MATHEMATICS

PRINCIPLES

PROCESS

Authors

FRANK EBOS, Senior Author
Faculty of Education
University of Toronto

BOB TUCK
Computer Consultant
Nipissing Board of Education

WALKER SCHOFIELD
Department Head of Mathematics
Banting Secondary School

DENNIS HAMAGUCHI
Vice Principal
West Vernon Elementary School
Vernon, British Columbia

Consultants

David Banting
Classroom Teacher
Chancellor School
Winnipeg, Manitoba

Donald Darling
Principal
Lawton Junior High School
Edmonton, Alberta

Timothy Quinn
Mathematics Teacher
Rothesay Junior High School
Rothesay, New Brunswick

Henry Remai
Head, Mathematics Department
Holy Cross High School
Saskatoon, Saskatchewan

NELSON CANADA

Published in 1988 by
Nelson Canada,
A Division of International Thomson Limited
1120 Birchmount Road
Scarborough, Ontario, MIK 5G4

ISBN 0-17-602614-2

Canadian Cataloguing in Publication Data

Ebos, Frank, 1939–
 Mathematics: principles and process, 9

For use in high schools.
Includes index.
ISBN 0-17-602614-2

1. Mathematics—1961–   .   I. Title.

OA107.E525 1987   510   C87-094627-7
 . . . . .

Project Editors
Sheila Bassett
Janice Nixon

The symbol for year is a. For the sake of clarity the word year has been used, in full, in place of a.

Printed and bound in Canada by John Deyell Company
   4567890   JD 89543210

Photo Credits

P. 19 Peter Gardiner/Pizza with Pizzazz, **P. 23** H. Armstrong Roberts/Miller Services, **P. 38** Miracle Food Mart, **P. 53** Camerique/Miller Services, **P. 76** H. Armstrong Roberts/Miller Services, **P. 83** E. Jane Mundy/Miller Services, **P. 92** H. Armstrong Roberts/Miller Services, **P. 107** Rob Stocks, **P. 121** Ted Grant/National Film Board, **P. 127** H. Armstrong Roberts/Miller Services, **P. 129** Halle Flygare/Miller Services, **P. 130** Donald Eldon, **P. 147** left Manitoba Govt. Photo **P. 147** right IPS, **P. 150** Alberta Govt. Services, **P. 157** G. S. McNatt/Miller Services, **P. 166** Camerique/Miller Services, **P. 176** H. Armstrong Roberts/Miller Services, **P. 187** Camerique/Miller Services, **P. 191** left Camerique/Miller Services, **P. 191** right H. Armstrong Roberts/Miller Services, **P. 217** NASA, **P. 260** H. Armstrong Roberts/Miller Services, **P. 273** Harold M. Lambert/Miller Services, **P. 301** H. Armstrong Roberts/Miller Services, **P. 316** Alan B. Stone/Miller Services, **P. 320** H. Armstrong Roberts/Miller Services, **P. 325** Air Canada, **P. 340** left National Health and Welfare Information Services, **P. 351** Harold M. Lambert/Miller Services, **P. 367** Gerry Cairns/Miller Services, **P. 368** F. Prazak/Miller Services, **P. 370** Harold M. Lambert/Miller Services, **P. 374** UPI/Bettman Newsphotos, **P. 381** H. Armstrong Roberts/Miller Services, **P. 384** Camerique/Miller Services, **P. 386** Harold M. Lambert/Miller Services, **P. 387** Richard Harrington/Miller Services, **P. 419** Toronto Stock Exchange, **P. 420** Reuters/Bettman Newsphotos, **P. 445** Camerique/Miller Services, **P. 476** National Gallery of Canada, Ottawa; Gift of George Escher, Mahone Bay, Nova Scotia, 1984; Copyright W. Veldholysen, Baarn, Holland.

The authors gratefully acknowledge the advice, assistance or contribution of RoseMary Ebos, Michael Ebos, Lesley Ebos, Bill Allan, Maggie Cheverie, Andrew Clowes, Debbie Davies, Dawna Day-Harris, Ruta Demery, Anna Jalandoni, Julie Kretchman, Gloria Lewsey, Peter Maher, Barbara Pawlicki, Claire Robitaille, Anthony Rodrigues.

Contents

4 Using Algebra: Language and Process

5 Using Equations: Solving Problems

6 Measurement: Concepts, Formulas and Applications

Using Mathematics: Principles and Process, 9

These pages explain how the text is organized. They tell you what to look for in each lesson and chapter.

Lesson Features

▶ Look for the lesson number and title.

Teaching
▶ The lesson begins with the information you need to learn. Look for photos that illustrate uses of mathematics. New words are printed in **bold type**.
▶ Examples and Solutions guide you step-by-step through new material.
▶ Always read the hints and learning comments printed in red type.

Exercise Features

▶ Each lesson gives you lots of practice. Exercises are graded as A, B and C according to their level of difficulty.

A These questions let you practise the skills and concepts taught in the lesson. Some of these questions can be done orally with the teacher and the class.

B These questions also give you practice with the skills you have learned, but they involve a combination of skills. There are also lots of problems and applications to practise with.

C These questions provide an extra challenge or may involve another approach.

Applications
These sections show how mathematics is a part of the everyday world. You will solve some problems and learn some interesting facts which apply or extend the topic.

2.9 Order of Operations: Integers

The order of operations you used in your work with whole numbers also applies in your work with integers.

For the following example, do the operations with multiplication and division first and then add or subtract.

Rules for the Order of Operations
▶ Perform the operations in brackets ( ) first.
▶ Then calculate the powers. Namely, find the value of expressions involving exponents.
▶ Then do multiplication and division in the order they appear.
▶ Then do addition and subtraction in the order they appear.

Example 1 Simplify
$(-8)(-4) \div 2 - (-3)(-2)$

Solution
$(-8)(-4) \div 2 - (-3)(-2)$
$= 32 \div 2 - (-3)(-2)$
$= 16 - (-3)(-2)$
$= 16 - 6$
$= 10$

4.5 Exercise

A 1 The cost, C, in cents of making cards is given by $C = 125 + 2n$ where n is the number of cards. Calculate the cost of making each number of cards.
(a) 100   (b) 150   (c) 200   (d) 1000

2 The amount, C, in dollars, charged by a delivery company to deliver a package is given by $C = 2.65 + 0.85d$ where d is the distance in kilometres. Find the charge to deliver each parcel.
(a) 8.5 km   (b) 3 km   (c) 25 km

B 3 In skydiving, once you leave the plane, your height, h, in metres above the earth's surface is given by
$h = a - 4.9t^2$ where a is the altitude of the plane in metres and t is the time in seconds after leaving the plane.
(a) Find Jennifer's height to the nearest metre after 6.5 s if she jumped from a height of 2500 m.
(b) Jackson jumped 2 s after Jennifer. How far apart were they, 4.5 s after

---

Applications: Designs in Business

Designs and logos are used by companies and advertisers so that people, when they see the logo, may think of their product.

10 Which shapes are used to construct each of the logos above?
11 Based on your impression of what the logo reminds you of, suggest in what type of business each company might be involved.

Reviews and Tests

These sections review and test skills and concepts *after* every chapter:

► **Practice and Problems: Review**
► **Practice Test**

This section helps you review and practise skills from *earlier* chapters:

► **Cumulative Review**
► **Year End Review**

Problem Solving Features

There are lots of opportunities to learn and practise problem solving skills and strategies as part of the lessons and also in special sections based on particular strategies for problem solving.

► Lessons in many chapters give you problem solving skills, such as, using patterns. using counter-examples, and working backwards.
► A **Problem Solving Plan** 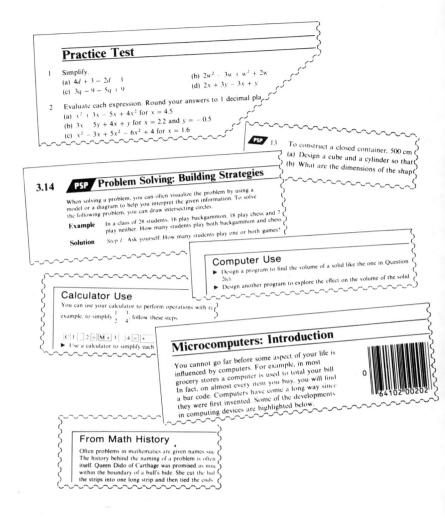 is provided to help you organize a framework for problem solving.
► **PSP** questions in the lessons give you an opportunity to do different types of problems and introduce you to interesting aspects of mathematics

Extension Features

► **Calculator Use** offers suggestions for using your calculator and for planning efficient procedures.
► **Computer Use** and **Microcomputers** investigate uses of the computer.

► **Math Tips** suggest methods for doing mathematics better. They offer suggestions for helping you learn mathematics and for planning your work.
► **From Math History** offers glimpes at people and problems that were part of the development of mathematics.

1 *Mathematics: An Essential Foundation*

Language of mathematics, symbols and words, inventory skills, using calculators, factors and exponents, variables and substitution, *Problem Solving Plan* **PSP**, problems to solve, applications, building strategies for problem solving

Introduction

Mathematics has many interesting facets. Throughout history a long list of people contributed to its development.
Mathematicians have come from different walks of life as well as from different countries. Some worked with numbers, some with space, and today some work with computers. Throughout this text, you will meet some of them in the feature *From Math History*.

Mathematics developed in the same way as you develop your own personal skills and understanding.

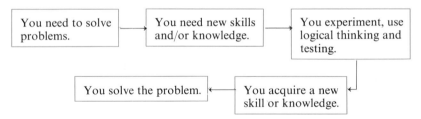

The stamps illustrate glimpses of the many problems solved by mathematics. As you learn mathematics throughout this text, you will experience some of the many facets of mathematics. For example,

- the language
- the people
- the enjoyment
- the excitement
- the power
- the applications
- the problem solving process
- the technology
- the nature

1.1 Inventory: Computation

Inventory 1: Whole Numbers

1 Add.

(a) 16
   $+38$

(b) 25
   $+47$

(c) 39
   $+24$

(d) 97
   $+56$

(e) 74
   $+26$

(f) $128 + 39 + 84$

(g) $4713 + 469 + 73$

(h) $3847 + 958 + 107$

2 Subtract.

(a) 61
   -25

(b) 83
   -47

(c) 90
   -56

(d) 413
   -68

(e) 923
   -75

(f) $618 - 49$

(g) $650 - 127$

(h) $805 - 196$

(i) $700 - 423$

3 Multiply.

(a) 63
   $\times 5$

(b) 27
   $\times 4$

(c) 19
   $\times 8$

(d) 87
   $\times 54$

(e) 92
   $\times 16$

(f) 35×68

(g) 683×27

(h) 924×51

(i) 735×68

4 Divide.

(a) $602 \div 7$ (b) $152 \div 4$ (c) $423 \div 5$ (d) $236 \div 6$ (e) $4828 \div 71$

Inventory 2: Decimals

1 Add.

(a) $0.47 + 2.5$ (b) $0.2 + 1.79$ (c) $4.35 + 3.6$ (d) $27.5 + 11.8$
(e) $0.7 + 1.83$ (f) $0.73 + 0.842$ (g) $3.94 + 7.4$ (h) $0.054 + 0.0092$

2 Subtract.

(a) $8.9 - 4.7$ (b) $8.48 - 3.07$ (c) $0.483 - 0.172$ (d) $9.3 - 4.7$
(e) $8.36 - 1.58$ (f) $12 - 0.569$ (g) $99.25 - 78.56$ (h) $7 - 4.85$

3 Multiply.

(a) 0.5×3 (b) 0.7×4 (c) 0.6×0.2 (d) 3.8×2.4
(e) 0.45×0.3 (f) 0.735×100 (g) $0.148\ 35 \times 1000$ (h) 179.5×0.01

4 Divide.

(a) $9.1 \div 7$ (b) $98.6 \div 29$ (c) $360.4 \div 53$ (d) $70.84 \div 23$
(e) $2.24 \div 0.4$ (f) $4.384 \div 100$ (g) $4.3 \div 0.1$ (h) $0.43 \div 0.01$

Inventory 3: Fractions

To write an **equivalent fraction**, you multiply or divide the numerator and the denominator by the same number.

$$\frac{4}{5} = \frac{4 \times 3}{5 \times 3} = \frac{12}{15} \qquad \frac{20}{25} = \frac{20 \div 5}{25 \div 5} = \frac{4}{5}$$

equivalent fractions   equivalent fractions

The fraction $\frac{4}{5}$ is said to be in **lowest terms**.

▶ $\frac{9}{8}$ is an **improper fraction**.   ▶ $2\frac{1}{4}$ is a **mixed number**.

1 Write each fraction in lowest terms.

(a) $\frac{4}{12}$ (b) $\frac{5}{30}$ (c) $\frac{35}{56}$ (d) $\frac{48}{60}$ (e) $\frac{36}{54}$

2 Write each fraction as a mixed number.

(a) $\frac{8}{5}$ (b) $\frac{13}{4}$ (c) $\frac{19}{7}$ (d) $\frac{10}{3}$ (e) $\frac{21}{8}$

3 Write each mixed number as an improper fraction.

(a) $1\frac{3}{4}$ (b) $2\frac{1}{3}$ (c) $5\frac{2}{7}$ (d) $4\frac{3}{4}$ (e) $3\frac{2}{5}$

4 Which fraction in each pair is greater?

(a) $\frac{2}{5}, \frac{4}{5}$ (b) $\frac{1}{2}, \frac{1}{3}$ (c) $\frac{5}{8}, \frac{7}{12}$ (d) $\frac{1}{3}, \frac{3}{8}$ (e) $\frac{7}{10}, \frac{7}{8}$

5 Add.

(a) $\frac{5}{9} + \frac{2}{9}$ (b) $\frac{1}{4} + \frac{7}{20}$ (c) $2\frac{2}{3} + \frac{5}{9}$ (d) $1\frac{4}{5} + 1\frac{7}{10}$ (e) $2\frac{13}{20} + 1\frac{3}{4}$

6 Subtract.

(a) $\frac{5}{9} - \frac{4}{9}$ (b) $\frac{3}{4} - \frac{2}{3}$ (c) $\frac{7}{8} - \frac{5}{6}$ (d) $2\frac{1}{5} - 1\frac{7}{10}$ (e) $3\frac{1}{6} - 2\frac{2}{3}$

7 Multiply.

(a) $\frac{1}{2} \times \frac{1}{5}$ (b) $\frac{4}{5} \times \frac{15}{32}$ (c) $\frac{4}{15} \times 9$ (d) $2\frac{1}{2} \times 1\frac{1}{15}$ (e) $3\frac{1}{5} \times 3\frac{3}{4}$

8 Divide.

(a) $\frac{1}{3} \div \frac{1}{2}$ (b) $\frac{2}{5} \div \frac{4}{15}$ (c) $1\frac{1}{4} \div 5$ (d) $2\frac{1}{3} \div \frac{7}{9}$ (e) $5\frac{1}{2} \div 3\frac{1}{3}$

Inventory 4: Rounding

To check whether an answer is reasonable, you estimate using rounded numbers.

$$\text{Estimate}$$
$$3.86 \times 71.3 = 275.218 \qquad 4 \times 70 = 280$$
$$\uparrow \qquad\qquad\qquad \uparrow$$
The answer is reasonable.

The charts show numbers rounded to different places.

	ten	hundred	thousand
776	780	800	1 000
3 812	3 810	3 800	4 000
86 515	86 520	86 500	87 000

	tenth	hundredth	thousandth
4.1693	4.2	4.17	4.169
38.1325	38.1	38.13	38.133
123.5159	123.5	123.52	123.516

to 1 decimal place ———————┘
to 2 decimal places ————————————┘
to 3 decimal places ——————————————————————┘

1   Round 19 356 to each place.
   (a) nearest ten   (b) nearest hundred   (c) nearest thousand

2   Round each number to the accuracy indicated.
   (a) 0.76 (tenth)   (b) 0.784 (hundredth)
   (c) 2.498 (2 decimal places)   (d) 9.4155 (3 decimal places)

3   Calculate. Round to the accuracy indicated.
   (a) 4.83×6.96 (thousandth)   (b) 1.96×3.9 (1 decimal place)
   (c) $21.0919 - 6.9$ (2 decimal places)   (d) $3.45 \div 1.6$ (2 decimal places)

4   Estimate the answer for each calculation. Then do the calculation.
   (a) $782 + 87.3$ (b) $16.0 - 9.38$ (c) 85×173 (d) 185×19
   (e) 8.3×9.4 (f) 0.87×1.7 (g) $12\ 558 \div 23$ (h) $42\ 504 \div 84$

5   Which costs more? Check whether your answer is reasonable.
   (a) 7 cans of soup at 63¢ each or 5 cans of soup at 83¢ each
   (b) 2 LP's at $9.79 each or 8 singles at $2.45 each
   (c) 3 shirts at $19.75 each or 2 slacks at $29.98 each

6   Estimate the answer to each problem. Then do the calculation.
   (a) Find the total cost of 7 packages of tape. Each package costs $1.15.
   (b) Find the change from a $20 bill if the total cost is $12.45.
   (c) A ball glove costs $27.45, a ball costs $8.75 and a bat costs $14.55. Find the total cost of buying the three items.

1.2 Language of Mathematics: Symbols and Words

You will come across many symbols in your everyday activities. Each symbol has a special meaning. Do you know what these symbols mean?

The language of mathematics often uses symbols to represent words. Symbols are used to represent sets of numbers.

the set of natural numbers

$$N = \{1, 2, 3, 4, \ldots\}$$

the set of whole numbers

$$W = \{0, 1, 2, 3, 4, \ldots\}$$

This symbol means and so on.

The symbol ∈ means *belongs to* or *is a member of* or *is an element of*.

$3 \in N$ means   *3 is a member of the set of natural numbers.*

$0 \in W$ means   *0 is a member of the set of whole numbers.*

In mathematics, symbols enable you to write concise statements. For example,

$5 + 4 < 10$ means   *five added to four is less than ten.*

Communicating in Mathematics

Have you ever tried to give directions to someone? If you make one error, then the person will probably not reach his or her destination. People who do mathematics try to communicate their thoughts and work to others. One of the most important aspects of understanding mathematics is learning the vocabulary: the meanings of words and symbols.

There is probably a very good reason for your not understanding what the message shown says.

トラベラーズ・チエツクいま

If you don't understand the above message it is because you probably don't know Japanese words or symbols. In Japanese, one symbol often stands for many words.

Similarly in mathematics, you must understand the meanings of the symbols used.

Symbols allow you to use a short form—a compact form of writing mathematics. Often *different* symbols are used to represent the *same* idea. For example,

$\frac{m}{2}$ and $m \div 2$ have similar meanings.

Sometimes the desire to write more compactly leads to misunderstandings.

$2 \times m$ is often written as $2m$.

When you are solving problems, you must remember that $2m$ means 2 times m.

▶ When you are learning to speak a language, you need to learn hundreds of words, their spellings and their pronunciation.

▶ When you are learning to communicate in mathematics, you need to learn fewer symbols and words *but* you need to know their *exact* meanings.

3^2 means *three multiplied by three.*

Translating sentences in English into sentences in mathematics is an important skill used for solving problems.

An **equality** is shown by an **equation** such as

$(6 + 4) \div 2 = 5$

$3^2 + 19 = 28$

An **inequality** is shown by an **inequation** such as

$(6 + 4) \div 2 < 6$

$3^2 + 19 > 26$

To do calculations you need to follow the *Rules for the Order of Operations* as shown in the example.

Rules for the Order of Operations

▶ Perform the operations in brackets ( ) first.

▶ Then do multiplication and division in the order they appear.

▶ Then do addition and subtraction in the order they appear.

Example Simplify $(14 + 4^2 \div 8) \div [(16 - 4) \div 3]$.

Solution

$(14 + 4^2 \div 8) \div [(16 - 4) \div 3]$

$= (14 + 4 \times 4 \div 8) \div [(16 - 4) \div 3]$

$= (14 + 16 \div 8) \div [(16 - 4) \div 3]$

$= (14 + 2) \div (12 \div 3)$

$= 16 \div 4$

$= 4$

1.2 Exercise

A Remember: Begin to place symbols and math words in your summary list.

1 What does each of these symbols mean?

(a) (b) (c) (d) (e)

2 Locate other examples of symbols that you have seen used. Give the meaning of each.

3 Match the symbol with the expression.
A symbol may be used more than once.

(a) sum   (b) is greater than   (c) product
(d) is equal to   (e) quotient   (f) increased by
(g) is less than   (h) decreased by

Symbols
$<$ $=$ $+$
$-$ $\div$
$>$ $\times$

4 Write an equation or inequation for each of the following.

(a) 25 added to 36 is greater than 50.

(b) 36 decreased by 12 is less than the product of 6 and 5.

(c) 12 increased by 30 is greater than 30 decreased by 12.

(d) One half of the sum of 36 and 48 is equal to the product of 7 and 6.

(e) 8 squared is less than the sum of 7 squared and 6 squared.

5   Simplify each of the following.
    (a) $36 \div 6 + 3$ (b) $23 + 12 \div 2$ (c) $8(5) \div 2$
    (d) $14 - 2(5)$ (e) $28 \div 4 - 2$ (f) $8 - 4 \div 2$
    (g) $2^2 + 3$ (h) $3^2 + 4^2$ (i) $8^2 - 3^2$

6   Simplify each of the following.
    (a) $\dfrac{15 - 3}{4 - 2}$ (b) $\dfrac{12 + 6}{9 - 3}$ (c) $\dfrac{(4 + 6) \times 6}{12 - (8 - 2)}$

    (d) $\dfrac{(6 - 4) \div 2}{8 \div (4 \times 2)}$ (e) $12 + \dfrac{16 + 4}{4 \times 5} - 3$ (f) $\dfrac{20 + 12 \div 3}{(4 + 4) \div 2}$

B Review the steps in the order of operations.

7   (a) Predict which has the greater answer, A or B.
    $$\text{A: } \frac{6 + 3 \times 6}{4^2 - 2^2} \qquad \text{B: } \frac{6^2 - (3 \times 6)}{6 - (2 + 1)}$$
    (b) Calculate your answer in (a).

8   Which has the greatest answer?
    (a) $\dfrac{20 \div 4 + 4}{6 + (6 - 3)}$ (b) $64 - \dfrac{144}{8 \times 3} + 2 \times 6$ (c) $\dfrac{(7 \times 5) \times 12}{4 \div (7 - 3)}$

9   Often more than one pair of grouping symbols are used. Simplify.
    (a) $12 - [2(3 + 6) - 15]$ (b) $8 - 2[3(3 - 2)]$
    (c) $112 - [125 - (40 - 4)]$ (d) $456 \div 2 + 3[4(5 - 3)]$

10 Simplify each of the following.
    (a) $(18 - 12)(18 + 12)$ (b) $[5 + 3^2] \div 2$ (c) $2 + 4^2 \div 2$
    (d) $(2 + 4)^2 \div 2$ (e) $(18 \div 3)(9 - 3)$ (f) $(18 \div 3) \div 3$
    (g) $(12 - 8 + 4 - 2) \div 3$ (h) $[8 \div 2 + 9 \div 3] - [2^2 + (2 - 1)]$
    (i) $12 - [3(2 + 5) - 3(2 + 5)]$ (j) $256 \div 2[2(2 + 2) + 4(4 - 2)]$

11 Use one of the symbols $<$, $>$ or $=$ in place of ⬤ to write an equation
    or inequation.
    (a) $36 \div 6 + 8$ ⬤ $40 + 9 \div 3$ (b) $8 \times 6 \div 3$ ⬤ $3 + 3 \div 3$

    (c) $8 - 25 \div 5$ ⬤ $16 \div 4 + 3$ (d) $\dfrac{12 + 3}{4 + 1}$ ⬤ $\dfrac{28 - 4}{4 \times 3}$

    (e) $\dfrac{16 + 16}{4^2 \times 2}$ ⬤ $\dfrac{7 \times 8 - 6}{8 \times 6 + 2}$ (f) $2^3 + 3 \times 4$ ⬤ $4^2 + 3^2$

    (g) $5^2 - 4^2 + 2$ ⬤ $6^2 - 5^2$ (h) $\dfrac{48 \div 12 + 4}{2^2 + 2}$ ⬤ $\dfrac{4 \times 4 - 8}{6^2 - 5 \times 6}$

12 The multiples of 3 are 1×3 2×3 3×3 4×3

                                 3   6   9   12

Write the multiples of 3 which meet each condition.

(a) greater than 28

(b) greater than 4 and less than 24

(c) between 4 and 14

(d) between 21 and 36

13 (a) Write the multiples of 4 between 25 and 36.

(b) Write the multiples of 3 between 25 and 36.

(c) Write the multiples common to (a) and (b).

14 Once you learn the meanings of individual words in mathematics, you can combine them. For each of the following, find the numbers that satisfy each property.

(a) the even natural numbers greater than 16

(b) the odd natural numbers less than 12

(c) the odd natural numbers greater than 12 and less than 20

(d) the odd multiples of 7 between 96 and 110

(e) the natural numbers with more than one digit

(f) the even multiples of 9 greater than 36

(g) the even natural numbers between 36 and 40

(h) the even multiples of 9 less than 96

C 15 Write a suitable equation or inequation using each set of symbols and numbers. You may also use brackets if the need arises.

(a) $\{1, 12, 36, 48, +, =, \div\}$

(b) $\{2, 3, 5, 28, \div, <\}$

(c) $\{2, 3, 4, 14, \times, +, =\}$

(d) $\{2, 13, 15, 27, +, \div, <\}$

(e) $\{2, 3, 4, 8, \times, +, <\}$

(f) $\{8, 6, 3, 2, +, -, >\}$

(g) $\{1, 2, 3, 4, 5, 8, \times, +, \div, <\}$

(h) $\{1, 2, 3, 4, 5, 6, \times, \div, +, -, >\}$

Math Tip

Once you learn the skills and concepts of a new topic in mathematics,

▶ Make a summary in your own words describing the skills and concepts.

▶ Illustrate the skills and concepts with examples of your own.

Continue the above procedure in the following sections as well as in the other chapters you study.

1.3 Using Calculators

A calculator is a useful tool but different calculators have different features. To use your calculator efficiently, you must be familiar with how it works. Study the manual provided with it. Try the following skills on *your* calculator. Always estimate the answer first.

| C and CE key |

When using your calculator, the first step is to clear it by pressing the $\boxed{C}$ key. If your calculator has a $\boxed{CE}$ key, it is used to erase the last entry that was made. Compare.

$$\boxed{C}\,5\,\boxed{\times}\,3\,\boxed{CE}\,2\,\boxed{=}\,10$$

This clears the 3 only.

$$\boxed{C}\,5\,\boxed{\times}\,3\,\boxed{C}\,2\,\boxed{=}\,2$$

This clears all earlier work.

| Does your calculator have a repeat function? |

If you press $\boxed{=}$ more than once after an operation, the calculator will repeat the operation using the input number. However different calculators do this function differently as shown. Read your manual.

$$3 \times 2 \times 2 \times 2$$

Calculator A

$$\boxed{C}\,3\,\boxed{\times}\,2\,\boxed{=}\,\boxed{=}\,\boxed{=}\,24$$

Calculator B

$$\boxed{C}\,2\,\boxed{\times}\,3\,\boxed{=}\,\boxed{=}\,\boxed{=}\,24$$

Note the order of the inputs.

| Does your calculator follow the order of operations? |

Do the following steps to calculate $36 + 12 \times 2$.

$$\boxed{C}\,36\,\boxed{+}\,12\,\boxed{\times}\,2\,\boxed{=}$$

Follows. Answer is 60.
Does not follow. Answer is 96.

Calculator Use

In each chapter you will find suggestions for calculators called *Calculator Use*. Refer to them to develop your skills with calculators.

| Does your calculator have a memory? |

Look for the $\boxed{MEM}$, $\boxed{M}$, $\boxed{M+}$, $\boxed{MI}$ or $\boxed{STO}$ key. When performing calculations, you can store answers in the memory. Do the following calculation.

Recalls the answer you placed in memory

$$4 \times 5.6 + 5 \times 6.8 \qquad \boxed{C}\,4\,\boxed{\times}\,5.6\,\boxed{=}\,\boxed{M+}\,5\,\boxed{\times}\,6.8\,\boxed{=}\,\boxed{+}\,\boxed{MR}\,\boxed{=}$$

1.3 Exercise

A   Remember: Estimate your answers.

1   What is the output for the following instructions? Check on your calculator.

(a) [C] 5 [+] 3 [CE] 6 [=]

(b) [C] 5 [×] 8 [+] 6 [CE] 2 [=]

(c) [C] 5 [+] 2 [=] [=] [=]

(d) [C] 625 [÷] 5 [=] [=] [=]

2   Estimate the results before calculating.

(a) [C] 687 [+] 987 [=]

(b) [C] 1824 [÷] 64 [=]

(c) [C] 617 [×] 83 [=]

(d) [C] 9046 [−] 975 [=]

3   Use the repeat function to calculate.
(a) $2 \times 2 \times 2 \times 2 \times 2$

(b) $3 \times 3 \times 3 \times 3 \times 3$

(c) $4 \times 2 \times 2 \times 2 \times 2$

(d) $2 \times 2 \times 2 \times 3 \times 3 \times 3$

B   Use your calculator to do the following. Use the memory key as needed.

4   Calculate. Read carefully.
(a) Find the sum of 9782 and 8965.
(b) Find the product of 96 and 39.6.
(c) Find the quotient of 849.6 and 36.

5   Follow these instructions.
A: Subtract the sum of 963 and 481 from 1500.
B: Divide the product of 82 and 45 by 18.
C: Multiply the sum of 481 and 293 by 28.
D: Divide the sum of 983 and 460 by 39.
E: Find the quotient when the sum of 939 and 486 is divided by 75.
Now add your answers in A to E.

6   (a) Find the difference of 963.2 and 794.9.
(b) What is the total of 43.6, 28.9 and 128.3?
(c) Find the product of 48.9 and 1.5.
(d) By how much does 16.89 exceed 9.91?
(e) What is the total of 486, 9832, 19 632 and 8?
(f) By how much does the product of 932 and 4.9 exceed the quotient of 153.6 and 48?

C 7   Investigate how to find the remainder when you divide using your calculator. (Hint: $50 \div 12 = 4$ R2 and $4 \times 12 + 2 = 50$)

Applications: Pizzas and Calculators

Would you believe that the largest pizza baked to date was 24 m across and served over 60 000 slices?

Pizzas like the ones you normally buy are shown in the price list. Use a calculator to solve the following.

INGREDIENTS		
PEPPERONI	GREEN OLIVES	ANCHOVIES
MUSHROOMS	GREEN PEPPERS	HOT PEPPERS
BACON	ONIONS	PINEAPPLES
TOMATOES	SALAMI	HAM

Prices	Small	Med.	Large	Ex. Large
Basic: Sauce and Cheese	5.25	7.25	8.50	9.75
With 1 ingredient	5.75	8.00	9.50	11.00
With 2 ingredients	6.25	8.75	10.50	11.75
With 3 ingredients	6.75	9.50	11.50	13.00
Each additional ingredient	0.50	0.75	1.00	1.25

8 Calculate the cost of each pizza.

   (a) large with pepperoni and tomatoes

   (b) small with olives, ham and tomatoes

   (c) extra large with pepperoni, mushrooms and hot peppers

9 Often people share a pizza. Find the cost for each person to the nearest cent.
   (a) Four people ordered a large pizza with 2 ingredients.
   (b) Three people ordered a medium with 3 ingredients.
   (c) Six people ordered 2 medium pizzas with 4 ingredients.

10 The school swim team (40 members) placed an order for the following pizzas. Calculate the cost for each person.
   ▶ 3 extra large pizzas with ham, bacon, olives and onions
   ▶ 3 extra large pizzas with peppers, salami and tomatoes
   ▶ 5 medium pizzas with hot peppers, pepperoni and pineapple

11 How many different pizzas can you order if you can order from the following ingredients? (Assume that every pizza has tomato sauce and cheese.)
   (a) pepperoni, mushrooms, tomatoes
   (b) salami, green peppers, olives, bacon
   (c) pepperoni, mushrooms, bacon, tomatoes, ham

1.4 Factors and Exponents

Certain words in mathematics can be analysed to understand their meanings. For example, to understand the meaning of *greatest common factor*, you need to understand each word.

 Each skill or word you learn will help you learn more advanced skills.

The **factors** of two different numbers are shown.
12 is divisible by 3. Thus 3 is said to be a *factor* of 12.

Factors of 12	Factors of 18
$1 \times 12 = 12$	$1 \times 18 = 18$
$2 \times 6 = 12$	$2 \times 9 = 18$
$3 \times 4 = 12$	$3 \times 6 = 18$

The set of factors of 12 is $\{1, 2, 3, 4, 6, 12\}$.

The set of factors of 18 is $\{1, 2, 3, 6, 9, 18\}$.

The set of **common factors** of 12 and 18 is $\{1, 2, 3, 6\}$.

From this set of common factors you can see that since 6 is the greatest number common to both sets of factors, 6 is the **greatest common factor** of 12 and 18.

 You can often analyze the meanings of complex-looking words in mathematics.

There are other important words you need to know.
▶ A **prime** number has 1 and itself as its only factors. For example, $11 = 1 \times 11$ and $31 = 1 \times 31$.
▶ A number that has more than two factors is called a **composite** number. For example, $12 = 1 \times 2 \times 6$ and $20 = 1 \times 2 \times 2 \times 5$.

A number can be written as a product of prime factors. For example, $24 = 2 \times 2 \times 2 \times 3$. The product of prime factors can be used to write the greatest common factor of two or more numbers using the alternative strategy in the following example.

 Often there is more than one way to solve a problem.

Example Find the greatest common factor of 18 and 24.

Solution

$24 = ② \times 2 \times 2 \times ③$ — Write each number as a product of prime factors.
$18 = ② \times ③ \times 3$
$② \times ③ = 6$ — Write the product of the common factors.

The greatest common factor of 18 and 24 is 6.

Symbols are used to express mathematics compactly and concisely. For example,

▶ You can write a sum of equal addends in a compact way.

$\underbrace{2 + 2 + 2 + 2 + 2}_{\text{5 equal addends}} = 10$ becomes $5 \times 2 = 10$ ← number of equal addends

▶ You can also write a product of equal factors in a concise way.

$\underbrace{2 \times 2 \times 2 \times 2 \times 2}_{\text{5 equal factors}} = 32$ becomes $2^5 = 32$ ← number of equal factors

2^5 is said to be in **exponential form**. Each part has a special name and meaning.

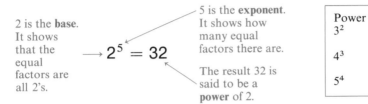

2 is the **base**. It shows that the equal factors are all 2's.

$\longrightarrow 2^5 = 32$

5 is the **exponent**. It shows how many equal factors there are.

The result 32 is said to be a **power** of 2.

Power	Read as
3^2	3 to the exponent 2 3 squared
4^3	4 to the exponent 3 4 cubed
5^4	5 to the exponent 4

1.4 Exercise

A 1 In each power, what is the base? the exponent?

(a) 2^3 (b) 3^2 (c) 2^4 (d) 3^4 (e) 4^3 (f) 4^2 (g) 5^2 (h) 2^5

2 The value of the power 2^4 is $2 \times 2 \times 2 \times 2 = 16$. Find the value of each power in the previous question.

3 Each expression is shown in expanded form. Write each in exponential form.

(a) $3 \times 3 \times 3 \times 3 \times 3$ (b) $2 \times 2 \times 2 \times 2$

(c) $5 \times 5 \times 5$ (d) $4 \times 4 \times 4 \times 4 \times 4 \times 4$

4 (a) Write 12 as a product of prime factors.

(b) Write 16 as a product of prime factors.

(c) Find the greatest common factor of 12 and 16 using (a) and (b).

5 Find the greatest common factor of each pair of numbers.

(a) 8, 6   (b) 16, 24   (c) 25, 30   (d) 18, 27   (e) 27, 45

(f) 16, 48   (g) 27, 36   (h) 75, 45   (i) 30, 40   (j) 32, 56

6 Find the greatest common factor of each of the following.

(a) 25, 30, 45   (b) 24, 36, 18   (c) 24, 48, 72   (d) 32, 24, 20

7   The **least common multiple** of 6 and 8 is obtained as shown.
    Step 1: List the multiples of 6.   6, 12, 18, 24, 30, 36, 42, 48, . . .
    Step 2: List the multiples of 8.   8, 16, 24, 32, 40, 48, . . .
    Step 3: List the *common* multiples of 6 and 8.   24, 48, 72, . . .
    Step 4: Identify the *least common* multiple of 6 and 8.   24
    Find the least common multiple of each of the following.
    (a) 4, 6   (b) 9, 4   (c) 10, 25   (d) 24, 36   (e) 8, 6, 12   (f) 8, 6, 16

8   An alternative method of finding $12 = 2 \times 2 \times 3$
    the least common multiple is
    based on using prime factors. $18 = 2 \times \quad 3 \times 3$ The least common
    Find the least common multiple   multiple of 12 and
    of the following numbers. $2 \times 2 \times 3 \times 3 = 36$ 18 is 36.

    (a) 18, 24   (b) 4, 18   (c) 72, 24   (d) 9, 12   (e) 16, 24, 36   (f) 9, 16, 12

B   9   (a) Write the set of factors of 25, 16, 36, 27, 48, 49, 72, 99.
        (b) Write all the numbers less than 50 with exactly three different factors.

10 Write the prime numbers between
    (a) 0 and 20   (b) 20 and 40   (c) 40 and 60   (d) 60 and 80

11 (a) Use your answers from the previous question to predict how many
        prime numbers you might expect to find between 120 and 140.
    (b) Now find the prime numbers between 120 and 140. How many prime
        numbers are there?

12 Which number less than 50 has the greatest number of prime factors?

13 (a) Find the value of (i) 2^3 (ii) 2^4 (iii) $2^3 \times 2^4$ (iv) 2^7
    (b) Compare your answers in (iii) and (iv). What do you notice?

14 (a) Based on your results from the previous question, write a probable
        conclusion about multiplying powers with like bases.
    (b) Use your answer in (a). Express each in exponential form.
        ▶ $2^2 \times 2^3$ ▶ $2^3 \times 2^3$ ▶ $3^2 \times 3^5$ ▶ $3^4 \times 3^2$ ▶ $10^3 \times 10^5$

15 (a) Find the value of (i) 10^5 (ii) 10^2 (iii) $10^5 \div 10^2$ (iv) 10^3.
    (b) Compare your answers in (iii) and (iv). What do you notice?

16 (a) Based on your results from the previous question, write a probable
        conclusion about dividing powers with like bases.
    (b) Use your answer from (a).   ▶ $\dfrac{8^6}{8^2}$ ▶ $\dfrac{5^6}{5^2}$ ▶ $\dfrac{2^9}{2^5}$ ▶ $\dfrac{8^5}{8^2}$
        Express each in exponential form.

1.5 Using Variables: Substitution

In hockey a team scores 2 points for each win. You can use a letter such as w to represent the number of games won. Then the number of points is given by

$2 \times w$ or $2w$. ← Multiplication is understood.

A **variable** is a symbol used to represent numbers. Thus the letter w is a variable. The **domain** of the variable w is the set of replacement values for w. For example, w is a member of the set of whole numbers; this is shown by $w \in W$. The set W is the domain of the variable.

You can use a relation rule, $n = 2w$, to show how the number of points, n, is related to the number of games won, w. If $w = 26$, you can find the value of n.

$n = 2w$ When you substitute
$n = 2(26)$ use brackets to show
$n = 52$ the substitution.

Similarities such as the following help you to learn mathematics.

▶ Each of the following is a **number expression**.

$3 + 8$ $3 \times 2 + 4$
$8 - 2 + 6$ $4^2 \div 8$

Numbers appear in a number expression.

▶ Each of the following is a **variable expression**.

$a + b$ $3a$ (means $3 \times a$)
$m \div 3$ a^2 (means $a \times a$)

Variable expressions include at least one variable.

You need to use the rules for the order of operations when you evaluate an expression.

Example   Evaluate $3a + 2b$ when $a = 4$ and $b = 5$.

Solution   Use $a = 4$ and $b = 5$.

$3a + 2b = 3(4) + 2(5)$
$= 12 + 10$
$= 22$

PSP To avoid errors, use brackets to show substitutions.

The value of an expression depends on the values used for the variables. If you use different values for a and b, you will obtain different values for the expression. The values of the variable expression are often referred to as the **range**.

A chart is useful for showing the values of the variable and variable expression. For example, the table of values at the right shows the values of $3x + 2$ for $x \in \{1, 2, 3, 4, 5\}$.

x	$3x + 2$
1	5
2	8
3	11
4	14
5	17

If $x = 1$, then
$3x + 2 = 3(1) + 2$
$= 3 + 2$
$= 5$

The domain is $\{1, 2, 3, 4, 5\}$.

The range is $\{5, 8, 11, 14, 17\}$.

1.5 Exercise

A 1 (a) Find the value of $3k + 2$ if $k = 3$.
 (b) Find the value of $3k^2 + 2$ if $k = 3$.
 (c) Find the value of $3(k + 2)$ if $k = 3$.

2 (a) Find the values of $3x + 5$ if $x \in \{1, 3, 5\}$.
 (b) Find the values of $3(x + 5)$ if $x \in \{1, 3, 5\}$.
 (c) Why do your answers in (a) and (b) differ?

3 (a) Find the values of $4(y - 1)$ if $y \in \{2, 4, 6\}$.
 (b) Find the values of $4y - 1$ if $y \in \{2, 4, 6\}$.
 (c) Why do your answers in (a) and (b) differ?

4 Copy and complete each table of values.

(a)
x	$3x - 1$
1	
2	
3	
4	
5	

(b)
y	$y^2 + 1$
5	
6	
7	
8	
9	

(c)
z	$2z^2 - 3z$
10	
11	
12	
13	
14	

5 Calculate each expression for the value of the variable given.
 (a) $3m - 2$, $m = 4$
 (b) $2(k + 5)$, $k = 4$
 (c) $(m^2 - 1) \div 8$, $m = 3$
 (d) $\dfrac{y^2 - 1}{y^2 - 5}$, $y = 3$

B 6 Evaluate each of the following expressions.
 (a) $2x + 6, x \in \{1, 3, 5, 7\}$
 (b) $(2y + 4) \div 2, y \in \{1, 5, 10\}$
 (c) $3d^2 - 2d, d \in \{3, 6, 9\}$
 (d) $\dfrac{(m^2 - 1)}{m + 1}, m \in \{1, 4, 10\}$
 (e) $\dfrac{a^2 + 2a + 1}{a + 1}, a \in \{1, 2, 3\}$
 (f) $(2y + 1)(2y - 1), y \in \{2, 3, 4, 5, 6\}$

7   Evaluate each expression using $x = 5$ and $y = 4$.
   (a) $5x - 3y$ (b) $3x + 2y$ (c) $2(x - y)$ (d) $3xy$
   (e) $3y - 2$ (f) $5x + y^2$ (g) $4x(y + 2)$ (h) $x^2 + y^2$
   (i) $x^2 - y^2$ (j) $3xy - 5$ (k) $\dfrac{4 + xy}{3y}$ (l) $\dfrac{x + y}{x - y}$
   (m) $x^2 - y^2 - 3^2$ (n) $2x^2y$ (o) $3xy^2$ (p) $(3xy)^2$
   (q) $(x + y)(x + y)$ (r) $x^2 + 2xy + y^2$ (s) $9 - x + y$ (t) $9 - (x + y)$

8   (a) Find the value of each expression if $x = 4$ and $y = 3$.
        (i) $4x^2y^2$ (ii) $(2xy)^2$
     (b) What do you notice about your answers?

9   (a) Use $x = 5$ and $y = 4$ in the previous question. What do you notice about the
          values of $4x^2y^2$ and $(2xy)^2$?
     (b) Try other values for x and y. What do you notice each time?

C 10 (a) Find the value of each expression if $y = 3$.
         (i) $y^2 + 2y + 1$ (ii) $(y + 1)^2$
      (b) What do you notice about your answers?

11   (a) Use $h = 5$ and $k = 3$. Find the value of each expression.
         (i) $h^2 - k^2$ (ii) $(h - k)(h + k)$
      (b) What do you notice about your answers?

From Math History

Karl F. Gauss (1777–1855) was the son of a bricklayer. He had an excellent
aptitude for calculations. At a very early age, he was asked by his teacher to find
the sum of the first 100 counting numbers. Karl had already developed a method
to find the answer and was able to do the calculation quickly, to the surprise
of his teacher. Karl used the expression

$$\frac{n(n + 1)}{2}$$ where n is the number of numbers to be added.

Thus to find the sum of the first 100 numbers, Karl used $n = 100$.

$$\frac{n(n + 1)}{2} = \frac{(100)[(100) + 1]}{2}$$

$$= 5050$$

By the time he was 19, Karl Gauss was developing concepts in mathematics
that are still studied today and bear his name. His natural interest in
mathematics led to his studying astronomy since both these studies are closely
related. Throughout this text, watch for other *From Math History* features.

1.6 Equations and Inequations

When you write $4 < 3$ or $4 > 3$ you can tell if it is true or false.
However if you write a sentence using a variable, you cannot tell if it is true or false. $x < 3$ may be true or false.

$x < 3$ is called an **open sentence** since it can be true or false.
If you replace x with numbers, then you can write true or false as shown below. Use $x \in W$. W is called the **replacement set** or the **domain**.

$0 < 3$	true	$3 < 3$	false
$1 < 3$	true	$4 < 3$	false
$2 < 3$	true	and so on	

Since the numbers 0, 1 and 2 make a true sentence for $x < 3$, the numbers 0, 1 and 2 are said to **satisfy** the inequation $x < 3$.

The **solution set** for the inequation $x < 3$, $x \in W$ is given by $\{0, 1, 2\}$.

To write the above ideas concisely, you use symbols as shown.

$$\{x \mid x < 3, x \in W\}$$

the set of all x such that $x < 3$ and $x \in W$

Thus you can write $\{x \mid x < 3, x \in W\} = \{0, 1, 2\}$.

Example   Find $\{n \mid n + 1 = 6, n \in N\}$.

Solution   Since $5 + 1 = 6$,
$\{n \mid n + 1 = 6, n \in N\} = \{5\}$

You say that the solution set for the equation $n + 1 = 6$ is $\{5\}$.
In the above example, 5 is also called a **root** of the equation $n + 1 = 6$.
The root satisfies the equation, since $n + 1 = 6$.

$$5 + 1 = 6$$

To find the solution set for an equation or inequation means to **solve** the equation or inequation. Later you will learn formal methods for solving equations and inequations. For now, you can solve the equations and inequations in the exercise by a trial and error method called **inspection**.

1.6 Exercise

A 1 For each equation, three numbers are given. Which one is the root?
(a) $x + 6 = 11$ 3, 5, 7 (b) $2m + 3 = 7$ 2, 5, 7   (c) $3x - 12 = 18$ 8, 9, 10
(d) $6(x + 2) = 30$ 7, 3, 5 (e) $y - 3 = 8$ 8, 11, 3   (f) $8 = k + 7$ 1, 2, 3

2   Find each solution set. What do you notice about your solution sets in
    (a) to (c)?
    (a) $\{x\,|\,x < 4,\, x \in W\}$ (b) $\{y\,|\,y \leqq 3,\, y \in W\}$ (c) $\{k\,|\,k + 2 < 6,\, k \in W\}$

B 3   Find the solution set for each equation by inspection. The domain is N.
    (a) $2x + 1 = 5$ (b) $2y - 1 = 7$ (c) $5 + 2x = 5$ (d) $y + 2y = 9$

4   Find the solution set of each of the following equations or inequations.
    The domain is W.
    (a) $x < 13$ (b) $a > 5$ (c) $y \leqq 6$ (d) $m \geqq 8$
    (e) $4 \leqq y$ (f) $6 > k$ (g) $x + 5 = 14$ (h) $2x = 8$
    (i) $y + y \geqq 8$ (j) $14 = 2 + 3m$ (k) $4y + 3 - y = 6$
    (l) $5y + 3 = 23$ (m) $8y + 3y = 22$ (n) $3y - 3 = y + 5$

5   Find the root of each equation by inspection. The domain is W.

    (a) $2k - 1 = 7$ (b) $\dfrac{x}{2} = 6$ (c) $y + 4 = 4$

    (d) $5k + 1 = 26$ (e) $4m + 2 = 42$ (f) $2x - 1 = x + 2$

6   Solve each of the following by inspection. The domain is W.
    (a) $x + 3 < 6$ (b) $14 \leqq y - 2$ (c) $k - 4 = 32$

    (d) $m + 3 \geqq 9$ (e) $3k \leqq 6$ (f) $\dfrac{4}{5}(k - 2) = 12$

    (g) $p - 1 \geqq 3$ (h) $\dfrac{2}{3}k > 6$ (i) $8m + 3m = 33$

7   Find each of the following.
    (a) $\{y\,|\,y \geqq 2,\, y \in W\}$ (b) $\{k\,|\,k < 2,\, k \in N\}$ (c) $\{p\,|\,p > 3,\, p \in W\}$
    (d) $\{m\,|\,m \div 3 \leqq 4,\, m \in N\}$ (e) $\{n\,|\,2n \leqq 6,\, n \in W\}$ (f) $\{a\,|\,2a + a \leqq 9,\, a \in W\}$

Computer Use

▶ On various pages in this text, information about microcomputers is
  provided. Use the *Contents* to locate these pages. Then read them.
▶ Refer to the various tips in the *Computer Use* features that occur in this
  text. Make a summary of the suggestions.
▶ Compile a list of the uses of computers. Compile another list of the
  misuses of computers. You may need to do some research to complete
  these lists.

1.7 PSP Problem Solving Plan

In previous years, you started to develop your skills for solving problems. Problems you are asked to solve fall into two categories.

Category I The skill or strategy you need to solve the problem is immediately evident. Once you recognize which skill or strategy to use, you plan your solution and solve the problem.

Category II The skill or strategy you need to solve the problem is not immediately evident. To solve this type of problem, you need a plan that allows you to look for clues, to ask yourself key questions, to try a strategy and so on.

Sometimes you can use a systematic approach to solve a problem. Other times you need to be creative. However to solve any problem successfully, you must understand the answers to these two questions.

I What information does the problem ask me to find?

II What information is given in the problem?

Once you clearly understand the answers to these questions, you need to develop your plan of attack. The flow chart at the right shows a simplified framework for a plan.

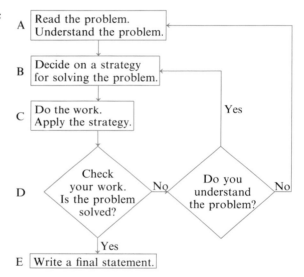

As you seek solutions to problems and acquire skills and strategies, you begin to develop a framework for your own particular plan for solving a problem. As well, you begin to accumulate a list of key questions to ask yourself to help you decide on a strategy. Some of these key questions follow.

▶ What information does the problem ask me to find?
▶ What information is given in the problem?
▶ Have I solved a similar problem before?
▶ Do I understand the meanings of all the words in the problem?
▶ What words or clues in the problem suggest a strategy or skill to try?
▶ If the strategy I choose does not work, what other strategies can I try?

To organize a problem solving plan, you need a framework. The *Problem Solving Plan* **PSP** is a framework to help you organize your plan of attack.

A list of possible strategies and other key questions for problem solving follows. Many of these you have used in your earlier work in mathematics. Throughout your work in mathematics you will practise these strategies, as well as learn others to add to the list.

▶ What information is needed?

▶ Is there enough information?

▶ Is there extra information?

▶ Is my answer reasonable?

▶ Have I made any assumptions?

▶ Can I solve the problem by

  • Drawing diagrams or graphs?

  • Making a list or a table?

  • Solving a simpler problem?

  • Guessing and testing?

  • Searching for a pattern?

  • Working backwards?

  • Using formulas or equations?

▶ Do I need to use more than one skill, operation or strategy?

PSP	**Problem Solving Plan**
Step A:	Understand the problem. • What are you asked to find? • What are you given? Make a list of other key questions to help you solve a problem.
Step B:	Decide on a strategy. Make a list of strategies.
Step C:	Apply the strategy. Do the work. Make a list of suggestions to help you.
Step D:	Check your solution. Make a list of ways of checking.
Step E:	Write a final statement. Make a checklist of reminders.

There is no simple approach to learn in order to solve problems. However the more practice and experiences you have, the better you will become at solving problems. By building a framework of the key questions, strategies and experiences you acquire, you equip yourself better to solve problems. On the next page many of the questions, strategies, etc., are listed in a suggested framework for a *Problem Solving Plan* **PSP**.

1.7 Exercise

B 1 Throughout the text, look for the symbol **PSP**. This symbol indicates skills, strategies and suggestions you might place in your plan. Refer to the chart on the next page. Record the chart, leaving sufficient space in each step to record additional skills, strategies and questions you acquire throughout your work in mathematics.

2 During your study of mathematics, continue to record the skills and strategies in your *Problem Solving Plan* **PSP**. Read Sections 1.8 and 1.9. Place any key questions or strategies you use in your *Problem Solving Plan*.

Step A: Read the problem carefully.

- Do I know the answer to these two questions?
  I What information am I asked to find?
  II What information am I given?
- Do I understand the meaning of each word and symbol given in the problem?

  > Record here other suggestions and key questions that will help you understand a problem.

Step B: Decide on a method or strategy for solving the problem.

- What words or clues in the problem suggest a strategy for solving the problem?
- Is the strategy immediately evident?
- Do I need to draw a diagram? a chart?
- Do I need to use a formula? an equation? a variable?

  > Record here other strategies and key questions that will help you decide on a strategy to use.

Step C: Do the work. Apply or test the method or strategy you have chosen in Step B to solve the problem.

- Do I understand each step of the solution?
- Have I made any incorrect assumptions?
- Is there enough given information to solve the problem?
- Is any of the given information not needed to solve the problem?
- If my strategy isn't working, what other strategy can I use? Choose this strategy and try again.

  > Continue to record other suggestions for this part of the *Problem Solving Plan.*

Step D: Check your work.

- Is my answer reasonable? Does my answer make sense?
- Is my method of solving the problem efficient?
- Did I check my answer in the original problem?
- Will I obtain the same answer if I use another strategy?
- Have I solved the problem?

  > Continue to record other suggestions for this part of the *Problem Solving Plan.*

Step E: Make a final statement.

- Did I answer the question asked in the original problem?
- Did I choose the correct units?
- Will my answer be understood by someone else reading it?
- Did I round off correctly? Is the accuracy of my answer consistent with the given information?

  > Continue to record other suggestions for this part of the *Problem Solving Plan.*

1.8 $\quad$ PSP $\quad$ Problems to Solve: Using a Plan

To solve any problem successfully, you must understand the answers to these two questions.

I What information does the problem ask me to find?
II What information is given in the problem?

Once you clearly understand the answers to these two questions you are ready to plan your solution. Refer to your *Problem Solving Plan* PSP In the problems that follow you need to decide on the operation or operations that help solve the problem.

Example At a paper drive Gino collected 1985 kg of newspapers. Maria collected 2396 kg. For each kilogram they received 8.2¢. How much money did they raise?

Solution $\quad$ *Step* 1: Find the sum. $\qquad$ *Step* 2: Calculate the amount.

Gino	1985 kg	1 kg is worth 8.2¢.
Maria	2396 kg	4381 kg are worth 4381 × 8.2¢
Total	4381 kg	or $359.24.

Check: Is the answer reasonable?
1985 is about 2000 $\quad$ 8.2¢ is about 10¢
2396 is about 2000 $\quad$ 10¢ × 4000
about 4000 $\quad$ or about $400

Gino and Maria raised $359.24.

1.8 $\quad$ Exercise

B Copy and complete the chart for each of the following questions. Express the information in your own words. Then solve the problem.

I What information are you asked to find?	II What information is given?

1 $\quad$ One of the largest airplanes in the world is the Boeing 747C which can carry 490 passengers. At the last census the population of Chilliwack, B.C. was 9135 people. If the residents were to go to Europe on a holiday, how many planes would be needed?

2 $\quad$ A 20-g serving of a cereal contains 4 g of bran. How many grams of bran are in a package that contains 800 g of cereal?

3　The length of a rectangle is 6 cm more than the width. If the perimeter is 76 cm, find the dimensions of the rectangle.

4　How would you divide $1000 among three people, A, B and C, if B receives $80 more than A and C receives twice as much as A?

5　Did you know that a human breathes faster when awake than asleep? A sleeping person breathes an average of 15 times per minute. How many breaths would you take during a 9-h sleep?

6　Have you ever heard of the midnight sun? North of the Arctic Circle there is a period of constant daylight. If there were 1752 h of constant daylight, how many consecutive days was this?

7　(a) Canada has 675 740 km of paved roads and 170 813 km of gravel roads. What is the total length of roads in Canada?
　　(b) Create another problem based on the information in (a). Solve the problem.

8　On election night across Canada it was reported that, out of a total of 2878 polling stations, 1235 had counted their votes and 325 stations were still counting. How many stations had not even started to count?

Often problems contain more information than you need. For the following questions,
▶ Identify which information you don't need.　　▶ Solve the problem.

9　A crate of raspberries holds 48 boxes. A shipment had 5325 crates. If 500 crates are going to Mississauga, how many boxes of raspberries are there?

10　This year the total number of points scored by the Rabbits is 8902. About 1250 points were scored on road trips. Last year they scored 3912 points. By how many points have they improved?

Often some problems do not have enough information as in the following question.

11　The Nile River is the longest in Africa and the Amazon the longest in South America. Which river is longer?
　　(a) Why are you not able to answer the problem?
　　(b) Use this data to answer the problem.
　　　　Amazon: 6280 km　　Nile: 6690 km
　　(c) You can travel at 12 km/h for 8 h each day. How long will it take you to travel the Amazon?

1.9 PSP Problem Solving: Building Strategies

To solve a problem, you need to make a decision.

I Is the strategy for solving the problem immediately evident?

II Is the strategy for solving the problem not immediately evident?

As you solve more problems and acquire strategies for problem solving, you will more frequently answer, "Yes, the strategy for solving the problem is immediately evident."

In sections such as this, specific strategies for problem solving, that you can record in your *Problem Solving Plan* **PSP**, will be illustrated.

Example   How many squares are in the diagram?

Solution   Think: Which strategy should I try?
To solve this problem, a useful strategy is to ask if you can solve a simpler problem.

Try a 1 × 1 square.   □   1 square

Try a 2 × 2 square.

4	1 × 1 squares
1	2 × 2 square
5	squares

Then a 3 × 3 square.

9	1 × 1 squares
4	2 × 2 squares
1	3 × 3 square
14	squares

The number of squares in the diagram is 14.

1.9 Exercise

B To solve the problems in Questions 1 to 4, think of a simpler problem.

1   How many equilateral triangles are in the diagram?

2   The first 4 triangular numbers are shown by the diagram. What is the tenth triangular number?

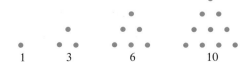

1   3   6   10

3   How many different ways can you connect
    4 squares so that they touch along at least
    one side, as shown in the diagram?

4   A cube is constructed from smaller cubes as shown.
    The outside surface is painted. How many small
    cubes have each number of painted faces?
    (a) 1   (b) 2   (c) 0   (d) 3   (e) 4

Solve the following problems. Refer to your *Problem Solving Plan* /PSP/

5   A digit is represented by the letter S. What is one value of S if S6SS6 is
    divisible by 4? Are there any other values of S that are suitable?

6   To answer these questions, you may need to interpret the question from a
    different point of view. Use the clues provided and answer the question
    asked!
    (a) Which sentence is correct, A or B?
        A: 243 and 431 are 664.   B: 243 and 431 is 664.
    (b) During a severe storm in Lake Erie, a sightseeing boat sank, killing
        23 of the 48 passengers. The accident occurred on the international
        boundary between United States and Canada. Where were the survivors
        buried?

7   Which of the following does not belong in the list?

        wot   xis   net   vife   gihet   rouf

8   A diagram is used to record the digits 1 to 9.
    Each digit is used only once. Use the clues
    below to place all 9 digits in the diagram.

    ⌐ × ⌐ = ☐   ☐ − ⌐ = ⌐

    ⌐ ÷ ⌐ = ⌐   ⌐ ÷ ⌐ = ⌐   ⌐ − ⌐ = ⌐

	?	?	?
	?	9	?
	?	?	?

Math Tip

To solve a problem, whether it is in mathematics or in another discipline, you
must understand the meaning of each word that occurs in the problem.

▶ Make a list of the new math words you have learned in this chapter. Provide
  an example of your own to illustrate each word.

▶ List any new problem solving strategies or key questions you have acquired
  and place them in your *Problem Solving Plan* /PSP/

Applications: Sports and Records

A chart frequently contains more information than may be needed. You must decide what information is relevant to solving a problem. Use the chart given for the team's standings to answer the following questions. Be sure to read carefully.

Team	Number of wins (W)	Number of losses (L)	Number of ties (T)	Number of goals scored for the team (F)	Number of goals scored against the team (A)
Montreal	37	8	9	228	114
Buffalo	29	24	3	182	184
Boston	21	23	8	216	211
Quebec	20	28	9	148	207
Hartford	5	42	6	148	279

9 (a) How many goals have been scored against Quebec?

   (b) How many more games has Montreal won than Hartford?

   (c) Which team has played the most games?

10 Two points are awarded for each game won and one point is awarded for each game tied.

   (a) Calculate the number of points Boston has.

   (b) Calculate the number of points Quebec has.

   (c) Why is Boston ahead of Quebec in the standings?

11 Use w to stand for the number of games won by a team and t to stand for the number of ties.

   (a) Explain why $2w + t$ represents the number of points for a team.

   (b) Calculate $2w + t$ for each team in the previous newspaper standings.

   (c) For which pair of teams could the order of standings change after *one* game? Why?

12 These headings were seen in the newspaper. Update the team standings chart to show these results.

13 The next day the standings in Question 12 changed as shown.

   (a) Which teams played?

   (b) Who won?

Team	W	L	T	F	A
Montreal	38	8	9	237	114
Buffalo	29	26	3	183	196
Quebec	21	28	9	154	212
Boston	21	24	8	221	217
Hartford	6	42	6	151	280

14 Make up a question of your own about the standings in the previous question. Write a solution to the question you made.

Practice and Problems: Review

1 Add.
   (a) $936 + 285$ (b) $1.84 + 0.67$ (c) $12.84 + 3.9$ (d) $\frac{1}{3} + \frac{2}{5}$ (e) $4\frac{3}{4} + 6\frac{1}{2}$

2 Subtract.
   (a) $1005 - 875$ (b) $7.98 - 5.125$ (c) $15 - 9.47$ (d) $\frac{5}{8} - \frac{1}{4}$ (e) $3\frac{1}{2} - 1\frac{3}{5}$

3 Multiply.
   (a) 42×18 (b) 1.7×0.5 (c) 3.6×0.001 (d) $\frac{9}{16} \times \frac{8}{21}$ (e) $5\frac{1}{4} \times 5\frac{1}{3}$

4 Divide.
   (a) $1976 \div 38$ (b) $29.25 \div 22.5$ (c) $0.88 \div 5.5$ (d) $\frac{7}{8} \div \frac{4}{5}$ (e) $9\frac{2}{3} \div 3\frac{3}{4}$

5 Calculate. Round your answers to 1 decimal place.
   (a) $18.65 - 9.483$ (b) 7.8×19.6 (c) $15.134 \div 2.3$

6 Calculate.
   (a) $3^2 + 4^2 \div 2$ (b) $6 - [(4 \times 2 + 1) \div 3]$ (c) $\frac{64 \times 8 - 8}{8 \div 4 + 4}$

7 Use your calculator. Use estimation to check the calculator display.
   (a) Add 49.6, 9.6, 100, 3 and 121.   (b) Subtract 6.96 from the sum of 14.93 and 9.89.
   (c) Divide the sum of 49.3 and 126.6 by the product 9.6 and 12.

8 Express each number as a product of repeated identical factors and then express in exponential form.
   (a) 100   (b) 64   (c) 10 000   (d) 8   (e) 125

9 Find the greatest common factor of each pair.
   (a) 12, 28   (b) 30, 72   (c) 18, 54

10 Find the least common multiple of each pair.
   (a) 6, 9   (b) 9, 12   (c) 16, 20

11 Evaluate.   (a) $3n - 2$ for $n = 4$ (b) $5(m - 4)$ for $m = 5$

12 Find each solution set. The domain is the set of whole numbers.
   (a) $3x - 2 = 10$ (b) $5 + 2y = 11$ (c) $n < 10$ (d) $2c + 1 \geq 7$ (e) $3n + 1 \leq 10$

13 A cassette tape is 3.5 cm narrower than it is long. If its perimeter is 33.0 cm, find its dimensions.

Practice Test

1 Use your calculator.
   (a) Find the sum of 26.5, 9.87, 3.42 and 0.91.
   (b) Subtract 2.47 from the product of 14.8 and 0.56.
   (c) Multiply the difference of 12.34 and 7.8 by the sum of 15.6 and 3.75.

2 Calculate.
   (a) $\dfrac{2}{5} + \dfrac{1}{3} \div \dfrac{4}{15}$
   (b) $\left(\dfrac{5}{8} - \dfrac{1}{4}\right) \div \dfrac{2}{3}$
   (c) $\dfrac{2}{3} \times \dfrac{5}{8} \div \dfrac{5}{6}$
   (d) $\dfrac{3}{4} + \left(\dfrac{1}{2} \times \dfrac{2}{3}\right)$

3 (a) Find the sum of 4.35, 19.1 and 0.765 rounded to the nearest hundredth.
   (b) Find the product of 0.765 and 9.4 to 3 decimal places.
   (c) Find the quotient of 11.9223 and 3.9 to 2 decimal places.

4 Calculate.
   (a) $14 + 9 \div 3$
   (b) $15^2 - 9^2$
   (c) $18 + [(4 \times 3 - 2) \div (4 + 1)] \times 0$

5 Copy and complete the chart.

	power	base	exponent	value
(a)	2^5	?	?	?
(b)	?	5	2	?
(c)	?	3	?	81

6 Evaluate.
   (a) $10^5 \times 10^3$
   (b) $10^4 \times 10^2$
   (c) $10^1 \times 10^2$
   (d) $10^5 \div 10^2$
   (e) $10^6 \div 10^4$
   (f) $10^4 \div 10^1$

7 (a) Find the greatest common factor of 54 and 80.
   (b) Find the least common multiple of 12 and 16.

8 Evaluate for $x = 3$, $y = 2$ and $z = 4$.
   (a) $x^2 - y$
   (b) $(x + y)^2 - z^2$
   (c) x^2yz
   (d) $xz \div y$

9 Find each solution set. The domain is the set of whole numbers.
   (a) $5m - 3 = 17$
   (b) $2n - 1 > 4$
   (c) $4c + 3 \leq 25$
   (d) $2h + 1 = 5$

10 What is each student's share if 17 students paid $76.50 for tickets to a play?

11 A number is multiplied by 3, then decreased by 5. If the result is 7, find the number.

Microcomputers: Introduction

You cannot go far before some aspect of your life is influenced by computers. For example, in most grocery stores a computer is used to total your bill. In fact, on almost every item you buy, you will find a bar code. Computers have come a long way since they were first invented. Some of the developments in computing devices are highlighted below.

▶ John Napier (1550–1617) invented Napier Bones and logarithms to assist computation.

▶ Blaise Pascal (1623–1662) and G.W. Leibniz (1646–1716) invented the first calculating machines. Pascal's machine did only addition and subtraction. Leibniz's machine did multiplication and division.

▶ John V. Atansoff designed and constructed a semielectronic computing device in 1939.

▶ The first computer, Mark I, was completed in 1944 and had a mass of 5000 kg.

▶ ENIAC 1946 (Electronic Numerical Integrator And Computer) was the first modern computer. It occupied a room about 9 m × 9 m and had a mass of 27 000 kg.

▶ In 1951 UNIVAC 1 was built as an improved computer and separated the input and the output from the computing unit.

▶ The first silicon chip (or integrated circuit) was developed in 1959. By 1970 a chip was available that could hold about 15 000 transistors. In 1980 over 70 000 transistors could be held on a single chip. With the use of a chip, the computer became faster and more compact.

▶ Today the IBM System/360 computer can perform 375 000 computations per second. This is a great improvement over 1954 when a computer could only perform 2500 computations per second.

1 Use a newspaper. Collect articles and make a list of other improvements and features that the computers of today have.

2 Use a newspaper. Collect ads that advertise for people with computer training.

3 Compile a list of ways that computers can affect or influence your everyday activities. Include in this list the different uses to which computers are put.

2 Integers: Essential Skills for Algebra

Vocabulary of integers, ordering and graphing, using models for operations, adding, subtracting, multiplying and dividing integers, using patterns, order of operations, skills with calculators, working with absolute value, applications, strategies for problem solving

Introduction

The study of mathematics has had a significant impact on many fields including medicine, engineering, social sciences, biology and others such as those shown on the stamps.

▶ For each stamp, suggest ways in which mathematics may have been involved or is displayed.

▶ How is what is displayed on each stamp important to us?

Mathematics has evolved in ways similar to other languages that are thousands of years old. At each stage of study, attempts were made to make the meanings of words clearer as well as to make the language more precise. The history of mathematics records achievements of the many people who contributed to the development of mathematics as a precise language. Many developments have occurred and the study of mathematics has progressively improved. Over the years, the symbols used in mathematics were invented and refined.

People have studied mathematics for thousands of years. However, many of the common symbols that are used today were invented only during the last five hundred years.

+ Our present-day symbols for addition
− and subtraction were first used in print by Johann Widman in 1489.
× The symbol for multiplication was first used by William Oughtred (1574–1660).
÷ The symbol for division first appeared in print in a book by Johann Heinrich Rahn (1622–1676).
= The first time the symbol for equals appeared was in 1557 in a book written by Robert Recorde.

In this chapter, you will learn about integers and their operations so that you will be able to work successfully with a powerful branch of mathematics, namely, algebra.

2.1 Ordering Integers

For thousands of years, whole numbers were the only numbers people needed in their everyday activities. However, as civilization became more complex, people needed a way to express opposite ideas involving numbers.

The numerals you use today have changed in form through the ages. The chart shows the transition in form from the twelfth to the twentieth century for the numerals 2 and 4.

To represent **opposite** ideas such as the following, a new set of numbers called **integers** was developed.

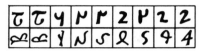

▶ 4°C above zero $+4$°C
  4°C below zero -4°C

▶ an increase of 12 mL $+12$ mL
  a decrease of 12 mL -12 mL

The set of integers, I, can be written as
$$I = \{\ldots, -3, -2, -1, 0, +1, +2, +3, \ldots\}.$$

Integers can be shown on a number line.
▶ Since $+3$ is to the right of -2, $+3 > -2$.
▶ Since -5 is to the left of -3, $-5 < -3$.

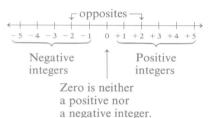

opposites

Negative integers

Positive integers

Zero is neither a positive nor a negative integer.

The positive integers are often written without their sign, but negative integers must always be written with the negative sign. Thus you can write
$$I = \{\ldots, -3, -2, -1, 0, 1, 2, 3, \ldots\}.$$

In the following example, you need to know that *ascending* means from least to greatest.

 PSP To solve a problem, you must understand the meaning of each word.

Example Arrange these integers in ascending order.
$$-2 \quad 0 \quad 4 \quad -5 \quad 6 \quad -3 \quad -7 \quad 8 \quad 9 \quad -11$$

Solution $-11 \quad -7 \quad -5 \quad -3 \quad -2 \quad 0 \quad 4 \quad 6 \quad 8 \quad 9$

↑ Farthest to the left on the number line

↑ Farthest to the right on the number line

2.1 Exercise

A 1 Use a suitable integer to show each of the following.
(a) 6 steps backwards
(b) a profit of $12
(c) a gain of 14 points
(d) an increase of 8 m²
(e) 8 steps down
(f) a loss of $6

2 Write the opposite of each integer.

(a) -2 (b) 1   (c) -3 (d) 18   (e) -36 (f) -48

3 *Left* and *right* are opposite ideas. If -2 m means 2 m to the left and $+2$ m means 2 m to the right, what do the following mean?

(a) -3 m   (b) $+4$ m   (c) -12 m   (d) $+15$ m   (e) -36 m   (f) 0 m

B 4 *Above sea level* and *below sea level* are opposite ideas used for elevation. Write an integer for each of the following.

(a) The peak of Mount Everest is 8840 m above sea level.

(b) A whale has been found at a depth of 1130 m below sea level.

(c) The highest motorway, 5630 m above sea level, is found in Tibet.

(d) Bacteria have been found 41 km above the earth's surface.

5 Which integer in each pair is greater?

(a) 3, 5   (b) -2, 1   (c) 0, 8   (d) -6, -3 (e) 5, -4 (f) -2, 2

6 Replace the symbol ⊘ with $<$ or $>$.

(a) 3 ⊘ 6   (b) 6 ⊘ -1 (c) 0 ⊘ -2 (d) 0 ⊘ 4

(e) -8 ⊘ -7 (f) -12 ⊘ -13 (g) 0 ⊘ 1   (h) -1 ⊘ 0

7 Arrange the integers in ascending order.

(a) -13, 2, -9, 6, 0   (b) -99, 101, -87, -103, 100

(c) -15, -21, -12, -5, -18 (d) 36, -17, 24, -13, -29

8 Arrange the integers in descending order.

(a) 45, -23, -19, 27, -8 (b) 13, -14, 15, -16, -17

(c) -3, -8, 5, -1, 1   (d) 109, -101, 95, -96, -108

PSP 9 (a) If 4 students can run a total of 48 km in one hour, how far can 3 students run in 20 min?

(b) What assumption(s) did you make?

Calculator Use

You can use your calculator to work with integers. Look for the $\boxed{+/-}$ key.

▶ Enter each of the following. What integers appear in the display?

(a) $\boxed{C}\,6\,\boxed{+/-}$ (b) $\boxed{C}\,8\,\boxed{+/-}\,\boxed{+/-}$ (c) $\boxed{C}\,12\,\boxed{+/-}\,\boxed{+/-}\,\boxed{+/-}$

▶ Enter these steps. What do you notice about your answers?

(a) $\boxed{C}\,4\,\boxed{+}\,8\,\boxed{=}$ (b) $\boxed{C}\,4\,\boxed{+/-}\,\boxed{+}\,8\,\boxed{=}$

(c) $\boxed{C}\,4\,\boxed{+}\,8\,\boxed{+/-}\,\boxed{=}$ (d) $\boxed{C}\,4\,\boxed{+/-}\,\boxed{+}\,8\,\boxed{+/-}\,\boxed{=}$

2.2 Graphing Integers

In the previous section you used the number line to compare and order integers. In this section you will graph sets of integers given by **inequations**. The **domain** of an inequation is the replacement set. In Example 1, the inequation, $n > -2$, has the set of integers as its domain given by $n \in I$.

Example 1   Find the solution set for $n > -2$, $n \in I$.
Draw a graph of the solution set.

Solution   Since $-1 > -2$, $0 > -2$, $1 > -2$ and so on, the solution set is $\{-1, 0, 1, 2, \ldots\}$.

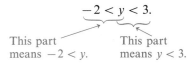

The arrow shows that the integers to the right of 3 also belong to the solution set.

When comparing three integers such as -8, -1 and 3, the inequalities $-8 < -1$ and $-1 < 3$ can be written in the **compact form**
$-8 < -1 < 3$.   This statement is read
"-8 is less than -1 and -1 is less than 3".

Similarly $-2 < y$ and $y < 3$ can be written in the **compact form**

$$-2 < y < 3.$$

This part means $-2 < y$.   This part means $y < 3$.

Example 2   Draw the graph of the solution set for $-1 \leq n \leq 3$, $n \in I$.

Solution   The integers greater than or equal to -1 are $-1, 0, 1, 2, 3, 4, \ldots$. The integers less than or equal to 3 are $3, 2, 1, 0, -1, -2, \ldots$. Thus the integers that satisfy both are $-1, 0, 1, 2, 3$.

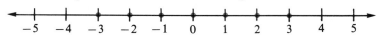

To solve some problems, you often need to work backwards. If you are given the solution set, you work backwards to find the inequation.

Example 3   Find an inequation that has the following solution.

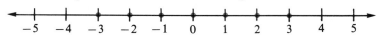

Solution $-3 \leq n \leq 3$, $n \in I$ Check: The solution set for $-3 \leq n \leq 3$, $n \in I$ is $\{-3, -2, -1, 0, 1, 2, 3\}$.

Each of the following inequations is also an answer to the previous example.
$$-3 \leq n < 4 \qquad -4 < n \leq 3 \qquad -4 < n < 4$$

PSP Often in mathematics you can obtain more than one answer to a problem.

2.2 Exercise

A Review the meaning of the symbols $<$, $>$, $\leq$ and $\geq$.

1 Write each of the following in a compact form.
(a) $-3 < -2$ and $-2 < 5$
(b) $4 > 3$ and $3 > -3$
(c) $-12 < 4$ and $4 < 12$
(d) $-8 < -3$ and $-3 < 1$
(e) $12 \geq -1$ and $-1 \geq -5$
(f) $-7 \leq 2$ and $2 \leq 7$

2 List the members of each of the following sets of integers. Then draw the graph.
(a) greater than 3
(b) less than 6
(c) less than -3
(d) greater than -4
(e) greater than 4 and less than 8
(f) less than 1 and greater than -1

3 Describe in words the set of integers represented by each of the following graphs.
(a)
(b)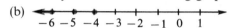

(c)
(d)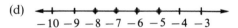

4 (a) Find the solution set for $-4 \leq y$, $y \in I$.
(b) Find the solution set for $-4 < y$, $y \in I$.
(c) How are the solution sets in (a) and (b) different? Why?

5 (a) Find the solution set for $k < 2$, $k \in W$.
(b) Find the solution set for $k < 2$, $k \in I$.
(c) How are the solution sets in (a) and (b) different? Why?

B Record the meanings of any new words that you learn.

6 Match each inequation with the graph of its solution set. The domain is I.
(a) $n > 3$
(b) $n \leq 1$
(c) $n < -2$
(d) $n \geq -3$

(i)

$$\begin{array}{ccccccccc} -4 & -3 & -2 & -1 & 0 & 1 & 2 & 3 & 4 \end{array}$$

(ii)

$$\begin{array}{ccccccccc} -4 & -3 & -2 & -1 & 0 & 1 & 2 & 3 & 4 \end{array}$$

(iii)

$$\begin{array}{ccccccccc} -4 & -3 & -2 & -1 & 0 & 1 & 2 & 3 & 4 \end{array}$$

(iv)

$$\begin{array}{ccccccccc} -4 & -3 & -2 & -1 & 0 & 1 & 2 & 3 & 4 \end{array}$$

7 List the members of each set. Then draw the graph.
(a) $\{x \mid x > 2, x \in I\}$
(b) $\{m \mid m \leq 3, m \in W\}$
(c) $\{y \mid -2 < y, y \in I\}$
(d) $\{k \mid -2 \geq k, k \in I\}$
(e) $\{d \mid d \leq 1, d \in W\}$
(f) $\{s \mid -12 < s, s \in I\}$

8   The domain for each inequation is given. Find the solution set. Then draw
    the graph.
    (a) $y > 3$, $y \in \{0, 1, 2, 3, 4\}$ (b) $s < -1$, $s \in \{-2, -1, 0, 1, 2\}$
    (c) $p > -3$, $p \in \{\ldots, -4, -2, 0, 2, 4, \ldots\}$ (d) $8 < y$, $y \in \{0, 2, 4, 6, 8, \ldots\}$

9   (a) Find the solution for each of the following. The domain is I.
        A: $-2 < y < 3$ B: $-2 \leq y < 3$ C: $-2 < y \leq 3$ D: $-2 \leq y \leq 3$
    (b) How are your solutions alike? How are they different?

10 Find the solution set for each of the following. Then draw the graph. The
    domain is I.
    (a) $3 < y < 6$ (b) $-3 < m < 3$ (c) $-3 \leq p < 0$
    (d) $-8 \leq s < -2$ (e) $-16 \leq t \leq -12$ (f) $-2 < a \leq 0$

11 The graphs of various solution sets are shown. Write an inequation for
    each solution set.

    (a)   (b)

    (c)   (d)

    (e)   (f)

    (g)   (h)

C 12   For each graph in the previous question, write another inequation to show
       the solution set.

Math Tip

Often words used in mathematics also occur as part of your everyday
language. Refer to the list of words.
▶ Use a dictionary to find the meaning of the everyday usage of each word.
▶ How are the everyday meanings of these words alike or different from
  their meanings in mathematics?

| positive | negative | minus | plus | product | multiply |
| opposite | solution | inequality | equality | set | model |

2.3 Using Models: Adding Integers

Often to illustrate a concept, whether in mathematics or other subjects, you can use a model as shown at the right. To help you learn mathematics, you use mathematical models. For example, integers can be represented by arrows on a number line. The *direction* of the arrow shows whether the integer is positive or negative. The *magnitude* of the integer is shown by the length of the arrow.

An important model used in hydrology, the science of water, is the **water cycle**. It is a model of the never-ending circulation of water and water vapour over the entire earth.

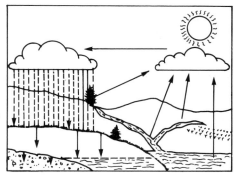

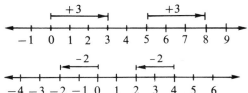

You can use this model to show how to find the sums of integers.

Example   Find each sum.

(a) $(+4) + (+3)$ (b) $(-4) + (-3)$ (c) $(-4) + (+3)$

Solution   (a)

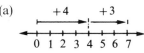

$(+4) + (+3) = +7$

(b)

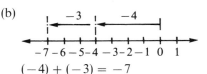

$(-4) + (-3) = -7$

(c)

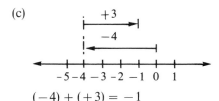

$(-4) + (+3) = -1$

Often you can use more than one model to illustrate a concept.   **PSP**
For example, you could think of each sum of integers as follows.

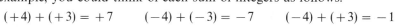

$(+4) + (+3) = +7$ $(-4) + (-3) = -7$ $(-4) + (+3) = -1$

Think: Think: Think:
     gain of 4   loss of 4   loss of 4
add gain of 3   add loss of 3   add gain of 3
    gain of 7 or +7   loss of 7 or −7   loss of 1 or −1

Patterns can be used to find the sums of integers.

$$(+5) + (+2) = 7$$
$$(+5) + (+1) = 6$$
$$(+5) + 0 = 5$$
$$(+5) + (-1) = ?$$
$$(+5) + (-2) = ?$$
$$(+5) + (-3) = ?$$

From the pattern, what do you expect the sums to be?

2.3 Exercise

A In the following questions, models help you to learn to add integers.

1   Use an arrow on a number line to represent each integer.

(a) $+3$ (b) -3 (c) $+4$ (d) -4 (e) -5 (f) -2

2   Write the integer shown by each model.

(a)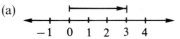

(b)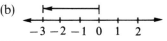

(c)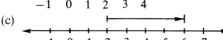

(d)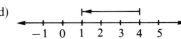

3   Find each sum.   Think of using a model.

(a) $(+2) + (+5)$

(b) $(-5) + (-2)$

(c) $(-2) + (+5)$

(d) $(+2) + (-5)$

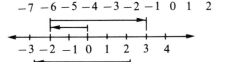

4   Find each sum.
(a) $(+3) + (+5)$ Think: (gain of 3) + (gain of 5) = ?
(b) $(+5) + (-3)$ Think: (gain of 5) + (loss of 3) = ?
(c) $(-5) + (-3)$ Think: (loss of 5) + (loss of 3) = ?
(d) $(-3) + (-5)$ Think: (loss of 3) + (loss of 5) = ?

5   Think of a model for each sum. Then find the sum.
(a) $(+2) + (+3)$ (b) $(-3) + (-2)$ (c) $(-2) + (+3)$ (d) $(+2) + (-3)$

B   In the following questions use a model or a pattern as needed to find the sum.

6. (a) $(+4) + (-3)$ (b) $(-3) + (+5)$ (c) $(-2) + (-3)$
    (d) $(+6) + (-5)$ (e) $(-8) + (+7)$ (f) $(-5) + (-4)$
    (g) $(+9) + (-9)$ (h) $(-3) + (+3)$ (i) $(-6) + 0$

7. Simplify. Remember: You can write $+2$ as 2.
    (a) $-6 + 3$ (b) $-6 + (-2)$ (c) $6 + (-3)$ (d) $2 + (-4)$
    (e) $-4 + 2$ (f) $-6 + (-3)$ (g) $3 + (+3)$ (h) $-6 + 6$
    (i) $3 + (-4)$ (j) $-3 + (-9)$ (k) $0 + (-8)$ (l) $-8 + 9$

8. The following procedure is used on a calculator to calculate $(-3) + (-4)$.

    $\boxed{C}\ 3\ \boxed{+/-}\ \boxed{+}\ 4\ \boxed{+/-}\ \boxed{=}$

    Use a calculator. Calculate the following.
    (a) $(+3) + (-7)$ (b) $(-4) + (-6)$ (c) $(-6) + (+3)$ (d) $-9 + 14$

9. Find each of the following sums. How many can you do mentally?
    (a) $-2 + (-4) + 8$ (b) $3 + 2 + (-1)$ (c) $2 + (-3) + 5$
    (d) $-4 + (-3) + 6$ (e) $12 + (-3) + (-2)$ (f) $6 + (-12) + 6$
    (g) $8 + (-8) + (-3)$ (h) $-3 + (-6) + 9$ (i) $-2 + 3 + (-8)$
    (j) $-8 + (-3) + 12$ (k) $-12 + 12 + (-12)$
    (l) $3 + (-8) + (-7) + 6$ (m) $-2 + (-1) + 3 + 9$
    (n) $-2 + (-3) + (-4) + 6 + (-8)$ (o) $4 + (-1) + (-3) + 9 + (-9)$

PSP 10. The parentheses have been left out of the following.
    $$8 \div 9 + 3 \div 12 + 2 \times 3 - 1 \times 2 + 1 = 11$$
    Place parentheses so that the equation will be true. (Hint: You may need to use parentheses within parentheses.)

C 11. Find the February 21 temperature in each city given in the table.

	Victoria	Jasper	Edmonton	Calgary	Yellowknife	Prince Albert	Saskatoon	Regina	Winnipeg	Ottawa	Montreal	Quebec City	Fredericton	Saint John	Moncton	Halifax
Temperature (°C) on Feb. 20	8	0	−8	4	−8	−8	−6	−8	−8	2	3	−1	2	2	0	3
Net change in temperature (°C) from Feb. 20 to Feb. 21	−3	−2	2	−3	4	2	−4	−3	2	−2	6	−3	−2	6	−3	−3

2.4 Using Patterns: Subtracting Integers

In the previous section you developed the skill of adding integers using the stages shown at the right. These stages are an important aspect of the development of any skill in mathematics.

Stage 1

You use a model or previously learned skills to help you understand and develop a new skill.

To develop the skill of subtracting integers, you repeat the stages.

Stage 1

You use your previous skills with addition of integers and the concept of inverse operations to learn to subtract integers.

Stage 2

You look for a pattern to help you simplify the skill.

Stage 3

You practise the skill to develop accuracy and speed.

Stage 4

You apply the skill to solve problems.

If you know that	then you know that
(Add) $\quad 8 + 7 = 15 \longrightarrow$	(Subtract) $\quad 15 - 7 = 8$
$36 + 42 = 78 \longrightarrow$	$78 - 42 = 36$

You can extend the concept of inverse operations to integers.

If you know that   then you know that

(Add) $(+3) + (+5) = +8 \longrightarrow$ (Subtract) $(+8) - (+5) = +3$

$(-3) + (-5) = -8 \longrightarrow \qquad (-8) - (-5) = -3$

Thus to subtract integers, you think of the inverse operation of addition.

$(-8) - (-3) = $ ▨   Think: ▨ $+ (-3) = -8$

What integer added to (-3) equals -8?

$(-8) - (-3) = (-5)$ Thus ▨ $= -5$.

Stage 2

It would be time-consuming to use the inverse operation of addition each time you wanted to subtract integers. Thus you look for a pattern.

 Often patterns help you to develop mathematics.

Think: How could these answers be used to obtain a pattern for subtracting integers?

Think: The same answer is obtained if you think of adding integers.

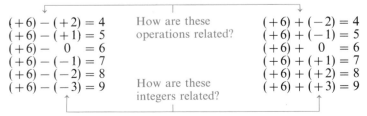

$(+6) - (+2) = 4$
$(+6) - (+1) = 5$
$(+6) - \quad 0 \ = 6$
$(+6) - (-1) = 7$
$(+6) - (-2) = 8$
$(+6) - (-3) = 9$

How are these operations related?

How are these integers related?

$(+6) + (-2) = 4$
$(+6) + (-1) = 5$
$(+6) + \quad 0 \ = 6$
$(+6) + (+1) = 7$
$(+6) + (+2) = 8$
$(+6) + (+3) = 9$

The previous examples suggest a pattern for subtracting integers.

To subtract an integer, add its opposite.

The opposite of an integer is its **additive inverse**.
The sum of an integer and its additive
inverse equals 0.

PSP Learn the precise
meanings of the
words of mathematics.

$(+4) + (-4) = 0$ $(-3) + (+3) = 0$ $(+12) + (-12) = 0$

additive $+4$ is the additive inverse of -4.
inverses -4 is the additive inverse of $+4$.

Example   Subtract.

(a) $(-3) - (-2)$ (b) $3 - (-4)$

Solution   (a) $(-3) - (-2) = (-3) + (+2)$ Think: To subtract an integer,
$= -1$ add its opposite.

(b) $3 - (-4) = 3 + (+4)$ Think: To subtract an integer,
$= +7$ add its additive inverse.

Stage 3 and Stage 4
You do Stage 3 in the exercise. Then you do Stage 4 as you apply your
skills with subtracting integers to solving problems.

2.4   Exercise

A In Questions 1 to 4 you will practise your skills with using the inverse
operation of addition and patterns to subtract integers.

1   Find the missing values.

(a) $(+4) - (-3) = $ ▨   Think: ▨ $+ (-3) = +4$
(b) $(-3) - (+2) = $ ▨   Think: ▨ $+ (+2) = -3$
(c) $(-6) - (-8) = $ ▨   Think: ▨ $+ (-8) = -6$
(d) $(-8) - (-6) = $ ▨   Think: ▨ $+ (-6) = -8$

2   To find each answer, use the inverse operation.

(a) $(+8) - (+9)$ (b) $(+10) - (+7)$ (c) $(+8) - (+10)$
(d) $(-3) - (-4)$ (e) $(-4) - (-3)$ (f) $(+6) - (-9)$
(g) $(-9) - (+6)$ (h) $(+9) - (-6)$ (i) $(-6) - (-9)$

3   Find the missing values ▨. Write the next three rows for each pattern.

(a) $(+2) - (-6) = +8$ (b) $(-8) - (-9) = +1$
$(+1) - (-6) = +7$ $(-8) - (-8) = 0$
$0 - (-6) = $ ▨ $(-8) - (-7) = $ ▨
$(-1) - (-6) = $ ▨ $(-8) - (-6) = $ ▨

4   Find the values of ▨ in each of the following patterns. What do you notice about your answers in (a) and in (b)?

(a) $(+8) - (+1) = $ ▨
$(+8) - 0 = $ ▨
$(+8) - (-1) = $ ▨
$(+8) - (-2) = $ ▨

(b) $(+8) + (-1) = $ ▨
$(+8) + 0 = $ ▨
$(+8) + (+1) = $ ▨
$(+8) + (+2) = $ ▨

B 5   Calculate.

(a) $(+5) - (-3)$
(b) $(+11) - (-8)$
(c) $(+15) - (+12)$
(d) $(-9) - (-3)$
(e) $(-5) - (-4)$
(f) $(-13) - (-8)$
(g) $(+18) - (+12)$
(h) $0 - (-4)$
(i) $(-9) - 0$

6   (a) What procedure would you use on a calculator to calculate $(+12) - (-3)$?

(b) Use a calculator. Calculate the following.

(i) $(+8) - (-9)$ (ii) $(-6) - (-3)$ (iii) $(-6) - (-8)$ (iv) $-5 - 13$

7   Calculate each of the following.

(a) $11 - 9$
(b) $11 - 14$
(c) $-14 - 11$
(d) $12 - (-5)$
(e) $-6 - 2$
(f) $35 - (-19)$
(g) $79 - 17$
(h) $-12 - (-6)$

8   Find the value of $a + b$ for each pair of values.

(a) $a = 3, b = -4$
(b) $a = -2, b = 3$
(c) $a = -4, b = -3$
(d) $a = -5, b = -3$
(e) $a = -6, b = 2$
(f) $a = 2, b = -8$

9   Find the value of $x - y$ for each pair of values.

(a) $x = 3, y = 4$
(b) $x = 3, y = -4$
(c) $x = -3, y = -4$
(d) $x = -4, y = -2$
(e) $x = -2, y = -4$
(f) $x = 2, y = -4$

10   These calculations involve addition and subtraction. Read carefully!

(a) $3 + (-4)$
(b) $3 - 8$
(c) $9 - (-2)$
(d) $-8 - 6$
(e) $6 + (-4)$
(f) $-4 + 4$
(g) $5 - (-3)$
(h) $-6 + 3$

11   Calculate.

(a) $-3 + (-5) - (-4)$
(b) $-11 + 3 - (-7)$
(c) $14 - (-8) + (-6)$
(d) $-5 + (-7) - 11$
(e) $26 - 17 - (-19)$
(f) $-7 - (-6) + (-8)$

12   Replace ⬤ with either $<$ or $>$.

(a) $13 - (-3)$ ⬤ $-12 + 24$
(b) $9 + (-3)$ ⬤ $-3 + (-4)$
(c) $5 - (-3)$ ⬤ $4 - (-5)$
(d) $-2 + (-3)$ ⬤ $-3 - (-2)$

PSP 13   What is the least positive integer that when divided by 5, 7 or 10 leaves a remainder of 2?

2.5 Problem Solving: Using Integers

Once you learn skills, you use them to solve problems. To solve a problem successfully, you must first answer these questions:

▶ What information does the problem ask me to find?
▶ What information is given in the problem?

Once you clearly understand the answer to these two questions you are ready to organize your solution. Refer to the *Problem Solving Plan* **PSP**

PSP	Problem Solving Plan

Step A: Understand the problem.
 • What are you asked to find?
 • What are you given?

Step B: Decide on a strategy.

Step C: Apply the strategy. Do the work.

Step D: Check your solution.

Step E: Write a final statement.

Example Jason's score in the first game was 87 points. His total score for two games was −136 points. What was his score in the second game?

PSP Think:
What am I asked to find? ▶ Score in the second game.
What information am I given? ▶ Score in first game was 87 points. Total score was −136 points.

Solution Subtract to find the score in the second game.
−136 − 87 = −223
Jason's score in the second game was −223 points.

PSP Check:
First game score	87
Second game score	−223
Total score	−136

2.5 Exercise

A 1 Find the change in temperature from A to B.
(a) A: 39°C B: 41°C   (b) A: −17°C B: 1°C   (c) A: 6°C B: −5°C

2 Find the new temperature for each of the following.
(a) −42°C, change of −5°C   (b) 12°C, change of 8°C
(c) 6°C, change of −11°C   (d) −19°C, change of 12°C

B   Remember: Ask yourself if your answer is reasonable.

3   On November 29 the temperature was $-3°C$. If the overnight temperature change was $-2°C$, what was the temperature on November 30?

4   On February 16 the temperature was $-12°C$. If the overnight temperature change was $3°C$, what was the temperature on February 17?

5   A store's temperature is $18°C$. Its cold storage room has a temperature of $-11°C$.
     (a) How much colder is the cold storage room than the store?
     (b) What change in temperature would you experience when you walked from the cold storage room into the store?

6   The temperature inside an igloo was $6°C$. If the temperature outside was $-18°C$, what change in the temperature would you experience if you went outside?

7   The highest shade temperature ever recorded was in Libya in 1922. It was $58°C$. The lowest temperature ever recorded was in Antarctica in 1960. It was $146°C$ below the Libyan temperature. What is the lowest temperature on record?

8   A balloon was released to record temperatures of the atmosphere. The results are shown. Find the change in temperature as the balloon rose from
     (a) S to B   (b) B to D   (c) D to E   (d) S to E

9   Use the results from the previous question. Which is the greatest change?
     (a) S to B   (b) B to C   (c) C to D   (d) D to E

Questions 10 to 13 are based on the chart which shows the extreme temperatures for some cities in Canada in one calendar year.

City	Highest temperature	Lowest temperature
Calgary	35°C	−36°C
Charlottetown	29°C	−28°C
Churchill	30°C	−38°C
Fredericton	37°C	−36°C
Frobisher Bay	19°C	−41°C
Halifax	31°C	−26°C
Kitchener	34°C	−24°C
Montreal	33°C	−31°C
Regina	37°C	−37°C
St. John's	46°C	−21°C
Whitehorse	30°C	−47°C
Vancouver	29°C	−23°C

10   Which city recorded the
     (a) mildest lowest temperature?
     (b) coolest highest temperature?

11   Which city had the
     (a) greatest change in temperature?
     (b) least change in temperature?

 12   (a) Make up a question of your own about the chart.
     (b) Provide a solution for your question.
     (c) What assumptions did you make in finding your solution?

C 13   (a) Which city experienced the greater change in temperature, Vancouver or Regina?
     (b) Which city experienced the greater change in temperature, Halifax or Regina?
     (c) Provide what you think is the reason for your answers in (a) and (b).

14 Integers are used in hockey to show a player's performance.

Plus-Minus Record

A If a player is on the ice and a goal is scored in favour of the player's team, the player receives +1.

B If a player is on the ice and a goal is scored against the player's team, the player receives −1.

The sum of A and B is called the player's Plus-Minus Record.

Copy and complete the chart to find each player's plus-minus record.

	Player	Plus	Minus	Plus-Minus Record
(a)	James	+18	−20	?
(b)	Henry	+43	−18	?
(c)	Carol	+8	−26	?
(d)	Karl	+30	−42	?
(e)	Mitzi	+76	−38	?

15

In golf, par has a special meaning. If a hole is Par 4, this means that the ball should be in the hole in 4 strokes. Par is shown by a score of 0.
- +2 means 2 strokes above par (or zero).
- −2 means 2 strokes below par (or zero).
- a score of −2 is better than a score of +2.

Calculate each golfer's results. Who played best?

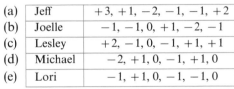

(a)	Jeff	+3, +1, −2, −1, −1, +2
(b)	Joelle	−1, −1, 0, +1, −2, −1
(c)	Lesley	+2, −1, 0, −1, +1, +1
(d)	Michael	−2, +1, 0, −1, +1, 0
(e)	Lori	−1, +1, 0, −1, −1, 0

16 In golf the following vocabulary is used.
▶ Birdie means 1 stroke below par (−1).
▶ Bogey means 1 stroke above par (+1).
▶ Eagle means 2 stokes below par (−2).

Find each golfer's results after 4 holes. Which golfer played best?

(a) Shirley: par, par, eagle, bogey

(b) John: bogey, bogey, par, birdie

(c) Barb: birdie, eagle, par, bogey

(d) Frank: bogey, eagle, par, bogey

2.6 Patterns for Multiplying Integers

The skills and concepts you learn in one area of mathematics extend to learning new skills. For example, in your work with whole numbers, you wrote the sum of like numbers in a simpler way by using multiplication.

Whole numbers:

as a sum
$3 + 3 + 3 + 3 = 12$

as a product
$4 \times 3 = 12$

For integers:

$(+3) + (+3) + (+3) + (+3) = +12$
$(-3) + (-3) + (-3) + (-3) = -12$

$(+4)(+3) = +12$
$(+4)(-3) = ?$

Since these answers must be the same, the example suggests $(+4)(-3) = -12$

As in your earlier work, you can use a pattern to show the product of integers. From the pattern at the right, it appears that:

$$\begin{bmatrix} \text{positive} \\ \text{integer} \end{bmatrix} \times \begin{bmatrix} \text{positive} \\ \text{integer} \end{bmatrix} = \begin{bmatrix} \text{positive} \\ \text{integer} \end{bmatrix}$$

$$\begin{bmatrix} \text{positive} \\ \text{integer} \end{bmatrix} \times \begin{bmatrix} \text{negative} \\ \text{integer} \end{bmatrix} = \begin{bmatrix} \text{negative} \\ \text{integer} \end{bmatrix}$$

These integers are decreasing by 1.

$(+4)(+3) = +12$
$(+4)(+2) = +8$
$(+4)(+1) = +4$
$(+4)(0) = 0$
$(+4)(-1) = -4$
$(+4)(-2) = -8$
$(+4)(-3) = -12$

These products are decreasing by 4.

The following suggest additional patterns for multiplying integers.

$(+3)(+3) = +9$
$(+2)(+3) = +6$
$(+1)(+3) = +3$
$(0)(+3) = 0$
$(-1)(+3) = -3$
$(-2)(+3) = -6$

How do these integers change?

How do these products change?

$(-3)(+3) = -9$
$(-3)(+2) = -6$
$(-3)(+1) = -3$
$(-3)(0) = 0$
$(-3)(-1) = +3$
$(-3)(-2) = +6$

From the previous example for multiplying integers, you observe the following pattern.

$(-2)(+3) = -6$

$$\begin{bmatrix} \text{negative} \\ \text{integer} \end{bmatrix} \times \begin{bmatrix} \text{positive} \\ \text{integer} \end{bmatrix} = \begin{bmatrix} \text{negative} \\ \text{integer} \end{bmatrix}$$

$(-3)(-2) = +6$

$$\begin{bmatrix} \text{negative} \\ \text{integer} \end{bmatrix} \times \begin{bmatrix} \text{negative} \\ \text{integer} \end{bmatrix} = \begin{bmatrix} \text{positive} \\ \text{integer} \end{bmatrix}$$

The results for multiplying integers are summarized in a chart.

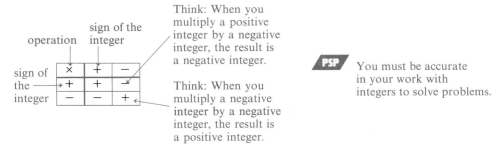

Think: When you multiply a positive integer by a negative integer, the result is a negative integer.

Think: When you multiply a negative integer by a negative integer, the result is a positive integer.

PSP You must be accurate in your work with integers to solve problems.

The exercise explores patterns which will help you learn how to multiply integers.

2.6 Exercise

B 1 (a) Find the values of ▨ in the pattern.
(b) Use the pattern to find the products.
$(+4)(-4) = $ ▨
$(+4)(-5) = $ ▨

$$(+4)(+2) = +8$$
$$(+4)(+1) = ▨$$
$$(+4)(0) = ▨$$
$$(+4)(-1) = ▨$$
$$(+4)(-2) = ▨$$
$$(+4)(-3) = ▨$$

2 Find the values of ▨ for each pattern.

(a) $(+4)(+2) = +8$
$(+4)(+1) = ▨$
$(+4)(▨) = 0$
$(▨)(-1) = -4$
$(+4)(-2) = ▨$

(b) $(+2)(+4) = +8$
$(▨)(+4) = +4$
$(0)(+4) = ▨$
$(▨)(+4) = -4$
$(-2)(▨) = -8$

3 Use the patterns in the previous question to find the products $(+4)(-3)$ and $(-3)(+4)$. What do you notice about your answers?

4 (a) Find the values of ▨ in the pattern.
(b) Use the pattern to find the products.
$(-3)(-3) = $ ▨
$(-4)(-3) = $ ▨

$$(+2)(-3) = -6$$
$$(+1)(-3) = ▨$$
$$(0)(-3) = ▨$$
$$(-1)(-3) = ▨$$
$$(-2)(-3) = ▨$$

5 Find the values of ▨ for each pattern. Continue each pattern for three more rows.

(a) $(+3)(-6) = ▨$
$(+2)(-6) = ▨$
$(▨)(-6) = -6$
$(0)(-6) = ▨$
$(-1)(▨) = +6$

(b) $(+2)(-7) = ▨$
$(+1)(-7) = ▨$
$(▨)(-7) = 0$
$(-1)(▨) = +7$
$(-2)(-7) = ▨$

6   Suggest a pattern to find each product.

    (a) $(+5)(-3)$ (b) $(-2)(+6)$ (c) $(-3)(-5)$ (d) $(-4)(+5)$

7   Copy and complete the following summary.

    (a) The product of a negative integer and a positive integer is a ▨▨▨ integer.

    (b) The product of a positive integer and a positive integer is a ▨▨▨ integer.

    (c) The product of a negative integer and a negative integer is a ▨▨▨ integer.

    (d) The product of a negative integer and a ▨▨▨ integer is a positive integer.

    (e) The product of a positive integer and a negative integer is a ▨▨▨ integer.

    (f) The product of a ▨▨▨ integer and a negative integer is a negative integer.

 8   To solve these problems you need to try all the possibilities.

    (a) Two letters in the word RAW are switched to form a new word.
        What is the new word?

    (b) Two letters in the word ABLE are switched to form a new word.
        What is the new word?

Computer Use

Computers have evolved over the years. The following people have made significant contributions towards the development of computing devices.

▶ Find out what contribution each person made.

▶ Find out two facts about each person.

    Napier   Pascal   Leibniz   Morland   Aiken   Van Heumann
    Baldwin   Babbage   Byron   Jacquard   Eckert   Mauchly

From Math History

Often problems in mathematics are given names such as *Dido's problem.* The history behind the naming of a problem is often a fascinating story in itself. Queen Dido of Carthage was promised as much land as would lie within the boundary of a bull's hide. She cut the hide into thin strips, tied the strips into one long strip and then tied the ends together. The largest area she could enclose occurred when she used a circle. To this day the problem *What is the maximum area that can be enclosed within a given perimeter?* is named in her honour.

▶ Who was Queen Dido?

▶ Find out how large an area the bull's hide did enclose.

2.7 Multiplying Integers

In the previous section you used patterns to show the results of multiplying integers. Use the table to remind you of the signs of products.

×	+	−
+	+	−
−	−	+

Example 1   Find each product.

     (a) $(-7)(23)$ (b) $(-13)(-9)$

Solution   (a) $(-7)(23) = -161$ (b) $(-13)(-9) = 117$

Once you have practised the skills of multiplying integers, you can combine these skills with your substitution skills.

Example 2   Find the value of each expression for $m = -6$ and $n = 2$.

     (a) $3mn$ (b) m^2n

Solution   (a) $3mn$ (b) m^2n

           $= 3(-6)(2)$ $= (-6)^2(2)$

           $= -36$ $= (-6)(-6)(2)$

                               $= 72$

PSP   Remember: Read carefully. $(-3)^2$ means $(-3)(-3) = 9$. -3^2 means $-(3 \times 3) = -9$

2.7 Exercise

A Skills for multiplying integers are important in your work in mathematics.

1   Calculate each of the following.

     (a) $(-1)(+1)$ (b) $(+3)(-4)$ (c) $(-1)(-4)$ (d) $(+7)(+4)$

     (e) $(+4)(-3)$ (f) $(-9)(-8)$ (g) $(-4)(+6)$ (h) $(0)(-6)$

     (i) $(-7)(-6)$ (j) $(+10)(-6)$ (k) $(+12)(+5)$ (l) $(-1)(+7)$

2   Find each product.

     (a) $4(-1)$ (b) $5(-3)$ (c) $-3(-4)$ (d) $-4(-3)$ (e) $3(-4)$

     (f) $-2(-3)$ (g) $-4(6)$ (h) $3(-6)$ (i) $8(-9)$ (j) $-9(-8)$

B List the meanings of any new words or symbols you learn.

3   Find the product bc for each pair of values.

     (a) $b = 2, c = -3$ (b) $b = -2, c = 3$ (c) $b = -3, c = -4$

     (d) $b = -6, c = -4$ (e) $b = 8, c = -4$ (f) $b = -9, c = 6$

4   Find the products. Which has the greatest value?

     (a) $(-3)(+4)$ (b) $(-5)(-6)$ (c) $(+3)(-2)$

Copy and complete each chart.

5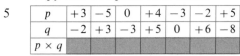

p	+3	−5	0	+4	−3	−2	+5
q	−2	+3	−3	+5	0	+6	−8
p × q							

6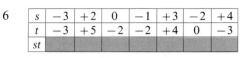

s	−3	+2	0	−1	+3	−2	+4
t	−3	+5	−2	−2	+4	0	−3
st							

7 Find each of the following products.
(a) $(−5)(−3)(+1)$ (b) $(+4)(−3)(−7)$ (c) $(+3)(−3)(−2)$
(d) $(−6)(+5)(−4)$ (e) $(−4)(−3)(−20)$ (f) $(+5)(−3)(−1)$
(g) $(−8)(+6)(−3)$ (h) $(0)(−12)(+8)$ (i) $(−9)(+4)(−3)$

8 Calculate.
(a) $(−2)^2$ (b) $(−3)^2$ (c) $(−4)^2$ (d) $(+4)^2$
(e) $(+2)^2$ (f) $(−5)^2$ (g) $(−2)^3$ (h) $(−1)^3$
(i) $(−3)^3$ (j) $(−2)(−3)^2$ (k) $(−3)(−2)^3$ (l) $(−4)^2(−2)^2$

9 Calculate each of the following.
(a) $−2^3$ (b) $(−2)^3$ (c) $−4^2$ (d) $(−4)^2$ (e) $(−6)^2$
(f) $(−1)^3$ (g) $−6^2$ (h) $−5^2$ (i) $(−5)^2$ (j) $(−5)^3$

10 (a) What procedure would you use on a calculator to calculate $(−3)(−4)$?
    (b) Use a calculator. Calculate the following.
        (i) $(+8)(−4)$ (ii) $(−5)(+7)$ (iii) $(−6)(−9)$ (iv) $(−13)(5)$

11 Find the value of each expression for $x = −1$ and $y = −2$.
(a) $5y$ (b) $−3x$ (c) y^2 (d) x^2y
(e) $3xy$ (f) $−2y^2$ (g) $3x^2y^2$ (h) $4xy^2$

12 Evaluate each number expression for the values given.
(a) $3k$ for $k = −3, −2, −1, 0, 1, 2$ (b) $−5y$ for $y = 3, 2, 1, 0, −1$
(c) $−3m$ for $m = −4, −2, 0, 2, 4$ (d) $4p$ for $p = −5, −3, −1, 3, 5$

PSP 13 You can use patterns to solve some problems. Study the pattern.
$$(−1)^2 = +1, (−1)^3 = −1, (−1)^4 = +1, (−1)^5 = −1, (−1)^6 = +1$$
(a) Which sign, + or −, can you use to complete each statement?
    $(−1)^m = \blacksquare 1$ if m is an even number.
    $(−1)^m = \blacksquare 1$ if m is an odd number.
(b) Evaluate. (i) $(−1)^{391}$ (ii) $(−1)^{1003}$ (iii) $(−1)^{5000}$

C 14 Use the integers shown and one of the operation signs, $+$, $−$ or $×$, and $=$ to write a true statement.
(a) $−2, −3, −5$ (b) $−2, +1, −3$ (c) $+5, +2, −3$ (d) $−4, −8, +2$

2.8 Using Patterns: Dividing Integers

Since multiplication and division are inverse operations, what you have learned about multiplying integers can be used to learn how to divide integers.

To find $\dfrac{-12}{-4} = \text{▨} \longrightarrow$ you can think: $(\text{▨})(-4) = -12$

What number multiplied by -4
gives -12? $\text{▨} = +3$

	If	If
Multiplication	$(-3)(+6) = -18$	$(-3)(-6) = +18$
	then	then
Division	$\dfrac{-18}{+6} = -3$	$\dfrac{+18}{-6} = -3$

Example   Find each quotient.

(a) $(-51) \div (-3)$ (b) $64 \div (-4)$ (c) $(-115) \div 5$

Solution

(a) $(-51) \div (-3) = 17$ Think: $\text{▨} \times (-3) = -51$ $17 \times (-3) = -51$

(b) $64 \div (-4) = -16$ Think: $\text{▨} \times (-4) = 64$ $(-16) \times (-4) = 64$

(c) $(-115) \div 5 = -23$ Think: $\text{▨} \times 5 = -115$ $(-23) \times 5 = -115$

In the exercise you will explore patterns to help you learn how to divide integers.

2.8 Exercise

A Questions 1 to 5 develop your understanding of dividing integers.

1 Use Column A to help you find the values of ▨ in Column B.

Column A	Column B	Column A	Column B
(a) $(+4)(+6) = +24$	$\dfrac{+24}{+6} = \text{▨}$	(b) $(-4)(+6) = -24$	$\dfrac{-24}{+6} = \text{▨}$
(c) $(+4)(-6) = -24$	$\dfrac{-24}{-6} = \text{▨}$	(d) $(-4)(-6) = +24$	$\dfrac{+24}{-6} = \text{▨}$

2 Find each answer. Use each *Think* to help you.

(a) $\dfrac{-32}{+8} = \text{▨}$ Think: $(\text{▨})(+8) = -32$ (b) $\dfrac{+32}{-4} = \text{▨}$ Think: $(\text{▨})(-4) = +32$

(c) $\dfrac{-32}{-8} = \text{▨}$ Think: $(\text{▨})(-8) = -32$ (d) $\dfrac{-32}{-4} = \text{▨}$ Think: $(\text{▨})(-4) = -32$

3   Find the value of ▨ in each of the following. You may wish to rewrite each
    question using multiplication to help you.

(a) $\dfrac{+30}{+6} = ▨$ (b) $\dfrac{-30}{+6} = ▨$ (c) $\dfrac{+30}{-6} = ▨$ (d) $\dfrac{-30}{-6} = ▨$ (e) $\dfrac{-42}{+7} = ▨$

(f) $\dfrac{+42}{-7} = ▨$ (g) $\dfrac{-42}{-7} = ▨$ (h) $\dfrac{-36}{-6} = ▨$ (i) $\dfrac{-36}{-6} = ▨$ (j) $\dfrac{-36}{+6} = ▨$

4   Examine your answers in the previous question.
    (a) When are your quotients positive?   (b) When are your quotients negative?
    (c) Use your answers in (a) and (b) to help you decide whether the answer
        to each of the following is positive or negative.

(i) $\dfrac{+25}{+5}$ (ii) $\dfrac{+25}{-5}$ (iii) $\dfrac{-25}{+5}$ (iv) $\dfrac{-25}{-5}$

5   Copy and complete each sentence.
    (a) The quotient of a positive integer and a positive integer is a ▨▨▨ integer.
    (b) The quotient of a negative integer and a positive integer is a ▨▨▨ integer.
    (c) The quotient of a negative integer and a negative integer is a ▨▨▨ integer.
    (d) The quotient of a positive integer and a negative integer is a ▨▨▨ integer.
    (e) The quotient of a negative integer and a ▨▨▨ integer is a positive integer.
    (f) The quotient of a negative integer and a ▨▨▨ integer is a negative integer.

B 6   For each of the following:
    ▶ Decide whether the quotient is positive or negative.
    ▶ Then write your answer.

(a) $\dfrac{-36}{+9}$ (b) $\dfrac{+54}{-9}$ (c) $\dfrac{+49}{+7}$ (d) $\dfrac{+100}{-10}$ (e) $\dfrac{-60}{-10}$

(f) $\dfrac{-49}{-7}$ (g) $\dfrac{+25}{-5}$ (h) $\dfrac{-54}{-9}$ (i) $\dfrac{-75}{+15}$ (j) $\dfrac{-19}{-19}$

(k) $(-24) \div (-6)$ (l) $(-36) \div (+9)$ (m) $(-36) \div (+18)$
(n) $(+50) \div (+25)$ (o) $(+75) \div (-3)$ (p) $(-90) \div (-2)$

7   Calculate.
    (a) $(-36) \div (-12)$ (b) $15 \div (-3)$ (c) $0 \div (-10)$
    (d) $64 \div (-32)$ (e) $(-72) \div 72$ (f) $72 \div (-9)$
    (g) $(-121) \div (-11)$ (h) $150 \div (-30)$ (i) $(-150) \div (-15)$

8   Copy and complete.

s	92	-80	-78	84	-104	105	-117
t	-4	5	-6	-7	8	-3	-9
$s \div t$							

9   The following procedure is used on a calculator to calculate $(-18) \div (-6)$.

$$\boxed{C}\,18\,\boxed{+/-}\,\boxed{\div}\,6\,\boxed{+/-}\,\boxed{=}$$

Use a calculator. Calculate the following.

    (a) $(+12) \div (-3)$ (b) $(-15) \div (+5)$ (c) $(-28) \div (-4)$ (d) $(-150) \div (-10)$

The following questions involve multiplying and dividing. Read carefully.   PSP

10   Calculate.

    (a) $(-9) \times (-7)$ (b) $(-15) \div 5$ (c) $18 \times (-3)$ (d) $48 \div (-6)$

    (e) $(-13) \times (-3)$ (f) $(-28) \div (-4)$ (g) $8 \times (-11)$ (h) $54 \times (-2)$

    (i) $-54 \div (-2)$ (j) $(-38) \times 0$ (k) $0 \times (-12)$ (l) $0 \div (-9)$

11   Find the value of the variable in each of the following. Remember: $-3y$ means $(-3)(y)$.

    (a) $(-36) \div y = -6$ (b) $x \div (-5) = -5$ (c) $(-12)(-4) = k$

    (d) $(-12) \div m = 4$ (e) $-4y = 24$ (f) $b \div (-2) = -24$

    (g) $(-48) \div p = -8$ (h) $8k = -24$ (i) $33 \div (-11) = h$

    (j) $-4m = -48$ (k) $60 \div t = -12$ (l) $y \div (-7) = -7$

12   Find the value of each expression for $w = -4$.

    (a) $w \div (-1)$ (b) $7w$ (c) $44 \div w$ (d) $-13w$

    (e) $72 \div w$ (f) $9w$ (g) $w \div 2$ (h) $(-52) \div w$

13   (a) Find the value of $36 \div b$ if $b = -12$.

    (b) Find the value of $y \div (-2)$ if $y = -48$.

    (c) Find the value of $-3k$ if $k = -6$.

    (d) Find the value of $17m$ if $m = -5$.

    (e) Find the value of $x \div (-7)$ if $x = 91$.

PSP   14   (a) A digit is represented by a letter A. What is the value of A if the number A1AA2 is divisible by 9?

    (b) Are there any other values of A that are suitable?

C 15   Do you know the answer to the following question?

       Where in Canada was one of the coldest temperatures ever recorded?

To find the answer you need to find the values of the variables. Then arrange your answers from least to greatest. The variables spell the place.

    (a) $(-5)(+2) = E$ (b) $R \div (-2) = +2$ (c) $F \div (-2) = +9$

    (d) $A \div (-4) = -2$ (e) $-8 + (+6) = G$ (f) $(-8) \div B = -2$

    (g) $-12 - (E) = -6$ (h) $(-3)(+5) = L$ (i) $(B)(+2) = -16$

    (j) $10 - (-12) = Y$ (k) $O - (-4) = -8$

2.9   Order of Operations: Integers

The order of operations you used in your work with whole numbers also applies in your work with integers.

For the following example, do the operations with multiplication and division first and then add or subtract.

Example 1   Simplify
$(-8)(-4) \div 2 - (-3)(-2)$.

Solution
$$(-8)(-4) \div 2 - (-3)(-2)$$
$$= 32 \div 2 - (-3)(-2)$$
$$= 16 - (-3)(-2)$$
$$= 16 - 6$$
$$= 10$$

To evaluate expressions, be sure you record the original expression as the first step of your solution.

Example 2   Evaluate $3y^2 - 2x$ for $x = -2$ and $y = 4$.

Solution
$$3y^2 - 2x = 3(4)^2 - 2(-2) \quad \text{Think: Evaluate powers first.}$$
$$= 3(16) - 2(-2)$$
$$= 48 + 4$$
$$= 52$$

The skills you learn for evaluating expressions occur over and over again in your study of mathematics.

 Remember: Read symbols carefully.
$(-4)^2$ means $(-4) \times (-4) = 16$.
-4^2 means $-(4 \times 4) = -16$.

2.9   Exercise

A Remember: Learn the order of operations.

1   Calculate.
(a) $(-3) \times 4 - 3$
(b) $(-8) - 3 \times (-6)$
(c) $(-8) + (-12) \div (-4)$
(d) $-12 \div (-3) + (-3)$
(e) $(-3)^2 - (-2)^2$
(f) $(-5)^2 - (-7) + (-12)$

2   Evaluate each of the following.
(a) $-4 + 20 \div (-4)$
(b) $[-4 + 20] \div (-4)$
(c) $-3 \times (-4) + 8^2$
(d) $-3 \times [(-4) + 8^2]$
(e) $(-16) - [(-8) \div 2]$
(f) $[-16 - (-8)] \div 2$

3 Explain each step in each of the following.

(a) $\dfrac{(-22 + 2) \div (-5)}{(-8) \div (8 \div 4)}$

$= \dfrac{(-20) \div (-5)}{(-8) \div 2}$

$= \dfrac{4}{-4}$

$= -1$

(b) $16 - [3(6 - 3) - 12]$
$= 16 - [3(3) - 12]$
$= 16 - [9 - 12]$
$= 16 - [-3]$
$= 16 + 3$
$= 19$

4 For each of the following, decide which steps need to be used. Then simplify.

(a) $48 \div (-6) + 3$ (b) $43 + 12 \div (-2)$ (c) $(-8)(-5) \div 2$

(d) $(-14) \div 2 - 6^2$ (e) $-9 + 5 \times (-3)$ (f) $8 \div (-4) + 4 \div (-2)^2$

B 5 Simplify each of the following.

(a) $36 \div (-4) - 9$ (b) $(-3)^2 + (-4)^2$ (c) $(-8)^2 - 3^2$

(d) $-2^2 - (4)(-2)$ (e) $(-3)^2 + (-8) \div (-2)$ (f) $(-8 + 2) \div (-3 + 2)$

6 Simplify each of the following.

(a) $\dfrac{-12 - 3}{-3 - 2}$ (b) $\dfrac{-18 + 6}{(-3)(4)}$ (c) $\dfrac{(-16 + 4) \div 2}{8 \div (-8) + 4}$ (d) $\dfrac{-5 + (-3)(-6)}{(-2)^2 + (-3)^2}$

7 Simplify. Use a calculator.

(a) $18 \div (-3) + 6$ (b) $25 - (-18) \div (-6)$ (c) $(-3)^2 \div (-9) + (-3)$

8 Simplify. Which has the greater answer, A or B?

A: $\dfrac{20 + (-12) \div (-3)}{(-4 + 12) \div (-2)}$ B: $\dfrac{7(-4)(12)}{-64 \div (7 - 3)}$

9 Write a solution to simplify each expression. You may do some steps mentally.

(a) $-9 - 3[2(2 - 3)]$ (b) $-4[(-3)(-2) + 4]$

(c) $160 \div (-4) + 2[3(8 - 4)]$ (d) $(-12) \div (-6) + (-3)(-2)$

10 Evaluate each expression for $x = -3$ and $y = -6$.

(a) $3x - 4y$ (b) $4x - 3y$ (c) $-2x + 3y$ (d) $x + 2xy$

(e) $x^2 - 1$ (f) $x^2 + y^2$ (g) $x^2 - y^2$ (h) $2x^2 - y^2$

PSP 11 If 6 goalies can make 768 saves in 4 games, how many saves can 5 goalies make in 2 games? What assumptions did you make?

C 12 Evaluate each expression for $x = -5$ and $y = -2$. Which has the greatest value?

(a) $\dfrac{x^2 - 1}{x + 1}$ (b) $\dfrac{y^2 + 2y + 1}{y + 1}$ (c) $3x(y + 6)$ (d) $-2y(x + 3)$ (e) $\dfrac{xy + y^2}{y}$

Properties of Integers

You have learned some new language related to integers.

-5 is a negative integer.

-5 is the **opposite** of 5, and 5 is the opposite of -5.

-5 is the **additive inverse** of 5, and 5 is the additive inverse of -5.

You also learned how to perform operations with integers. The following exercise explores some properties related to these operations.

13 Copy and complete.

(a) $9 + \boxtimes = 0$ (b) $(-7) + \boxtimes = 0$ (c) $(-8) + 8 = \boxtimes$

(d) $(-6) \times \boxtimes = 0$ (e) $8 \times 0 = \boxtimes$ (f) $0 \times (-5) = \boxtimes$

(g) $12 \times \boxtimes = 12$ (h) $(-7) \times \boxtimes = 7$ (i) $(-5) \times 1 = \boxtimes$

14 Complete the following statements.

(a) The sum of an integer and its additive inverse is ▨▨▨.

(b) The product of an integer and 1 is ▨▨▨.

(c) The product of an integer and 0 is ▨▨▨.

15 Compare the answers to each pair.

(a) $(-5)(3)$ and $(3)(-5)$ (b) $(-11)(6)$ and $(6)(-11)$

(c) $(-4)(-13)$ and $(-13)(-4)$ (d) $(-9) + 3$ and $3 + (-9)$

(e) $(-7) + (-14)$ and $(-14) + (-7)$ (f) $(-6) + 15$ and $15 + (-6)$

(g) $(-9) - (-5)$ and $(-5) - (-9)$ (h) $6 - (-12)$ and $(-12) - 6$

(i) $(-7) - (-18)$ and $(-18) - (-7)$ (j) $8 - 7$ and $7 - 8$

16 Which of the following statements are true?

(a) The order of the integers does not affect the sum.

(b) The order of the integers does not affect the difference.

(c) The order of the integers does not affect the product.

17 Simplify each expression. Match the expressions with the same answer.

(a) $(-9)[(-6) + 2]$ (b) $(12)(-3) - (-4)(-3)$ (c) $(-36) \div (-12) + (-36) \div 3$

(d) $13[(-9) + 11]$ (e) $(-9)(-6) + (-9)(2)$ (f) $(-11)(-3) + (-11)(1)$

(g) $(-36) \div [(-12) + 3]$ (h) $13(-9) + 13(11)$ (i) $[12 - (-4)](-3)$

18 You explored the distributive property in the previous question. Use this property to express each of the following in an equivalent form.

(a) $3[(-5) + 7]$ (b) $6(-3) - 6(8)$ (c) $(-5)(-7) + (-5)(3)$

2.10 ◢PSP◣ Problem Solving Strategy: Making Decisions

Before you can solve a problem in mathematics you must know the answers to these two questions:

  I What information am I asked to find?
 II What information am I given?

To solve a problem, you need to decide on the method to use. Often the words in a problem suggest the method to use to solve the problem. For your work with integers, think: Do I add, subtract, multiply or divide? The *Problem Solving Plan* will help you think in an organized way.

◢PSP◣	Problem Solving Plan
Step A:	Understand the problem. • What are you asked to find? • What are you given?
Step B:	Decide on a strategy. Which clues in the problem suggest a method of solution?
Step C:	Apply the strategy. Do the work.
Step D:	Check your solution.
Step E:	Write a final statement.

Example   The temperatures on six consecutive days at Fredericton were $-6°C$, $-3°C$, $-5°C$, $+3°C$, $-2°C$ and $-5°C$. Find the average temperature for the 6 d.

Solution   Find the sum of the integers.
$$(-6) + (-3) + (-5) + (+3) + (-2) + (-5) = -18$$
Divide by the number of days.
$$\frac{-18}{6} = -3$$

The average temperature was $-3°C$.

2.10 Exercise

A To solve problems, you need to know the vocabulary. ◢PSP◣

1   (a) Add -38 to the sum of -43 and 85.
      (b) Find the average of -14, -24, -15, $+9$.
      (c) Subtract -36 from -28.   (d) Multiply the sum of -24 and -14 by -25.

2   (a) Divide the product of -10 and -8 by 4.
      (b) Divide the sum of -144, -48, and 96 by -12.
      (c) Subtract the sum of -49 and 46 from 45.   (d) Subtract -48 from 86.

B For each problem, write a final statement to complete your solution.

3 The low temperatures recorded one week in Kamloops are shown. What was the average low temperature for the week?

Monday	−4°C	Friday	0°C
Tuesday	−5°C	Saturday	1°C
Wednesday	−5°C	Sunday	2°C
Thursday	−3°C		

4 The temperatures recorded at noon in Aklavik are shown for one week. What was the average noontime temperature?

Wednesday	−18°C	Sunday	−24°C
Thursday	−24°C	Monday	−22°C
Friday	−20°C	Tuesday	−18°C
Saturday	−28°C		

5 The points scored in a dart game are shown. Find the total points scored by each person.

Belive	−2	3	−1	−2	−5
Klarke	−3	−1	4	−1	0
Sholtz	−2	−1	0	−6	−3

6 (a) How would you use multiplication to find the sum of the values −22, −22, −22, −22, −22?

(b) The temperature was 8°C. Over the next 4 h the average change per hour was −3°C. Find the final temperature.

7 During a recent expedition, this profile of the bottom of a lake was drawn. Based on the results, what is the average depth of the lake?

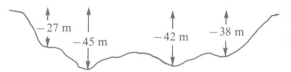

8 The table at the right gives the depths of some of the trenches on the floor of the Pacific Ocean. Find the average depth of these trenches.

Trench	Depth
Mid America Trench	−6669 m
Ryukyu Trench	−7507 m
New Hebrides Trench	−7570 m
Peru Chile Trench	−8064 m
Aleutian Trench	−8100 m
Palau Trench	−8138 m
Japan Trench	−8412 m

9 The needle of a detector moves up and down as shown. (Up is positive and down is negative.) The readings appear at 1-s intervals.

(a) Find the sum of the readings shown.

(b) Find the average.

(c) From your answer in (b), would you expect the needle to point more often in the negative part or positive part in the next 8 s? Why?

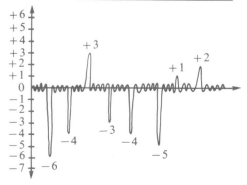

PSP 10 It is often helpful to use a chart to sort information given in a problem. Solve the problem.

Samuel, James and Joseph are married to Jennifer, Samantha and Christina. Samantha's sister is married to Joseph. Samuel has never met Christina. Christina is an only child. Who is married to whom?

C 11 A veterinarian recorded the changes in mass of an animal during the first 8 weeks of its life as -118 g, -89 g, -45 g, -10 g, 25 g, 80 g, 110 g and 115 g.
(a) Find the net change in mass.   (b) Find the average weekly change in mass.

12 At noon the temperature was $6°C$. During the first 6 h after noon the average change was $0°C/h$. For the next 6 h the average change was $-2°C/h$. Find the temperature at midnight.

13 An experiment was set up in which the daily temperature changes for a week were recorded. The average change was $-1°C$. If six of the daily temperature changes were $-3°C$, $-6°C$, $-2°C$, $4°C$, $2°C$ and $-8°C$, what was the seventh daily temperature change?

From Math History

Many people of many nationalities contributed to the development of mathematics. Here are a few of them.

▶ Neils Abel (1802–1829) was a Norwegian. Much of his work involved studying the structure of mathematics, in particular, the mathematical group.

▶ Michael Stifel (1486–1567) has been described by some as the greatest German algebraist (one who studies algebra). Much of his work was published in *Arithmetica Integra*.

▶ Augusta Ada Byron (1815–1852) was the English Countess of Lovelace. She wrote a set of instructions, which is considered to be the first computer program, for Charles Babbage's machine to compute Bernoulli numbers.

For each of the following people of mathematics,

▶ Find out in which country they were born.

▶ List three facts about their lives.

▶ Find out what contribution each person made.

Clairaut (1713–1765)	Boole (1815–1864)
Cantor (1845–1918)	Kovalevski (1850–1891)
Bolzano (1781–1848)	Sylvester (1814–1897)
Archimedes (287–212 B.C.)	Stevin (1546–1620)
Descartes (1596–1650)	Pierce (1809–1880)

Applications: Wind Chill Factor

An important skill in mathematics is using a table to summarize data.
For example, scientists have recorded data to explore the apparent change
in temperature when the wind is blowing.

Speed (km/h)	Actual thermometer reading (°C)												
	10	5	0	−5	−10	−15	−20	−25	−30	−35	−40	−45	−50
8	9	3	−3	−8	−13	−18	−23	−28	−33	−38	−44	−50	−57
16	4	−2	−9	−15	−21	−26	−33	−38	−44	−50	−57	−64	−72
24	2	−6	−13	−20	−26	−33	−40	−45	−51	−58	−65	−73	−81
32	0	−8	−16	−22	−30	−37	−44	−49	−55	−63	−71	−79	−88
40	−1	−9	−18	−25	−32	−40	−47	−53	−59	−67	−76	−83	−93
48	−2	−11	−19	−27	−34	−41	−50	−55	−62	−70	−78	−87	−97
56	−3	−12	−20	−28	−36	−42	−52	−57	−64	−72	−81	−89	−99

The table shows the combined effect of the temperature of the air with
the speed of the wind. In the Arctic or the Antarctic, you can get severe
frostbite without knowing it. If you are travelling at a speed of 32 km/h,
or if the wind speed is 32 km/h, then an actual air temperature of −20°C
feels like a temperature of −44°C. This apparent temperature of −44°C
is called the **wind chill factor**.

14 Complete the table for the following places in the Arctic.

Check your work with a calculator.

	Location	Temperature	Wind speed	Wind chill factor
(a)	Innuik	−10°C	40 km/h	?
(b)	Tiksi	−25°C	?	−45°C
(c)	Zemlya	?	32 km/h	−71°C
(d)	Point Barrow	−15°C	56 km/h	?

15 At Shackleton, Antarctica, the temperature was −25°C with no wind.

(a) Find the wind chill factor when the wind started to blow at 8 km/h.

(b) A wind of 32 km/h would cause the wind chill factor to drop by how
many degrees?

16 On Ellesmere Island in the Arctic the wind chill factor was −50°C. If the
wind speed was 16 km/h, what was the actual air temperature?

17 A survey crew used sleds to move from Knox Coast to Kemp Land in
the Antarctic. If they travelled at 24 km/h and the air temperature was
−20°C, estimate the wind chill factor.

18 Scientists had protective clothing made to withstand temperatures as low
as −65°C. What maximum wind speed for an air temperature of −40°C
could they withstand?

2.11 Working with Absolute Value

The cars shown in the diagram have driven the same distance but in opposite directions. To show the directions, you can use integers.

The magnitude or size of the distance driven is the same. The directions are different.

If you wanted to compare the gas consumption of the two cars, you would only be interested in the distance travelled not the direction. You would only be concerned with the *size* or *magnitude* of $+5$ and -5, and not with whether it is positive or negative. This is called the **absolute value** of the integer. The symbol $|\ \ |$ is used to show the absolute value of -5 and $+5$.

$$|+5| = 5 \qquad |-5| = 5 \qquad \text{This symbol is read as "the absolute value of } -5\text{".}$$

For any integer, n, $|n| = n$ if $n \geq 0$,
$$|n| = -n \text{ if } n < 0.$$

To calculate with absolute value, you need to understand each step of the solutions to the following example.

Example Evaluate.

(a) $|+3|$ (b) $|-6|$ (c) $|+3-5|$ (d) $|+3| + |-5|$

Solution

(a) $|+3|$ (b) $|-6|$ (c) $|+3-5|$ (d) $|+3| + |-5|$
    $= 3$ $= 6$ $= |-2|$ $= 3 + 5$
                                    $= 2$ $= 8$

2.11 Exercise

A 1 Find the value of each of the following.

(a) $|-2|$ (b) $|+3|$ (c) $|-5|$ (d) $|-10|$ (e) $|+8|$

2 Simplify each of the following.

(a) $|-3| - |4|$ (b) $|-6| - |-3|$ (c) $|-2| + |3|$ (d) $3|-6| - |-3|$
(e) $2|6| - 3|-4|$ (f) $|3 - 8|$ (g) $|8 - 3|$ (h) $|4 - 2| + |6 - 3|$

3 Use either $<$, $>$ or $=$ in place of ⊘.

(a) $|-6|$ ⊘ $|5|$ (b) $|-3|$ ⊘ $|-4|$ (c) $|-6|$ ⊘ $|-5|$ (d) $|5|$ ⊘ $|-6|$

B   Remember: $3|8 - 3|$ means $3 \times |8 - 3|$. Multiplication is understood.

4   Simplify.
(a) $3|-2| + 2|-6| - 3|8 - 5|$ (b) $3|8 - 3| + 2|4 - 8| - 6|9 - 12|$
(c) $|4 - 2| + |2 - 6| + |8 - 5|$ (d) $|6 - 9| + 2|3 - 4| + |6 - 1|$

5   Use $<$, $>$ or $=$ in place of ⊘ for each of the following.
(a) $|-3 + 8|$ ⊘ $|-8 + 5|$ (b) $|-2 + 6|$ ⊘ $|-2| + |6|$
(c) $|-2 - 3|$ ⊘ $|-2| + |-3|$ (d) $|-5 + 3|$ ⊘ $|-5| + |3|$

6   Simplify each of the following.
(a) $-3|2|$ (b) $-6|-2|$ (c) $-3(-3)$
(d) $-4(-2) + |-3|$ (e) $2(-3) + |-6|$ (f) $-2|-2| - |-3|$
(g) $-4(-3) - 3(-2)$ (h) $|-6 - (-3)|$ (i) $|-3 - 2| - |-3 - (-2)|$
(j) $|4 - 8| - 3(4 - |3|)$ (k) $(6 - |3|) - 4(|3| - |2|)$ (l) $4|8 - 11| - 4(|8| - |11|)$

7   If $x = 5$ and $y = -3$, evaluate $|x| + 2|y| + xy$.

8   If $x = -1$, $y = 3$ and $z = -2$, evaluate each of the following.
(a) $|x| - |y|$ (b) $|x - y|$ (c) $|x| + |y|$
(d) $|x + y|$ (e) $|x + y + z|$ (f) $|x| + |y| + |z|$
(g) $2|x| + 3|y|$ (h) $|2x + 3y|$ (i) $|x + y| \times z$
(j) $(x + y)z$ (k) $|x + y| + |z|$ (l) $|xy| - |yz|$

9   (a) Find the values of $|3y|$ and $3|y|$ for each value of y.
       (i) $y = 0$ (ii) $y = -4$ (iii) $y = 4$
    (b) Use your answers to explain why $|3y| = 3|y|$.

C 10   (a) Find the values of $|x^2|$ and x^2 for each value of x.
       (i) $x = 0$ (ii) $x = -4$ (iii) $x = 4$
    (b) Use your answers to explain why $|x^2| = x^2$.

Math Tip

To solve a problem, whether it is in mathematics or in another discipline, you must understand the meaning of each word that occurs in the problem.

▶ Make a list of all the new math words you have learned in this chapter. Provide an example of your own to illustrate each word.

▶ Place any new problem solving strategies you have acquired in your *Problem Solving Plan* **PSP** .

2.12 **PSP** Problem Solving: Building Strategies

Often while solving a problem you need to ask yourself important questions.

▶ Do I understand the meaning of all the words used in the problem?

▶ Is there enough information given to solve the problem?

▶ Can I use a diagram or a model to help me record the given information?

▶ Can I use a pattern, a table or a chart to help me solve the problem?

▶ Can I solve a simpler but related problem?

▶ If I can't solve the problem, should I think of the problem from a different point of view?

PSP	Problem Solving Plan

Step A: Understand the problem.
  • What are you asked to find?
  • What are you given?

Step B: Decide on a strategy.

Step C: Apply the strategy. Do the work.

Step D: Check your solution.

Step E: Write a final statement.

To develop a problem solving plan of your own, you have been listing questions like those above in your *Problem Solving Plan* as shown by the shaded regions in the chart.
(Refer to the problem solving sections in Chapter 1.)

To solve a problem, you need to make decisions.

You can use different strategies or a combination of strategies to help you solve the following problems.

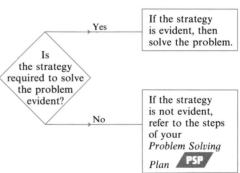

Is the strategy required to solve the problem evident?

Yes → If the strategy is evident, then solve the problem.

No → If the strategy is not evident, refer to the steps of your *Problem Solving Plan* **PSP**

Example 1   How many ways can 4 different books be arranged on a shelf?

PSP Sometimes to solve a problem you need to make assumptions.
Assume that all the books are placed on the shelf in a normal vertical arrangement.

1	2	3	4	

PSP Think: Is the strategy immediately evident?

Solution   You can use a diagram to help you list all the possibilities. Organize your work carefully as shown.

Use A, B, C and D to represent the 4 books.

ABCD	BACD	CABD	DABC
ABDC	BADC	CADB	DACB
ACBD	BCAD	CBAD	DBAC
ACDB	BCDA	CBDA	DBCA
ADBC	BDAC	CDAB	DCAB
ADCB	BDCA	CDBA	DCBA

Thus 4 books can be arranged 24 different ways on a shelf.

The above would not be an efficient method to find the number of ways to arrange 6 books on a shelf, but it suggests another strategy as shown in the next example.

Example 2   How many ways can 6 different books be arranged on a shelf?

Solution   Think of a simpler problem. Use a pattern.

Number of Books	Diagram	Number of Arrangements
2	AB BA	2
3	ABC ACB BAC BCA CAB CBA	6
4	See Solution 1	24

Think: Look for a pattern.
$$2 = 2 \times 1$$
$$6 = 3 \times 2 \times 1$$
$$24 = 4 \times 3 \times 2 \times 1$$

Continue the pattern to obtain the answer.

Number of Books		Number of Arrangements
5		$5 \times 4 \times 3 \times 2 \times 1 = 120$
6		$6 \times 5 \times 4 \times 3 \times 2 \times 1 = 720$

Based on the pattern, you can arrange 6 books in 720 different ways on a shelf.

As shown by the above solutions, to list all the possibilities for 6 books as in Example 1 would not be efficient, but the method would *eventually solve the problem*. The advantage of the solution in Example 2 is that it allows you to generalize the solution for any number of books.

2.12 Exercises

B 1 (a) At a water fountain, how many ways can 2 people line up? 3 people line up? 4 people line up?

(b) Use the pattern in (a). How many ways can 5 people line up at a water fountain?

(c) Use your results in (a) and (b). How many ways can 10 people line up at a water fountain?

2 (a) Two people are to send Valentines to each other. How many Valentines are needed?

(b) Three people are to send Valentines to each other. How many Valentines are needed?

(c) Use the pattern in (a) and (b) to predict how many Valentines are needed if 4 people send Valentines to each other. Justify your answer.

3 How many different ways can 9 baseball players be organized for a batting order?

4 If you use the letters A, B and C, you can write a "word" that makes sense like CAB or a "word" like BAC that makes no sense (nonsense).

(a) How many different words can you create using the three letters, A, B and C?

(b) How many of these words make sense?

5 How many times does the digit 1 or the digit 3 occur in writing the natural numbers from 1 to 100?

6 (a) How many different committees of 2 people can you make if 3 people volunteer?

(b) How many different committees of 3 people can you make up from 5 people?

7 What is the next number you would write? Justify your answer.

2   6   11   20   30

8 What is the least positive integer that when divided by 3, 5 or 7 leaves a remainder of 2?

9 A truck can carry 4 cows and 12 calves. Alternately it can carry 8 cows and 2 calves. How many calves can the truck carry if it only carries calves?

10 Two clocks are placed side by side. One clock works perfectly while the other clock loses 5 min each hour. If both clocks start at noon one day, how long will it take before the two clocks read the same time again?

Practice and Problems: Review

1   Use a suitable integer to show
    (a) a profit of 6 dollars   (b) 5 steps down   (c) an increase of 4 km

2   Arrange the integers in ascending order.
    (a) $-1, 9, -13, -4, 8$ (b) $-13, -19, 12, 18, -15$

3   Find the solution set and draw the graph for $k \in I$.
    (a) $k < -2$ (b) $k \geqq -1$ (c) $-2 < k < 4$ (d) $-4 \leqq k \leqq -3$

4   Find each sum.
    (a) $(+2) + (+5)$ (b) $(-2) + (-5)$ (c) $(-2) + (+5)$
    (d) $(+2) + (-5)$ (e) $(-8) + (+4)$ (f) $(-8) + (+8)$
    (g) $(-8) + (-2) + (+6)$ (h) $(+6) + (-3) + (-2)$

5   Copy and complete the chart.

	(a)	(b)	(c)	(d)	(e)	(f)	(g)	(h)
m	-2	$+4$	$+7$	-3	-8	-1	-3	$+7$
n	$+4$	-4	-2	$+6$	$+4$	$+6$	-5	-6
$m - n$	?	?	?	?	?	?	?	?

6   Calculate.
    (a) $(+4)(+2)$ (b) $(+4)(-2)$ (c) $(-4)(+2)$ (d) $(-4)(-2)$
    (e) $(+9)(-6)$ (f) $(-3)^2$ (g) $(-6)^2$ (h) $(+11)(-5)$

7   Find the answer.
    (a) $\dfrac{+15}{+3}$ (b) $\dfrac{-15}{+3}$ (c) $\dfrac{+15}{-3}$ (d) $\dfrac{-28}{-7}$ (e) $\dfrac{+18}{-18}$ (f) $\dfrac{+121}{-11}$

8   Simplify.
    (a) $(-48) \div 8 + 2$ (b) $12 \div (-6) + 16 \div 4$ (c) $(-2)^2 - (-3)^3$

9   Evaluate for $a = -2$ and $b = -3$.
    (a) $2a - 3b$ (b) $a + 2b$ (c) $-4a + b^2$ (d) $-3a - b^2$

10 The coldest place on average is Polus Nedostvpnostic with a temperature of $-58°C$. The hottest place has a temperature of $34°C$. By how much do the extremes differ?

11 Simplify.
    (a) $|4| - |-6|$ (b) $|4 - (-6)|$ (c) $3|5 - 8|$ (d) $3(|5| - |8|)$

Practice Test

1   Arrange the integers from greatest to least.
    (a) $-99, 101, -95, -102, 97$ (b) $33, -3, 333, -33, 3$

2   Find the solution set for $n \in I$. Then draw the graph.
    (a) $n \leq -3$ (b) $-5 \leq n < -1$ (c) $-3 \leq n \leq 2$

3   Calculate.
    (a) $3 + (-2)$ (b) $-2 + 3$ (c) $4 + (-4)$ (d) $4 - 5$ (e) $-3 + (-3)$
    (f) $-4 - 3$ (g) $-5 - (-6)$ (h) $4 - (-4)$ (i) $5 + (-2)$ (j) $(-4) + (-5)$

4   Simplify.
    (a) $3 + (-8) + (-7) + 6 + 3 - (-8)$ (b) $-4 - 2 + (-1) - (-1) - 3 - (-2)$

5   Calculate.
    (a) $(-4)(2)$ (b) $-12 \div 4$ (c) $16 \div (-4)$ (d) $(-2)^3$
    (e) $(-3)(-4)$ (f) $-14 \div (-7)$ (g) $(-64) \div (-4)$ (h) $72 \div (-6)$

6   Perform the operation indicated.
    (a) $(-6)(-3)$ (b) $(-6) + (-3)$ (c) $-6 - 3$
    (d) $(-6) \div (-3)$ (e) $(-8) \div 4$ (f) $16 \div (-4)$
    (g) $+4(-3)$ (h) $(-36) \div 9$ (i) $54 - (-9)$

7   Simplify.
    (a) $-3 + (-12) \div (-3)$ (b) $12 - (-2)(9) \div 3$
    (c) $40 \div (-4) - 2 + 2(-8 \div 2)$ (d) $-3 + (-2)^2 + (-3)^2$

8   (a) Evaluate $3a - 4b$ if $a = 3, b = 2$.   (b) Evaluate $2k^2 - 3w$ if $k = -6, w = 2$.

9   The metal mercury is a liquid at room temperature. Its freezing point is
    $-39°C$. The freezing point of alcohol is $-114°C$. How much colder is the
    freezing point of alcohol than the freezing point of mecury?

10 The temperatures recorded for a week were $-8°C, -6°C, -4°C, -3°C,$
    $0°C, 2°C, -2°C$.
    (a) Calculate the average daily temperature.
    (b) How much did the temperature change from the start of the week to
         the end of the week?

11 Simplify.
    (a) $-4|-7|$ (b) $|8 - 13|$ (c) $|-5| - |-4|$ (d) $7|-4 - 1|$

Microcomputers: Components

Two key terms associated with computers are hardware and software.

▶ **Hardware** is the equipment you see.

▶ **Software** is the programs or the routines and codes which are used to direct the operation of a computer.

The operation of a computer is as follows:

Step 1 A computer operator places data called the **input** into the computer and gives the instructions as to what is to be done with the data. These instructions are written as a **computer program**. Data are input into a computer in a variety of ways such as from a magnetic tape, a disk or a keyboard.

Step 2 Once the computer has been programmed, it acts on the data using the **central processing unit** or **CPU**.

Step 3 The responses or the results of the computer program are referred to as the **output**. Outputs from the computer are provided in a variety of ways such as on a video screen, through a printer, on punched cards or tape or by a synthesized voice.

Each computer also has

▶ a **primary memory** in which is stored particular data relating to the problem the computer is working on.

▶ a **secondary memory** in which is stored data, instructions and so on, which the computer has been programmed to keep regardless of the data in the primary memory.

1 Each of these terms is used when working with computers. Find the meaning of each. Illustrate each word by an example.

(a) keyboard (b) cursor (c) function key

(d) output screen (e) shift key (f) CLR button

(g) punched card (h) magnetic tape (i) printer

(j) disk (k) chip (l) on line terminal

2 Compile a list of other words you want to know about that appear in a computer manual, in newspapers or in other resources.

3

Real Numbers: Process and Properties

Building rational numbers, operations with rational numbers, using calculators, rationals as decimals, vocabulary and properties, square roots and formulas, real numbers and their graphs, Pythagoras and right triangles, constructing irrational numbers, applications, problem solving skills and strategies

Introduction

Often mathematics is developed from a need. As needs change, more mathematics is introduced and developed. For example, the first set of numbers you encountered were the natural or counting numbers.

$$N = \{1, 2, 3, 4, 5, \ldots\}$$

The Ancient Romans used the following symbols for the natural numbers.

I	II	III	IV	V	VI	VII	VIII	IX	X	L	C	D	M
1	2	3	4	5	6	7	8	9	10	50	100	500	1000

The Ancient Greeks used yet another set of symbols.

α	β	γ	δ	ε	F	ζ	η	θ	L	K	λ	μ	v	ξ	o	π	G	ρ
1	2	3	4	5	6	7	8	9	10	20	30	40	50	60	70	80	90	100

The ancient systems lacked a symbol for zero. It was not until centuries later, about the 15th century, that the first printed use of zero occurred. With the inclusion of 0, the set of whole numbers evolved.

$$W = \{0, 1, 2, 3, 4, \ldots\}$$

In 1489 the first appearance of our present $+$ and $-$ signs occurred. It was the need to represent opposite ideas that led to the development of negative numbers. When these are included with the set of whole numbers, the set of integers is formed.

$$I = \{\ldots, -2, -1, 0, 1, 2, \ldots\}$$

It was the Pythagoreans that first showed the existence of points on the number line that did not correspond to rational numbers. This discovery was important to the study of mathematics. Since the numbers were not rational, they became known as irrational numbers. Rationals and irrationals combined make up the real numbers which you will study in this chapter. The concepts and properties of the real number system provide an important foundation for the study of all mathematics.

3.1 Building Rational Numbers

In your earlier work you graphed integers on a number line. You can also name points between the integers. The number $\frac{1}{2}$ is midway between 0 and 1. You can also mark the number $-\frac{1}{2}$ midway between 0 and -1.

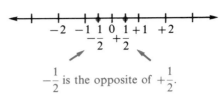

$-\frac{1}{2}$ is the opposite of $+\frac{1}{2}$.

Using the set of integers, $I = \{\ldots, -3, -2, -1, 0, 1, 2, 3, \ldots\}$, you can build another set of numbers called the **rational numbers**.

$$\frac{-2}{3} \qquad \frac{3}{-2} \qquad \frac{2}{3} \qquad \frac{4}{-1} \qquad \frac{5}{1}$$

Each rational is of the form $\frac{a}{b}$ where a and b are integers and b is not equal to zero. The set of all rational numbers, Q, is written as

$$Q = \left\{ \frac{a}{b} \middle| a \in I, b \in I, b \neq 0 \right\}.$$
  The set of rational numbers $\frac{a}{b}$ where a and b are integers, $b \neq 0$.

Every integer is a member of the set Q, since any integer can be written in the form $\frac{a}{b}$ by using $b = 1$. For example, $-3 = \frac{-3}{1}$.

You can work with rational numbers in much the same way as with fractions. To do so, you need to use your skills with integers.

You can write equivalent rational numbers.

$$\frac{-2}{3} = \frac{-2(2)}{3(2)} \qquad \frac{4}{-5} = \frac{4(-1)}{-5(-1)}$$
$$= \frac{-4}{6} \qquad\qquad = \frac{-4}{5}$$

You can also write rational numbers in lowest terms.

$$\frac{6}{-9} = \frac{6 \div (-3)}{-9 \div (-3)} \qquad \frac{0}{-5} = \frac{0 \div (-5)}{-5 \div (-5)}$$
$$= \frac{-2}{3} \text{ or } -\frac{2}{3} \qquad = \frac{0}{1} \text{ or } 0$$

The following rational numbers are equivalent and mark the same point on the number line. Use the form $-\frac{1}{2}$ for final answers. $\qquad \dfrac{-1}{2} \qquad \dfrac{1}{-2} \qquad -\dfrac{1}{2}$

To compare rationals, you follow the same procedure as for integers.

Since $-\frac{2}{3}$ is to the left of $-\frac{1}{3}$, $-\frac{2}{3} < -\frac{1}{3}$.

Since $\frac{3}{4}$ is to the right of $\frac{1}{4}$, $\frac{3}{4} > \frac{1}{4}$.

3.1 Exercise

A 1 A rational number is of the form $\dfrac{a}{b}$, a, $b \in I$. Write the rational number.

(a) $a = -3$, $b = 2$ (b) $a = -10$, $b = -3$ (c) $a = -2$, $b = 5$

2 In each of the following, which rational numbers are equivalent?

(a) $\dfrac{-1}{2}, \dfrac{2}{-4}, \dfrac{-2}{-4}, \dfrac{1}{-2}$ (b) $\dfrac{4}{5}, \dfrac{-4}{-5}, \dfrac{-4}{5}, \dfrac{4}{-5}$ (c) $\dfrac{7}{8}, \dfrac{-7}{8}, \dfrac{7}{-8}, \dfrac{7}{8}, \dfrac{-7}{-8}$

3 In each of the following, which rationals are expressed in lowest terms?

(a) $\dfrac{2}{-8}, \dfrac{1}{-4}, \dfrac{-1}{4}$ (b) $\dfrac{-8}{12}, \dfrac{-4}{6}, \dfrac{-2}{3}$ (c) $\dfrac{-10}{-6}, \dfrac{-5}{-3}, \dfrac{5}{3}$

4 Write equivalent forms for each of the following.

(a) $-\dfrac{3}{4}$ (b) $\dfrac{2}{-3}$ (c) $\dfrac{-2}{5}$ (d) $\dfrac{3}{5}$ (e) $-\dfrac{5}{7}$ (f) $\dfrac{-2}{-9}$

5 Simplify each of the following rationals where possible.

(a) $\dfrac{-4}{2}$ (b) $\dfrac{-8}{-4}$ (c) $\dfrac{12}{6}$ (d) $\dfrac{-16}{-4}$ (e) $\dfrac{16}{-4}$ (f) $\dfrac{-25}{-5}$

6 Use $<$ or $>$ for ⊘ in each of the following.

(a) $\dfrac{1}{4}$ ⊘ $\dfrac{3}{4}$ (b) $-\dfrac{1}{4}$ ⊘ $\dfrac{1}{4}$ (c) $\dfrac{-3}{8}$ ⊘ $\dfrac{-7}{8}$ (d) $\dfrac{-5}{4}$ ⊘ $\dfrac{-3}{4}$

B   Remember: These rationals are equivalent: $-\dfrac{1}{2} = \dfrac{-1}{2} = \dfrac{1}{-2}$

7 Write two equivalent rationals for each of the following. (Write your answers with *positive* denominators.)

(a) $\dfrac{4}{-5}$ (b) $\dfrac{-2}{3}$ (c) $\dfrac{1}{-2}$ (d) $\dfrac{-3}{5}$ (e) $\dfrac{1}{3}$ (f) $\dfrac{3}{-4}$

8 Show that   (a) $-\left(\dfrac{-2}{3}\right) = \dfrac{2}{3}$ (b) $-\left(\dfrac{-2}{-3}\right) = \dfrac{-2}{3}$

9 Express each of the following rationals in lowest terms. Write each of your results with a positive denominator.

(a) $\dfrac{-4}{10}$ (b) $\dfrac{6}{-30}$ (c) $\dfrac{-8}{12}$ (d) $\dfrac{-30}{-100}$ (e) $-\dfrac{-4}{-8}$

(f) $-\dfrac{12}{-10}$ (g) $-\dfrac{-25}{5}$ (h) $-\dfrac{-75}{-100}$ (i) $\dfrac{-8}{10}$ (j) $\dfrac{-15}{-10}$

10   Find the rational number represented by each of the following expressions if $x = -1$, $y = 2$ and $z = -3$. Express each rational in lowest terms.

   (a) $\dfrac{z}{-3}$ (b) $\dfrac{2x}{y}$ (c) $\dfrac{x+y}{z}$ (d) $\dfrac{x^2+y}{z}$

11   Find the missing numerator or denominator in each of the following.

   (a) $-\dfrac{4}{5} = -\dfrac{x}{20}$ (b) $-\dfrac{3}{4} = -\dfrac{x}{20}$ (c) $\dfrac{5}{6} = \dfrac{15}{x}$

   (d) $-\dfrac{9}{18} = \dfrac{3}{x}$ (e) $\dfrac{5}{-12} = \dfrac{x}{36}$ (f) $-\dfrac{9}{15} = \dfrac{3}{x}$

12   Use $>$ or $<$ in place of ⊘ for each of the following.

   (a) $-\dfrac{2}{3}$ ⊘ $-\dfrac{5}{6}$ (b) $\dfrac{2}{3}$ ⊘ $\dfrac{3}{4}$ (c) $\dfrac{-2}{5}$ ⊘ $\dfrac{3}{10}$ (d) $-\dfrac{3}{5}$ ⊘ $\dfrac{-4}{7}$

13   Write these rational numbers in order from least to greatest.

   (a) $\dfrac{-3}{5}, \dfrac{1}{-3}, -\dfrac{4}{3}$ (b) $\dfrac{-2}{5}, \dfrac{-3}{2}, \dfrac{1}{3}$ (c) $\dfrac{3}{10}, -\dfrac{2}{5}, \dfrac{-1}{2}$

14   Express each of the following in mixed form.

   (a) $\dfrac{-11}{4}$ (b) $\dfrac{-10}{3}$ (c) $\dfrac{12}{-5}$ (d) $\dfrac{15}{4}$ (e) $\dfrac{-20}{7}$

15   Express each of the following in improper form.

   (a) $-3\dfrac{1}{2}$ (b) $-5\dfrac{1}{4}$ (c) $2\dfrac{2}{3}$ (d) $-1\dfrac{7}{10}$ (e) 6

16   Use $>$, $<$ or $=$ in place of ⊘ in each of the following.

   (a) $-2\dfrac{1}{2}$ ⊘ $-\dfrac{9}{4}$ (b) $\dfrac{17}{5}$ ⊘ $3\dfrac{3}{10}$ (c) $\dfrac{-11}{3}$ ⊘ $-3\dfrac{1}{3}$

   (d) $-1\dfrac{8}{12}$ ⊘ $\dfrac{-5}{3}$ (e) $\dfrac{18}{-4}$ ⊘ $-4\dfrac{1}{2}$ (f) $2\dfrac{3}{5}$ ⊘ $\dfrac{12}{5}$

Calculator Use

Refresh your calculator skills. Refer to the manual provided with your calculator to review the functions of the following keys.

$$\boxed{\sqrt{x}} \quad \boxed{\dfrac{1}{x}} \quad \boxed{+/-} \quad \boxed{\%} \quad \boxed{x^2} \quad \boxed{y^2} \quad \boxed{MS} \quad \boxed{MR} \quad \boxed{M+} \quad \boxed{M-} \quad \boxed{\times} \quad \boxed{C} \quad \boxed{AC} \quad \boxed{\sqrt[x]{x}}$$

Are there examples in your manual to illustrate the use of the above keys as well as any other keys that are new to you?

3.2 Rational Numbers: Adding and Subtracting

To add and subtract rationals, you follow the same principles as you did when you added and subtracted fractions.

Fractions $\qquad\qquad\qquad\qquad$ Rationals

$$\frac{1}{2} + \frac{3}{8} = \frac{4}{8} + \frac{3}{8} \longleftarrow \text{Find a common} \longrightarrow \frac{1}{2} + \frac{-3}{8} = \frac{4}{8} + \frac{-3}{8}$$
$$\text{denominator.}$$

$$= \frac{4+3}{8} \qquad\qquad\qquad\qquad\qquad = \frac{4+(-3)}{8}$$

$$\text{Remember:}$$

$$= \frac{7}{8} \qquad \frac{a}{-b} = \frac{-a}{b} = -\frac{a}{b} \qquad = \frac{1}{8}$$

Sometimes you have to express numbers given in mixed form as improper fractions before adding or subtracting.

Example   Simplify.

$$\text{(a) } \frac{2}{-3} + \frac{-1}{6} \qquad\qquad \text{(b) } \frac{2}{-9} - 1\frac{1}{3}$$

Solution   (a) $\quad \dfrac{2}{-3} + \dfrac{-1}{6} \qquad$ (b) $\quad \dfrac{2}{-9} - \dfrac{4}{3} \qquad 1\dfrac{1}{3}$ is equivalent to $\dfrac{4}{3}$.

$$= \frac{-2}{3} + \frac{-1}{6} \qquad\qquad = \frac{-2}{9} - \frac{4}{3}$$

$$= \frac{-4}{6} + \frac{-1}{6} \qquad\qquad = \frac{-2}{9} - \frac{12}{9}$$

$$= \frac{(-4) + (-1)}{6} \qquad\qquad = \frac{-2}{9} + \frac{-12}{9} \qquad \text{To subtract, add the opposite.}$$

$$= -\frac{5}{6} \qquad\qquad\qquad = \frac{(-2) + (-12)}{9}$$

PSP   Always ask yourself: Is the answer in lowest terms?

$$= -\frac{14}{9}$$

3.2 Exercise

A 1   Use equivalent rationals to write each pair with a positive common denominator.

$$\text{(a) } \frac{-1}{2}, \frac{1}{4} \qquad \text{(b) } \frac{3}{4}, \frac{-5}{8} \qquad \text{(c) } \frac{-2}{3}, \frac{3}{-4} \qquad \text{(d) } \frac{-1}{3}, \frac{2}{-5} \qquad \text{(e) } \frac{1}{-2}, \frac{3}{-10}$$

2   Find the missing numerator in each of the following.

$$\text{(a) } -2\frac{1}{4} = \frac{x}{4} \qquad \text{(b) } 1\frac{1}{2} = \frac{x}{2} \qquad \text{(c) } -1\frac{2}{3} = \frac{x}{3} \qquad \text{(d) } -2\frac{3}{4} = \frac{x}{4} \qquad \text{(e) } 3\frac{3}{5} = \frac{x}{5}$$

B Remember: Express each answer in lowest terms.

3 Add each of the following.

(a) $\dfrac{-3}{4} + \dfrac{1}{4}$ (b) $\dfrac{3}{8} + \dfrac{-7}{8}$ (c) $\dfrac{-3}{4} + \dfrac{-7}{10}$ (d) $\dfrac{-1}{5} + \dfrac{3}{10}$

(e) $\dfrac{-2}{5} + \dfrac{-3}{10}$ (f) $\dfrac{4}{3} + \dfrac{-3}{5}$ (g) $\dfrac{1}{2} + \dfrac{-2}{3}$ (h) $\dfrac{3}{-5} + \dfrac{-3}{4}$

4 Subtract each of the following.

(a) $\dfrac{3}{4} - \dfrac{1}{4}$ (b) $-\dfrac{2}{3} - \dfrac{-1}{3}$ (c) $\dfrac{-4}{5} - \dfrac{-3}{5}$ (d) $\dfrac{7}{8} - \dfrac{-1}{4}$

(e) $\dfrac{-3}{4} - \dfrac{-2}{3}$ (f) $\dfrac{1}{3} - \dfrac{-1}{8}$ (g) $\dfrac{4}{5} - \dfrac{3}{-4}$ (h) $\dfrac{-1}{3} - \dfrac{1}{4}$

5 Simplify each of the following. Watch the operation!

(a) $\dfrac{3}{4} - \dfrac{-1}{4}$ (b) $\dfrac{-2}{5} + \dfrac{1}{-2}$ (c) $\dfrac{3}{5} - \dfrac{-1}{10}$ (d) $-\dfrac{3}{4} + \dfrac{-1}{8}$

(e) $\dfrac{1}{-4} + \dfrac{-1}{3}$ (f) $\dfrac{-3}{4} - \dfrac{2}{3}$ (g) $\dfrac{-3}{4} - \dfrac{1}{-4}$ (h) $\dfrac{5}{-12} + \dfrac{-3}{4}$

(i) $\dfrac{-1}{4} + \dfrac{-4}{5}$ (j) $\dfrac{3}{5} - \dfrac{-2}{3}$ (k) $\dfrac{1}{-8} - \dfrac{-3}{4}$ (l) $\dfrac{-3}{5} + \dfrac{7}{-10}$

6 For each of the following, find the common denominator for the three rationals and then simplify.

(a) $\dfrac{3}{4} + \dfrac{-1}{4} - \dfrac{-1}{-2}$ (b) $\dfrac{-1}{8} + \dfrac{1}{-4} - \dfrac{-1}{2}$ (c) $\dfrac{1}{3} - \dfrac{-1}{2} + \dfrac{1}{-6}$

(d) $\dfrac{3}{5} - \dfrac{-3}{4} - \dfrac{-9}{10}$ (e) $\dfrac{7}{4} + \dfrac{5}{-3} - \dfrac{1}{4}$ (f) $\dfrac{11}{-10} + \dfrac{6}{5} - \dfrac{-3}{20}$

7 Use $m = \dfrac{3}{4}$, $n = -\dfrac{2}{3}$ and $s = -\dfrac{1}{2}$ to evaluate each expression.

(a) $m + n$ (b) $m - s$ (c) $n - m$
(d) $m + n - s$ (e) $m - n + s$ (f) $m - n - s$

8 Evaluate $p - q + r$ for each set of values.

(a) $p = \dfrac{2}{3}, q = -\dfrac{1}{3}, r = \dfrac{1}{6}$ (b) $p = \dfrac{5}{-8}, q = \dfrac{1}{4}, r = \dfrac{-3}{8}$

(c) $p = \dfrac{1}{-5}, q = \dfrac{-3}{10}, r = \dfrac{2}{5}$ (d) $p = \dfrac{-1}{8}, q = \dfrac{3}{-4}, r = \dfrac{-3}{-8}$

9   To qualify for a trip to a
    sugaring off party in Quebec,
    follow these instructions.

    Step A: Add $\dfrac{2}{3} + \dfrac{1}{-3}$ to $\dfrac{3}{4} - \dfrac{-2}{3}$.

    Step B: Subtract $\dfrac{2}{-3}$ from your
    answer in A.

    Step C: Add $\dfrac{-3}{4}$ to your answer
    in B.

    Step D: Increase your answer in
    C by $\dfrac{3}{-8}$. What is your
    final answer?

*For the early settlers in Canada, maple trees were one
of their only sources of sugar. In early spring the sugar
maple provides sap which is then boiled to make maple
syrup.*

10 Simplify.

    (a) $-\dfrac{-3}{2} - 1\dfrac{1}{3}$ (b) $-\dfrac{3}{8} + 2\dfrac{1}{4}$ (c) $\dfrac{7}{8} - 1\dfrac{1}{2}$ (d) $\dfrac{-8}{10} - 1\dfrac{5}{10}$

    (e) $-8\dfrac{1}{4} + 9$ (f) $-2\dfrac{1}{3} + 1\dfrac{2}{3}$ (g) $\dfrac{-9}{10} - 2\dfrac{2}{5}$ (h) $8 - 4\dfrac{3}{4}$

    (i) $\dfrac{-1}{4} + 1\dfrac{1}{3}$ (j) $\dfrac{1}{-3} - \dfrac{1}{8}$ (k) $\dfrac{1}{-2} + 1\dfrac{1}{3}$ (l) $\dfrac{3}{4} - 2\dfrac{1}{2}$

    (m) $-3\dfrac{1}{8} + 2\dfrac{1}{4}$ (n) $2\dfrac{1}{10} - \dfrac{-1}{5} + 3\dfrac{1}{2}$ (o) $\dfrac{1}{3} + \dfrac{-5}{6} - 1\dfrac{1}{3}$

11 Use $>$ or $<$ in place of ⊘ for each of the following.

    (a) $\dfrac{-3}{4} - \dfrac{-1}{4}$ ⊘ $\dfrac{-3}{4} - \dfrac{2}{3}$

    (b) $-\dfrac{3}{5} - \dfrac{-2}{3}$ ⊘ $\dfrac{1}{-8} - \dfrac{3}{-4}$

PSP 12 (a) Follow these instructions.
            Start with the number 5.
            Add 12.
            Double your answer.
            Add your original number.
            Divide by 3.
            Subtract 8.
            What final answer did you get?

         (b) Follow the instructions in (a) starting
             with 12, 36, −3, 126, 12.8 and −13.5.
             Are your final answers surprising?
             Try to show why this works for any
             number. (If you are wondering why
             you always end up with a surprising
             result, you can find the clue in
             Chapter 4.)

C 13 Use $p = -3$ and $q = 4$. Evaluate each of the following.

    (a) $\dfrac{p}{2} - \dfrac{q}{5}$ (b) $\dfrac{6}{p} - \dfrac{3}{q}$ (c) $\dfrac{p+q}{q} - \dfrac{p}{q}$ (d) $\dfrac{p-q}{p} - \dfrac{q}{p}$

3.3 Rational Numbers: Multiplying and Dividing

When you are developing a skill you often follow the steps shown at the right. For example, to learn the skill of multiplying or dividing rational numbers, you can use your previously-learned skills of multiplying or dividing fractions and of determining the sign of the product or quotient of integers.

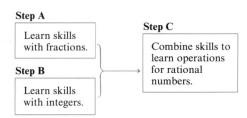

Step A

Learn skills with fractions.

Step B

Learn skills with integers.

Step C

Combine skills to learn operations for rational numbers.

Compare the following.

Fractions

$$\left(\frac{2}{3}\right)\left(\frac{4}{5}\right) = \frac{(2)(4)}{(3)(5)}$$

$$= \frac{8}{15}$$

Rationals

$$\left(\frac{-2}{-3}\right)\left(\frac{-4}{5}\right) = \frac{(-2)(-4)}{(-3)(5)}$$

$$= \frac{8}{-15} \text{ or } -\frac{8}{15}$$

When you learned to multiply fractions you also learned to simplify before you actually multiplied. This skill also extends to multiplying rationals as shown in the following example.

Example 1 Simplify $\dfrac{2}{3} \times \dfrac{-6}{5} \times \dfrac{-10}{-8}$.

Solution

$$\frac{2}{3} \times \frac{-6}{5} \times \frac{-10}{-8} = \frac{2}{3} \times \frac{-6}{5} \times \frac{10}{8}$$

Remember: $\dfrac{-10}{-8} = \dfrac{10}{8}$

$$= \frac{\overset{1}{2}}{\underset{1}{3}} \times \frac{\overset{-2}{-6}}{\underset{1}{5}} \times \frac{\overset{2}{10}}{\underset{4}{8}}$$

First divide by the common factors. Then multiply the rationals.

$$= \frac{-4}{4}$$

Think: $\dfrac{1(-2)(2)}{1(1)(4)}$

$$= -1$$

You have already learned that to divide by a fraction, you multiply by its reciprocal.

The reciprocal of $\dfrac{1}{2}$ is 2 since $\dfrac{1}{2} \times 2 = 1$.

The reciprocal of $-\dfrac{3}{2}$ is $-\dfrac{2}{3}$ since $\left(-\dfrac{3}{2}\right)\left(-\dfrac{2}{3}\right) = 1$.

Compare the following.

Fractions	Rationals

PSP To develop a new skill, often you can relate to a similar, but simpler, situation that you already know how to deal with.

$$\frac{8}{3} \div \frac{4}{5} = \frac{8}{3} \times \frac{5}{4} \qquad \frac{-8}{3} \div \frac{-4}{5} = \frac{-8}{3} \times \frac{5}{-4}$$

$$= \frac{\overset{2}{\cancel{8}}}{3} \times \frac{5}{\cancel{4}_1} \qquad = \frac{-\overset{2}{\cancel{8}}}{3} \times \frac{5}{-\cancel{4}_1}$$

$$= \frac{10}{3} \qquad\qquad = \frac{10}{3}$$

When multiplying or dividing mixed numbers, they should first be expressed as improper fractions. Then simplify where possible before multiplying or dividing.

Example 2   Simplify.

(a) $\left(-2\frac{1}{2}\right) \div \left(-\frac{1}{2}\right)$ (b) $\left(-\frac{-2}{3}\right) \div \left(-1\frac{1}{5}\right)$

Solution   (a) $\left(-2\frac{1}{2}\right) \div \left(-\frac{1}{2}\right)$ (b) $\left(-\frac{-2}{3}\right) \div \left(-1\frac{1}{5}\right)$

Remember: Your first step is to record the original equation.

$$= \left(\frac{-5}{2}\right) \div \left(\frac{-1}{2}\right) \qquad = \left(\frac{2}{3}\right) \div \left(\frac{-6}{5}\right)$$

$$= \frac{-5}{2} \times \frac{2}{-1} \qquad\qquad = \frac{\overset{1}{\cancel{2}}}{3} \times \frac{5}{\underset{-3}{\cancel{-6}}}$$

$$= \frac{-5}{\cancel{2}_1} \times \frac{\overset{1}{\cancel{2}}}{-1} \qquad\qquad = -\frac{5}{9}$$

$$= \frac{5}{1} \text{ or } 5$$

Example 3   Use $m = -\frac{1}{2}$ and $n = \frac{3}{-4}$ to evaluate $4mn$.

Solution $4mn = 4\left(-\frac{1}{2}\right)\left(\frac{3}{-4}\right)$

$$= 4\left(\frac{-1}{2}\right)\left(\frac{3}{\underset{-1}{\cancel{-4}}}\right)$$

$$= \frac{3}{2}$$

Math Tip

You can use this chart to help you find the signs of products and quotients of rational numbers.

$\times, \div$	Positive rational	Negative rational
Positive rational	$+$	$-$
Negative rational	$-$	$+$

3.3 Exercise

A 1 Multiply. Express each answer with a positive denominator.

(a) $\dfrac{1}{2} \times \dfrac{1}{-5}$

(b) $\left(\dfrac{-1}{3}\right)\left(\dfrac{2}{-5}\right)$

(c) $\dfrac{1}{2} \times \left(-\dfrac{2}{5}\right)$

(d) $\dfrac{-3}{4} \times \dfrac{1}{3}$

(e) $\left(-\dfrac{6}{10}\right)\left(\dfrac{1}{-2}\right)$

(f) $\dfrac{-2}{3} \times \dfrac{-3}{2}$

2 Find the following products.

(a) $\left(-\dfrac{2}{3}\right)\left(1\dfrac{1}{3}\right)$

(b) $\left(\dfrac{-3}{4}\right)\left(2\dfrac{1}{2}\right)$

(c) $\left(\dfrac{0}{-2}\right)\left(\dfrac{-3}{8}\right)$

(d) $\left(-2\dfrac{1}{5}\right)\left(-\dfrac{2}{3}\right)$

(e) $\left(-3\dfrac{1}{4}\right)\left(\dfrac{-2}{-3}\right)$

(f) $\left(-\dfrac{2}{3}\right)\left(-\dfrac{1}{3}\right)(0)$

3 Write the reciprocals of the following. Use a positive denominator.

(a) $\dfrac{1}{3}$

(b) $\dfrac{-2}{3}$

(c) 3

(d) $-\dfrac{1}{3}$

(e) $2\dfrac{1}{2}$

(f) $-4\dfrac{1}{2}$

4 Divide. Express each answer with a positive denominator.

(a) $\dfrac{9}{10} \div \dfrac{3}{5}$

(b) $\dfrac{4}{3} \div \dfrac{2}{3}$

(c) $\dfrac{-1}{3} \div \dfrac{1}{8}$

(d) $\dfrac{3}{-2} \div \dfrac{-1}{3}$

B Remember: Write your answers in lowest terms.

5 Simplify each of the following. Watch the signs.

(a) $\dfrac{4}{5} \times \dfrac{-20}{25}$

(b) $\dfrac{3}{-2} \div \dfrac{-1}{3}$

(c) $-6 \div \dfrac{4}{5}$

(d) $\dfrac{0}{-10} \times 2\dfrac{1}{4}$

(e) $10\dfrac{1}{2} \div \dfrac{3}{4}$

(f) $-7\dfrac{1}{8} \times \dfrac{-2}{3}$

(g) $\dfrac{-1}{2} \div 2\dfrac{1}{3}$

(h) $-1\dfrac{1}{10} \times 4\dfrac{1}{5}$

6 Simplify each product.

(a) $\left(\dfrac{3}{5}\right)\left(\dfrac{1}{-6}\right)\left(\dfrac{-2}{3}\right)$

(b) $\dfrac{-1}{10} \times \dfrac{5}{-6} \times \dfrac{3}{-5}$

(c) $\dfrac{4}{10} \times \dfrac{5}{-8} \times \dfrac{-6}{8}$

(d) $\dfrac{-3}{4} \times 0 \times \dfrac{8}{-10}$

(e) $\left(2\dfrac{3}{4}\right)\left(-1\dfrac{1}{4}\right)\left(\dfrac{-3}{8}\right)$

(f) $(-8)\left(2\dfrac{3}{4}\right)\left(\dfrac{-3}{4}\right)$

7 Simplify each of the following.

(a) $\left(-\dfrac{2}{3}\right)^2$

(b) $\left(\dfrac{1}{-3}\right)^2$

(c) $\left(-\dfrac{3}{2}\right)^2$

(d) $\left(-\dfrac{2}{5}\right)^2$

(e) $\left(\dfrac{-3}{2}\right)^2\left(-\dfrac{1}{3}\right)$

(f) $\left(-\dfrac{2}{3}\right)\left(\dfrac{1}{2}\right)^2$

(g) $\left(\dfrac{-2}{3}\right)^2\left(\dfrac{1}{-2}\right)^3$

8   Simplify each of the following.

(a) $\dfrac{4}{-5} \times \dfrac{5}{4} \times \dfrac{-3}{8}$

(b) $\dfrac{-5}{7} \times \dfrac{28}{5} \div \dfrac{-8}{6}$

(c) $\left(\dfrac{-5}{8}\right)\left(\dfrac{16}{4}\right)\left(\dfrac{-3}{10}\right)$

(d) $\dfrac{2}{-3} \times \dfrac{6}{-8} \div \dfrac{-3}{12}$

(e) $-1\dfrac{1}{5} \times \dfrac{-2}{3} \div \dfrac{-12}{7}$

(f) $\dfrac{-1}{3} \div \dfrac{-10}{9} \times \dfrac{5}{6}$

9   Evaluate each expression. Use $m = \dfrac{-2}{3}$, $n = \dfrac{3}{-4}$ and $p = \dfrac{-4}{-3}$.

(a) $2m$

(b) $-3n$

(c) $-\dfrac{4}{5}m$

(d) $\dfrac{1}{2}p$

(e) mnp

10 Evaluate each of the following. Use $p = -\dfrac{1}{2}$, $q = -\dfrac{3}{4}$ and $r = \dfrac{4}{3}$.

(a) pq

(b) rq

(c) qrp

(d) p^2r

(e) q^2r

PSP 11   How many different ways can four stamps be attached? Two ways are shown.

Math Tip

Why can you not divide by zero?

Suppose you could divide by zero. Then dividing -8 by 0 would give you some answer A.

$$\dfrac{-8}{0} = A$$

Since multiplication and division are inverse operations, you know

$$\dfrac{-8}{0} = A \text{ means } -8 = 0 \times A.$$

But $0 \times A = 0$ for any A. Thus $-8 = 0$. As a result of dividing by 0, you have shown that $-8 = 0$ which you know is not true. **Dividing by 0 is not permissible.**

Applications: Stock Exchange

Many companies offer stocks to the public who then buy the stocks and thus own a share of the company. These stocks are sold on a stock exchange. The amount sold each day is reported in most newspapers in the financial section.

The prices and the price changes represent dollars and cents. For example, $17\frac{1}{2}$ means $17.50, $+\frac{1}{2}$ means up $0.50.

Stock Exchange Report				Date: February 8	
					Net
Stock	Sales	High	Low	Close	change
Bridger	3499	$10\frac{3}{4}$	$10\frac{1}{2}$	10	$-\frac{1}{2}$
Brunswick	3900	420	410	410	-2
C.S. Pete	18 110	335	345	345	-2
C. Curtis	1500	44	44	44	$+3$
Comb Met	5000	$17\frac{1}{2}$	$16\frac{3}{4}$	16	$+\frac{7}{8}$
C. Durham	8000	66	63	63	-3
Marcana	3633	13	12	12	$+2$
Merland E.	13 690	278	271	271	-8
Norlex	14 000	$16\frac{1}{4}$	$14\frac{3}{4}$	$15\frac{1}{2}$	$-\frac{1}{2}$
Ponder	500	60	60	60	-2
VanDer	621	360	360	360	$+12$
Westfield	13 800	155	150	155	-8

change from yesterday's final price

name of company

number of shares (stocks) sold

highest price paid per share

lowest price paid per share

final price per share

---

12 If all the Norlex shares were sold at the high price, what would they cost?

13 What would all the shares of VanDer cost at the high price?

14 If all the Westfield shares were bought at the low price, what would they cost?

15 (a) What would be your maximum (most) cost to buy all the Bridger shares that were sold?
   (b) What would be your minimum (least) cost to buy all the shares in (a)?
   (c) What is the difference in cost in (a) and (b)?

16 (a) The net change for C. Curtis is $+3$. Calculate the net gain on 1500 shares.
   (b) The net change for Merland E is -8. Calculate the net loss for the shares sold.

17 Which of the following transactions at the closing involves more money?
   (a) Selling all the Brunswick shares.
   (b) Selling all the Norlex shares.

18 A number of shares in Newell stock were purchased and then sold. When sold, the shares had a net change of $-\frac{1}{8}$. If the loss was $280, how many shares were purchased?

3.4 Order of Operations: Rationals

The rules for the order of operations which apply to whole numbers and integers also apply to rationals as shown in the example.

Rules for the Order of Operations
- ▶ Perform the operations in brackets ( ) first.
- ▶ Then calculate the powers. Namely, find the value of expressions involving exponents.
- ▶ Then do multiplication or division in the order they appear.
- ▶ Then do addition or subtraction in the order they appear.

Example   Simplify $-\dfrac{3}{4} + \dfrac{2}{3} \times \left(-5\dfrac{1}{4}\right)$.

Solution

$$\dfrac{-3}{4} + \dfrac{2}{3} \times \left(-5\dfrac{1}{4}\right)$$

$$= \dfrac{-3}{4} + \dfrac{2}{\underset{1}{3}} \times \left(\dfrac{\overset{-7}{-21}}{4}\right)$$

$$= \dfrac{-3}{4} + \dfrac{-14}{4}$$

$$= -\dfrac{17}{4} \text{ or } -4\dfrac{1}{4}$$

Remember: Record the original expression as the first step.

3.4 Exercise

A Remember to apply the rules for the order of operations.

1   (a) Calculate $\dfrac{3}{4} + \left(\dfrac{1}{2} + \dfrac{3}{8}\right)$ and $\dfrac{3}{4} + \dfrac{1}{2} + \dfrac{3}{8}$.

   (b) Why are the answers the same?

2   (a) Calculate $\dfrac{2}{3} - \left(\dfrac{3}{4} - \dfrac{1}{8}\right)$ and $\dfrac{2}{3} - \dfrac{3}{4} - \dfrac{1}{8}$.

   (b) Why are the answers different?

3   (a) Calculate $-\dfrac{4}{5} - \left(\dfrac{2}{3} - \dfrac{1}{6}\right)$ and $-\dfrac{4}{5} - \dfrac{2}{3} - \dfrac{1}{6}$.

   (b) Why are the answers different?

4   (a) Calculate $-\dfrac{3}{4} \div \left(\dfrac{3}{4} \div \dfrac{4}{5}\right)$ and $-\dfrac{3}{4} \div \dfrac{3}{5} \div \dfrac{4}{5}$.

   (b) Why are the answers different?

5   (a) Calculate $-\dfrac{5}{8} \times \left(\dfrac{3}{4} \times \dfrac{4}{5}\right)$ and $-\dfrac{5}{8} \times \dfrac{3}{4} \times \dfrac{4}{5}$.

   (b) Why are the answers the same?

B 6 Two solutions, A and B, are provided for the same question.

Solution A

$$-\frac{4}{5}\left(-\frac{3}{4}+\frac{1}{3}\right)=\frac{-4}{5}\left(\frac{-9}{12}+\frac{4}{12}\right)$$

$$=\frac{-4}{5}\left(\frac{-5}{12}\right)$$

$$=\frac{\overset{-1}{-4}}{\underset{1}{5}}\left(\frac{\overset{-1}{-5}}{\underset{3}{12}}\right)$$

$$=\frac{1}{3}$$

Solution B

$$-\frac{4}{5}\left(-\frac{3}{4}+\frac{1}{3}\right)=\left(-\frac{4}{5}\right)\left(-\frac{3}{4}\right)+\left(-\frac{4}{5}\right)\left(\frac{1}{3}\right)$$

$$=\frac{3}{5}+\frac{-4}{15}$$

$$=\frac{9}{15}+\frac{-4}{15}$$

$$=\frac{5}{15}\text{ or }\frac{1}{3}$$

(a) How are the solutions alike?

(b) How are they different?

(c) Simplify $\dfrac{3}{4}\left(\dfrac{3}{5}+\dfrac{-7}{5}\right)$.

(d) Simplify $-\dfrac{2}{3}\left(\dfrac{9}{10}-\dfrac{4}{5}\right)$.

7 Calculate. Use the rules for the order of operations.

(a) $\dfrac{1}{3}+\dfrac{2}{3}-\dfrac{1}{2}$

(b) $\dfrac{3}{4}-\dfrac{1}{2}+\dfrac{1}{3}$

(c) $\left(\dfrac{2}{3}\right)\left(-\dfrac{1}{4}\right)\left(-\dfrac{3}{4}\right)$

(d) $\left(\dfrac{3}{4}\right)\div\left(-\dfrac{1}{2}\right)\div\left(\dfrac{2}{3}\right)$

(e) $\left(\dfrac{3}{4}\right)\left(-\dfrac{2}{3}\right)\div\left(-\dfrac{1}{4}\right)$

(f) $\dfrac{5}{8}\div\left(-\dfrac{3}{4}\right)\times\left(\dfrac{2}{3}\right)$

8 Simplify each of the following.

(a) $\dfrac{3}{2}-\left(\dfrac{3}{4}-\dfrac{-1}{4}\right)$

(b) $\dfrac{3}{5}-\dfrac{-1}{10}+\dfrac{-1}{2}$

(c) $\left(\dfrac{-3}{5}+\dfrac{7}{10}\right)\div\dfrac{-1}{2}$

(d) $-\dfrac{4}{5}\left(\dfrac{-3}{4}+\dfrac{-1}{4}\right)$

(e) $\dfrac{-4}{5}-\left(\dfrac{-1}{4}+\dfrac{-4}{5}\right)$

(f) $\dfrac{-3}{5}\div\left(\dfrac{-3}{4}-\dfrac{-9}{10}\right)$

9 Simplify. Which answer is greatest?

(a) $\dfrac{-3}{4}-\left(\dfrac{-3}{4}+\dfrac{4}{-5}\right)$

(b) $\dfrac{-3}{5}-\dfrac{-3}{4}-\dfrac{9}{-10}$

(c) $6\div\dfrac{-1}{5}-\dfrac{1}{-2}$

10 Simplify. Which answer is least?

(a) $-\dfrac{3}{2}+\dfrac{-1}{-2}-\dfrac{-3}{5}$

(b) $\dfrac{-4}{3}\div\left(\dfrac{-3}{4}\div\dfrac{2}{3}\right)$

(c) $\dfrac{-2}{3}\div\dfrac{-4}{5}\div\dfrac{-3}{4}$

11 (a) What is your first step in simplifying

$$\left(\frac{-2}{5}+\frac{1}{-2}\right)\div\left(\frac{5}{-8}-\frac{-1}{2}\right)?$$

(b) Simplify the expression.

12 Simplify each of the following.

(a) $\left(\dfrac{2}{3} - \dfrac{-1}{3}\right) \div \left(\dfrac{-3}{4} - \dfrac{-2}{3}\right)$

(b) $\left(\dfrac{-1}{8} + \dfrac{1}{-4}\right)\left(\dfrac{-1}{-2} + \dfrac{1}{-6}\right)$

(c) $\left(\dfrac{2}{-3} - \dfrac{-1}{2}\right) \div \left(\dfrac{-3}{2} - \dfrac{3}{2}\right)$

(d) $\left(\dfrac{4}{5} - \dfrac{3}{-4}\right)\left(\dfrac{-1}{3} - \dfrac{1}{4}\right)$

13 Find the value of the expression $x^2 - pq$ for the following.

(a) $x = \dfrac{1}{2}, p = -\dfrac{1}{3}, q = -\dfrac{1}{4}$

(b) $x = \dfrac{-3}{4}, p = \dfrac{1}{2}, q = -\dfrac{2}{3}$

14 Use $x = -\dfrac{2}{3}$, $y = \dfrac{1}{2}$ and $z = \dfrac{3}{4}$. Evaluate each expression.

(a) $xy + z$

(b) $y - xz$

(c) $yz \div x$

(d) $2x - 3y$

(e) $\dfrac{1}{2}y - \dfrac{2}{3}x$

(f) $\dfrac{3}{4}x - \dfrac{3}{8}y$

(g) $2x + 3y - 2z$

(h) $\dfrac{1}{4}x - \dfrac{2}{3}y \div 4z$

PSP 15 In a store there were children's wagons, bicycles and tricycles displayed for sale.

(a) If the total number of wheels was 40, how many of each were there?

(b) Can you obtain more than one answer? How many different answers can you find?

(c) What assumptions did you make?

C 16 Simplify the expression. Plan ahead as to what each step should be.

$$\dfrac{\dfrac{-4}{5} - \dfrac{-3}{5}}{\dfrac{1}{3} - \dfrac{-1}{5}} + \dfrac{\dfrac{3}{5} - \dfrac{-1}{10}}{\dfrac{-1}{4} - 1\dfrac{2}{3}} - \dfrac{\dfrac{1}{-4} + \dfrac{-1}{3}}{\dfrac{5}{-12} + 1\dfrac{3}{4}}$$

Calculator Use

You can use your calculator to perform operations with rationals. For example, to simplify $\dfrac{1}{2} - \dfrac{3}{4}$, follow these steps.

Output

$\boxed{C}\ 1\ \boxed{\div}\ 2\ \boxed{=}\ \boxed{M+}\ 3\ \boxed{\div}\ 4\ \boxed{=}\ \boxed{+/-}\ \boxed{+}\ \boxed{MR}\ \boxed{=}$ -0.25

▶ Use a calculator to simplify each of the following.

$$\dfrac{-2}{3} + \dfrac{1}{4} \qquad \dfrac{-3}{4} - \dfrac{-2}{3}$$

▶ Choose calculations from the questions on this page. Use a calculator to simplify them.

3.5   Problem Solving: Using Rationals

One of the main reasons for learning mathematics is to acquire skills and strategies for solving problems. To solve a problem you need to analyse the given information carefully. The given information often suggests a strategy for solving the problem. Refer to the steps in your *Problem Solving Plan* to solve problems involving rational numbers.

> You learn skills.
>
> You learn strategies.
>
> You apply skills and strategies to solve problems.

Example

A freight train is carrying steel pipes, plastic drums and aluminum rods. If $\frac{3}{5}$ of the freight cars have steel pipes and $\frac{1}{4}$ of them have plastic drums, what fraction of the freight cars carry aluminum rods?

Solution

Known information:

steel pipes in $\frac{3}{5}$ of freight cars
plastic drums in $\frac{1}{4}$ of freight cars
all of the freight cars make a whole, 1

number with aluminum rods
= all − (those with steel pipes and plastic drums)

$$= 1 - \left(\frac{3}{5} + \frac{1}{4} \right) \qquad \text{Use the order of operations.}$$

$$= \frac{20}{20} - \left(\frac{12}{20} + \frac{5}{20} \right)$$

$$= \frac{20}{20} - \frac{17}{20}$$

$$= \frac{3}{20}$$

Thus $\frac{3}{20}$ of the freight cars are carrying aluminum rods.

3.5 Exercise

A 1 Maria spent $2\frac{1}{4}$ h raking leaves and $1\frac{3}{4}$ h washing windows. How much time, in total, did she spend on these two tasks?

2 A bus trip is $\frac{3}{4}$ h longer than the same trip by train. If the train trip is $2\frac{1}{6}$ h long, how long is the bus trip?

B Check your answers to see if they are reasonable. **PSP**

3 It rained for $3\frac{1}{2}$ h on Monday and for $1\frac{3}{4}$ h on Tuesday. How many times as long was the period of time it rained on Monday as on Tuesday?

4 The ski lift ride is $5\frac{1}{2}$ min long. Garry skis down the slope in $4\frac{1}{4}$ min. Brad skis down the slope in $3\frac{5}{6}$ min. How much more time does each skier spend on the lift than on the ski slope for each run?

5 Julia feeds her dogs $\frac{2}{3}$ of a can of dog food twice a day. How much dog food does she feed them in a week?

6 Glenda ran $2\frac{3}{4}$ laps of the track in 9 min. How long did it take her to run 1 lap?

7 Water evaporates from a storage drum at a rate of $\frac{1}{20}$ of the drum's volume each week. What fraction of the drum's volume evaporates in $5\frac{1}{2}$ weeks?

8 Rita and Ron were playing a game. After 1 h Rita's score was $15\frac{1}{2}$ points and Ron's score was $-7\frac{3}{4}$ points. How far apart were their scores?

9 A complete trip of a bus route uses $\frac{1}{10}$ of a tank of fuel. If the fuel tank is $\frac{7}{8}$ full, how many trips can be made without refuelling?

10 A recipe for a cake calls for $3\frac{1}{4}$ cups of flour and $\frac{3}{4}$ cup of sugar. How much more flour is used than sugar?

11 Alain can plant 1 flat of begonias in $\frac{3}{4}$ h. If he plants begonias for his entire shift of $7\frac{1}{2}$ h, how many flats does he plant?

12 If $12\frac{1}{4}$ bags of seed are planted in each hectare field, how many bags are needed to plant $6\frac{1}{2}$ 1-ha fields?

13 Alex's scores for 5 rounds of a game were $3\frac{1}{2}$ points, $-1\frac{1}{4}$ points, $-2\frac{3}{4}$ points, $5\frac{1}{4}$ points and $1\frac{1}{4}$ points. What was his total score?

14 At a muffin shop, the types of muffins sold one morning were recorded. One quarter were banana-bran, $\frac{2}{5}$ were carrot-nut, $\frac{1}{8}$ were chocolate chip and $\frac{1}{8}$ were blueberry-oatmeal.

(a) What fraction of the muffins sold were carrot-nut or blueberry-oatmeal?

(b) How much greater was the fraction of carrot-nut muffins than the fraction of banana-bran muffins?

(c) What fraction of the muffins sold were all the muffins other than carrot-nut?

(d) Which type of muffin was the most popular that morning?

PSP 15 365 is a special number. It is the number of days in a year, but it also has other properties.

(a) Find three consecutive whole numbers such that the sum of their squares is 365.

(b) Find two consecutive whole numbers such that the sum of their squares is 365.

C 16 A music shop sells cassette tapes, L.P. records and compact discs. Half of the space is used for L.P. records, $\frac{3}{10}$ for cassette tapes and $\frac{1}{5}$ for compact discs.

(a) If $\frac{1}{3}$ of the cassette tape space is used for Top 40 music, what fraction of the whole store is used for Top 40 cassette music?

(b) If $\frac{3}{5}$ of the L.P. record space is used for Top 40 music, what fraction of the whole store is used for Top 40 L.P. music?

(c) If $\frac{1}{4}$ of the compact disc space is used for Top 40 music, what fraction of the whole store is used for Top 40 music in any form?

From Math History: George Polya

George Polya's works cover an impressive range of mathematics. His endeavours have led to developments in the fields of probability, number theory, geometry and real analysis, among others. When asked how he came to solve so many problems in so many fields, he described what he studied before he became involved with mathematics, "I did not come straight to mathematics. I started by studying law. Then I studied languages and literature. I also had an interest in biology."

He was influenced by the work of previous mathematicians such as Euler, "because Euler explained how he found his results and I am deeply interested in that. It has to do with my interest in problem solving." George Polya is best known for his book *How To Solve It* which has been translated into at least 15 languages. His name is associated with the art of problem solving.

▶ What do you think his book *How To Solve It* is about?

▶ List the strategies that you have learned about "how to solve it."

3.6 Decimals for Rationals

To find the decimal equivalent of a rational number, you divide the numerator by the denominator.

$\frac{1}{2}$ is written as 0.5.

$$\begin{array}{r} 0.5 \\ 2 \overline{\smash{)}1.0} \end{array}$$

$-1\frac{1}{2}$ is written as -1.5.

Decimal numerals such as 0.5, 0.25 and 0.125 are called **terminating decimals**. In each case the division terminates.

Example 1 Write $\frac{5}{11}$ as a decimal.

$$\begin{array}{r} 0.4545 \\ 11 \overline{\smash{)}5.0000 \ldots} \\ 44 \\ \hline 60 \\ 55 \\ \hline 50 \\ 44 \\ \hline 60 \\ 55 \\ \hline 5 \end{array}$$

Solution $\frac{5}{11} = 0.4545 \ldots$

$= 0.\overline{45}$ or $0.\dot{4}\dot{5}$

Bars and dots are compact ways of showing which digits repeat. The dots appear above the first and last digits that repeat.

Decimals such as 0.4545 . . . are called **periodic decimals**. The period of $0.\overline{45}$ is 45, and the **length of the period** is 2 because 2 digits repeat.

To compare two rationals, you can express them as decimals.

Example 2 Which is greater, $\frac{-12}{29}$ or $-\frac{13}{31}$?

Solution Using your calculator,

$$\frac{-12}{29} = -0.413\ 793\ 1 \text{ and } -\frac{13}{31} = -0.419\ 354\ 8$$

The digits differ after the hundredths place.

Thus since $-0.413 > -0.419$, then $\frac{-12}{29} > -\frac{13}{31}$.

3.6 Exercise

A 1 Write each decimal in a compact way.

(a) 3.232323 . . .   (b) 3.777 . . .   (c) 2.35555 . . .   (d) 0.01232323 . . .

2 Express each of the following rationals as a decimal.

(a) $\frac{1}{4}$ (b) $\frac{2}{3}$ (c) $\frac{3}{4}$ (d) $\frac{1}{8}$ (e) $\frac{2}{11}$ (f) $\frac{1}{-9}$

3   For each rational number, is the decimal terminating or periodic?

(a) $\dfrac{3}{8}$ (b) $\dfrac{5}{12}$ (c) $\dfrac{7}{11}$ (d) $-\dfrac{5}{8}$ (e) $\dfrac{1}{9}$ (f) $\dfrac{7}{8}$

B 4   Find the period and the length of the period of each of the following.

(a) $\dfrac{35}{99}$ (b) $\dfrac{2}{-11}$ (c) $\dfrac{1}{15}$ (d) $-\dfrac{3}{22}$ (e) $\dfrac{34}{27}$ (f) $2\dfrac{2}{3}$

(g) $-\dfrac{7}{11}$ (h) $\dfrac{49}{54}$ (i) $\dfrac{7}{15}$ (j) $\dfrac{17}{36}$ (k) $\dfrac{11}{27}$ (l) $\dfrac{3}{7}$

5   For each pair, which is the greater rational?

(a) $\dfrac{12}{23}, \dfrac{14}{29}$ (b) $-\dfrac{3}{17}, -\dfrac{5}{26}$ (c) $\dfrac{3}{28}, \dfrac{2}{17}$ (d) $-\dfrac{4}{25}, -\dfrac{3}{20}$ (e) $\dfrac{7}{30}, \dfrac{6}{26}$

(f) $\dfrac{5}{29}, \dfrac{1}{6}$ (g) $-\dfrac{4}{25}, -\dfrac{3}{17}$ (h) $\dfrac{26}{27}, \dfrac{27}{29}$ (i) $\dfrac{21}{22}, \dfrac{25}{27}$ (j) $-\dfrac{17}{36}, -\dfrac{11}{27}$

6   To calculate the batting average, A, for a baseball player, you use the formula $A = \dfrac{h}{b}$ where h is the number of hits and b is the number of times at bat. Calculate the batting average for each player to 3 decimal places.

	Player	Number of hits, h	Number of times at bat, b
(a)	Johnson	16	28
(b)	Jefferson	17	32
(c)	Adams	19	34
(d)	Limpett	15	29
(e)	Harris	16	33

Which player had the best batting average? The worst batting average?

7   Each of the following players won the batting average champion title in the National League in the year shown. Calculate the batting average of each.

	Player	Year	Times at bat	Number of hits
(a)	Jesse Burbett	1895	556	235
(b)	Roger Hornsby	1925	504	203
(c)	Stan Musial	1946	625	228
(d)	Willie Mays	1954	565	195
(e)	Pete Rose	1968	627	210

PSP 8   To solve problems you must carefully read and understand the meaning of *each word* used in the problem. Solve this problem.

How old am I? I have lived for more than a quarter century, but less than a half. My age this year is a multiple of 6. My age last year was a multiple of 5.

You can explore mathematics with a calculator.
Use your calculator to express rationals as periodic decimals.

9 (a) Calculate decimals for $\dfrac{1}{11}, \dfrac{2}{11}$ and $\dfrac{3}{11}$.

   (b) Use the pattern to predict the decimal for $\dfrac{4}{11}$.

   (c) Check your prediction by calculating the decimal for $\dfrac{4}{11}$.

10 (a) Calculate decimals for $\dfrac{1}{2}$ and $\dfrac{1}{20}$.

   (b) Use the pattern to predict the decimal for $\dfrac{1}{200}$.

   (c) Check your prediction by calculating the decimal for $\dfrac{1}{200}$.

11 (a) Calculate the first 3 decimal places for each of $\dfrac{11}{47}, \dfrac{12}{47}$ and $\dfrac{13}{47}$.

   (b) Use the pattern to predict $\dfrac{14}{47}$ to 3 decimal places.

   (c) Check your prediction by calculating $\dfrac{14}{47}$ to 3 decimal places.

12 (a) Find the decimal represented by $\dfrac{1}{7}, \dfrac{2}{7}$ and $\dfrac{3}{7}$.

   (b) Use the pattern to predict the decimals for $\dfrac{4}{7}$ and $\dfrac{5}{7}$. Check your predictions.

   (c) Which rational is represented by the decimal $0.\overline{857\ 142}$?

Calculator Use **PSP**

You can easily find the period of a rational number using a calculator as long
as the period can be identified on the display of your calculator. For example,

$$\frac{1}{3} = 0.333\ldots \qquad\qquad \frac{4}{99} = 0.0404040\ldots$$

Devise a method to find the period of a rational number when the period is
longer than the digits on your calculator display.

$$\frac{2}{71} = 0.028\ 169\ 01??\ldots \qquad\qquad \frac{5}{17} = 0.294\ 117\ 64??\ldots$$

3.7 Rationals for Decimals

The two types of decimal equivalents for rationals are
- terminating decimals
- periodic decimals.

To find the rational number represented by a terminating decimal, you use your skills with place value.

$$0.55 = \frac{55}{100} \quad \text{or} \quad \frac{11}{20}$$

Express your answer in lowest terms.

To find the rational number represented by a periodic decimal, use these steps. Use x to represent the decimal. $\quad x = 0.222 \ldots$

Since the period length is 1, multiply both sides by 10.

$$10x = 10(0.222 \ldots)$$
$$10x = 2.222 \ldots$$
$$x = 0.222 \ldots \qquad \text{Use the original equality.}$$

Subtract. $\quad 10x - x = 2.0000 \ldots$
Simplify. $\qquad 9x = 2$

PSP You can check your work by finding the decimal for $\frac{2}{9}$.

$$x = \frac{2}{9}$$

Thus $\qquad 0.\bar{2} = \frac{2}{9}$

Check: $\quad 9\overline{)2.000 \ldots}$ ✓

$$0.222 \ldots$$

Example Find a rational number for
(a) $0.\overline{32}$
(b) $0.1\bar{6}$.

Solution (a) Use x to represent $0.\overline{32}$.

$$x = 0.323232 \ldots$$
Then $\qquad 100x = 32.3232 \ldots$
Also $\qquad x = 0.3232 \ldots$
Subtract. $\quad 99x = 32$
Solve. $\qquad x = \frac{32}{99}$

Thus $0.\overline{32} = \frac{32}{99}$.

(b) Use x to represent $0.1\bar{6}$.

$$x = 0.166666 \ldots$$
$$100x = 16.666666 \ldots$$
$$10x = 1.666666 \ldots$$
$$90x = 15$$
$$x = \frac{15}{90} \quad \text{or} \quad \frac{1}{6}$$

Thus $0.1\bar{6} = \frac{1}{6}$.

3.7 Exercise

A Check your answers. Use a calculator to help you.

1 What is the length of the period for each decimal?
(a) $4.\bar{3}$ (b) $-2.1\bar{3}$ (c) $0.\overline{65}$ (d) -4.892

2   Find a rational number for each terminating decimal. Express your
    answer in lowest terms.
    (a) 0.2   (b) −0.25   (c) 0.62   (d) −1.75   (e) 0.3
    (f) −0.36   (g) 0.15   (h) 0.32   (i) 0.125   (j) −0.05

3   Which would you multiply by, 10, 100 or both, to find the rational for
    each decimal?
    (a) $0.\overline{6}$ (b) $-3.\overline{35}$ (c) $0.0\overline{6}$ (d) $-1.\overline{45}$

B 4   Write a rational number for each periodic decimal.
    (a) 1.3333 . . .   (b) −1.2323 . . . (c) 0.4444 . . .   (d) 3.1212 . . .   (e) −2.4545 . . .

5   Find a rational number for each of the following.
    (a) $0.\overline{5}$ (b) $0.\overline{3}$ (c) $0.\overline{8}$ (d) $1.\overline{4}$ (e) $3.\overline{6}$ (f) $0.\overline{15}$
    (g) $2.\overline{63}$ (h) $0.\overline{82}$ (i) $1.\overline{36}$ (j) $0.\overline{315}$ (k) $1.\overline{057}$ (l) $2.\overline{825}$

6   Find a rational for each of the following.
    (a) $0.3\overline{5}$ (b) $0.4\overline{9}$ (c) $0.6\overline{8}$ (d) $0.5\overline{9}$ (e) $0.3\overline{15}$ (f) $3.\overline{15}$
    (g) $0.04\overline{6}$ (h) $2.\overline{3}$ (i) $0.4\overline{13}$ (j) $4.4\overline{5}$ (k) $0.32\overline{3}$ (l) $0.03\overline{2}$

7   (a) Find the rational numbers represented by 0.5 and $0.4\overline{9}$.
    (b) What do you notice about your answers?

8   (a) Find the rational numbers for the decimals $0.5\overline{9}$ and 0.6.
    (b) What do you notice about your answers?
    (c) Predict what rational number is represented by $0.2\overline{9}$. Check your answer.

9   (a) Find the rational represented by $0.\overline{4}$.
    (b) Use your answer to predict the rational represented by $0.\overline{2}$.
    (c) Predict the rationals represented by $0.\overline{3}$, $0.\overline{5}$ and $0.\overline{8}$. Check your answers.

10 (a) Find the rational represented by $0.0\overline{4}$.
    (b) Use your answer to predict the rationals represented by $0.0\overline{5}$, $0.0\overline{8}$ and
        $0.9\overline{8}$. Check your answers.
    (c) Use your previous results to predict the rationals for $0.00\overline{4}$ and $0.00\overline{9}$.
        Check your predictions.

PSP 11   Sometimes when solving a problem, you are stumped because you don't
    know the meaning of each word.
    (a) Read the following problem. Do you understand all the words? In how
        many different orders can you eat a seven-course meal?
    (b) Solve the problem. (A seven-course meal is served with seven different parts.)

3.8 Working with Square Roots

The area of this square is 25 m². To find the
measure of each side of the square, you find the
square root of 25. $25 = (5)(5)$

$$25 \text{ m}^2$$

The number 25 has an exact square root. However not all numbers have
square roots that are exact.

Example 1   Find the length of each side of the square
to 1, 2 and 3 decimal places.

$$45 \text{ m}^2$$

Solution   45 is between 36 and 49.
$\sqrt{45}$ is between $\sqrt{36}$ and $\sqrt{49}$, or 6 and 7.
Estimate and use your calculator.

Estimate	Calculator key press using automatic constant	Result	
6.5^2	C 6.5 × =	42.25	Too low
6.7^2	C 6.7 × =	44.89	Too low
6.71^2	C 6.71 × =	45.0241	Too high
6.705^2	C 6.705 × =	44.957 025	Too low
6.708^2	C 6.708 × =	44.997 264	Too low
6.709^2	C 6.709 × =	45.010 681	Too high

6.71^2 is closer than 6.70^2 to 45.
6.708^2 is closer than 6.709^2 to 45.
Thus the length of each side is 6.7 m to 1 decimal place;
6.71 m to 2 decimal places;
6.708 m to 3 decimal places.

There are tables which provide the square roots
of numbers to a specified accuracy. On page 489,
a table of square roots of the whole numbers
from 1 to 100 accurate to 3 decimal places
is provided.

You can also obtain negative square roots.
For example, 25 is a product of the factors
shown.
$$(5)(5) = 25 \text{ or } (-5)(-5) = 25$$
The square root of 25 is either 5 or -5.

Calculator Use

Your calculator may have a
key marked $\sqrt{}$, for finding
the square root of a number.

number		display
45	$\sqrt{}$	6.7082039

This number is the positive or
principal square root of 45.

When you work with perimeters of square areas such as lawns, you find the positive or principal square root of numbers. The positive or principal square root of 25 is 5.

$$\sqrt{25} = 5 \quad \text{The symbol } \sqrt{} \text{ means the principal square root.}$$

Example 2   Find the principal square root of each number.

(a) 144   (b) 0.64   (c) 85   (d) 240

Solution

(a) $12^2 = 144$ (b) $8^2 = 64$ (c) From the tables,
$\sqrt{144} = 12$ $0.8^2 = 0.64$ $n = 85, \sqrt{n} = 9.220$
                          $\sqrt{0.64} = 0.8$ $\sqrt{85} = 9.220$

(d) Using a calculator, $\boxed{\text{C}}\,240\,\boxed{\sqrt{}}\,15.491933$
$\sqrt{240} = 15.492$ (to 3 decimal places)

3.8   Exercise

A 1   Estimate the positive square root of each number to 1 decimal place.

(a) 10   (b) 18   (c) 34   (d) 12   (e) 50

2   Estimate the principal square root of each number to the nearest hundredth.

(a) 40   (b) 75   (c) 89   (d) 21   (e) 55

3   Use the table of square roots to write the square root of each number to 2 decimal places.

(a) 6   (b) 24   (c) 58   (d) 76   (e) 49   (f) 94   (g) 65   (h) 13

Which of the values above did you find without using the table of square roots?

4   From the square root table, $\sqrt{83} \doteq 9.110$.

(a) Without multiplying, what answer would you predict for $(9.110)^2$?

(b) Calculate $(9.110)^2$.

(c) Why do your answers in (a) and (b) differ? By how much do they differ?

5   Evaluate without using tables or a calculator.

(a) $\sqrt{25}$ (b) $-\sqrt{9}$ (c) $\sqrt{64}$ (d) $\sqrt{100}$ (e) $-\sqrt{225}$
(f) $\sqrt{256}$ (g) $\sqrt{0.36}$ (h) $\sqrt{0.81}$ (i) $\sqrt{2.25}$ (j) $\sqrt{6.25}$

B 6 The area of each square stamp is shown. Calculate the dimensions of each stamp to 1 decimal place.

(a)

(b)

(c)

225 mm²   350 mm²   435 mm²

7 How much fencing to 1 decimal place would be needed to enclose each of the following fields?

(a) Area is 6 m².

(b) Area is 42 m².

(c) ABFG is a square.
CDEF is a square.

A   B

Area is 65 m².

C   D

Area is 27 m².

G   F   E

8 Find each of the following to 2 decimal places.
(a) $\sqrt{300}$ (b) $\sqrt{208}$ (c) $\sqrt{800}$ (d) $\sqrt{350}$
(e) $\sqrt{240}$ (f) $\sqrt{700}$ (g) $\sqrt{175}$ (h) $\sqrt{1300}$

9 The area of a square gymnasium is 500 m². Calculate the dimensions of the gymnasium to 1 decimal place.

10 The area of a square field is 380 m².
(a) Calculate the dimensions of the field to 2 decimal places.
(b) How much wire fencing would be needed to enclose the field? Express your answer to 1 decimal place.
(c) Use the information in the ad to calculate the cost of the fencing in (b) to the nearest cent.

Fencing
Wire mesh
20-m roll, $78.95

PSP 11 To solve some problems, you can begin by listing possible answers and deciding which ones are not correct.

Write the year (in the last two hundred) that reads the same backwards or forwards or upside down.

C 12 A square rug with area 18 m² is placed in the centre of a square room with area 22 m². Find the width in centimetres of the strip of floor left uncovered.

Applications: Distance to the Horizon

When the ships of the early explorers set across the sea, the mast was the last part of the ships to be seen at the horizon. Many people at that time did not realize that the earth's surface was curved and believed that, when the masts disappeared, the ships dropped off the edge of the earth.

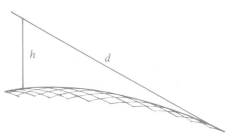

To calculate how far away the horizon is you can use a formula. The distance to the horizon, d, in kilometres is given by the formula $d = 3.572\sqrt{h}$ where h is the height in metres of the observer.

Round all answers to 1 decimal place when necessary.

13 How far away is the horizon for each height?
    (a) 45 m   (b) 90 m   (c) 120 m   (d) 200 m   (e) 450 m   (f) 1000 m

14 The tallest flagpole ever built is in San Francisco. It has a height of 92 m. How far away is the horizon as seen from the top?

15 The original Ferris Wheel was 79 m high. How far away was the horizon from the top seat?

16 The tallest block of apartments is in Chicago. It has 70 stories and each storey is 2.8 m high. How far can you see from the top of this building?

17 The world's tallest self-supporting structure is the C.N. Tower in Toronto. The observation tower is at the 335 m level. How far away is the horizon?

18 Forest rangers often fly in planes to watch for the start of fires.
    (a) How far away is the horizon if the plane is 900 m high?
    (b) How much further away is the horizon if the plane flies 300 m higher than in (a)?

Computer Use

To find the distance, d, to the horizon you can use a computer program. Try values for h from this page to calculate d.

```
10 INPUT "THE HEIGHT IS"; H
20 LET D = 3.572 * SQR(H)
30 PRINT "THE HORIZON IS"; D
40 IF D = 0 THEN 60
50 GOTO 10
60 END
```

3.9 Historical Math: Newton's Method

Most of what you do in mathematics was invented by someone.

The table of square roots was obtained by programming a computer to find successively better approximations to the required square root. The process involves a sequence of estimating, dividing and averaging, and is called **Newton's Method**, after its inventor Sir Isaac Newton.

Find $\sqrt{75}$ to 2 decimal places.

Step 1: Estimate the square root.
75 is between 64 and 81. Thus $\sqrt{75}$ is between $\sqrt{64}$ and $\sqrt{81}$, or 8 and 9. Try 8.7.

Step 2: Divide the number by the estimate. Use your calculator.
$\boxed{\text{C}}\ 75\ \boxed{\div}\ 8.7\ \boxed{=}\ 8.6206896$

Step 3: Is the quotient equal to the estimate? If yes, then you are finished. But, since 8.620 689 6 $\neq$ 8.7 to 2 decimal places, go to Step 4.

Step 4: Average the estimate and the quotient to produce a new estimate. Continue with your calculator.
$\boxed{+}\ 8.7\ \boxed{=}\ \boxed{\div}\ 2\ \boxed{=}\ 8.6603445$

Step 5: Repeat step 2 using the new estimate you obtained in Step 4. Continue with your calculator.
$\boxed{\text{M}+}\ 75\ \boxed{\div}\ \boxed{\text{MR}}\ \boxed{=}\ 8.6601635$

Step 6: Same as Step 3. Since 8.660 163 5 = 8.660 344 5 to 2 decimal places, $\sqrt{75}$ = 8.66 to 2 decimal places.

3.9 Exercise

B 1 Use Newton's Method to find each value to 2 decimal places.

(a) $\sqrt{85}$ (b) $\sqrt{30}$ (c) $\sqrt{11}$ (d) $\sqrt{23}$ (e) $\sqrt{110}$
(f) $\sqrt{153}$ (g) $\sqrt{5.8}$ (h) $\sqrt{13.2}$ (i) $\sqrt{2.1}$ (j) $\sqrt{17.6}$

From Math History

Very often, things you use are named after the people who invented them. For example, Ford cars are named after Henry Ford, and Salk Vaccine, used to prevent polio, is named after Jonas Salk. Many names used in mathematics honour people. Find out in whose honour the following are named.

Cartesian Co-ordinates	Boolean Algebra	Möbius Strip
Witch of Agnesi Curve	Euclidean Geometry	Zeno's Paradox
Pythagorean Triplets	Ovals of Cassini	Sieve of Eratosthenes
Gaussian Integers	Klein Bottle	Newton's Method
Mercator Chart	Vitali Set	Taylor Series

3.10   Pythagoras and Square Roots

The side opposite the right angle in a right triangle is called
the **hypotenuse**.

A Greek named Pythagoras was one of the first to formalize
a proof about the relationship between the hypotenuse and
the other two sides.
To show this relationship,

▶ Draw a right triangle with two sides
   4 units and 3 units on grid paper
   as shown.

▶ Draw a square on each of the two
   known sides.

▶ Cut out the squares. Cut them to form
   a square on the hypotenuse.

What is the area of the square on the hypotenuse?
What is the length of the hypotenuse?
Pythagoras proved that the area of the square on the
hypotenuse was equal to the sum of the areas of the
squares on the other two sides.

$$c^2 = a^2 + b^2$$

Example 1   Find the length of $\overline{EF}$ in $\triangle DEF$.

Solution   In $\triangle DEF$, $\angle D = 90°$, $e = 5$ units, $f = 12$ units.
Then $d^2 = e^2 + f^2$
$$d^2 = 5^2 + 12^2$$
$$d^2 = 25 + 144$$
$$d^2 = 169$$
$$d = \sqrt{169}$$
$$d = 13 \qquad \text{Thus } \overline{EF} = 13 \text{ units.}$$

Example 2   A tower is 20 m in height. A guy wire 25 m
in length is secured a distance from its
base. Find the distance from the base.

Solution   If d represents the distance from the base in
metres, then
$$25^2 = 20^2 + d^2 \qquad \boxed{PSP} \text{ Use a}$$
$$625 = 400 + d^2 \qquad\qquad \text{variable.}$$
But $625 = 400 + 225$
Thus $d^2 = 225$
$$d = \sqrt{225}$$
$$d = 15 \qquad \text{Thus the distance from the base is 15 m.}$$

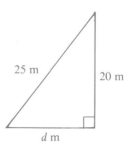

3.10 Exercise

A Round your answers to 1 decimal place.

1 Find the missing measure in each triangle.

(a)

(b)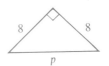

(c)

(d)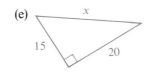

(e)

(f)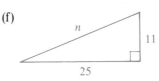

2 Find the value of each variable.

(a) $x^2 = 12^2 + 5^2$ (b) $y^2 = 9^2 + 4^2$ (c) $k^2 = 3^2 + 6^2$

(d) $14^2 = x^2 + 4^2$ (e) $20^2 = y^2 + 12^2$ (f) $31^2 = 20^2 + m^2$

(g) $14^2 + 12^2 = x^2$ (h) $13^2 + 15^2 = y^2$ (i) $p^2 + 6^2 = 15^2$

3 Find the missing measures in each triangle.

(a)

(b)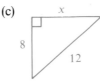

(c)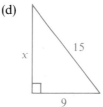

(d)

B 4 Calculate the length of the ramp in each diagram.

(a)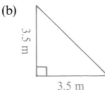

(b)

(c)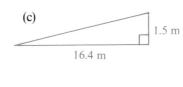

5 Three hills at a ski resort are shown. Calculate the height of each hill.

(a)

56.0 m

(b)

125.0 m

(c)

160.0 m

6   Calculate the length of the guy wire in each diagram.

(a)

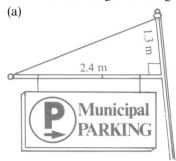

1.3 m

2.4 m

Municipal
PARKING

(b)

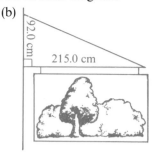

92.0 cm

215.0 cm

(c)

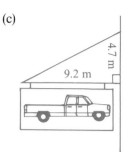

4.7 m

9.2 m

7   A ladder leans against a wall as shown. Use the
information in the photograph to calculate the
length of the ladder.

8   A ladder 7.0 m long is placed against a wall.
The foot of the ladder is 2.0 m from the wall.
Calculate how far up the wall the ladder reaches.

9   As a short cut to school, Joelle cuts across a
rectangular field along the diagonal. If the sides
of the field are 120.0 m by 160.0 m, how much
walking does Joelle save?

2.1 m

PSP   10   The palindromic number 484 is obtained
from the calculations shown. The numbers
94 and 49 are the palindromic roots of 484.

(a) Find two other palindromic roots
for the number 484.

(b) Find two palindromic roots for
the number 363.

$$\begin{array}{r} 94 \\ + 49 \\ \hline 143 \\ + 341 \\ \hline 484 \end{array}$$

Computer Use

Use the program shown to calculate
the length of the hypotenuse in
a right triangle. Choose numerical
values from problems on this page as
inputs for A and B.

```
10 PRINT "PYTHAGORAS"
20 INPUT A, B
30 LET V = A ↑ 2 + B ↑ 2
40 LET H = SQR(V)
50 PRINT "THE HYPOTENUSE IS"; H
60 END
```

3.11   Irrational and Real Numbers

In your earlier work you found that terminating and periodic decimals represent rational numbers.

$$\frac{1}{8} = 0.125 \qquad \frac{2}{3} = 0.6666\ldots \qquad 1\frac{45}{99} = 1.454545\ldots$$

There is another type of decimal that is neither terminating nor periodic.

$$0.131\ 131\ 113\ 111\ 131\ldots \qquad 0.123\ 456\ 789\ 101\ 112\ldots$$

Decimals such as those above cannot be written in rational form and are called **irrational numbers**. An irrational number you have used when you worked with the circle is π. The first 100 decimal places of π are

$$\pi = 3.141\ 592\ 653\ 589\ 793\ 238\ 462\ 643\ 383\ 279\ 502\ 884\ 197\ 169\ 399\ 375\ 105$$
$$820\ 974\ 944\ 592\ 307\ 816\ 406\ 286\ 208\ 996\ 628\ 034\ 825\ 342\ 117\ 067\ 9.$$

In the previous sections you found the square roots of numbers. You calculated values such as $\sqrt{2}$ and $\sqrt{45}$. The decimals for $\sqrt{2}$ or $\sqrt{45}$ are also non-repeating and non-terminating. Thus $\sqrt{2}$ and $\sqrt{45}$ are examples of irrational numbers. Symbols are used to represent the rational numbers and irrational numbers.

$$Q = \text{set of rational numbers} \qquad \bar{Q} = \text{set of irrational numbers}$$

Together, the set of rationals Q and irrationals $\bar{Q}$ form the set of **real numbers**, denoted by the symbol R.

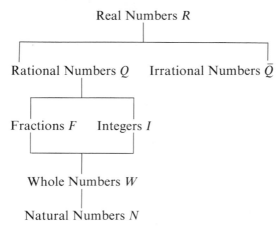

PSP To solve problems you need to know the meaning of special words and symbols.

$$N = \{1, 2, 3, \ldots\}$$
$$W = \{0, 1, 2, 3, \ldots\}$$
$$F = \left\{ \frac{a}{b} \,\middle|\, a, b \in W, b \neq 0 \right\}$$
$$I = \{\ldots, -2, -1, 0, 1, \ldots\}$$
$$Q = \left\{ \frac{a}{b} \,\middle|\, a, b \in I, b \neq 0 \right\}$$
$$\bar{Q} = \text{irrationals}$$
$$R = \{Q \text{ and } \bar{Q}\}$$

Each set of numbers has certain properties. Not all properties are true for all sets of numbers.

An operation is said to be **commutative** if, when the operation is performed on two numbers, the result is not affected by the order of the numbers. Subtraction of integers is not commutative. $-3 - 4 \neq -4 - (-3)$

An operation is said to be **associative** if, when the operation is performed on three numbers, the result is not affected by which two are combined first.

Addition of rationals is associative. $\left(\frac{1}{2}+\frac{1}{3}\right)+\left(-\frac{1}{2}\right)=\left[\frac{1}{2}+\left(-\frac{1}{2}\right)\right]+\frac{1}{3}$

One example does not prove,
but one example can disprove.

An operation is said to be **distributive** over another if the result is the same whether the operation is performed before or after the other operation.

Multiplication of natural numbers is distributive over subtraction. $\qquad 3(9-2)=3(9)-3(2)$

A set of numbers is said to be **closed** for a given operation if, when the operation is performed on any two numbers of the set, the result is a number of the set.

The natural numbers are not closed under subtraction $\qquad 3-5=-2$ but $-2 \notin N$

An operation has an **identity** element if there is a number that can be combined with any other number and the result is always the other number.

Addition of real numbers has an identity element, 0. $\qquad -\frac{7}{8}+0=-\frac{7}{8}$

An operation has **inverse** elements if there are pairs of numbers that can be combined and the result is always the identity element.

Addition of real numbers has inverse elements. $\qquad -\frac{7}{8}+\frac{7}{8}=0$

A set of numbers is said to be **dense** if between any two numbers of the set, there is another number of the set.

The rationals are dense. $\qquad 0.11 \underset{\uparrow}{} 0.12$

There are many rationals between
these two numbers.

3.11   Exercise

A 1   Are the following numbers rational or irrational?

(a) $-\sqrt{16}$ (b) 6   (c) $\sqrt{4}$ (d) $-\frac{2}{3}$ (e) $-\sqrt{9}$

(f) $\sqrt{2}$ (g) $2\frac{3}{5}$ (h) $-\sqrt{36}$ (i) $\sqrt{6}$ (j) 0.136

(k) $\frac{-8}{3}$ (l) $-\sqrt{100}$ (m) $\sqrt{3}$ (n) 0.151 515 151 . . .

2 (a) Write three examples of periodic decimals.

   (b) Which type of number, rational or irrational, is each of the decimals in (a)?

B 3 The decimal for π is 3.141 592 653 6 to 10 decimal places.

   (a) The rational $\dfrac{22}{7}$ is often used as an approximate value for π. For which decimal places do the decimals for $\dfrac{22}{7}$ and π match?

   (b) The rational number $\dfrac{355}{113}$ was used by Tsu Ch'ung-chih to give an approximate value for π. For which decimal places do the decimals for $\dfrac{355}{113}$ and π match?

   (c) Which is a better approximation to π, the rational $\dfrac{22}{7}$ or the rational $\dfrac{355}{113}$? Why?

4 Make a chart summarizing the properties of numbers. Use a column for each set of numbers, N, W, F, I, Q, $\bar{Q}$, R and check ($\checkmark$) each property that is true.

5 Identify the property being illustrated.

   (a) $3, 6 \in N, \quad 3 - 6 \notin N$

   (b) $-2, 7, 8 \in I,$
       $7 \times [8 \times (-2)] = (7 \times 8) \times (-2)$

   (c) $\dfrac{5}{8}, 1 \in F, \quad \dfrac{5}{8} \times 1 = \dfrac{5}{8}$

   (d) $\dfrac{-5}{6}, \dfrac{3}{4} \in Q,$
       $\dfrac{3}{4} \div \left(\dfrac{-5}{6}\right) \neq \left(\dfrac{-5}{6}\right) \div \dfrac{3}{4}$

   (e) $3, 5, 9 \in W,$
       $(9 + 5) \div 3 = 9 \div 3 + 5 \div 3$

   (f) $0.101\ 101\ 110\ldots,$
       $0.010\ 010\ 001\ldots \in \bar{Q},$
       $0.101\ 101\ 110\ldots$
       $+\ 0.010\ 010\ 001\ldots \notin \bar{Q}$

Property	
Commutative	Addition
	Subtraction
	Multiplication
	Division
Associative	Addition
	Subtraction
	Multiplication
	Division
Distributive	Multiplication over addition
	Division over addition
	Multiplication over subtraction
	Division over subtraction
Closed	Addition
	Subtraction
	Multiplication
	Division
Identity	Addition
	Subtraction
	Multiplication
	Division
Inverse	Addition
	Multiplication
Denseness	

3.12 PSP Problem Solving Strategy: Using Diagrams

Often to solve a problem you can draw a diagram to help you plan your solution.
Locate the number $\sqrt{2}$ on the number line.

▶ To solve the problem, you need to
remember that $\sqrt{2}$ suggests the
previous work you did with right
triangles. The diagram suggests
a method of locating the
number $\sqrt{2}$ on the number line.

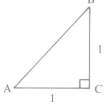

$$AB^2 = 1^2 + 1^2$$
$$AB^2 = 1 + 1$$
$$AB^2 = 2$$
$$AB = \sqrt{2}$$

Step 1 Construct $\triangle ABC$.

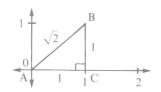

Step 2 Draw an arc. Locate $\sqrt{2}$ on the
number line.

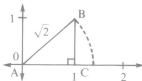

By thinking visually, you can find some other interesting results.

The area of a square
is 2 square units.

2 square
units

The length of each side
is $\sqrt{2}$ units.

$\sqrt{2}$ units

$$(\sqrt{2})(\sqrt{2}) = 2$$

side of   side of   area of
square   square   square

3.12 Exercise

B 1 Use each equation to draw a triangle and to locate each irrational number
on a number line.
(a) $\sqrt{5} = \sqrt{2^2 + 1^2}$ (b) $\sqrt{8} = \sqrt{2^2 + 2^2}$

2 To find $\sqrt{3}$ on the number line, a sketch is shown.
(a) Why is $\overline{AD}^2 = \overline{AB}^2 + \overline{DB}^2$?
(b) Use the sketch. Locate $\sqrt{3}$ on the number line.

3 Refer to the previous method. Locate each
irrational number on the number line.
(a) $\sqrt{6}$ (b) $\sqrt{7}$ (c) $\sqrt{10}$ (d) $\sqrt{12}$ (e) $\sqrt{13}$

4 (a) Construct a square with sides that measure $\sqrt{5}$ cm.
(b) Construct a diagram to show $(\sqrt{10})(\sqrt{10}) = 10$.

3.13 Real Numbers and Their Graphs

Skills you learned previously can be extended to learn new skills. For example, in the previous chapter you learned to graph integers. In this section you will extend your skills to graphing real numbers. In an earlier section in this chapter you learned that real numbers are dense. This means that between any two real numbers there is another real number. Thus it is impossible to list all the real numbers. As a result, when you are graphing real numbers, a continuous line is used to show the denseness of the real numbers.

Recall that the domain is the replacement set. In the following example, the domain is the set of real numbers shown by $x \in R$.

Example   Draw each graph.
(a) $\{x \mid x \leq -3, x \in R\}$
(b) $\{x \mid -4 < x \leq 1, x \in R\}$
(c) $\{x \mid x < 0 \text{ or } x \geq 2, x \in R\}$

Solution   (a)

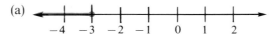

The -3 is included. Use a solid dot.

(b)

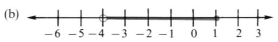

The -4 is not included. Use an open dot.

(c)

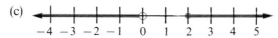

3.13 Exercise

A Remember the meaning of the inequality symbols, $<, >, \leq, \geq$, in order to draw graphs of real numbers.

1   The graph of two sets are shown.

$A = \{x \mid x < 3, x \in R\}$ $B = \{x \mid x < 3, x \in I\}$

(a) Name the domain of A.   (b) Name the domain of B.
(c) How are the graphs alike? How do they differ?

2   Draw each graph.

(a) $\{x \,|\, x \geq 3, x \in R\}$　　　(b) $\{x \,|\, x \geq 3, x \in I\}$　　　(c) $\{x \,|\, x \geq 3, x \in W\}$

How are the graphs alike? How do they differ?

3   Graphs are shown for A and B.

$$A = \{x \,|\, -1 < x \leq 3, x \in R\} \qquad\qquad B = \{x \,|\, -1 < x \leq 3, x \in I\}$$

(a) Why is a solid line used in the graph of set A?

(b) Why is -1 not included in both graphs?

(c) Why is $2\frac{1}{2}$ not included in the graph for set B?

B Remember: To draw graphs you must read the symbols carefully. **PSP**

4   Draw the graph of each set.

(a) $\{x \,|\, x > 1, x \in I\}$　　　(b) $\{x \,|\, x \geq 1, x \in R\}$　　　(c) $\{x \,|\, x \leq 6, x \in I\}$

(d) $\{x \,|\, 6 > x, x \in R\}$　　　(e) $\{x \,|\, x \geq 2, x \in R\}$　　　(f) $\{x \,|\, -2 < x, x \in R\}$

(g) $\{x \,|\, x \geq 0, x \in I\}$　　　(h) $\{x \,|\, x \leq -3, x \in R\}$　　　(i) $\{x \,|\, x \leq 0, x \in I\}$

(j) $\{x \,|\, -8 < x, x \in R\}$　　　(k) $\{x \,|\, x < -8, x \in R\}$　　　(l) $\{x \,|\, 8 > x, x \in R\}$

5   Each graph represents a set of numbers. Use symbols to show the sets.

(a)
$-4 \;\; -3 \;\; -2 \;\; -1 \;\;\;\; 0$

(b)
$-3 \;\; -2 \;\; -1 \;\;\;\; 0 \;\;\;\; 1 \;\;\;\; 2$

(c)
$0 \;\;\;\; 1 \;\;\;\; 2 \;\;\;\; 3$

(d)
$1 \;\;\;\; 2 \;\;\;\; 3 \;\;\;\; 4 \;\;\;\; 5 \;\;\;\; 6$

(e)
$0 \;\;\;\; 1 \;\;\;\; 2 \;\;\;\; 3$

(f)
$-8 \;\; -7 \;\; -6 \;\; -5 \;\; -4 \;\; -3$

(g)
$-6 \;\; -5 \;\; -4 \;\; -3 \;\; -2$

(h)
$5 \;\;\;\; 6 \;\;\;\; 7 \;\;\;\; 8 \;\;\;\; 9 \;\;\; 10$

(i)
$5 \;\;\;\; 6 \;\;\;\; 7 \;\;\;\; 8 \;\;\;\; 9$

(j)
$-1 \;\;\;\; 0 \;\;\;\; 1 \;\;\;\; 2 \;\;\;\; 3$

6   Draw a graph of each of the following sets.

(a) $\{x \,|\, 4 < x \leq 8, x \in R\}$　　　　(b) $\{x \,|\, -8 < x < -4, x \in I\}$

(c) $\{x \,|\, -2 \leq x < 0, x \in I\}$　　　(d) $\{x \,|\, 1 \geq x \geq -1, x \in R\}$

(e) $\{x \,|\, -3 \leq x < 3, x \in I\}$　　　(f) $\{x \,|\, -2 < x < 3, x \in R\}$

(g) $\{x \,|\, 8 \geq x \geq -3, x \in R\}$　　　(h) $\{x \,|\, 0 < x \leq 3, x \in I\}$

(i) $\{x \,|\, -12 < x < -8, x \in R\}$　　(j) $\{x \,|\, -3 < x \leq 3, x \in R\}$

7 Use symbols to describe each set.

(a)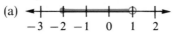

(b) ◄─┼──┾──┼──┼──┼──┾─►
     6   7   8   9 10 11

(c) ◄─┼──┿──┿──┿──┿──┼─►
  −1 0   1   2   3   4

(d) ◄─┾──┼──┼──┼──┼──┼─►
  −6 −5 −4 −3 −2 −1

(e) ◄─┼──┼──┿──┿──┿──┼─►
   4   5   6   7   8   9

(f) ◄─┾──┿──┿──┿──┿──┼─►
  −3 −2 −1 0   1   2

(g) ◄─┼──┼──┿──┿──┼──┼─►
  −1 0   1   2   3   4

(h) ◄─┾──┿──┿──┼──┼──┼─►
  −4 −3 −2 −1 0   1

8 Draw the graph of each set.

(a) $\{x \mid x \leq -3 \text{ or } x > 3, x \in R\}$

(b) $\{x \mid x > 2 \text{ or } x \leq -1, x \in R\}$

(c) $\{x \mid x \geq 4 \text{ or } x < 0, x \in R\}$

(d) $\{x \mid x < -2 \text{ or } x > 0, x \in R\}$

(e) $\{x \mid x < -4 \text{ or } x \geq -2, x \in R\}$

(f) $\{x \mid x \geq 8 \text{ or } x < 4, x \in R\}$

9 To write the opposite of $=$, you write $\neq$. What is the meaning of each of the following symbols?

(a) $\not>$ (b) $\not<$ (c) $\not\geq$ (d) $\not\leq$

 10 In the history of mathematics, many people have made a contribution.

(a) Diophantus was a Greek mathematician. When he died his epitaph read as shown. Based on the information, how long did Diophantus live?

(b) Find out about Diophantus and his contributions to the study of mathematics.

> Diophantus passed $\frac{1}{6}$ of his life in childhood, $\frac{1}{12}$ in youth and $\frac{1}{7}$ as a bachelor. His son was born 5 years after his marriage but died 4 years before his father did, and only lived to $\frac{1}{2}$ of his father's age.

C 11 Draw the graph of each of the following.

(a) $\{x \mid x - 5 \neq 3, x \in R\}$ (b) $\{x \mid x + 3 \neq 5, x \in R\}$ (c) $\{x \mid x - 3 \neq -2, x \in R\}$

(d) $\{x \mid 2x + 1 \neq 5, x \in R\}$ (e) $\{x \mid x \not> 3, x \in R\}$ (f) $\{x \mid x \not< -2, x \in R\}$

Math Tip

Remember to look over your work in this chapter.

▶ Record all the new math words you have dealt with. Use an example of your own to illustrate each word.

▶ Record any new questions, statements, strategies, etc. into your *Problem Solving Plan* **PSP**

3.14 **PSP** Problem Solving: Building Strategies

When solving a problem, you can often visualize the problem by using a model or a diagram to help you interpret the given information. To solve the following problem, you can draw intersecting circles.

Example   In a class of 28 students, 16 play backgammon, 18 play chess and 7 play neither. How many students play both backgammon and chess?

Solution   *Step 1:* Ask yourself: How many students play one or both games?

Total number of students	28
Number of students that play neither game	-7
Number of students that play one or both	21

Step 2:

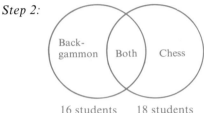

PSP Think: To interpret the given information, use the intersecting circles shown.

16 students   18 students

$16 + 18 = 34$
But there are only 21 students that play one or both games. Thus the overlap is $34 - 21 = 13$.

PSP Check your answer in the *original* problem.

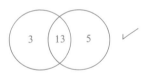

The number of students that play both backgammon and chess is 13.

Think: Refer to your *Problem Solving Plan* **PSP** .

▶ Does your answer satisfy all the given information?
▶ Does your answer solve the original problem?
▶ Are there any other possible solutions?
▶ Can you solve this problem in another way?
▶ Did you place this strategy in your list in your *Problem Solving Plan* **PSP** ?

3.14 Exercise

B 1   (a) Read the following problem.
   In a sample of 34 families, 16 own a dog, 14 own a cat and 8 own neither. How many families own both a cat and a dog?

(b) Draw a diagram to help you interpret the problem.

(c) Solve the problem.

2 (a) Read the following problem. What strategy is suggested?

   In a sample of 26 designers, 18 designers are working in advertising, 6 designers are working in publishing and 6 designers are not working presently. How many designers are working in both advertising and publishing?

   (b) Draw a diagram to help you interpret the problem.

   (c) Solve the problem.

   (d) Check whether you have answered what the problem asked you to find.

Solve the following problems. You may need to use other strategies to solve the problems.

3 A diagram is often helpful to plan a solution to a problem. Use a diagram to help you solve the following.

   (a) A ladder has 40 uniformly-spaced rungs. If each rung had been 2 cm more apart, only 36 rungs would have been required. Find the distance between rungs.

   (b) What assumption(s) did you make?

4 Three views of a cube are shown. What is opposite the black circle?

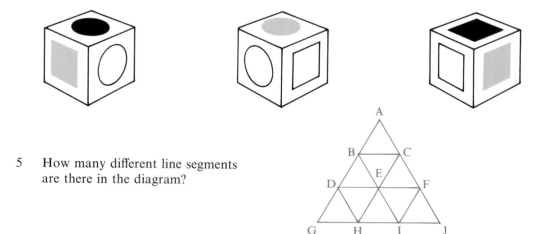

5 How many different line segments are there in the diagram?

6 In a gym class of 28 students, 14 are on the wrestling team, 12 are on the swim team and 8 are on neither. How many students are on both the swim team and the wrestling team?

7 On an expedition Pat saw a large pod of whales and a school of sharks. The sharks had 7 fins each and the whales had 3 fins each. If there were 100 tails and 448 fins, how many sharks and how many whales did she see?

3.15 PSP Problem Solving: Using Strategies

Refer to your *Problem Solving Plan* **PSP**

▶ Record any questions, statements, strategies, etc. that you have recently learned in the appropriate place in your *Problem Solving Plan* **PSP**

▶ Then solve the following problems. After you solve each problem and you have obtained a solution, look over your work.

- Does your solution answer the original problem you were asked to solve?
- Are there other solutions?
- Place in your *Problem Solving Plan* any new strategies, questions, statements, features of the problem, etc., that will assist you later to solve problems.

PSP	Problem Solving Plan

Step A: Understand the problem.
- What are you asked to find?
- What are you given?

Step B: Decide on a strategy.

Step C: Apply the strategy. Do the work.

Step D: Check your solution.

Step E: Write a final statement.

3.15 Exercise

B 1 (a) In December each person in our class decided to give each other a candy cane. If there are 22 people in our class, how many candy canes will we need to purchase in all?

(b) The school athletic council makes 25¢ on each candy cane sold. How much profit will be made from our class?

2 How would you place the numbers 7 to 15 so that each triple (⑦—⑦—⑦) has the same sum? You can only use each number once.

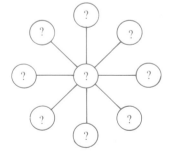

3 A two-digit number is equal to 21 times the difference of its digits. Find the number.

4 Examples of palindromic words are shown.
MOM   NOON   RADAR

(a) Find two more words that are palindromic with three letters; two more with four letters; two more with five letters.

(b) Make a sentence that is palindromic.

Practice and Problems: Review

1   Write each rational number in lowest terms.

(a) $\dfrac{-3}{-15}$ (b) $-\dfrac{6}{9}$ (c) $\dfrac{-12}{-9}$ (d) $-\dfrac{24}{3}$ (e) $\dfrac{-8}{-42}$

2   Calculate.

(a) $\dfrac{-3}{5} + \dfrac{1}{5}$ (b) $\dfrac{1}{-6} - \dfrac{-1}{3}$ (c) $\dfrac{-3}{5} - \dfrac{-1}{-10}$ (d) $\dfrac{-5}{-12} + \dfrac{-1}{-4}$

3   Calculate.

(a) $\left(\dfrac{-1}{2}\right)\left(\dfrac{1}{-3}\right)$ (b) $\left(-2\dfrac{1}{3}\right)\left(\dfrac{-9}{-14}\right)$ (c) $\left(\dfrac{2}{3}\right) \div \left(\dfrac{-4}{-9}\right)$ (d) $\left(\dfrac{-2}{3}\right)^2$

4   Simplify.

(a) $\dfrac{-3}{5} + \left(\dfrac{2}{3} - \dfrac{1}{-5}\right)$ (b) $\dfrac{-1}{2} \div \left(\dfrac{-1}{3} + \dfrac{-1}{-2}\right)$ (c) $\left[\dfrac{1}{8} + \left(\dfrac{-2}{3}\right)\right] \times \dfrac{12}{13}$

5   Substitute and evaluate for $m = \dfrac{-1}{2}$, $n = -\dfrac{1}{4}$ and $t = \dfrac{-3}{4}$.

(a) $mn - t$ (b) $2m - 4n + 3t$ (c) $mt - mn$

6   Find the period and the length of the period for each rational.

(a) $\dfrac{73}{99}$ (b) $-\dfrac{17}{22}$ (c) $\dfrac{13}{27}$ (d) $-\dfrac{5}{7}$

7   Find a rational number for each decimal.

(a) 0.75   (b) 0.45   (c) $0.\overline{37}$ (d) $1.2\overline{9}$

8   The bottom of a cardboard box is square and has an area of 453.0 cm². Find the lengths of the sides.

9   (a) To find $\sqrt{71}$ to 1 decimal place using Newton's Method, start with the estimate 8.5. Show the steps to find the root.
    (b) Evaluate $\sqrt{135}$ and $\sqrt{19.5}$ to 1 decimal place using Newton's Method.

10 A guy wire is used to brace a newly planted tree. Find the length of the wire to 1 decimal place.

3.2 m

2.0 m

11 Draw each graph.
    (a) $\{n \mid n \geq -1, n \in I\}$
    (b) $\{k \mid -1 < k \text{ or } k \leq -3, k \in R\}$

Practice Test

1   Replace ◉ by $>$ or $<$ to make each of the following true.

(a) $\dfrac{-2}{3}$ ◉ $\dfrac{3}{4}$ (b) $\dfrac{-1}{2}$ ◉ $\dfrac{2}{-3}$ (c) $\dfrac{2}{5}$ ◉ $\dfrac{3}{-16}$ (d) $\dfrac{-3}{4}$ ◉ $\dfrac{2}{-3}$

2   Calculate.

(a) $\dfrac{1}{-2} + \dfrac{1}{6}$ (b) $\left(\dfrac{2}{3}\right)^2 - \dfrac{-4}{9}$ (c) $\dfrac{-3}{10} - 1\dfrac{1}{5}$ (d) $\left(\dfrac{-3}{5}\right)\left(\dfrac{-10}{21}\right)$

(e) $2\dfrac{1}{3} + \left(-\dfrac{1}{2}\right)$ (f) $-\dfrac{1}{2} - 2\dfrac{1}{3}$ (g) $\dfrac{7}{3} \times \left(-3\dfrac{1}{2}\right)$ (h) $\left(-3\dfrac{1}{4}\right) \div \left(\dfrac{-2}{3}\right)$

(i) $\dfrac{-2}{3} + \left(\dfrac{-1}{2} - \dfrac{1}{3}\right)$ (j) $\dfrac{2}{5} \div \left(\dfrac{-2}{5} + \dfrac{1}{10}\right)$ (k) $\dfrac{-5}{6} + \dfrac{-2}{3} \times \dfrac{3}{4}$

3   Express each rational as a decimal.

(a) $\dfrac{7}{10}$ (b) $-\dfrac{3}{8}$ (c) $1\dfrac{7}{9}$ (d) $\dfrac{-5}{6}$

4   Write a rational number in lowest terms for each.

(a) 0.08   (b) $0.\overline{4}$ (c) $1.\overline{69}$ (d) $-0.41\overline{6}$

5   Kim's scores for 5 rounds of a game were $12\dfrac{1}{2}$, $-5\dfrac{1}{4}$, $-3\dfrac{1}{2}$, $6\dfrac{3}{4}$ and $2\dfrac{1}{4}$. What was her total score?

6   Leon can unload 1 carton of wooden figurines in $\dfrac{3}{4}$ h. If he unloads cartons for $3\dfrac{1}{2}$ h, how many cartons does he unload?

7   Find the perimeter of a square field whose area is 272.25 m².

8   A guy wire is used to support the sign. Find the length of the wire to 1 decimal place.

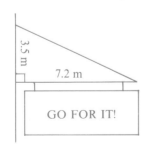

9   Perry wanted to place a small rectangular table in the corner of the room as shown. How far is A from the corner to 1 decimal place?

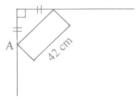

10   Use the inequality $1.3 < x < 1.5$.
(a) Write 3 values of x such that it is a repeating decimal.
(b) Write 3 values of x such that it is a non-repeating, non-terminating decimal.

11   Draw each graph.   (a) $\{a\,|\,a \leqq 2,\ a \in I\}$ (b) $\{k\,|\,-3 < k \leqq 0,\ k \in R\}$

Microcomputers: Computer Programs

A program is a sequence of instructions that the computer follows. The programmer gives the instructions to the computer in a specific computer language. Some examples of computer languages are

BASIC   Beginners All Purpose Symbolic Instruction Code

ALGOL   ALGorithmic Oriented Language

FORTRAN   FORmula TRANslation

COBOL   COmmon Business Oriented Language

These are the symbols used in the BASIC computer language.

+	add
−	subtract
*	multiply
/	divide
↑	exponent
>	greater than
> =	greater than or equal to
< >	not equal to
<	less than
< =	less than or equal to

In this book, the program language you will use is BASIC. Many of the computer symbols are already familiar to you.

To learn the special skills and intricacies of computer programming is a study in itself. A computer programmer learns skills in translating a problem into the steps of a program that the computer can follow. *A computer does not think for itself.* You must tell it every step that it is to do. Flow charts assist the computer programmer in organizing the steps of the computer program.

Line 10 gives your program a title.

Line 20 gives the computer the values of m and n you want to use. Use $m = 2$, $n = -3$.

In Line 30 the computer evaluates the expression.

$V = 3 * N + 5 * M ↑ 2$
$V = 3(-3) + 5(2)^2$
$V = -9 + 20$
$V = 11$

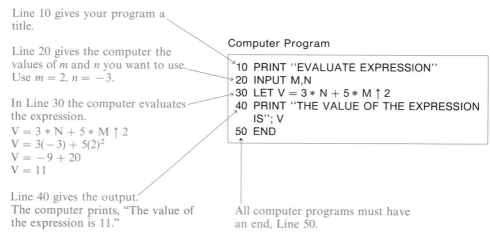

Computer Program

```
10 PRINT "EVALUATE EXPRESSION"
20 INPUT M,N
30 LET V = 3 * N + 5 * M ↑ 2
40 PRINT "THE VALUE OF THE EXPRESSION
   IS"; V
50 END
```

Line 40 gives the output. The computer prints, "The value of the expression is 11."

All computer programs must have an end, Line 50.

1   Use the above program as a sample. Write a computer program in BASIC that evaluates these expressions. Try the program. Do a RUN.

(a) Evaluate $8m^2 - 3n$. Try a RUN for $m = -6$ and $n = 3$.

(b) Evaluate $y = 3x^2 - 2x + 5$. Try a RUN for $x = -3, -2, -1, 0, 1, 2$ and 3.

4 Using Algebra: Language and Process

Language for algebra, symbols and variables, adding and subtracting polynomials, translation skills, simplifying expressions, using fundamental principles, solving problems, applications, strategies for problem solving

Introduction

An important characteristic of mathematics is that often skills and concepts learned in one branch of mathematics can be extended to learning and understanding skills and concepts in another branch of mathematics. In *arithmetic*, you learned the language and concepts related to working with numbers. In *algebra*, the skills and concepts of arithmetic are generalized. Read the comparisons that follow and then read the article on the right.

Arithmetic numerical expression	Algebra algebraic expression
$3 + 3$	$x + x$
$2(3) - 6$	$2(x) - 6$
$2(6) + 3(8)$	$2(x) + 3(y)$

Mathematics uses a language of symbols. Once you learn the meanings of the symbols and how to operate with them, you can use algebra to solve problems that you might otherwise not have been able to solve. A knowledge of algebra today is essential in many different fields such as engineering, space exploration, accounting, insurance, architecture and, of course, all the sciences. The photograph displays the end result of using algebra to solve many complex problems.

What is Algebra?
To most people the word *algebra* conjures up notions of letters and symbols. The word itself comes from the title of an Arabic publication, Al-jabr-w'al-muqabalah *Al-jabr* means "the reunion of broken parts, bone setting".

The mathematical ideas in these writings were passed on from generation to generation until they reached the Western World. Eventually *al-jabr* became the name for the powerful branch of mathematics, algebra.

As the problems that people were confronted with became more and more complicated, more and more mathematics was invented.

The impact of algebra on the study of mathematics is considered to be greater than the impact of computers on today's society.

4.1 Language for Algebra: Inventory

The language you have learned in order to work with numbers extends to your work in this chapter. Do the inventory below.

4.1 Exercise

1 Find the greatest common factor of
  (a) 32, 48   (b) 36, 54, 72   (c) 18, 24, 30

2 Find the lowest common multiple of
  (a) 3, 5   (b) 3, 6, 4   (c) 3, 4, 5

3 Simplify.
  (a) $(-3) + (+4)$ (b) $(-6) - (+2)$ (c) $(-9) \div (+3)$
  (d) $(-6) \times (+3)$ (e) $(-9) - (-3)$ (f) $(-4) + (-8)$
  (g) $(+27) \div (-9)$ (h) $(-18) \div (-6)$ (i) $(+6) + (-3)^2$
  (j) $(0) \times (-2)$ (k) $(-3) \times (+8)$ (l) $(+8)^2 - (-12)$
  (m) $(-25) \div (+5)$ (n) $(+6) + (-12)$ (o) $(+9) + (-7) - (-8)$
  (p) $(-12) \div (+3) \times (-2)$ (q) $(+32) \times (-8) \div (-4)$ (r) $(-8)^2 \div (+4) \div (-2)$

4 Calculate.
  (a) $8(-3)$ (b) $-3(-2)$ (c) $-6 - (-3)$ (d) $0 - (-3)$
  (e) $10 - (-3)$ (f) $-6(-4)$ (g) $16 \div (-4)$ (h) $-18 \div 2$

5 Simplify.
  (a) $3 + (-2) + 6 + (-2) + (-3) + (-5)$ (b) $-3 - 2 + 6 - 3 + 4 - 6 + 7$

6 Simplify.
  (a) $(-3)^2 + (-2)^2$ (b) $\dfrac{-6 + 8}{-3 + 1}$ (c) $\dfrac{(3 - 6)(-2)}{-6 \div 2}$ (d) $\dfrac{-40 \div 20 + 6}{-16 \div 4}$

7 Follow the instructions.
  (a) Subtract the sum of -2 and 3 from -8. (b) How much more is 8 than 4?
  (c) How much less is -8 than 12?   (d) Find the sum of $3(-2)$ and $-2(-3)$.

8 Use an example with integers to illustrate the meaning of each word.
  (a) square   (b) factor   (c) quotient   (d) exponent
  (e) product   (f) substitution   (g) base   (h) solution set
  (i) equation   (j) power   (k) multiple   (l) inequation

4.2 Simplifying Expressions: Using Symbols

Methods you learn in arithmetic often suggest patterns in algebra.

Arithmetic	Algebra
$\underbrace{3 + 3 + 3 + 3}$	$\underbrace{a + a + a + a}$
4×3	$4 \times a$ or $4a$

$a = 1a$
$a + a = 2a$
$a + a + a = 3a$
and so on

PSP Remember the strategy, *similar but simpler.*

Multiplication is understood.

$a + a + a + a$ and $4a$ are **equivalent expressions**.

Equivalent expressions can also be written for more than one variable.

$$\underbrace{a + a + a}_{3a} + \underbrace{b + b}_{2b} = 3a + 2b$$

$3a$ is called a **term**.

$2b$ is called a **term**.

Each of these terms has a **numerical coefficient** and a **literal** (letter) **coefficient**.

$$3a$$

3 is the **numerical coefficient**.

a is the **literal coefficient**.

Terms that have the same literal coefficients are called like **terms**. Terms with different literal coefficients are called unlike **terms**.

$3a, 4a, 5a$ are **like terms**. $3a, 4b, 5a^2$ are **unlike terms**.

Special names are used to describe expressions formed by adding and subtracting terms as shown in the chart at the right. **Polynomials** is the general name for monomials, binomials, trinomials, etc.

To simplify a polynomial means to collect like terms. You add or subtract like terms by adding or subtracting the numerical coefficients of the like terms.

Name	Examples
monomial ↑ 1 term	$2x, 3ab, 7, m^3$
binomial ↑ 2 terms	$2x + 3y, 3a^2 - 2a$
trinomial ↑ 3 terms	$2x + 3y - 4k,$ $-4a + 2b - 6$

Example 1 Simplify.
(a) $2c + 3c + 4$
(b) $(2x^2 + 3) + (-4x^2 + 8)$

Solution

(a) $2c + 3c + 4$
$= 5c + 4$

Since these are unlike terms, you cannot simplify any further.

(b) $(2x^2 + 3) + (-4x^2 + 8)$
$= 2x^2 + 3 - 4x^2 + 8$
$= 2x^2 - 4x^2 + 3 + 8$
$= -2x^2 + 11$

Rearrange to collect like terms.

To evaluate a polynomial means to find its value for given values of the variable.

Example 2   Evaluate $3x^2 - 5y + 4$ for $x = -2$ and $y = 3$.

Solution   Use $x = -2$ and $y = 3$.

Think: First substitute and then evaluate. Use brackets to show substitution.

$$3x^2 - 5y + 4 = 3(-2)^2 - 5(3) + 4$$
$$= 3(4) - 15 + 4$$
$$= 1$$

4.2   Exercise

A 1   Write an equivalent expression for each of the following.

(a) $x + x + y + y + y$ (b) $a + a + a + a$ (c) $b + b + b$

(d) $x + x + y + y$ (e) $a + b + b + b$ (f) $m + m + m + m + n + n + n$

2   All your answers in the previous question were polynomials. Which expressions were

(a) monomials?   (b) binomials?

3   Which terms are like terms?

(a) a, $2b$, $3a$, $4b$, $-a$, $-6b$ (b) $2x$, $-3y$, $-2y$, $-4x$, $-5y$

(c) $2x^2$, $-2x^2$, $-3x^2$, $4y^2$, $-x^2$ (d) a^2, $2a$, $-3a$, $4a^2$, $-5a$

(e) x^2, y^2, $2xy$, $-y^2$, $-x^2$, $-3xy$ (f) $6y$, 8, $-3y$, $-2y^2$, 6, $-2y$

4   (a) Find the value of each expression for $m = 2$ and $n = 3$.

A: $m + n + m + n$ B: $2m + 2n$

(b) Why are the values the same?

5   (a) Simplify each expression.

A: $3x^2 - 2x + 3x - 2x^2$ B: $2x^2 - 8 + x - x^2 + 8$

(b) Why are the expressions equivalent?

6   Simplify each of the following polynomials.

(a) $a + b + a + b + a + b + a + b$ (b) $a + 2a + b + b + b$

(c) $a + b + a + c + b + a + c + b$ (d) $m + 3m + n + 2n$

(e) $k + m - 2k + 2m + k + 3m$ (f) $x + y + x + y + z + y + z + x$

(g) $2a + 3b + a + b$ (h) $x + y + 2x + y + 2x + y$

(i) $2a + 3b + c + a + b + 2c$ (j) $2a + 3b + 2a + 3b + 2a + b$

For the above answers, which expressions are monomials, binomials or trinomials?

B   Check whether your answers are reasonable.   **PSP**

7   Simplify.
   (a) $3x + 2x - 3y - 2y$ (b) $3x + 2x$ (c) $2y - 5y$
   (d) $2a + 3a + 2a$ (e) $2a + a - 3a$ (f) $-x + x + 3x$
   (g) $8y - 3y$ (h) $2y + 2y - 6y$ (i) $3y + 4 + 2y$

8   Simplify each of the following. Which expressions are equivalent?
   (a) $a + 3a - a - b$ (b) $6x - 8 + 3x$ (c) $3x - 2x + 4y - 3y$
   (d) $2x^2 + 3x - 2x^2$ (e) $a + a - 3b + 2b$ (f) $3a - a + 2b - 3b$
   (g) $4x + 2y - x - 2y$ (h) $-3y + 3x + 4y - 2x$ (i) $x^2 + x - x^2 + 2x$
   (j) $2x - y - x + 2y$ (k) $(6y - 2y) + (3x - 8x)$ (l) $(8k - 3m) + (2k - 5m)$

9   Find the value of each expression for $a = -3$, $b = 5$ and $c = -2$.
   (a) $2a + 3a + 7a$ (b) $3a - 2a + c$
   (c) $2a - 3b + 4b$ (d) $-2a + 3c + 6c$
   (e) $3a + 2b - a + c - 2b$ (f) $-3c + 2a + 3c - 3b + 4a$

10   Use $a = -1$, $b = 2$ and $c = 3$.
   ▶ Estimate which expression, A, B or C, has the least value.
   ▶ Calculate which has the least value.
      A: $8a + 2b - 6a - 2b + 3c$
      B: $-9a - 2b + 7a - 6b + 2a - 3c + 4c$
      C: $a^2 - 6a + 2a^2 - 3a^2 - 8 + 7a + 8$

11   ▶ Round the values given and estimate the value of each expression.
   ▶ Find the value of each expression to 1 decimal place for the given values.
   ▶ Use a calculator to check your answers.
      (a) $3x + 2y - 4x + 5y$ $x = 3.6$, $y = 4.9$
      (b) $x^2 - 3y^2 - 2x^2 + y^2$ $x = 2.5$, $y = -3.1$
      (c) $2m + 6n - 3m + 5n$ $m = 4.69$, $n = -3.62$

PSP   12   To solve some problems, you need to combine your skills. Which skills do you need to use to solve this problem? Solve it!
   (a) A digit is represented by the letter A. What is the value of A if A1AA2 is divisible by 36?
   (b) Are there any other values of A that are suitable?

C   13   Each of the following expressions is equivalent to $3x - 5y + z$. Find the value of each missing numerical coefficient.
   (a) $x + 2y - 2z + ?x - 7y + ?z$ (b) $-x + 2y - 3z + 4x + ?y + ?z$

Applications: Building Algebraic Expressions

When you are finding the value of an expression, the number of calculations is reduced if the expression is simplified first.

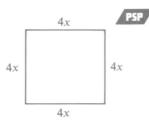

PSP Use a diagram to help you visualize the problem.

The perimeter of a square is given by $P = 4x + 4x + 4x + 4x$.
What is the perimeter if $x = 6$?

How many calculations do you do to find the value of the perimeter?
$P = 4x + 4x + 4x + 4x$
$P = 4(6) + 4(6) + 4(6) + 4(6)$
$P = 24 + 24 + 24 + 24$
$P = 96$ Did you get 7 calculations?

How many calculations do you do now to find the perimeter?
$P = 4x + 4x + 4x + 4x$
$P = 16x$
$P = 16(6)$
$P = 96$ Did you get fewer calculations?

14   A path, AB, is shown. Each distance is given in kilometres. Find the total length of the path if $m = 3$ and $n = 2$.

15   Find an expression for the perimeter of each of the following figures.

(a)

(b)

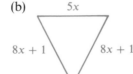

(c)
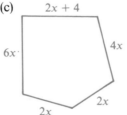

(d)
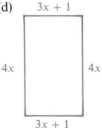

16   Find the perimeter of each figure in the previous question for
(a) $x = 6$ (b) $x = 10$

17   (a) The perimeter of a square is $16x$ units. What is the length of one side in terms of x?
(b) The perimeter of a rectangle is $16y$ units. If the length is $5y$ units, find an expression for the width.

18   (a) The perimeter of a rectangle is $24x$ units. If the width is $4x$ units, find an expression for the length.
(b) Find the dimensions of the rectangle if $x = 12$.

4.3 Polynomials: Addition and Subtraction

In the previous section you added polynomials.

$$(2a + b) + (3a - 2b)$$
$$= 2a + b + 3a - 2b$$
$$= 5a - b$$

To subtract polynomials, you need to use your earlier skills with opposites. The opposite is also called the additive inverse.

Arithmetic

The opposite of 3 is -3.
The opposite of -4 is 4.

Algebra

The opposite of $3a$ is $-3a$.
The opposite of $-4x$ is $4x$.
The opposite of $2a - b$ is
$-(2a - b)$ or $-2a + b$.

To subtract an integer you added its opposite. Similarly, to subtract a polynomial you add its opposite, as shown in the following example.

To plan the construction of a building, an engineer needs to simplify and evaluate many polynomials. To calculate the stresses and strains in the building, the engineer also needs to use algebra.

Example 1 Simplify each of the following.
(a) $3a - (-2a)$ (b) $(2a + b) - (3a - 2b)$

Solution
(a) $3a - (-2a)$
 $= 3a + 2a$
 $= 5a$

(b) $(2a + b) - (3a - 2b)$
 $= 2a + b - 3a + 2b$
 $= -a + 3b$

When you are finding the value of an expression, it is quicker if you simplify the expression first as shown in the next example.

Example 2 Find the value of $4m - 2n - (2m + 3n)$ for $m = 2$ and $n = -3$.

Solution
Step 1: Simplify the expression.
$$4m - 2n - (2m + 3n)$$
$$= 4m - 2n - 2m - 3n$$
$$= 4m - 2m - 2n - 3n$$
$$= 2m - 5n$$

Step 2: Substitute and then calculate.
$$2m - 5n$$
$$= 2(2) - 5(-3)$$
$$= 4 + 15$$
$$= 19$$

The **degree** of a polynomial is the greatest degree that occurs in any one of its terms. The degree of a term is the sum of the exponents of the variables of the term.

$2x^4$ has degree 4. $\qquad$ b^2c has degree 3.

In $3x^2 + 2xy^2 - 5$, $3x^2$ has degree 2, $2xy^2$ has degree 3, -5 has degree 0.

Thus $3x^2 + 2xy^2 - 5$ has degree 3.

4.3 Exercise

A 1 Match each binomial in Column I with its opposite in Column II.

Column I	Column II		Column I	Column II
(a) $2x - 3y$	A $-6 + 3n$		(d) $6 - 3n$	D $-2x + 3y$
(b) $x^2 - y^2$	B $2x + 3y$		(e) $-2x - 3y$	E $-3n - 6$
(c) $3n + 6$	C $x^2 - y^2$		(f) $-x^2 + y^2$	F $-x^2 + y^2$

2 (a) If $x = 2$ and $y = 3$, find the value of each expression.

(i) $2x - 3y$ $\quad$ (ii) $-(2x - 3y)$ $\quad$ (iii) $2x + 3y$ $\quad$ (iv) $-2x - 3y$

(b) Which expressions are opposites?

3 Find the value of each pair of expressions. Use $m = 2$ and $n = -1$.

(a) $3m - 2n$, $-3m + 2n$ $\qquad$ (b) $-4m - n$, $4m + n$

(c) $-(3m - 4n)$, $3m - 4n$ $\qquad$ (d) $-(4m + n)$, $4m + n$

4 To subtract a polynomial, you need to write its opposite. Write the opposite of each of the following.

(a) $3x$ $\qquad$ (b) $-2x$ $\qquad$ (c) $-4x^2$ $\qquad$ (d) $2xy$

(e) $-4x^2y$ $\qquad$ (f) $-g + h$ $\qquad$ (g) $-(a + b)$ $\qquad$ (h) $-(-e + f)$

(i) $x^2 + 2x - 5$ $\qquad$ (j) $-k^2 - 3k + 6$ $\qquad$ (k) $3x - 2y$ $\qquad$ (l) $-(-y^2 + 2y + 5)$

5 What is the degree of each polynomial?

(a) $3x^2 - 2xy + y^3$ $\qquad$ (b) $5abc - 6b^2c^2$ $\qquad$ (c) $-mn + 2m^2n - 4$

(d) $7a - 5b + 9$ $\qquad$ (e) $6m^3n - m^2n^3$ $\qquad$ (f) $4p^2 + 2pq - q$

B 6 Simplify.

(a) $2m - (m - 3)$ $\qquad$ (b) $3x - (2x - y)$ $\qquad$ (c) $(3m - 2n) - (2m - 3n)$

(d) $(3x - 4y) - (2x + 2y)$ $\qquad$ (e) $(2a + 3b) - (-2a + b)$

(f) $x - 2 - (x - 4)$ $\qquad$ (g) $9m - 3n - (-5m - 2n)$

7 Find the value of each of the following. Use $a = 3$ and $b = -2$.

(a) $2a - 3b - (4a + b)$ $\quad$ (b) $3a - 2b - (2a - b)$ $\quad$ (c) $-(6a - b) + (3a - 2b)$

8   Simplify.
     (a) $(2x - 3y) - (3x - 2y)$ (b) $(4a - 2b) + (3a + b)$ (c) $(2m - n) - (4m - n)$
     (d) $(y^2 - 2x^2) - (x^2 - 3y^2)$ (e) $(2xy + y^2) + (2y^2 - xy)$
     (f) $(3x^2 - 2x + 5) - (2x^2 + x - 6)$ (g) $(4m^2 - m - 4) + (-8m^2 - 2m + 1)$

9   Simplify.
     (a) $(5x^2 - 9) + (3 - x^2)$ (b) $(3ab + 4b) - (2b - 5ab)$
     (c) $(6g^2 - g) - (2g - g^2)$ (d) $(4m^2 - 2m - 4) + (-3m^2 - 2m + 5)$
     (e) $(7p^2 - 2p + 8) + (3p - 4p^2)$ (f) $(2x^2y - 3xy + 7) + (xy - 3x^2y - 2)$

10   Do you know why Elk Island
     National Park is important?
     (Refer to the caption for the
     photograph.) The size of Elk
     Island National Park in square
     kilometres is given by the answer
     to this question. Find the value
     for $m = 16$ and $n = 19$.
     $(12m + 3n) - (6m - 5n) - (-2m + 4n)$

*Did you know that the world's largest
herds of wood bison are found in Elk
Island National Park?*

11   For each expression, use $x = 3$ and $y = -2$.
     ▶ Estimate which has the greatest value.   ▶ Then evaluate the expressions.
     A: $3x - 2y - (2x - 5y) + 3x + 2y$ B: $-(x^2 - y) + x^2 + y - (x^2 - 3y)$
     C: $(x + 2y) - (x - 7y) + (x + 5y)$

PSP 12   Have you ever wondered whether Smarties candies have the exact
             same shape and size?
                 Seven of eight Smarties are identical in mass. One is heavier.
             How could you determine which Smartie is heavier than the others using
             a balance scale only twice?

C 13   Use $m = 3$ and $n = 2$. Which trip is longer, A or B? By how much?

14   The following polynomials are equivalent to $5m - 3n$. Find the unknown
     expressions.   A: $4m + n - (?)$ B: $-m + n - (?)$

Applications: Algebra for Perimeter

Computers can be used to simulate designs and to do calculations. Often computers are programmed to determine the minimum amount of material needed in the design of aircraft, machinery and so on.

A triangular region is given. The perimeter of the region is given by $P = 16x - 12$. Find the expression for side $\overline{BC}$.

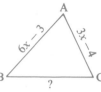

Step 1: Find the sum of the two known sides.

$$(3x - 4) + (6x - 3) = 3x - 4 + 6x - 3$$
$$= 9x - 7$$

Step 2: Find the expression for $\overline{BC}$.

$$\overline{BC} = \text{Perimeter} - \text{sum of two sides}$$
$$= 16x - 12 - (9x - 7)$$
$$= 16x - 12 - 9x + 7$$
$$= 7x - 5$$

The expression for side $\overline{BC}$ is $7x - 5$.

15 The perimeter of the figure is given by the expression $11x + 6$.

(a) Find the expression for side $\overline{LN}$.

(b) Find each of the sides when $x = 8$.

(c) Find the perimeter when $x = 8$.

(d) How could you use the expression $11x + 6$ to check your answer in (c)? **PSP**

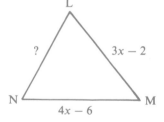

16 (a) Use the results in the previous question. Find the perimeter when

(i) $x = 6$ (ii) $x = 11$ (iii) $x = 20$

(b) For which of the values is the perimeter the greatest (a maximum)?

(c) Explain how you could check your answers in (a).

17 The expressions for the dimensions of an aircraft part are given in the diagram.

(a) Write an expression for the length of side $\overline{FA}$.

(b) Write an expression for the length of side $\overline{AB}$.

(c) Write an expression for the perimeter.

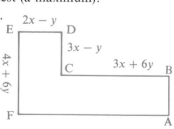

4.4 PSP Problem Solving Strategy: Translating to Mathematics

When you are solving problems, you can use the *Problem Solving Plan* PSP to help you organize your solution. One important skill you need to learn in order to solve word problems is to be able to translate from English to mathematics. An important strategy for *B Decide on a method* is *Use a variable to translate words to symbols*.

English
A number is increased by 12.

Mathematics
Use *n* to represent the number.
$n + 12$

To solve problems about age, you first need to translate into variable expressions as shown in the example.

Example 1   Bob's age today is *b* years. Write an expression for
(a) his age 2 years from now   (b) his age 6 years ago

Solution   All variable expressions represent years.
(a) $b + 2$ (b) $b - 6$

In many problems you are given relationships that need to be translated.

Example 2   The length of a rectangle is 6 m more than the width. Write its dimensions using variable expressions.

Solution   Let *w* represent the width in metres.
Then $(w + 6)$ represents the length in metres.

4.4 Exercise

A 1   Translate each of the following.
(a) Five times the sum of *y* and 23.   (b) $\frac{1}{3}$ of *n* is subtracted from $\frac{1}{2}$ of *n*.

2   Find the value in cents of each of the following.
(a) *n* dimes   (b) $(n - 1)$ nickels   (c) $2n$ quarters

B 3   Choose a variable to represent the number and write an expression for each of the following.
(a) A number is decreased by 15.
(b) Two thirds of a number.
(c) A number is doubled.
(d) A number is decreased by $\frac{1}{2}$ of itself.

4   Kevin's present age is k years. Write an expression for each of the following.
(a) Natalie is 3 years older than Kevin.   (b) Jeannette is twice as old as Kevin.
(c) Jim is $\frac{1}{2}$ of Kevin's age 3 years ago.   (d) Steve is $\frac{2}{3}$ of Kevin's age next year.

5   Write variable expressions for the dimensions of the following rectangles.
(a) The width is 8 m less than the length.
(b) The length is double the width.
(c) The width is 3 m shorter than $\frac{1}{2}$ of the length.
(d) The length is 3 m longer than twice the width.
(e) The width is 2 m longer than $\frac{1}{3}$ of the length.

6   Find the total value in cents of each sum of money.
(a) n dimes, $(n + 1)$ quarters
(b) n nickels, $(n - 2)$ dimes
(c) n cents, $(n + 2)$ nickels
(d) $3n$ dimes, $(3n + 1)$ quarters
(e) $(n + 2)$ cents, $2n$ dimes
(f) n cents, $(n + 1)$ dimes, $(n + 2)$ nickels
(g) n dimes, $(n + 2)$ quarters, $(n + 4)$ cents
(h) $3n$ nickels, $(3n - 2)$ quarters, $(3n + 2)$ cents

PSP 7   A family of cats guards the strawberry patch by chasing away flocks of birds. If there are 89 heads and 232 legs in the strawberry patch, how many cats are there?

PSP 8   What property do these words have in common?
           HI   COD   DOCK   HIKE
Suggest another word that has the same property. Justify your answer.

C 9   Often it is helpful to work backwards to solve a problem. For example, each variable expression occurred in translating a word problem. Use words to describe each one.
(a) $2n + 5$
(b) $n - 8$
(c) $6n$
(d) $3n - 1$
(e) $5n - n$
(f) $7 + \frac{1}{2}n$
(g) $15 - 2n$
(h) $\frac{2}{3}(n + 1)$
(i) $\frac{1}{2}(n - 1)$
(j) $\frac{n + 2n}{2}$

The first step when you are solving a word problem is to ask yourself the two key questions:

I   What information am I asked to find?

II   What information am I given?

It is important that you read a word problem carefully so that you understand exactly what it is that you are asked to find.

Following instructions is an important part of problem solving.

The following questions review some of the words and instructions you frequently encounter when solving problems.

10   Find the sum of $3x - 2y$, $x - y$ and $x - 3y$.

11   Subtract $2x - 3y$ from $x - 5y$.

12   How much less than $4x - 2y$ is $-3x + 2y$?

13   Subtract the sum of $2a$ and $-3a + 4b$ from $-6a - 2b$.

14   Find the sum of $a + 2b$, $6a - 3b$ and $-4a + 6b$.

15   Subtract $4a - 2b$ from $-6a + 4b$.

16   How much more than $6x - 6y$ is $2x - 3y$?

17   Find the sum of $2a$, $3a + 4b$ and $6a - 2b$.

18   Subtract the sum of $a + b$ and $2a - b$ from $4a - 4b$.

19   By how much is $3x^2 - 4xy$ greater than $7xy + 5x^2$?

20   Increase the sum of $2m - n$ and $8n + m$ by $5m - 7n$.

21   Find the result of decreasing $\frac{1}{2}ab + 2a$ by the total of $b - 5a$ and $\frac{3}{2}ab + 7a$.

22   The result of increasing $5m^2 + 2n^3$ by $-8n^3 - 5m^2$ is subtracted from $2m^2 + 3n^3$.

23   Find how much less than $2v + 11w + 8vw$ the sum of $5vw - 3v + 2w$ and $4w - 7vw$ is.

4.5 Applications with Polynomials

The skills you have learned with polynomials are applied to solve problems that use your skills with substitution.

$\boxed{\textit{PSP}}$

Example   The total cost, T, in thousands of dollars of digging trenches for underground cables is given by

$T = 6.8n + 2.6n - 2n$ where n is the length in metres of the trench.

Find the total cost for $n = 8.6$.

Solution   *Step 1:* Simplify.   *Step 2:* Substitute and then evaluate.

$$T = 6.8n + 2.6n - 2n \qquad\qquad T = 7.4(8.6) \quad \text{Remember: } T \text{ is in}$$
$$= 7.4n \qquad\qquad\qquad\qquad\quad = 63.64 \quad \text{thousands of}$$

Thus the total cost is $\$(63.64 \times 1000)$ or $\$63\ 640$.   dollars.

4.5 Exercise

A   **1**   The cost, C, in cents of making cards is given by $C = 125 + 2n$ where n is the number of cards. Calculate the cost of making each number of cards.

(a) 100   (b) 150   (c) 200   (d) 1000

2   The amount, C, in dollars, charged by a delivery company to deliver a package is given by $C = 2.65 + 0.85d$ where d is the distance in kilometres. Find the charge to deliver each parcel.

(a) 8.5 km   (b) 3 km   (c) 25 km

B   **3**   In skydiving, once you leave the plane, your height, h, in metres above the earth's surface is given by

$h = a - 4.9t^2$ where a is the altitude of the plane in metres and
t is the time in seconds after leaving the plane.

(a) Find Jennifer's height to the nearest metre after 6.5 s if she jumped from a height of 2500 m.

(b) Jackson jumped 2 s after Jennifer. How far apart were they, 4.5 s after Jackson jumped?

4   The cost of renting a car, C, in dollars is given by

$C = 21t + 0.12d + 9.50t$ where t is the time in days and
d is the distance driven in kilometres.

Find the cost for each distance and time.

(a) 1296 km, 3 d   (b) 1375 km, 5 d   (c) 1424 km, 4 d

5 An elevator can hold 8 children and 6 adults. Alternatively it can hold 12 children and 3 adults.

(a) If everyone on the elevator is an adult, how many people are on the elevator?

(b) What assumption did you make?

6 After camp ended, everyone in our cabin promised to write to each other once a month.

(a) If there were 15 in our cabin, how many letters will be sent each month?

(b) How many letters will be sent in one year?

(c) How many letters will each person write in one year?

C 7 The total cost, C, in dollars of producing a brochure is given by

$$C = 5.25p + 0.18b + 0.32b + 2.80p$$

where p is the number of pages in the brochure and b is the number of brochures.

By how much does the cost of printing 10 000 copies of an 8-page brochure exceed the cost of printing 9000 copies of a 12-page brochure?

Calculator Use

Does your calculator have a constant feature?
If you press any of the keys $+$, $-$, $\times$ or $\div$ twice, you establish a constant. On some calculators, the first number entered is stored as the constant and on other calculators, the second number entered is stored as the constant. Remember to read your calculator manual to see how it is done on your calculator.

The constant function $+$ $+$ is useful when you want to add the same number to different inputs. The following illustrates the constant feature.

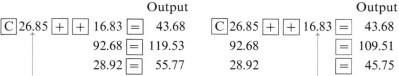

	Output			Output
C 26.85 + + 16.83 =	43.68		C 26.85 + + 16.83 =	43.68
92.68 =	119.53		92.68	= 109.51
28.92 =	55.77		28.92	= 45.75

When the first number entered is stored as a constant.

When the second number entered is stored as a constant.

Try the constant feature for $-$ $-$, $\times$ $\times$ and $\div$ $\div$.
Refer to your manual for the procedure related to your calculator.

4.6 A Fundamental Property: Simplifying Polynomials

You will find that there are some properties that are true for different branches of mathematics. One such property is the distributive property.

> Multiplication is distributive over addition.
> $$3(2 + 7) = 3(2) + 3(7)$$

Think:
$3(2 + 7) = 3(9)$
$= 27$

Think: $3(2) + 3(7) = 6 + 21$
$= 27$

Since variables represent real numbers, the distributive property also applies to addition and subtraction in algebra.

▶ Multiplication is distributive over addition.

$a(b + c) = a(b) + a(c)$

▶ Multiplication is distributive over subtraction.

$a(b - c) = a(b) - a(c)$

Skills and concepts can be extended to develop new skills. Thus the distributive property can be used along with your skills in collecting terms to simplify expressions as shown in the following example.

PSP

Example 1 Simplify $3(x - 2y) + 2(x + 4y)$.

Solution

$3(x - 2y) + 2(x + 4y)$
$= 3x - 6y + 2x + 8y$
$= 3x + 2x - 6y + 8y$
$= 5x + 2y$

Think:
$3(x - 2y) = 3x - 6y$
$2(x + 4y) = 2x + 8y$

Now that your skills in simplifying expressions have been extended, you will be able to reduce the work needed to evaluate expressions such as the one in the following example. Remember to simplify before evaluating.

Example 2 Find the value of $2(x^2 - y) - 3(x^2 + y)$ for $x = -1$ and $y = -3$.

Solution

Step 1: Simplify the expression.
$$2(x^2 - y) - 3(x^2 + y)$$
$$= 2x^2 - 2y - 3x^2 - 3y$$
$$= -x^2 - 5y$$

Step 2: Substitute and evaluate.
$$-x^2 - 5y = -(-1)^2 - 5(-3)$$
$$= -1 + 15$$
$$= 14$$

4.6 Exercise

A 1 Simplify each product.

(a) $2(3x)$ (b) $3(-2y)$ (c) $-2(5k)$ (d) $3(-y)$ (e) $-2(-3y)$

(f) $-3(-x)$ (g) $5(4x^2)$ (h) $-3(2xy)$ (i) $6(-3ab^2)$ (j) $-2(3y^2)$

2 Write each of the following expressions without brackets.

(a) $3(x + 6)$ (b) $2(y + 4)$ (c) $8(6 + y)$

(d) $2(3x + 4)$ (e) $-4(4y + 1)$ (f) $-3(2y - 1)$

(g) $(x - 2y)(-6)$ (h) $-8(7 - 3y)$ (i) $3(x - 6y)$

(j) $(m - 3n)(-2)$ (k) $5(3m + 7n)$ (l) $(6m - 2n)(-2)$

3 Find each product.

(a) $3(x - 2)$ (b) $-(y + 3)$ (c) $-2(2y - 5)$

(d) $-(2y - 4)$ (e) $(3x - 2y)(-2)$ (f) $(2a + 5b)(-3)$

(g) $(3a - 2b)(4)$ (h) $-5(6y - 3x)$ (i) $(5x - 2y)(-3)$

B 4 Simplify each of the following.

(a) $2x + 3(x + 2)$ (b) $3x - 2(x - 5)$ (c) $4y - 3(4 + 2y)$

(d) $6 - 3(a - 6)$ (e) $-6a - (2a - 5)$ (f) $-4(2m - 3) - 12$

(g) $3(2a + 5) - 6a$ (h) $12 + (-4)(a - 4)$ (i) $-16x - (x + 4)$

(j) $-2(x - 4) - x$ (k) $25m - 2(m - 6)$ (l) $3x - 4(3x + 5)$

5 Simplify each of the following.

(a) $3x + 2 - 2(x + 4)$ (b) $2m - 3 + 3(m - 4)$

(c) $0 - 4m - 3(m - 6) + 5$ (d) $0 - 6m - (8 - 3m) - 6$

(e) $-8(9 - y) - y + 9$ (f) $-8(9 - y) - (y + 9)$

(g) $3(x - 2) + (x + 2)(3)$ (h) $4(m + 5) + (m + 2)(-3)$

6 (a) Evaluate $3(x - y) - 2(2x - 3y)$ for $x = 2$ and $y = 3$.

(b) Simplify first and then evaluate the expression in (a) for $x = 2$ and $y = 3$.

(c) Which solution required fewer computations, (a) or (b)?

7 Copy and complete the chart. Remember to simplify first.

	Expression	Value of expression for		
		$x = 3$	$x = 0$	$x = -1$
(a)	$3(x - 5) - 2(x + 1)$			
(b)	$-2(4 - x) - 3(x - 2)$			
(c)	$5(2x - 1) + 3(2x - 1)$			

8 The profit in cents on the sale of plants is given by the expression
$0.05(3t - 25)$ where t is the number of plants sold. Find the profit for
(a) $t = 10$ (b) $t = 100$ (c) $t = 50$

9 Simplify.
(a) $0.5(k - 3) + 4.5(k + 1)$ (b) $3.2(p - 1) - 2.5(4 - p)$
(c) $2.7(w + 2) - 5.4(w - 1)$ (d) $0.8(m - 0.5) + 0.6(1.5 + m)$
(e) $1.5(q - 0.4) - 2.4(q + 0.5)$ (f) $3.7(b - 9) - 3.2(1.1 + b)$

10 Evaluate each expression for the value given.
(a) $2(x - 3) - (x - 3)$, $x = 3.2$ (b) $6(k - 6) - (k - 3)$, $k = 2.5$
(c) $8(s - 2) - 3(s - 5)$, $s = -5.4$ (d) $-4(2 - y) - 2(y + 5)$, $y = -3.5$

11 The parts of each path are shown by variable expressions. Find a
simplified expression for each path.

(a)
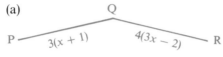

(b)

12 (a) Find an expression for the
perimeter of the rectangle.
(b) Find the perimeter for $x = 5$
and $x = 10$.

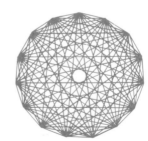

13 The design shown is made from line
segments. How many line segments
are there altogether in the design?

Math Tip

An important mathematical skill is learning methods of checking work. One
method is to substitute convenient values for the variable (e.g. $a = 1$, $b = 1$)
in both the original expression and the simplified expression. The answers
should be the same! Try this to check your work in this chapter.

4.7 **PSP** Problem Solving Strategy: Using Variables

People often do amazing number tricks and you ask "How did they do that?" *Using a variable* is an important problem solving strategy that can be used to provide an explanation. For example, follow the set of instructions for different choices of a number.

Instructions		Choose 4.	Choose 6.	Choose −3.
Think of a number.	⟶	4	6	−3
Add 5.	⟶	9	11	2
Multiply by 2.	⟶	18	22	4
Add your original number.	⟶	22	28	1
Subtract 4.	⟶	18	24	−3
Divide by 3.	⟶	6	8	−1
Subtract 2.	⟶	4	6	−3

For the above set of instructions, no matter how many different numbers you try, the result appears to be always the number you started with. Try some other numbers.

You can use a variable to show why you always obtain this result. For example, use the variable n to represent any number. As each instruction is translated to a variable expression, you can analyze the result.

Instructions		Translation
Think of a number.	⟶	n is the number chosen.
Add 5.	⟶	$n + 5$
Multiply by 2.	⟶	$2(n + 5) = 2n + 10$
Add your original number.	⟶	$(2n + 10) + n = 3n + 10$
Subtract 4.	⟶	$(3n + 10) − 4 = 3n + 6$
Divide by 3.	⟶	$(3n + 6) ÷ 3 = n + 2$
Subtract 2.	⟶	$(n + 2) − 2 = n$ ←

You can interpret the variable expression as follows. For any number, n, you always obtain the final result n.

4.7 Exercise

B **1** (a) Follow the set of instructions.

(b) Use algebra to show that you can predict the result.

(c) Would this work if you picked a number that is not a whole number?

> Pick any whole number.
> Add 4.
> Multiply by 3.
> Subtract your original number.
> Divide by 2.
> Subtract 6.

2   Try each of the following. Use algebra to show what answer to expect.

(a)
| Pick any whole number. |
| Double your number. |
| Add 6. |
| Add your original number. |
| Divide by 3. |
| Subtract your original number. |

(b)
| Pick any whole number. |
| Subtract 5. |
| Double your answer. |
| Add one more than your original number. |
| Divide by 3. |
| Add 3. |

3   Study each of the following. What would you do to the final answer to obtain the original number?

(a)
Instructions	Algebra
Pick any number.	x
Add 5.	$x + 5$
Multiply by 3.	$3x + 15$
Subtract your original number.	$2x + 15$
Subtract 15.	$2x$

(b)
Instructions	Algebra
Pick a number.	x
Add 10.	$x + 10$
Double the result.	$2x + 20$
Add one more than your original number.	$3x + 21$
Divide by 3.	$x + 7$

4   To make a set of instructions, translate your steps in algebra to words. For example, the following steps are translated as shown.

$x \longrightarrow$ Pick a number.

$3x \longrightarrow$ Multiply by 3.

$3x + 12 \longrightarrow$ Add the number of months in a year.

$4x + 12 \longrightarrow$ Add your original number.

$x + 3 \longrightarrow$ Divide by 4.

Ask for the final answer. The algebra shows you that all you need to do is subtract 3 from the final answer to get the original number.

(a) Make up a set of instructions of your own as shown above.

(b) Test it by choosing a number and following the instructions.

Computer Use

A computer can be used to investigate patterns with numbers and their properties. The numbers 7, 24 and 25 have a special relationship shown by

$$7^2 + 24^2 = 25^2.$$

Use the computer program to test for other numbers that share this property.

```
10 INPUT A, B, C
20 LET D = A ↑ 2 + B ↑ 2 − C ↑ 2
30 IF D = 0 THEN 60
40 PRINT A, B, C, "IS NOT A TRIPLE."
50 GO TO 70
60 PRINT A, B, C, "IS A TRIPLE."
70 END
```

4.8   Problem Solving: Building Strategies

In solving some problems, you have used diagrams to relate the given information to what you are asked to find. Using a diagram helps to suggest a strategy.

In the following problem, try relating the given information to numbers. Using numbers may suggest a strategy for solving the problem.

Example   What is the next letter in the following pattern of letters?

      A   C   F   J   O ...

Solution

> **PSP** Think: What letters are missing? Can I relate the letters to numbers to help me interpret the problem?

Assign a number to each letter.

A	B	C	D	E	F	G	H	I	J	K	L	M
1	2	3	4	5	6	7	8	9	10	11	12	13

N	O	P	Q	R	S	T	U	V	W	X	Y	Z
14	15	16	17	18	19	20	21	22	23	24	25	26

The pattern is interpreted using numbers.

     A   C   F   J   O
     ↑   ↑   ↑   ↑   ↑
     1   3   6   10   15

> Think: The next number in the pattern is 21.21 relates to the letter U.

The next letter in the pattern is U.

4.8   Exercise

A 1   A pattern is shown using letters.

     A   C   E   G   I ...

(a) Assign numbers to the letters.
(b) Interpret the problem using numbers.
(c) What is the next letter in the pattern?

2   A pattern is shown using letters.

     W   U   S   Q   O ...

(a) Interpret the problem using numbers.
(b) What is the next letter in the pattern?

B   Review the strategies you have listed in your *Problem Solving Plan* **PSP** . How many of them will you need to use to solve the following problems?

3   What is the next letter in each pattern?

(a) D F I M R ...
(b) G I K M O ...
(c) T R P N L ...
(d) B D G I L ...

4   To find the next letter in each of these patterns, you need to find other ways in which the letters may be related. (Hint: The letters are the first letters of related words.)

(a) O T T F F S S E...   (b) T F S E T T F...

(c) M T W T F S...   (d) J F M A M J J A...

5   The letters in the following patterns are related in some way. Identify the relationship and then find the next letter in each pattern.

(a) B C D E P...   (b) A E F H I...

6   To solve the following problem,

▶ Ask yourself, "How can letters and numbers be related?"

▶ Try a strategy that relates letters and numbers. Then apply this strategy to solve the problem.

(a) The value of CAMPING is 63. What value would you suggest for CANOEING? Justify your answer.

(b) The value of DANCING is 137. What value would you suggest for MUSIC? Justify your answer.

7   Each letter in the addition question shown represents a digit. Each letter represents only one digit. No digit is used for more than one letter.

$$\begin{array}{r} ON \\ + \ YOUR \\ \hline MARK \end{array}$$

(a) What is the addition question?

(b) Can you find more than one solution?

8   Use the digits 0, 1, 2, ... , 8, 9 to represent each letter in the subtraction.

$$\begin{array}{r} BRUSH \\ - \ YOUR \\ \hline TEETH \end{array}$$

C 9   If TELEVISION has a value of 10, what value would you give MOVIE? (Hint: Think more than natural.)

Math Tip

To solve problems, whether in mathematics or other disciplines, you must understand the meaning of each word that occurs.

▶ Make a list of the new math words you have learned in this chapter. Provide an example of your own to illustrate each word.

▶ List any new problem solving strategies that you have added to *Step B* of your *Problem Solving Plan* PSP

Practice and Problems: Review

1   Simplify.
(a) $\dfrac{(5-9)(3)}{-6}$
(b) $\dfrac{-8+12}{-3+1}$
(c) $\dfrac{(-5)^2+3^2}{-19+2}$
(d) $\dfrac{(-8)^2}{15\times(-2)-2}$

2   Simplify.
(a) $3a+4a+2+7$
(b) $4c-2+c-6$
(c) $-2mn-4m^2-mn+2m^2$
(d) $(x^2-3x)+(2x^2+5x)+6$

3   Evaluate for $x=2$.
(a) $(5x^2-x)+(3x^2+2x)$
(b) $(3x^2+x)-(x^2+5x)$
(c) $(7x^2-5)+(6-2x^2)$
(d) $(x^2-2x+3)-(5x^2+x-1)$

4   Find the distance around the figure.

5   Write expressions for the following.
(a) Auldean's age, k, 3 years from now
(b) Alan's age, c, 2 years ago
(c) The length is 3 m longer than the width, w.
(d) the value of k nickels
(e) the value of $(m+1)$ dimes

6   The cost of renting a chainsaw, C, in dollars is given by $C=5+7.5t$ where t is the time in days. Find the cost of renting a chainsaw for each time.
(a) 3 d
(b) 5 d
(c) 6 d
(d) 14 d

7   (a) Find the sum of $2a-3b$, $4a-b$ and $5b-3a$.
(b) Subtract $4a-3b$ from $3a-4b$.
(c) From the sum of $6a+b$ and $a-3b$, subtract $4a-2b$.

8   Find the value of each expression if $y=-2$.
(a) $3y+2(y+1)$
(b) $2y-3(y-1)$
(c) $4(2y-3)+4y$
(d) $-(3y-2)-5y$
(e) $-2(y+1)-3y$
(f) $2y+3(y-1)$

PSP 9   How many times does the digit 1 occur in writing the natural numbers from 1 to 100 inclusive?

PSP 10   What is the least positive integer that when multiplied by 48 is a cube?

Practice Test

1   Simplify.
   (a) $4d + 3 - 2d - 1$ (b) $2w^2 - 3w + w^2 + 2w$
   (c) $3q - 9 - 5q + 9$ (d) $2x + 3y - 3x + y$

2   Evaluate each expression. Round your answers to 1 decimal place.
   (a) $x^2 + 3x - 5x + 4x^2$ for $x = 4.5$
   (b) $3x - 5y + 4x + y$ for $x = 2.2$ and $y = -0.5$
   (c) $x^2 - 3x + 5x^2 - 6x^2 + 4$ for $x = 1.6$

3   Find the length of path AB if $m = -2$ and $n = 3$.

4   Simplify.
   (a) $2x - (x - 5)$ (b) $(3p - 2q) - (2p + 3q)$
   (c) $(5k + 7) + (11 - 2k)$ (d) $(5y^2 - 9y + 3) - (8y^2 - 4)$
   (e) $(7x - 9y) + (4y - x)$ (f) $(a^2 - ab + 2b^2) - (a^2 + 3ab - b^2)$

5   Choose a variable to represent the number. Then write an expression.
   (a) one half of a number   (b) 9 times a number
   (c) a number decreased by 3 and then multiplied by 4
   (d) a number increased by two thirds of itself

6   (a) Subtract $3u - 4c$ from $2u - 5c$.
   (b) Find the sum of $d - 2h$, $2d + 3h$ and $-d + 4h$.

7   The fare for a taxi ride, E, in dollars is given by $E = 1.5 + 0.75d$ where
   d is the distance in kilometres. Find the fare for each distance.
   (a) 2 km   (b) 12 km   (c) 15 km   (d) 28 km

8   Simplify.
   (a) $5(p - 7q)$ (b) $8 - 2(y + 9)$
   (c) $(3x - 4)(-2) + 7x$ (d) $-2(k - 4) + 3(k + 2)$
   (e) $-3(w^2 - w) - (w^2 + 2w)$ (f) $8(p^2 - 5) - (3p^2 + 6)$
   (g) $2.5(m - 1) - (1.5m + 2)$ (h) $3.2(y - 2z) + 1.3(z - 0.5y)$

PSP   9   One line in hockey consists of 3 forwards, 2 defence and 1 goalie. How
   many different lines can be formed from a team consisting of 2 goalies, 9
   forwards and 4 defence?

Cumulative Review (1–3)

1   Calculate. Round each answer to 1 decimal place.
- (a) $69.3 + 29.8$
- (b) $194.6 - 39.8$
- (c) 0.9×4.3
- (d) 3.96×1000
- (e) $67.93 \div 8$
- (f) $486 \div 9$
- (g) $8.9 + 29.3 - 3.6$
- (h) $19.6 - 3.8 + 4.9$
- (i) $83.65 \div 0.1$
- (j) $1000 - 96.8$
- (k) $43.2 \times 9.6 \div 2$
- (l) $6.832 \div 1.6$
- (m) $\dfrac{69.83 + 29.62}{1.96}$
- (n) $\dfrac{39.3 - 14.9}{3.8 + 1.3}$
- (o) $\dfrac{28.25 + 7.64 - 3.97}{7.6 \times 2}$

2   Express each number as a product of repeated identical factors and then express in exponential form.
- (a) 1000
- (b) 32
- (c) 27
- (d) 125
- (e) $100\ 000$

3   Evaluate each of the following.
- (a) 2^5
- (b) $2^3 + 3^2$
- (c) $3^3 - 3^2$
- (d) $2^3 \times 3^2$
- (e) $\dfrac{4 + 6 - 2}{2^2}$
- (f) $3(8 - 2) \div 9$
- (g) $\dfrac{8^2 \times 4 - 8 \times 2}{16 \div 4 + 8}$
- (h) $158 \div 2 + 3[6(8 - 5)]$
- (i) $\dfrac{12^2 - 3 \times 12}{2 + 4 \div 2}$

4   Find the following sums.
- (a) $-3 + (-2) + (-1) + (-4) + (-5) + (-6)$
- (b) $-1 + 6 + (-7) + 8 + (-3) + 3$
- (c) $4 + (-8) + 6 + (-12) + 3 + (-10)$

5   Simplify.
- (a) $(-3)^2$
- (b) $(-2)(-3)$
- (c) $(-2)(-3)^2$
- (d) $(-1)^4$
- (e) $(-1)^5$
- (f) $(-2)^3$
- (g) $(-3)(0)(-2)$
- (h) $(-2)(-3)(-1)(-6)$
- (i) $(3 + 5)(2 + 6)$
- (j) $8 \div 4 - 2$
- (k) $(9 - 9) \div (16 \div 4)$
- (l) $(12 \div 2 + 6) \div 3$

6   (a) Find the average of $-3,\ -4,\ 7,\ 9,\ -8,\ -7,\ -6,\ -5,\ 5$.
       (b) How much more or less is -6 than the average in (a)?

7   Evaluate for $p = -\dfrac{1}{8}$, $q = \dfrac{3}{-4}$ and $r = \dfrac{3}{8}$.
- (a) $p + q + r$
- (b) $pq + r$
- (c) $pr - pq$
- (d) pqr
- (e) $2qr - 3p$

8   A 3.5-m long ladder is leaning against a house. The base of the ladder is 1.8 m from the house. Find the height the ladder reaches up the house to the nearest tenth of a metre.

9   Draw each graph.   (a) $\{x \mid -5 \leqq x \leqq -1,\ x \in I\}$ (b) $\{y \mid -2 \leqq y$ or $y < -4,\ y \in R\}$

Microcomputers: Special Programs

A computer is often used for specific purposes. Computer programs or software are available to do many tasks, such as

▶ to find the balance of your account.

▶ to determine the cost of remodelling a home.

▶ to keep track of patients' records.

▶ to help you make financial forecasts.

Each of the programs that follow is written for a specific purpose.

You can use a program to find the results of any computation you need to do.

```
10 PRINT "OPERATIONS"
20 INPUT "THE NUMBERS ARE"; A, B
30 LET S = A + B
40 LET D = A − B
50 LET P = A * B
60 LET Q = A/B
70 PRINT "THE ANSWERS ARE"; S, D, P, Q
80 END
```

You can use a program to find your percent on a test.

```
10 PRINT "PERCENT ON TEST"
20 INPUT "TEST OUT OF"; T
30 INPUT "MY MARK IS"; M
40 LET P = 100 * M/T
50 PRINT "MY PERCENT IS"; P
60 END
```

You can use a program to do measurement problems.

```
10 PRINT "AREA OF A CIRCLE"
20 INPUT "THE RADIUS IS"; R
30 Let A = 3.14 * R ↑ 2
40 PRINT "THE AREA IS"; A
50 END
```

You can use a program to print a table of values.

```
10 PRINT "TABLE OF VALUES"
20 FOR X = 0 TO 10
30 LET F = 2 * X ↑ 2 − 3 * X + 5
40 PRINT "THE VALUES ARE"; F, X
50 NEXT X
60 END
```

1   Try a RUN for each program shown above. Use variables of your own choice.

2   Write a program to calculate the area of a

(a) rectangle.   (b) triangle.

3   Write a program to find a table of values for squares of whole numbers.

4   You want to check your skills with fractions. Write a program to do each computation.

(a) $\dfrac{a}{b} + \dfrac{c}{d}$ (b) $\dfrac{a}{b} - \dfrac{c}{d}$ (c) $\left(\dfrac{a}{b}\right)\left(\dfrac{c}{d}\right)$ (d) $\left(\dfrac{a}{b}\right) \div \left(\dfrac{c}{d}\right)$

5 *Using Equations: Solving Problems*

Language for solving equations, skills and strategies for solving equations, writing equations, using a *Problem Solving Plan* 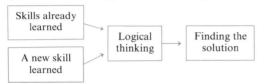, translating English to mathematics, organizational skills for solving problems, using formulas, applications, strategies for problem solving

Introduction

The process shown applies to the study of equations and solving problems.

```
┌─────────────────┐
│ Skills already  │ ⟍
│    learned      │   ⟍   ┌──────────┐      ┌──────────────┐
└─────────────────┘      │ Logical  │ →    │ Finding the  │
                         │ thinking │      │  solution    │
┌─────────────────┐   ⟋  └──────────┘      └──────────────┘
│  A new skill    │ ⟋
│    learned      │
└─────────────────┘
```

The skills you learned in algebra in the previous chapter are used to develop a plan to solve an equation. Solving an equation is then applied as a crucial part of solving problems. The photographs shown illustrate various achievements that were accomplished with the help of solving equations.

The fundamental skills you learn to solve equations are not only essential for solving the equations you will meet in this chapter, but also serve as a foundation for solving more advanced equations that occur in engineering, scientific research, economics and so on.

5.1 Vocabulary with Equations

A statement is translated from words into symbols. The result is an **equation**.

Twice a number, then increased by 4 is equal to 14.

A value of n that makes the equation true is called a **solution** or **root** of the equation. By systematically choosing different values of n and applying your substitution skills, you can find the solution. This method of finding a solution to an equation is called **systematic trial**.

$$2n + 4 = 14$$

Left side of equation: L.S.   Right side of equation: R.S.

Example 1   Find the solution of $2n + 4 = 14$.

Solution

Try $n = 3$.
L.S. $= 2n + 4$
$= 2(3) + 4$
$= 10$
R.S. $= 14$
L.S. $\neq$ R.S.

Try $n = 4$.
L.S. $= 2n + 4$
$= 2(4) + 4$
$= 12$
R.S. $= 14$
L.S. $\neq$ R.S.

Now try $n = 5$.
L.S. $= 2n + 4$
$= 2(5) + 4$
$= 14$
R.S. $= 14$
L.S. $=$ R.S.

Thus $n = 5$ is the solution of the equation.

Each of these statements has the same meaning.
► -2 is the root of the equation.
► $x = -2$ is the solution of the equation.
► $\{-2\}$ is the solution set of the equation.
Equations with the same root are called **equivalent equations**.

Example 2   Find the root of $11.5 - 4x = x - 0.5$. Use your calculator.

Solution

Try $x = 2$.

$\boxed{C}\boxed{CM}4\boxed{\times}2\boxed{=}\boxed{+/-}\boxed{M+}11.5\boxed{+}\boxed{MR}\boxed{=}3.5$ L.S. $= 3.5$

$\boxed{C}2\boxed{-}0.5\boxed{=}1.5$ R.S. $= 1.5$

Try $x = 2.5$.   Thus L.S. $\neq$ R.S.

$\boxed{C}\boxed{CM}4\boxed{\times}2.5\boxed{=}\boxed{+/-}\boxed{M+}11.5\boxed{+}\boxed{MR}\boxed{=}1.5$ L.S $= 1.5$

$\boxed{C}2.5\boxed{-}0.5\boxed{=}2$ R.S. $= 2$

Try $x = 2.4$.   Thus L.S. $\neq$ R.S.

$\boxed{C}\boxed{CM}4\boxed{\times}2.4\boxed{=}\boxed{+/-}\boxed{M+}11.5\boxed{+}\boxed{MR}\boxed{=}1.9$ L.S. $= 1.9$

$\boxed{C}2.4\boxed{-}0.5\boxed{=}1.9$ R.S. $= 1.9$

The root of $11.5 - 4x = x - 0.5$ is 2.4.   Thus L.S. $=$ R.S.

5.1 Exercise

A 1 Show that 4 is the root of the equation $5n - 3 = n + 13$.

Copy and complete the steps.

$$\text{L.S.} = 5n - 3 \qquad \text{R.S.} = n + 13$$
$$= 5(?) - 3 \qquad\qquad = (?) + 13$$
$$= ? \qquad\qquad\qquad = ?$$

2 Which value of the variable shown is the root?

(a) $3n + 1 = 16 \qquad 3, 4, 5$ (b) $2k - 3 = -7 \qquad -1, -2, -3$

(c) $5n + 5 = 30 \qquad 5, 6, 7$ (d) $15 - p = 9 \qquad 4, 5, 6$

3 (a) Estimate a solution for the equation $8k + 6 = 62$.

(b) Find the root of the equation.

B 4 Two values are given for each equation. Substitute both values in the equation to find which one is the root.

(a) $4x + 6 = 26 \qquad 5, 8$ (b) $4k - 3 = 2k + 9 \qquad 6, 3$

(c) $3(a + 2) = -6 \qquad 4, -4$ (d) $\dfrac{x}{3} - x = 2 \qquad -3, 3$

(e) $6x - 1 = 2(2x - 1) \qquad -\dfrac{1}{2}, -6$ (f) $7y + 28 = 5y + 6 \qquad 12, -11$

5 Which solution set is correct for each equation?

(a) $25 = 5(7 - y) \qquad \{2\}, \{-2\}$ (b) $\dfrac{3x + 12}{4} = 3 + x \qquad \{3\}, \{0\}$

(c) $5 = \dfrac{2x}{3} + x \qquad \{3\}, \{1\}$ (d) $3(x + 1) = 4(6 - x) \qquad \{0\}, \{3\}$

(e) $10 - \dfrac{3y}{5} = y - 6 \qquad \{3\}, \{10\}$ (f) $\dfrac{1}{3}x + 1 = \dfrac{1}{2}x \qquad \{1\}, \{6\}$

6 Two values of the variable are shown for each equation. Which is the root? Use your calculator.

(a) $6p + 8.1 = 32.1 \qquad 4, 3$ (b) $3q - 2.1 = 12.9 \qquad -5, 5$

(c) $9.6 + 2p = 21.6 \qquad 6, 7.5$ (d) $12.8 - 3q = -11.2 \qquad 8, 4$

(e) $2p + 3.1 = p + 9.1 \qquad 5.5, 6$ (f) $3q - 2.6 = 2q - 0.6 \qquad 2, -2$

7 The root of each of the following equations is one of the three numbers 2, -3 or 4. Find which equations are equivalent. Use your calculator.

(a) $2x + 5 = 9$ (b) $3x - 6 = 6$ (c) $2x + 8 = 2$

(d) $11 = 3x - 1$ (e) $3(2x + 8) = 6$ (f) $-25 = 5x - 10$

(g) $2x + 3 = x + 5$ (h) $\dfrac{3x - 6}{2} = 3$ (i) $3x - 9 = 4x - 6$

(j) $\dfrac{1}{2}x + 10 = 3x$ (k) $\dfrac{2}{3}x + x = 2x + 1$ (l) $3x + 2x + x = 2(2x + 2)$

8 The solution of $3x + 1 = 13$ is $x = 4$. Which of the following equations
have the same solution?

(a) $2x + 2 = 10$ (b) $3x - 2 = 14$ (c) $4x - 2 = 2x + 6$

(d) $4x - 2 = 2x + 4$ (e) $4x - 1 = 15$ (f) $\dfrac{2x + 4}{3} = 12$

(g) $2(5x - 6) = 28$ (h) $3x + x = 12 + 2x$ (i) $3(4x - 20) = 3x + 75$

9 The solution set for $23 - x = 2x - 22$ is $\{15\}$. Which of the following
have the same solution set?

(a) $2x = 15 + x$ (b) $15 - x = x + 5$ (c) $2x - 12 = x + 3$

(d) $3 = \dfrac{3x - x}{10}$ (e) $2.3x - 6 = 1.9x$ (f) $\dfrac{1}{5}(2x - 5) = 6$

10 I have $3.54 in change in my pocket. I have twice as many dimes as nickels and
half as many pennies as quarters. How many of each coin do I have?

C 11 Crownest Mountain was named because of
the crows that nest below its peak. Crowsnest
Pass is one of the lowest routes through the
Rockies. Answer the question to find the
height of the pass above sea level.

Find the value of $45a + 41b - 19c$.	a, b, c are the roots of $2a - 8 = 22$ $16 - 2b = 8$ $3c - 5 = -35$

From Math History

Symbols in mathematics have evolved over the centuries. People who first
use the symbols are often given credit for inventing them. Did you know
that the concepts of "is greater than" and "is less than" were used many
years before the symbols $>$ and $<$ were invented? Thomas Harriot
(1560–1621) is given credit for using these symbols for the first time.

5.2 Solving Equations: Using Properties

The skills you learn with numbers extend to your skills with algebra. For example, the properties of equality are important in developing methods of solving equations. Being able to identify inverse operations is also an important skill.

▶ If the same number is added to each side of an equation, the resulting sums are equal.

$8 = 8$	To isolate x, add 3 to each side	$x - 3 = 5$
$8 + 5 = 8 + 5$	(the inverse of *subtract 3*).	$x - 3 + 3 = 5 + 3$
$13 = 13$		$x = 8$

▶ If the same number is subtracted from each side of an equation, the resulting differences are equal.

$8 = 8$	To isolate x, subtract 5 from each	$x + 5 = 13$
$8 - 3 = 8 - 3$	side (the inverse of *add 5*).	$x + 5 - 5 = 13 - 5$
$5 = 5$		$x = 8$

▶ If each side of an equation is multiplied by the same number, the resulting products are equal.

$$\frac{x}{2} = 4$$

$8 = 8$	To isolate x, multiply each side by 2
$2 \times 8 = 2 \times 8$	(the inverse of *divide by 2*).
$16 = 16$	

$$2\left(\frac{x}{2}\right) = 2(4)$$

$$x = 8$$

▶ If each side of an equation is divided by the same number, the resulting quotients are equal.

$8 = 8$	To isolate x, divide each side by 2	$2x = 16$
$\dfrac{8}{2} = \dfrac{8}{2}$	(the inverse of *multiply by 2*).	$\dfrac{2x}{2} = \dfrac{16}{2}$
$4 = 4$		$x = 8$

Example   Solve.   (a) $3x = 42$ (b) $5y = 9 + 4y$

Solution   (a) $3x = 42$

$$\frac{3x}{3} = \frac{42}{3}$$

$$x = 14$$

Check:
L.S. $= 3x$
$= 3(14)$
$= 42$
$=$ R.S. ✓

The solution is $x = 14$.

(b)
$$5y = 9 + 4y$$
$$5y - 4y = 9 + 4y - 4y$$
$$y = 9$$

Check:
L.S. $= 5y$	R.S. $= 9 + 4y$
$= 5(9)$	$= 9 + 4(9)$
$= 45$	$= 45$

L.S. $=$ R.S. ✓

The solution is $y = 9$.

Recall the *Problem Solving Plan*. You now have a new skill for "Do the work".

Solve the equation.

When solving equations, you should always check your answer by substituting the root into the original equation. This process is called **verification**.

5.2 Exercise

A 1 What is the inverse of each step?
(a) add 8   (b) divide by 4   (c) multiply by 6
(d) subtract 6   (e) add -3 (f) divide by -2

2 ▶ Decide what number must be added or subtracted to solve the equation.
  ▶ Then solve the equation.
(a) $x + 5 = 9$ (b) $y - 3 = 7$ (c) $5 + p = -4$
(d) $-5 + x = 4$ (e) $2 = m - 10$ (f) $2 = 10 + w$

3 ▶ Decide whether you need to multiply or divide to solve the equation.
  ▶ Then solve the equation.
(a) $4x = 12$ (b) $\dfrac{y}{3} = 4$ (c) $\dfrac{1}{3} = 2y$ (d) $\dfrac{m}{8} = 3$

(e) $6p = 12$ (f) $6 = \dfrac{m}{4}$ (g) $-3k = 18$ (h) $\dfrac{x}{3} = -5$

B   Always verify your answers by substituting into the original equation. **PSP**

4 Find the root of each of the following equations.
(a) $p - 4 = 19$ (b) $-2y = -34$ (c) $w \div 7 = -8$ (d) $7y = -9 + 6y$
(e) $15 = x - 3$ (f) $m \div 2 = -13$ (g) $7 + k = -1$ (h) $12 - 8n = -7n$

5 Solve each of the following equations.
(a) $12 \div p = 1$ (b) $3m = 5 + 2m$ (c) $q \div 4 = -13$ (d) $17 = d - 3$
(e) $5x = 12$ (f) $9 + 6n = 7n$ (g) $13 - k = 11$ (h) $4 + y = -1$

C 6 Use your calculator to find the solution set of each of these equations.
(a) $k + 3.8 = 7.1$ (b) $9.5 - p = 1.8$ (c) $7.8 \div y = 2.4$
(d) $-6.5m = 22.1$ (e) $2.1 + q = -8.7$ (f) $-3.5 = x - 9.4$
(g) $a \div 1.5 = 2.2$ (h) $5.5n = -68.2$ (i) $-3.6 = 7.5 + q$

PSP 7 I am the smallest square that becomes a cube when you add me to some other square. Who am I?

5.3 Solving Equations: More Than One Step

You often need to use more than one property of equality to solve an equation.

Example 1   Solve $-8 = 3n - 14$.

Solution

$$-8 = 3n - 14$$
$$-8 + 14 = 3n - 14 + 14$$
$$6 = 3n$$
$$\frac{6}{3} = \frac{3n}{3}$$
$$2 = n \text{ or } n = 2$$

Thus $n = 2$ is the solution.

Check:
R.S. $= 3n - 14$
$= 3(2) - 14$
$= -8$
$= $ L.S. ✓

Example 2   Find the root of $5y - 8 = 3y - 10$.

Solution

$$5y - 8 = 3y - 10$$
$$5y - 8 - 3y = 3y - 10 - 3y$$
$$2y - 8 = -10$$
$$2y - 8 + 8 = -10 + 8$$
$$2y = -2$$
$$\frac{2y}{2} = \frac{-2}{2}$$
$$y = -1$$

Thus -1 is the root.

Check:
L.S. $= 5y - 8$ R.S. $= 3y - 10$
$= 5(-1) - 8$ $= 3(-1) - 10$
$= -5 - 8$ $= -3 - 10$
$= -13$ $= -13$
L.S. $=$ R.S. ✓

5.3 Exercise

A 1 Solve each of the following equations.

(a) $k + 9 = 15$ (b) $x + 4 = -7$ (c) $5 + n = 0$ (d) $10 = y + 8$

(e) $y - 5 = 4$ (f) $a - 4 = -3$ (g) $-3 + x = 7$ (h) $12 = b - 3$

(i) $3k = 27$ (j) $-4g = 32$ (k) $-26 = 13x$ (l) $18 = -6m$

(m) $\dfrac{x}{-7} = 6$ (n) $\dfrac{p}{9} = -8$ (o) $\dfrac{12}{w} = -2$ (p) $14 = \dfrac{42}{q}$

2 For each pair of equations, explain how the second one is obtained from the first one.

(a) $\quad 3x + 5 = 11$ (b) $\quad 4x - 3 = -11$ (c) $\quad 17 = 4y - 3$
$\quad 3x + 5 - 5 = 11 - 5$ $\quad 4x - 3 + 3 = -11 + 3$ $\quad 17 + 3 = 4y - 3 + 3$

(d) $\quad 6k + 8 = 3k - 7$ (e) $\quad 9p - 6 = 10 - p$
$\quad 6k + 8 - 3k - 8 = 3k - 7 - 3k - 8$ $\quad 9p - 6 + p + 6 = 10 - p + p + 6$

3 The first steps of the solutions are shown. Find the remaining steps.

(a) $\qquad 2x + 8 = 20$
$2x + 8 - 8 = 20 - 8$
▓▓▓▓▓▓▓▓▓▓▓▓▓

(b) $\qquad 3x - 2 = 13$
$3x - 2 + 2 = 13 + 2$
▓▓▓▓▓▓▓▓▓▓▓▓▓

(c) $\qquad 7 + \frac{1}{2}y = 10$
$7 + \frac{1}{2}y - 7 = 10 - 7$
▓▓▓▓▓▓▓▓▓▓▓▓▓

B Always verify your answers. **PSP**

4 The equations in each of the following pairs are related. Explain how the second equation is obtained from the first. Then solve.
(a) $4x - 2 = 18, \quad 4x = 20$
(b) $19 = 8y + 3, \quad 16 = 8y$
(c) $\frac{1}{2}x + 8 = 16, \quad \frac{1}{2}x = 8$
(d) $-18 = 3x - 12, \quad -6 = 3x$
(e) $7 - 4k = 5k - 2, \quad 7 = 9k - 2$
(f) $18 + 3k = k + 30, \quad 2k = 12$

5 Solve each equation.
(a) $3x - 2 = 16$
(b) $7y = 2y + 10$
(c) $\frac{1}{4}x - 3 = 4$
(d) $3 = \frac{3}{2}x - 3$
(e) $30 - 3n = 3n$
(f) $20 = 7y + 6$

6 Find the root of each equation.
(a) $8t - 14 = 26$
(b) $8 = 5 + 3y$
(c) $6 - 2m = m$
(d) $3r + 8 = 23$
(e) $20 + 7y = 12y$
(f) $1 - 5n = -9$

7 Find the solution set.
(a) $3a - 2 = -17$
(b) $40 + m = 6m$
(c) $7 = 1 + \frac{2}{3}x$
(d) $\frac{4}{5}x - 3 = 5$
(e) $4 - 3m = 10$
(f) $5 + 2a = 25$

8 Solve each equation. Check whether your answer is reasonable.
(a) $2m + 6.1 = 16.5$
(b) $4x - 2.8 = 4.8$
(c) $15.8 - 6m = 5$
(d) $8y = 16.5 + 3y$
(e) $8y - 6.9 = 3y + 3.6$
(f) $12.8 - 3m = 8m - 33.4$

PSP 9 A commuter plane begins a trip with 150 people and makes 4 stops before its final destination. At each of these stops the plane picks up 25 people and 50 people get off. How many people are there for the final destination?

C 10 In writing the following, Harriet accidently omitted the parentheses. Where should they be placed to make the equation true?
$$4 \times 8 + 4 \div 2 - 8 - 3 \times 3 - 3 = 0$$

5.4 Applying Skills: Solving Equations

The skills you learn about algebra, Step A, are used to develop more skills for solving equations. In this section you will learn skills for Step B. In Example 1, skill in using the distributive property is needed.

Step A Learn skills about algebra.

Step B Apply these skills to solve equations.

Step C Apply skills for solving equations to solve problems.

Example 1   Solve $4x + 3(20 - x) = 80$.

Solution

$$4x + 3(20 - x) = 80 \quad \text{Use the}$$
$$4x + 60 - 3x = 80 \quad \text{distributive}$$
$$x + 60 = 80 \quad \text{property.}$$
$$x + 60 - 60 = 80 - 60$$
$$x = 20 \quad \text{Check the solution.}$$

Thus $x = 20$ is the solution.

As you solve more equations you may find that you can complete certain steps mentally.

Example 2   Find the root of $y + 6(y - 3) = 5(y + 2)$.

Solution

$$y + 6(y - 3) = 5(y + 2)$$
$$y + 6y - 18 = 5y + 10$$
$$7y - 18 = 5y + 10$$
$$7y - 5y = 10 + 18$$
$$2y = 28$$
$$y = 14$$

Check:
$$\text{L.S.} = y + 6(y - 3) \qquad \text{R.S.} = 5(y + 2)$$
$$= 14 + 6(14 - 3) \qquad = 5(14 + 2)$$
$$= 14 + 66 \qquad\qquad = 5(16)$$
$$= 80 \qquad\qquad\quad = 80$$

Thus 14 is the root.

$$\text{L.S.} = \text{R.S.} \checkmark$$

To solve some equations, you simplify the equation first as shown.

Example 3   Find the solution set for $\frac{3}{4}t - 2 = \frac{1}{2}(t + 2)$.

Solution

$$\frac{3}{4}t - 2 = \frac{1}{2}(t + 2)$$

$$4\left(\frac{3}{4}t - 2\right) = 4\left[\frac{1}{2}(t + 2)\right] \quad \begin{array}{l}\text{Multiply both sides}\\\text{of the equation by 4.}\end{array}$$

$$3t - 8 = 2(t + 2) \qquad \text{Apply the distributive property.}$$
$$3t - 8 = 2t + 4$$
$$3t - 2t = 4 + 8$$
$$t = 12 \qquad\qquad \text{Check the solution.}$$

Thus the solution set is $\{12\}$.

5.4 Exercise

A Questions 1 to 5 review your earlier skills needed to solve equations.

1 Simplify each of the following expressions.
   (a) $2(y - 3)$
   (b) $3(6 - y)$
   (c) $-2(x - 6)$
   (d) $-4(2y - 6)$
   (e) $3(3 - 2y)$
   (f) $-2(3y - 6)$
   (g) $3x - x + 8$
   (h) $2 - 3x + 8$
   (i) $4x - 3x + 8$
   (j) $2x + 3x + 5x$
   (k) $3(x - 2) - 6$
   (l) $4(x - 5) - 7x$

2 Simplify each of the following expressions.
   (a) $\dfrac{1}{2}x - \dfrac{1}{3}x$
   (b) $\dfrac{y}{3} + \dfrac{y}{4}$
   (c) $\dfrac{4y}{5} - \dfrac{2y}{3}$

3 (a) What is the first step needed to solve $3y + \dfrac{3}{4} = \dfrac{9}{4}$?   (b) Solve the equation.

4 Solve. First you need to simplify like terms.
   (a) $3a + 8a - 8a = 42$
   (b) $5y - 4y + 2y = 18$
   (c) $5a + 8 - a = 20$
   (d) $12 + 6x - 3x = 36$
   (e) $50 = 7y + 4y - y$
   (f) $7x + 3 - 2x = 23$
   (g) $8n - 3 = 6n - 8$
   (h) $13x + 6 = 11x + 5$

5 The instructions are basically the same. Find each answer.
   (a) Solve $-2(2x - 3) + 6x = 36$.
   (b) Find the root of $2x - 6 = 3(x - 2)$.
   (c) What is the solution set of $6(y - 2) = 3y + 3$?

B Once you solve an equation, check whether your answer is reasonable. **PSP**

6 Find the solution set for each of the following equations.
   (a) $3(n + 4) = 5n$
   (b) $3y - 10 = 2(y - 3)$
   (c) $2(x - 2) = 2(3 - x)$
   (d) $4(x - 2) = 3(x + 1)$
   (e) $8(n - 1) = 4(n + 4)$
   (f) $2(x + 3) = 3(x - 3)$
   (g) $4(3 - m) = 5(2m + 1)$
   (h) $12(2m - 3) = 2(m + 4)$

7 Find the root of each equation.
   (a) $0.3y + 1.1 = 0.4(2y - 1)$
   (b) $0.3(4 - 5x) + 0.7 = 1.1 + 0.5x$
   (c) $2(0.2m - 0.1) - 0.8 = -3.9 - 0.3(m - 5)$
   (d) $0.2(n - 3) + 0.3 = 1.5 - n$
   (e) $0.3(y - 2) + 0.1y = 0.2(y + 1)$
   (f) $0.5(m + 2) = 0.1m + 0.6(m - 3)$
   (g) $1.4 + 0.5(x - 20) = 0.3(x - 2)$

8 Solve.

(a) $2y + \dfrac{1}{2} = \dfrac{2}{3}$

(b) $\dfrac{3m}{2} = 15$

(c) $\dfrac{3}{5}n - 4 = 14$

(d) $\dfrac{7}{6}x - 2 = \dfrac{1}{3}$

(e) $\dfrac{n}{4} - 1 = \dfrac{n}{5}$

(f) $3 - \dfrac{m}{2} = 5 - \dfrac{m}{3}$

(g) $\dfrac{2}{3}y - 3 = \dfrac{4}{5}y - 5$

(h) $\dfrac{3}{5}x - 2 = \dfrac{2}{3}x + 3$

(i) $16 = \dfrac{2}{3}k - 6$

9 To qualify for a trip on a freighter out of Vancouver Harbour, you need to answer the skill-testing question.

A: $5(m - 1) = 27 + m$ B: $6(n - 2) = 3n - 36$ C: $6(n + 1) = 3(n - 1)$

Step 1:
Double the root of A.

Step 2:
Subtract $\dfrac{1}{2}$ of the root of B from your answer to Step 1.

Step 3:
Multiply your answer to Step 2 by the root of C.

10 Solve.

(a) $\dfrac{1}{3}(2x - 1) = 1$

(b) $\dfrac{1}{6}(6 + 2y) = 2$

(c) $\dfrac{1}{2}(x - 5) = \dfrac{x}{4}$

(d) $x - 1 = \dfrac{x}{2}$

(e) $\dfrac{1}{2}(y + 2) = \dfrac{y}{3}$

(f) $\dfrac{3}{5}(2x + 15) = 3$

11 Solve.

(a) $\dfrac{x}{2} = \dfrac{1}{3}(x + 2)$

(b) $\dfrac{y}{2} = \dfrac{1}{5}(y + 4)$

(c) $\dfrac{1}{2}(x - 1) = \dfrac{1}{4}(x + 1)$

(d) $\dfrac{1}{3}(y + 4) = \dfrac{1}{2}(y + 1)$

(e) $\dfrac{4x - 1}{5} = \dfrac{2x + 3}{2}$

(f) $\dfrac{y - 7}{3} = \dfrac{y - 2}{4}$

PSP 12 Steve, Michael, Sandra and Lesley are standing in line to buy tickets for a movie. In how many different ways can they stand in line?

PSP 13 Find an expression for 30 using three 3's.

Applications: Mathematics for Fact Finding

The root of the equation is the answer to the question asked.

Question

Today more than 100 nations compete in the Olympics. How many nations competed in the first modern Olympics in 1896?

n represents the number of nations.

Equation

$$6n - 3 = 5n + 6$$
$$6n - 3 + 3 = 5n + 6 + 3$$
$$6n = 5n + 9$$
$$6n - 5n = 5n + 9 - 5n$$
$$n = 9$$

In the first Olympics 9 nations competed.

Solve each equation to answer the question.

14 How many climatic zones are there on the earth's surface?

n represents the number of zones.
Solve $8n - 3 = 4n + 17$.

15 You may have visited a performance of Ringling Brothers' Circus. How many Ringling brothers were there?

m represents the number of brothers.
Solve $16 - 3m = 1 - 2m$.

16 How long is a "day" on the planet Mercury?

k represents the number of hours.
Solve $\frac{1}{4}(k + 1) = 2(k - 29)$.

17 How many times in the Olympics has Canada won the men's 200 m race?

k represents the number of times.
Solve $4k + 6 = 3k + 8$.

18 How many time zones are there in Canada?

y represents the number of zones.
Solve $3(y + 2) = \frac{1}{2}(5y + 18)$.

19 In the famous Daniel Defoe book, Robinson Crusoe was shipwrecked on an island. How many years did he spend there?

y represents the number of years.
Solve $-(20 + y) = 2(4 - y)$.

20 The pentathlon is an event in the Olympics. How many events are in the pentathlon?

x represents the number of events.
Solve $\frac{1}{2}x - 7 = \frac{1}{2} - x$.

5.5 Writing Equations

To learn a skill well, you often need to practise each step. For example, to learn to solve problems, you need to practise writing equations. Once the equations are written, you use your earlier skills to solve them.

Example The amount of money in dollars that Natalie and Linda had was $3x$ and $2x + 4$. If they had a total of $44, how much did each girl have?

Solution The sum of money was $3x + 2x + 4$.

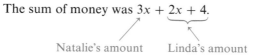

Natalie's amount   Linda's amount

Write the equation. Then solve.

$$3x + 2x + 4 = 44$$
$$5x + 4 = 44$$
$$5x + 4 - 4 = 44 - 4$$
$$5x = 40$$
$$\frac{5x}{5} = \frac{40}{5}$$
$$x = 8$$

Natalie: $3x = 3(8)$
$= 24$
Linda: $2x + 4 = 2(8) + 4$
$= 20$
Check: $20 + 24 = 44$ ✓

Thus Natalie had $24 and Linda had $20.

5.5 Exercise

A Check your answer in the original problem.

1 A path is shown. The total length of the path is 40 m.
Write an equation for the total length.

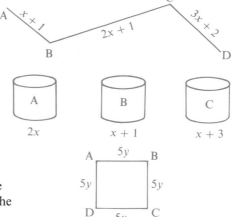

2 The amount of money in dollars in each container is shown. The total amount of money in the three containers is $160.
Write an equation for the total amount of money.

3 The dimensions of a square are shown. The perimeter is 400 m. Write an equation for the perimeter.

4   The dimensions of a rectangle are shown. The perimeter is 154 m. Write an equation for the perimeter.

x

$2x - 1$

B Write an equation for each problem and then solve. Be sure to write a final statement. **PSP**

5   The dimensions of a triangle are shown. The perimeter is 37 m. Find the length of each side.

6   A path used by spectators to travel to and from the baseball games is shown. The path is 535 m.
   (a) Find the length of
       (i) $\overline{AB}$ (ii) $\overline{BC}$ (iii) $\overline{CD}$
   (b) How can you check your answers?

7   Find the lengths of the sides of each figure.
   (a) Perimeter is 34 m.   (b) Perimeter is 56 m.

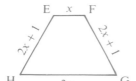   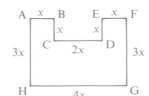

8   For selling magazines, Jana makes $(2n + 1)$ dollars where n represents the number of subscriptions sold. During one week Jana made $65. How many subscriptions did she sell?

9   To feed the cattle each day Fred uses $(12n - 6)$ bales of hay, where n represents the number of cattle. If 378 bales of hay were used in one day, how many cattle are there?

PSP 10   Two pieces fell out of the rectangle.
   Which of the pieces are they?

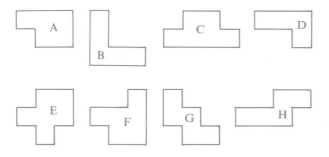   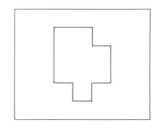

Applications: Mathematics for Science

Each of the following problems deals with some aspect of science. As in your earlier work, you need to know the answers to these two questions:

I What information am I asked to find? **PSP**
II What information am I given?

Once you know the answers to these two questions, you can use the *Problem Solving Plan* to organize your solution.

---

11 The human hand has $(3h + 2)$ bones in the wrist, $(2h + 1)$ bones in the palm and $(7h)$ bones in the fingers.
   (a) Write an expression for the total number of bones in the hand.
   (b) If the total number of bones is 27, find the number of bones in each part.

12 The tiger shark can grow to a length of $(3k - 0.6)$ m while the Great Blue shark can grow to a length of $(2k - 0.2)$ m.
   (a) Write an expression for the difference in length.
   (b) A research team determined the difference in length to be 1.6 m. Find the length of the tiger shark.

13 The snapping turtle has a mass of $(3t + 1.7)$ kg while the alligator snapping turtle has a mass of $(12t - 0.1)$ kg. Each turtle is shipped separately to an aquarium in a case with a mass of $(t + 5.2)$ kg.
   (a) Write an expression for the total mass to be charged for shipping.
   (b) If the total mass is 138 kg, find the mass of each turtle.

14 A fertilizer for fruit and vegetables is made up of $(2k - 4)$ kg of nitrogen, $(4k)$ kg of phosphorus and $(5k - 1)$ kg of potash.
   (a) Write an expression for the total mass of the fertilizer.
   (b) Find the mass of each element in a 50-kg bag of fertilizer.

15 The amount of air inhaled into the lungs is $(4a + 1)$ cm^3 of oxygen and $(16a - 1)$ cm^3 of nitrogen.
   (a) Write an expression for the total inhaled air.
   (b) How much oxygen and nitrogen would be found in 240 cm^3 of inhaled air?

16 Costume jewelry is made from an alloy or mixture of silver, tin and lead. The amount of silver is $(4a + 2)$ g, of tin is $(3a + 3)$ g and of lead is $(5a + 1)$ g.
   (a) Write an expression for the total mass.
   (b) How much tin is contained in a necklace with a mass of 90 g?

5.6 **PSP** Problem Solving Strategy: Organizational Skills

It is important to organize your work when you are solving a problem. The first step is to answer these two questions:

I What information am I asked to find?
II What information am I given?

The next step is to translate from English to mathematics. To do this you must first choose a variable.

Each of the following variables helps you remember what it represents.
- the height, h
- the width, w
- Peter's age, p
- the number of goals, g

Once you have decided on a suitable variable, use it to translate the information in the problem from English to mathematics.

PSP	**Problem Solving Plan**
Step A:	Understand the problem. • What are you asked to find? • What are you given?
Step B:	Decide on a strategy. Choose a variable and translate.
Step C:	Apply the strategy. Do the work.
Step D:	Check your solution.
Step E:	Write a final statement.

Example 1   Jeff, Dawn and Ajit shared lottery winnings of $90 000. Jeff received twice as much as Dawn and Ajit received three times as much as Dawn. How much did each receive?

Solution   Let d represent the amount of money Dawn received in dollars. Then Jeff received $2d$ and Ajit received $3d$.

$$d + 2d + 3d = 90\ 000$$
$$6d = 90\ 000$$
$$\frac{6d}{6} = \frac{90\ 000}{6}$$
$$d = 15\ 000$$

Dawn: $d = 15\ 000$
Jeff: $2d = 30\ 000$
Ajit: $3d = 45\ 000$
Check: $15\ 000 + 30\ 000 + 45\ 000 = 90\ 000$ ✓

Thus Dawn, Jeff and Ajit received $15 000, $30 000 and $45 000 respectively.

In some problems, you need to know the meanings of special words as shown in the next example.

Example 2   The sum of three *consecutive* whole numbers is 138. Find the numbers.

Solution   Let the numbers be represented by n, $n + 1$ and $n + 2$.

Consecutive numbers increase by 1.

$$n + (n + 1) + (n + 2) = 138$$
$$3n + 3 = 138$$
$$3n + 3 - 3 = 138 - 3$$
$$3n = 135$$
$$\frac{3n}{3} = \frac{135}{3}$$
$$n = 45$$

Can you do these steps mentally?

The consecutive numbers are 45, 46 and 47.

Did you check the answers?

5.6   Exercise

A   It is important that you translate word problems accurately from English to mathematics.

1   Jennifer has j dollars. Write an equation if
   (a) Kevin has $2 less than Jennifer and together they have $20.
   (b) Gino has $5 more than Jennifer and together they have $30.
   (c) Maria has twice as much as Jennifer and the difference in their amounts is $8.

2   The width in metres of a rectangle is w. Write an equation if
   (a) the length is 2 m more than the width and the perimeter is 30 m.
   (b) the length is 1 m less than double the width and the area is 40 m².

3   Sarah received s votes in an election. Write an equation if
   (a) Johann received 200 fewer votes than Sarah and together they received 750 votes.
   (b) Katrina received 150 votes more than Sarah and together they received 890 votes.
   (c) Hans received twice as many votes as Sarah and the difference in the number of votes was 330.

B 4   (a) One number is 8 more than another number. If the sum of the numbers is 48, what are the numbers?
   (b) A number is doubled and the result is increased by 4. If the answer is 100, what is the number?

(c) Three times a number decreased by 8 is equal to the number increased by 22. Find the number.

5 (a) Find three consecutive integers whose sum is 75.

   (b) Find three consecutive integers whose sum is -147.

6 (a) The length of a field is three times its width. If the perimeter is 96 m, find its dimensions.

   (b) The length of a rectangle is 8 cm more than the width. If the perimeter is 64 cm, find its dimensions.

7 The height of the Fenwick Towers in Halifax is 1 m less than the Peace Tower in Ottawa. Lombard Place in Winnipeg is 32 m higher than the Peace Tower. If the total height of the three structures is 307 m, find the height of each structure.

8 Andrea, Julie and Laura received $2250. Julie received $250 more than Andrea but Laura received $250 less than Andrea. How much did each girl receive?

9 Max has $2 less than Scott. Sam has $5 more than Scott. If they have $30 altogether, how much does each have?

10 Abigail, Jerome and Klaus were given a total of $2750 in scholarships. Klaus received 3 times the amount Abigail received. Jerome received $250 more than Abigail. How much did each student receive?

11 Bridget, Kelsey and Wayne shared $1926 from a lottery prize. Kelsey and Wayne received 2 and 3 times as much money as Bridget. How much money did each receive?

12 Bruce received 200 fewer votes in an election than Samantha. Lesley received 150 more votes than Samantha. If the total number of votes was 1135, how many votes did each person receive?

PSP 13 Each letter is represented by one of the digits 0, 1, 2, 3, 4, 5, 6, 7. Which digit does each letter represent?

$$\begin{array}{r} \text{HOW} \\ + \text{ARE} \\ \hline \text{YOU} \end{array}$$

PSP 14 The last digit of 4^3 is 4. What is the last digit of 4^{40}?

C 15 Jason jogs an average of 4.2 km each weekday. On the weekend his average is 7.0 km each day. What is Jason's average jog per day for an entire week?

5.7 PSP Problem Solving Strategy: Using Clues

To translate words to symbols and write equations, you must know the different words that represent the same symbol. Some of these clue words are shown.

Words	Symbols
plus, increased by, added to, and, sum	+
subtract, less than, difference, decreased by, diminished by, minus, exceeds	−
product, multiplied by, times	×
divided by, quotient	÷
equals, is equal to, is, is as much as, is the same as, the result is	=

Example The sum of two numbers is 148. Five times the lesser of the two numbers decreased by 8 is equal to twice the greater number increased by 4. Find the numbers.

Solution Let n represent the lesser number. Then $148 - n$ represents the greater number. Write the equation.

$$5n - 8 = 2(148 - n) + 4$$
$$5n - 8 = 296 - 2n + 4$$
$$5n - 8 = 300 - 2n$$
$$5n + 2n = 300 + 8$$
$$7n = 308$$
$$n = 44$$

lesser number: $n = 44$
greater number: $148 - n = 104$

 Think: Check your answer in the original problem.

Thus the numbers are 44 and 104.

5.7 Exercise

A 1 Translate each of the following to an equation.
(a) Three times a number plus 1 is equal to 13.
(b) The product of 8 and a number is 24.
(c) A number decreased by 5 is 19.
(d) Six less than double a number is 8.

2 The variable n represents a number. Write in words what each of the following represents.

(a) $2n$　　　(b) $n + 5$　　　(c) $n - 5$　　　(d) $2n + 1$　　　(e) $3 - 2n$

(f) $\frac{2}{3}n$　　　(g) $n + 2n$　　　(h) $\frac{n}{2} + 3$　　　(i) $10 - \frac{n}{2}$　　　(j) $\frac{n}{3} - 5$

B 3 Find two consecutive integers so that 3 times the lesser exceeds 2 times the greater by 43.

4   Two integers are consecutive. Twice the lesser increased by one half of the greater is 63. Find the numbers.

5   (a) One fifth of a number is added to one third of the same number. If the sum is 96, find the number.
     (b) One fourth of a number is subtracted from one third of the same number. If the difference is 18, find the number.

6   In each deck of 52 cards there are eyes, but how many are there? The number of eyes doubled and increased by 21 is equal to 3 times the number of eyes decreased by 21. How many eyes are there?

7   (a) The sum of two numbers is 75. Find the numbers if the greater exceeds twice the lesser by 24.
     (b) Four times a number decreased by 5 equals 45 diminished by 6 times the number. Find the number.

8   The difference between the number of girls and the number of boys in the outdoors club is 12. Four times the number of girls decreased by 25 equals 3 times the number of boys. Find the number of girls and the number of boys in the club.

9   The higher of two scores is equal to 3 times the lower score. The lower score is equal to the higher score decreased by 30. Find the scores.

 10   A positive prime number is greater than one and divisible only by 1 and itself.
     (a) Is the average of all prime numbers less than 24 also a prime number?
     (b) Investigate the averages of other sets of prime numbers.

C 11   One half of a number is subtracted from the sum of one third of the number and one quarter of the number. If the result is 16, find the number.

From Math History

Why is x as a variable used so frequently to write equations and solve problems? In early Arabic manuscripts the unknown quantity in algebra was written as *sai*. Spanish writers translated *sai* as $X_{\epsilon\iota}$ which means thing. Later only the first letter, X, was used to represent the unknown. Finally X was changed to x. Today mathematicians use x more than any other letter in their work in algebra.

5.8 PSP Problem Solving Strategy: Extraneous Information

In real life there is often more information given in a problem than is needed to solve it. Thus it is important to be able to sort through the given information and decide what you need to solve the problem and what information is extra or extraneous.

Example The number of cookies in a 500 g package is 12 less than twice the number in a 300 g package. Five 300 g packages have the same number of cookies as three 500 g packages. Two 300 g packages have more cookies than one 500 g package.

(a) How many cookies are in each size of package?

(b) What information is extraneous?

Solution (a) Let n represent the number of cookies in the smaller package. Then $2n - 12$ is the number of cookies in the larger package.

$$5n = 3(2n - 12)$$
$$5n = 6n - 36$$
$$36 = 6n - 5n$$
$$36 = n$$

For the smaller package, $n = 36$.
For the larger package, $2n - 12 = 2(36) - 12$
$$= 60.$$

PSP Check the answer in the original problem.

Thus the number of cookies in the smaller package is 36 and in the larger package, 60.

(b) Information not required: 500 g, 300 g and two 300 g packages have more cookies than one 500 g package.

5.8 Exercise

B For each of the following problems,
▶ Identify the extraneous information.
▶ Solve the problem.

1 Virja has $500 in the bank. Yannak and Virja are to share the profit of $1100. If Yannak is to receive $100 less than Virja, what is each person's share?

2   The sum of three consecutive integers is 84. The numbers are less than 35 and greater than 19. Find the numbers.

3   Tanya has $9 more than Janet. Fraser has 3 times as much as Janet. Janet and Tanya have $7 less than Fraser. If they have $89 altogether, how much does each person have?

4   Two numbers differ by 16. Their sum divided by 2 is greater than the lesser number. If their sum is 30, find the numbers.

5   A diskette costs $0.75 less than twice the cost of a cassette tape. A diskette works 25 times faster than a tape. If 4 diskettes and 3 tapes cost $24.50 altogether, find the cost of 1 tape and 1 diskette.

6   A number doubled and increased by 3 is equal to the number increased by 19. The sum of the digits of the number is 7. Find the number.

7   A small can of soup holds 150 mL less than a large can. A large can costs $0.15 more than a small can. If 8 small cans cost $0.37 less than 7 large cans, find the cost of each can of soup.

PSP 8   (a) If the value of COTTAGE is 118, what do you think the value of WEEKEND is?
      (b) The natural numbers 1 to 100 are written as shown with no spaces.
              1234567891011121314 . . .
         In what positions will you find the digits of the number 72?

From Math History

Throughout the history of mathematics, problems occurred that, when solved, developed new skills to solve further problems. However there are often problems posed that, although they seem reasonable, cannot be solved. For example, Goldbach (1690–1794) noticed that every even number except 2 can be expressed as a sum of prime numbers.

$$8 = 5 + 3 \qquad 18 = 7 + 11$$
$$22 = 11 + 11 \qquad 50 = 47 + 3$$

To this day, no one has proved that this observation is true for all even numbers. Even though Goldbach could not prove the result for every even number, history honoured him. This observation is now called **Goldbach's Conjecture**.

5.9 PSP Problem Solving Strategy: Using Charts

When you are solving a word problem, it is important to work in an organized way. One strategy for organizing your work is to use a chart to sort the information given in the word problem.

Example Dexter is 9 times the age of his son. In 3 years he will be 5 times the age of his son. How old are they now?

Solution Let n represent the age of the son in years.

	Present age	Age in 3 years
Dexter	$9n$	$9n + 3$ ← Dexter's age in 3 years
son	n	$n + 3$ ← son's age in 3 years

$$9n + 3 = 5(n + 3)$$
$$9n + 3 = 5n + 15$$
$$4n = 12$$
$$n = 3$$

The chart has included all the facts given in the problem except one. In 3 years Dexter will be 5 times as old as his son. From this fact, an equation can be written.

son: $n = 3$
Dexter: $9n = 27$

Check: In 3 years, Dexter will be 30 years, his son will be 6 years. Dexter will be 5 times his son's age. ✓

Thus Dexter's age is 27 years and his son's is 3 years.

5.9 Exercise

A 1 Copy and complete the chart.

	Coin	Number	Value
(a)	nickel	n	?
(b)	dime	$5n$	?
(c)	quarter	$d + 6$	?
(d)	dime	$3n - 1$	?
(e)	nickel	$q - 4$	?

2 Copy and complete the chart.

	Person	Present Age	Age in 5 years	Age 6 years ago
(a)	Sandra	k	?	?
(b)	Stephen	$k + 2$	?	?
(c)	Tobey	$m - 3$	?	?
(d)	Chris	$2p$	?	?
(e)	Lori	$25 - p$	?	?

Watch for extraneous information. **PSP**

3　Eight years from now Blair will be 6 times as old as he was 2 years ago. His brother is twice as old as Blair is today. Find Blair's present age.

4　Joya has $3.75 in nickels, dimes and quarters. The number of quarters is twice the number of dimes. The number of dimes is twice the number of nickels. How many of each type of coin does Joya have?

5　The greatest age reached by a marsupial is three times the greatest age reached by an orangutan. If each had lived 3 years longer, the sum of their ages would have been 82 years. What is the greatest age reached by a marsupial and by an orangutan?

6　My age increased by my son's age is 48 years. In 15 years his age increased by 4 times mine will equal 234 years. How old are we presently?

7　I was 26 years old when my daughter was born. Today the sum of 3 times my age and twice my daughter's age is 103 years. How old are we today?

8　If I had a quarter I would have $4.00. However I have only nickels and dimes. The number of dimes is 1 less than 3 times the number of nickels. How many of each coin do I have?

9　Three years ago Elaine was 5 times as old as Jerry. Today she is 3 times as old as Jerry. Jerry is 1 year older than Samantha was 4 years ago. How old are Jerry and Elaine today?

10　The number of quarters is 2 more than 3 times the number of dimes. I have 4 less nickels than dimes. If the value of the dimes and quarters is $6.45, find the number of dimes and quarters.

PSP 11　Three squads of cheerleaders have to sell 448 raffle tickets. The senior squad consists of 12 cheerleaders, the junior squad of 10 and the midget squad of 8. If the junior squad has to sell the most number of tickets and the midget squad has to sell the least, how many tickets does the senior squad have to sell?

C 12　The sum of my age and my father's age is 60 years. In 20 years my age increased by 3 times my father's age will equal 230. How old are we now?

13　Two years ago I was 4 times as old as my daughter. In 3 years I will be only 3 times as old as my daughter. How old are we today?

5.10   PSP   Problem Solving Strategy: Using Diagrams

Although there are many different types of problems, the *Problem Solving Plan* can be used to help you solve any of them.

There are different strategies that you can use to plan your solution to a word problem. One of these strategies is to use a diagram to help you visualize the problem. You can sort the information given in the word problem by recording it on the diagram.

For example, to solve problems about perimeter, it is helpful to draw a sketch and record the given information.

PSP   **Problem Solving Plan**

Step A: Understand the problem.
- What are you asked to find?
- What are you given?

Step B: Decide on a strategy.
Draw a diagram.

Step C: Apply the strategy.
Do the work.

Step D: Check your solution.

Step E: Write a final statement.

Example

The length of a rectangular auditorium is 1 m more than twice its width. If the perimeter is 170 m, find the dimensions.

Solution

Let w represent the width in metres. Then the length is $(2w + 1)$ metres.
From the diagram:
Perimeter $= 2w + 1 + w + 2w + 1 + w$
            $= 6w + 2$
Perimeter $= 170$ m
Thus $6w + 2 = 170$ width: $w = 28$
       $6w = 168$ length: $2w + 1 = 57$
         $w = 28$
The width is 28 m. The length is 57 m.

Record the information on the diagram.

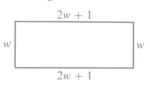

PSP   Check the answer in the original problem.

Once you have solved the problem, you can often obtain other useful information. For example, in the previous example, you are now able to find the area of the auditorium,

w, width $= 28$ m $A = l \times w$
l, length $= 57$ m $= 57 \times 28$
                $= 1596$ The area of the auditorium is 1596 m².

A Remember: Draw a diagram and sort the given information by recording ◢**PSP**◣ it on the diagram.

1   Each diagram shows the dimensions as variable expressions.
   ▶ Find variable expressions for the missing dimensions.
   ▶ Write an expression for the perimeter.
   ▶ Simplify the expression.

(a) 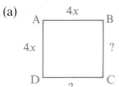   (b) 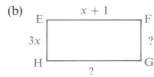   (c)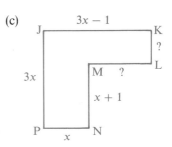

2   The dimensions for some rectangles are given below.
   ▶ Draw a diagram to show the dimensions as variable expressions.
   ▶ Write a variable expression for the perimeter.
   ▶ Simplify the expression.
   (a) The length is 2 cm shorter than twice the width.
   (b) The length is 4 cm longer than four times the width.
   (c) The width is $\dfrac{1}{3}$ of the length.   (d) The width is 3 m shorter than $\dfrac{1}{2}$ of the length.

B Remember: Use a diagram to help.

3   The length of a rectangle decreased by 6 cm is equal to the width. If the perimeter is 68 cm, find its dimensions.

4   The length of a room is 2 m more than twice the width. Find its dimensions if the perimeter of the room is 34 m.

5   The difference between the width and the length of a barn floor is 6 m. The perimeter of the floor is 76 m.
   (a) Find the dimensions of the floor.   (b) Find the area of the floor.

6   The length of a piece of land is 30 m more than six times the width.
   (a) Find the width if the perimeter is 172 m.   (b) Find the area of the land.

7   Shirley is presently 2 years more than 4 times Rose's age. In 12 years Rose will be one half of Shirley's age. How old are they presently?

8   The largest flag ever made had a perimeter of 378 m. Twice the width is
     3 m more than the length.
     (a) Find the dimensions of the flag.   (b) What is the area of the flag?
     (c) The area of a football field is 0.54 ha. Which has the greater area, the
         flag or the football field? By how much?

9   The width of a rectangle is one third the length. The difference between
     the length and the width is 18 m. If you double the width and increase it
     by the length, the result will be 45 m. Find the dimensions of the rectangle.

10   A pigpen is marked off so that its width is one half of its length. If 4 m are
     subtracted from the length and 24 m added to the width, the pigpen would
     be square.
     (a) Find the dimensions of the pigpen.   (b) Find the perimeter.

11   The perimeter of a pool is 24.0 m and it is 3.5 m deep at the deep end. The
     length of the pool is twice the width of the pool. What is the width of
     the pool?

PSP 12   You have a piece of plywood that measures 40 cm by 60 cm. Find the
     minimum number of cuts you would need to make to cover an area
     30 cm by 80 cm.

Computer Use

A computer can be programmed to solve an equation. The principles used
are the same as you have used, but the computer program uses the properties
of equality in a different way. The computer tries different values of the
variable and isolates the approximate value of the root as shown by the
following program. This important method of solving equations is called an
iterative method.

Try this program to solve the equation

$$6x + 2 = 3x + 3.$$

You will see the approximate value
of the root of this equation. When
the value of F equals zero, the
corresponding value of X is the
root. When the value of F is close to
zero, X is near the root. What is the
approximate root of the equation?

```
10 PRINT "SOLVING EQUATIONS"
20 FOR X = -4 TO 4 STEP 0.25
30 LET L = 6 * X + 2
40 LET R = 3 * X + 3
50 LET F = L - R
60 PRINT "VALUES ARE"; F, X
70 NEXT X
80 END
```

5.11 Nature of Mathematics: Using Interest

In mathematics you continually use the skills you learned previously. For example, the following problems use your earlier skills based on interest calculations. To solve these problems, you must have a clear understanding of the concepts and skills involving percent.

When you deposit money as an investment, you are paid **interest** for the use of your money. The ad shows a rate of interest of 8% per year. If you invest $500 at 8% for a year, the interest would be

TERM DEPOSIT
Earn **8%**.
Plan for a bright future.

$$8\% \text{ of } \$500 = 0.08 \times \$500 \qquad \% \text{ means per hundred.}$$
$$= \$40.$$

Example A sum of money invested in a savings account at 8% provides the same interest at the end of one year as a sum of money $400 less invested in bonds at 10%. Find the sums of money invested.

Solution Let m represent the sum of money in dollars invested at 8%. Then $m - 400$ represents the amount in dollars invested at 10%.

Investment ($)	Rate	Interest earned
m	8%	$0.08m$
$m - 400$	10%	$0.10(m - 400)$

$$0.08m = 0.10(m - 400)$$
$$8m = 10(m - 400)$$
$$8m = 10m - 4000$$
$$4000 = 2m$$
$$2000 = m \text{ or } m = 2000$$

Thus $2000 is invested at 8% and $1600 is invested at 10%.

Use the fact: Both accounts provide the same amount of interest.

savings account: $m = 2000$
bonds: $m - 400 = 1600$

Check: 8% of $2000 = $160
10% of $1600 = $160
Same interest for both accounts. ✓

5.11 Exercise

A Round your answers to 1 decimal place or to the nearest cent.

1 Find the interest if $125 is invested for one year at each rate.
   (a) 6%   (b) 12%   (c) 6.5%   (d) 12.5%

2 Find the interest earned for a year.
   (a) $x invested at 8%   (b) $y invested at 12%
   (c) $m invested at 6.5%   (d) $(m + 500)$ invested at 9%

3   Find the total interest earned in a year on
    (a) $300 invested at 10% and $200 at 8%.
    (b) $500 invested at 6.5% and $400 at 8.5%.
    (c) $m invested at 8% and $(1000 − m) invested at 10%.
    (d) $n invested at 9.5% and $(600 − n) invested at 7.5%.

4   To solve the equation $0.06x + 0.08(100 − x) = 7$
    Melanie simplified it to obtain $6x + 8(100 − x) = 700$.
    (a) What did she do to obtain the second equation?
    (b) Solve. Find the root of the equation.

5   Solve each equation.
    (a) $0.08(200 − x) + 0.06x = 15$ (b) $0.09x + 0.05(400 − x) = 24$

B   Refer to the *Problem Solving Plan* to organize your solution.   *PSP*

6   A businesswoman invested $6000; part of it at 8% and the rest at 12%. If
    the total interest in one year is $560, find the amount she invested at each
    rate of interest.

7   A sum of money invested at 8% earns the same amount of interest as an
    amount $800 greater invested at 6%. How much is invested at 8%?

8   Ramon's mother won $1000 in a lottery. She invested part of it at 8% and
    the rest at 10%. If she earned $88 interest in one year, how much did she
    invest at 8%?

9   Sheila invested an amount of money at 8% and an amount twice as large
    at 11%. If the annual interest is $75, how much money did she invest at
    each rate of interest?

10 A sum of money invested at 9% earns the same amount of interest as a
    sum $1200 less invested at 12%. How much money is invested at each rate?

PSP 11   Jeffrey takes six subjects and in two of these his average is 75%. His
    average in the other four subjects is 90%. What is his average in all six subjects?

C 12   Adam bought two oil paintings as an investment. He later sold them at
    $100 each. On one painting he made 20% profit, on the other he had a loss
    of 20%.
    (a) Without calculating the answer, estimate whether he broke even, lost
        money or made money.
    (b) Solve the problem. How does your estimate compare?

Applications: Mathematics for Leisure

Mathematics skills can be applied to solve problems in various types of hobbies as shown by the following questions. To solve each of the following problems, you need to use your skills with equations. Remember, to solve any problem, you must know the answer to these two questions.

  I What information am I asked to find?
  II What information am I given? **PSP**

13 Herbert's collection of coloured gems has 40% amethyst and 15% moonstone. If he has 33 amethysts and moonstones in total, how many moonstones are in his collection?

14 Yakona's hobby is woodcarving. Of a number of carvings he has completed, 20% are songbirds and 15% are ducks. If there are 14 carvings of songbirds and ducks in all, how many carvings are there altogether?

15 Freida's hobby is working with computer programs. 58% of her programs were purchased and 12% were traded. This totalled 175 programs. How many programs does she have altogether?

16 Dana keeps tropical fish as a hobby. By doubling the number of fish and increasing it by 5, her fish population increases by 225%. How many fish did she start with?

17 Cleo makes models. She completed 40% of a model. If she had worked 1 h more, she would have completed 60% of it. How long had she been working on it?

18 Juan collects miniature figurines. Of his collection, 20% were made of bone china. He bought 10 more figurines, 6 of which were bone china. If 30% of the figurines are now bone china, how many does he have?

19 Teneya takes photographs. She had 15 more photographs of non-sporting events than of sporting events. If 40% of all her photographs are about sports, how many of each does she have?

5.12 Formulas and Equations

In the previous sections, you learned that to solve a word problem, you write an equation by translating the given information from English to mathematics. Then you solve the equation to find the answer to the problem

A formula may be thought of as an equation that has more than one variable.

One method of using a formula is to substitute the given values into the formula and then solve for the remaining variable, as shown in the following example.

Example 1   The perimeter of a rectangle is 464 m. Find the width if the length is 140 m.

Solution   *Step 1:* Write an equation.

$$P = 2l + 2w$$

Step 2: Substitute $P = 464$ and $l = 140$ to simplify the equation.

$$464 = 2(140) + 2w$$
$$464 = 280 + 2w$$

Step 3: Solve for w.

$$464 - 280 = 280 + 2w - 280$$
$$184 = 2w$$
$$92 = w$$

You might do these steps in your solution mentally, but be aware of computational mistakes!

Thus the width is 92 m.

PSP Check your answer in the original problem.

You can also use the properties of equality to express the formula in terms of a particular variable. To express $P = 2l + 2w$ in terms of w, you isolate w.

$$P = 2l + 2w$$
$$P - 2l = 2l + 2w - 2l$$
$$\frac{P - 2l}{2} = \frac{2w}{2}$$
$$\frac{P - 2l}{2} = w$$

Sometimes one variable of a formula is to be evaluated for several values of the other variables. You can use your calculator to reduce the amount of work. First rearrange the formula so that the variable to be evaluated is isolated on one side. Then substitute the given values of the other variables.

Example 2   The income, I, in dollars from a concert is given by the formula
$$I = 4.5A + 2.5S$$
where A is the number of adult tickets sold and S is the number of student tickets sold. Find the number of student tickets sold for each of these values of A and I.

(a) $A = 120$, $I = 700$ (in dollars)
(b) $A = 150$, $I = 800$ (in dollars)
(c) $A = 275$, $I = 1487.5$ (in dollars)

Solution   *Step 1:* Write the formula in terms of S.
$$I = 4.5A + 2.5S$$
$$I - 4.5A = 4.5A + 2.5S - 4.5A$$
$$\frac{I - 4.5A}{2.5} = \frac{2.5S}{2.5}$$
$$\frac{I - 4.5A}{2.5} = S \qquad \text{Use this formula to calculate the number of student tickets.}$$

Step 2: Evaluate S for the values of A and I.

(a) Use $A = 120$, $I = 700$.
$$S = \frac{700 - 4.5(120)}{2.5}$$
$$= 64 \qquad \text{Use your calculator to find this value.}$$

$$\boxed{C}\,\boxed{CM}\,4.5\,\boxed{\times}\,120\,\boxed{=}\,\boxed{+/-}\,\boxed{M+}\,700\,\boxed{M+}$$
$$\boxed{MR}\,\boxed{\div}\,2.5\,\boxed{=}\,64$$

There were 64 student tickets sold.

(b) Use $A = 150$, $I = 800$.
$$S = \frac{800 - 4.5(150)}{2.5}$$
$$= 50 \qquad \boxed{C}\,\boxed{CM}\,4.5\,\boxed{\times}\,150\,\boxed{=}\,\boxed{+/-}\,\boxed{M+}\,800\,\boxed{M+}$$
$$\boxed{MR}\,\boxed{\div}\,2.5\,\boxed{=}\,50$$

There were 50 student tickets sold.

(c) Use $A = 275$, $I = 1487.5$.
$$S = \frac{1487.5 - 4.5(275)}{2.5}$$
$$= 100 \qquad \boxed{C}\,\boxed{CM}\,4.5\,\boxed{\times}\,275\,\boxed{=}\,\boxed{+/-}\,\boxed{M+}\,1487.5\,\boxed{M+}$$
$$\boxed{MR}\,\boxed{\div}\,2.5\,\boxed{=}\,100$$

There were 100 student tickets sold.

5.12   Exercise

A 1   Substitute the values given. Then evaluate.
(a) $P = 2l + 2w$, $l = 16$, $w = 9$ (b) $C = 2.5a + c$, $a = 43$, $c = 35$
(c) $R = 25j + 15w$, $j = 12$, $w = 36$ (d) $V = (a + b)h$, $a = 3$, $b = 5$, $h = 4$

2   (a) Solve for l in $A = lw$.   (b) Solve for T in $TS = V$.
(c) How are your solutions in (a) and (b) alike?

3   (a) Solve for m in $V = k + 2m$.   (b) Solve for t in $V = u + at$.
(c) How are your solutions in (a) and (b) alike?

4   (a) Solve for p in $t = 3(p + s)$.   (b) Solve for w in $P = 2(l + w)$.
(c) How are your solutions in (a) and (b) alike?

5   In each of the following equations, express x in terms of y.
(a) $x + y = 6$ (b) $2x + 4y = 6$ (c) $2x - y = 4$
(d) $2x - y = 8$ (e) $3y + 2x = 6$ (f) $3y - x = 4$

6   The formula for simple interest is $I = Prt$. Express the formula in terms
of each variable.
(a) P (b) r (c) t

7   The formula for the amount accumulated with simple interest is
$A = P(1 + rt)$. Express the formula in terms of each variable.
(a) P (b) r (c) t

B 8   Express each formula in terms of the unknown variable and then find the
value for this variable.

(a) $A = lw$, $A = 464$, $w = 4$ (b) $A = \dfrac{1}{2}bh$, $A = 288$, $h = 24$

(c) $A = \dfrac{1}{2}(a + b)h$, $A = 96$, $a = 4$, $b = 8$ (d) $P = 2l + 2w$, $P = 80$, $w = 8$

(e) $A = s^2$, $A = 1849$ (f) $A = bh$, $A = 4984$, $b = 56$

9   Each formula is used in different fields of study. Find the missing values.

(a) $D = \dfrac{m}{v}$ $v = 25$ $D = 26$ (b) $D = \dfrac{m}{v}$ $D = 36$ $m = 648$

(c) $W = fd$ $W = 144$ $f = 24$ (d) $P = I^2R$ $P = 230.4$ $I = 12$
(e) $W = aV$ $W = 1728$ $a = 36$ (f) $W = fd$ $W = 1748$ $d = 46$
(g) $P = I^2R$ $P = 6771.2$ $I = 3.2$ (h) $W = aV$ $W = 1125$ $V = 25$

10   In each formula, you expect to calculate 10 or more values of the variable shown. Rewrite each formula in a more convenient form for doing your calculations.

(a) $y = 2x + b$, x

(b) $y = mx + b$, x

(c) $V = k(3 - m)$, m

(d) $A = \frac{1}{2}bh$, b

11   The variables A, b and h are related by the formula $A = \frac{1}{2}bh$.

(a) Express h in terms of A and b.

(b) Use your results in (a). Copy and complete the table.

A	b	h
24	6	?
54	12	?
15.3	6.8	?
4.5	3.6	?

12   The accumulated points, P, for a season are given by the formula $P = 2w + t$, where w is the number of wins and t is the number of ties. If the Vancouver Canucks have 69 points and 7 ties, find their number of wins.

13   The number of points, P, scored by a basketball player is given by the formula $P = 2g + f$ where g is the number of goals and f is the number of fouls. Find the number of fouls scored if Bernie scored

(a) 17 points and 6 goals.

(b) 21 points and 10 goals.   Use your calculator.

(c) 24 points and 8 goals.

C 14 In one pile Don has enough loam to cover uniformly a triangular flower bed that has a base 12 m and a height 20 m. In another pile there is enough loam for a triangular flowerbed with a base 36 m and a height of 16 m. If all the loam is used to make one triangular flower bed having a base 24 m, find the height of the triangle.

Calculator Use

Did you know that Earth's path around the sun is not circular but elliptical (a flattened circle)? The eccentricity, e, of the path shows how much the orbit is "off" from a circular orbit. The eccentricity is given by the formula

$$e = \frac{\sqrt{a^2 - b^2}}{a}.$$

Use a calculator to find the eccentricity of the orbit of Earth. Use the values $a = 149.515 \times 10^6$ and $b = 149.494 \times 10^4$.

Applications: Mathematics for Computers

To write a program for a computer, you express one variable in terms of the other variables.

15 A computer is given different inputs for s, t and d in order to calculate V where $d = (V - s)t$.

s	t	d	V
4	3	12	?
12	5	70	?
3.2	5.5	35.2	?

   (a) Rewrite the formula in a more convenient form.

   (b) Test your formula. Copy and complete the table.

   (c) Write a BASIC program to calculate V when given values of s, t and d.

16 The circumference, C, of a circle for values of the radius r is given by $C = 2\pi r$.

   (a) Write a BASIC program to calculate r for given values of C.

   (b) Try your program for $C = 6.5$, 8.0, 9.8, 12.6 and 15.0.

17 The area of a trapezoid is given by $A = \dfrac{1}{2}(a + b)h$

   where a and b are the lengths of the parallel sides and h is the height of the trapezoid.

   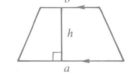

   (a) Write a BASIC program to calculate h for the input values, a, b and A.

   (b) Use your program to complete the table.

a	b	A	h
6	10	32	?
3.5	2.9	4.8	?

   (c) Try input values of your own for a, b and A to calculate the height, h.

18 Use the program to calculate the shaded area, called an annulus, for $R_1 = 8.5$ m and $R_2 = 6.9$ m.

```
10 PRINT "AREA OF ANNULUS"
20 INPUT "RADIUS R1"; R1
30 INPUT "RADIUS R2"; R2
40 IF R1 = 0, THEN 80
50 LET A = 3.14 * R1 ↑ 2 − 3.14 * R2 ↑ 2
60 PRINT "AREA OF ANNULUS"; A
70 GOTO 20
80 END
```

19 The formula to find R_2 when values of A and R_1 are given is

$$R_2 = \sqrt{R_1{}^2 - \frac{A}{\pi}}.$$

Write a BASIC program to calculate R_2 for input values of R_1 and A.

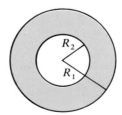

5.13 Solving Inequations

To solve an inequation, you use your skills to obtain a simpler but equivalent inequation. You need to use the properties of inequality shown as follows.

If you multiply or divide both sides of an inequality by a *positive* number, the inequality sign *is not* changed.

Multiply both sides by 4.	Divide both sides by 4.
$3 < 4$	$8 > 4$
$4(3) < 4(4)$	$\dfrac{8}{4} > \dfrac{4}{4}$
$12 < 16$	$2 > 1$

However, if you multiply or divide both sides of an inequality by a *negative* number, the inequality sign *is* changed.

Multiply both sides by -4.	Divide both sides by -4.
$3 < 4$	$8 > 4$
$-4(3) > -4(4)$	$\dfrac{8}{-4} < \dfrac{4}{-4}$
$-12 > -16$	$-2 < -1$

Once you have solved an inequation, you can draw a graph of the solution set as shown in the following example.

Example 1 Solve $3x - 6 \leq x + 8$, $x \in R$. Draw a graph of your solution set.

Solution Solve the inequation. Draw the graph of the solution set.

$$3x - 6 \leq x + 8$$
$$3x - 6 + 6 \leq x + 8 + 6$$
$$3x \leq x + 14$$
$$3x - x \leq x + 14 - x$$
$$2x \leq 14$$
$$\frac{2x}{2} \leq \frac{14}{2}$$
$$x \leq 7$$

To show that 7 is part of the solution set, a solid dot is used.

The following graphs show the solution set of different inequations.

▶ How are they alike?   ▶ How are they different?

$x < 7, x \in I$ $x \leq 7, x \in I$ $x \leq 7, x \in R$ $x < 7, x \in R$

To show that 7 is not part of the solution set, an open dot is used.

You should verify your solution by substituting a number from the
solution set into the original inequation as shown in the next example. **PSP**

Example 2   Find the solution set of the inequation
$2(x - 3) - 3(2x - 2) < 16$, $x \in I$.

Solution   Solve the inequation.

$$2(x - 3) - 3(2x - 2) < 16$$
$$2x - 6 - 6x + 6 < 16$$
$$-4x < 16$$

$$\frac{\overset{1}{-\cancel{4}x}}{\underset{1}{-\cancel{4}}} > \frac{\overset{-4}{\cancel{16}}}{\underset{1}{-\cancel{4}}}$$

$$x > -4$$

Check: Use $x = 0$. $(0 > -4)$
L.S. $= 2(x - 3) - 3(2x - 2)$
$= 2[(0) - 3] - 3[2(0) - 2]$
$= -6 + 6$
$= 0$
R.S. $= 16$
$0 < 16$
L.S. $<$ R.S. ✓
Why was -4 not used?

The solution set is $\{x \mid x > -4, x \in I\}$.

5.13   Exercise

A 1   For each inequation,
▶ Decide what your first step would be to write a simpler equivalent inequation.

▶ Find the solution.
(a) $3m - 5 > 4$ (b) $30 - 3p < 3p$ (c) $3x - 2 \leq 16$
(d) $7x \geq 2x + 10$ (e) $-14 > 3p - 8$ (f) $20 \leq 7t + 6$
(g) $3t - 12 \geq -18$ (h) $2r + 6 < 22$ (i) $8t < 35 + 3t$

2   (a) Solve $2x + 8 > 10$, $x \in I$.   (b) Draw a graph of your solution set.

3   (a) Find the solution set of $8 \leq 3y - 1$, $y \in I$.
(b) Draw a graph of your solution set.

4   Draw a graph for the solution set of each of the following.
(a) $8k - 5 < 35$ (b) $3 - y > 12$ (c) $4 - 6p \leq 16$

B   After you solve an inequation, check whether your answer is reasonable. **PSP**

5   Solve and check each of the following.
(a) $8y - 15 < 5y + 9$ (b) $5x + 8 \geq 3x + 26$
(c) $7y - 47 \leq 5y - 3$ (d) $18 + 3x < x + 30$
(e) $5m - 9 > 9 + 4m - 2m$ (f) $3k + 2k - 5 \geq 2k + k - 7$

6   Solve and check each of the following.
    (a) $3(2x - 4) \geqq 9$ (b) $3(y + 4) < 5y$ (c) $3(y + 2) \leqq 2y$
    (d) $10 > 2(m + 3)$ (e) $2(2p + 3) \geqq -10$ (f) $5(x - 1) < 7 + x$
    (g) $3p - 10 \geq 2(p - 3)$ (h) $3(2k - 1) \leq -12$ (i) $6(y - 2) > 3y - 11$

7   (a) Solve $2(x + 3) < 3(x + 5)$, $x \in R$.   (b) Draw a graph of your solution set.

8   Solve and check each of the following.
    (a) $-1 - 4y < 6 + 3(5 - 2y)$ (b) $2(x - 3) + 3 > 15 - x$
    (c) $3 - (6m - 15) \geq 4m + 88$ (d) $6(y + 1) \leq 3(y - 1) - 6$

9   (a) Solve $5(y + 2) \leqq y + 6(y - 3)$, $y \in I$.
    (b) Draw a graph of your solution set.

10 Draw the graph of all whole numbers such that 8 less than 4 times the
    number is greater than 12.

11 A rational number is doubled and then decreased by 9. The result is less
    than 7 more than 3 times the rational number. What rational numbers are
    possible?

12 An integer when doubled and increased by 6 is less than the integer
    increased by 30. Find the possible integers.

13 A cooler will hold a maximum of 48 cans of pop. If there are 3 more cola
    than orange and twice as many ginger ale as cola, what is the maximum
    number of each in the cooler?

C 14 The number of quarters is twice the number of nickels and the number of
       nickels is 3 more than the number of dimes. If the total amount is less
       than $3.75, find the possible numbers of each coin.

Math Tip

Remember: A common error made when working with inequalities is
forgetting to do the following.

Multiplying by a negative number   Dividing by a negative number

$$-x < 6$$
don't forget
$$(-1)(-x) > (-1)(6)$$
$$x > -6$$

$$-2x < 6$$
don't forget
$$\frac{-2x}{-2} > \frac{6}{-2}$$
$$x > -3$$

5.14 Problem Solving: Choosing a Strategy

One of the most important reasons for learning mathematics is to be able to solve problems.

In your earlier work, you not only learned to solve equations, but also to organize your solution to a problem.

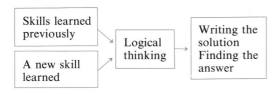

An important aspect of solving problems is deciding which skills and strategies to use. The following is a list of some strategies you have used.

> **PSP** | **Problem Solving Plan**
>
> *Step A:* Understand the problem.
> - What are you asked to find?
> - What are you given?
>
> *Step B:* Decide on a strategy.
>
> *Step C:* Apply the strategy. Do the work.
>
> *Step D:* Check your solution.
>
> *Step E:* Write a final statement.

▶ Look for clues in the problem that suggest a skill or strategy you have learned.

▶ Use a diagram or chart to sort and organize your work.

▶ Express the problem in your own words.

▶ Use a formula.

▶ Organize your written solution. Refer to the *Problem Solving Plan* **PSP** .

The more problems you solve, the better problem solver you will become.

5.14 Exercise

A 1 Write an equation for each of the following.

(a) x quarters and 5 more dimes than quarters have a total value of $1.55.

(b) 7 more than double a number, n, is 5 less than triple the number.

(c) Lila's age in years is 2 more than her brother's age, b, in years. The sum of their ages 3 years ago was 22 years.

(d) Franco's score, f, doubled and then increased by $\frac{2}{3}$ of his score gives 200.

(e) For four consecutive integers, the sum of the second integer and the third integer minus the fourth integer results in the first integer, n.

In the local camera club the number of boys is 15 more than 3 times the number of girls. If there are 79 students in the club, how many girls are there?

3 During a hike Craig went twice as far as Cliff. If the total distance they hiked was 144 km, how far did each of them hike?

4 The sum of two numbers is 36. If twice the greater number is 6 times the lesser number, find the numbers.

5 For the end-of-term concert 209 tickets were sold. There were 23 more student tickets sold than twice the number of adult tickets sold.
(a) How many of each were sold?
(b) The total receipts were $292.25. How much did adult tickets cost if they were 50¢ more than student tickets?

6 (a) A rectangular field needs 684 m of fencing to enclose it. If the width is 42 m, find the length.
(b) A square yard has an area of 460 m². Find the dimensions of the yard to 1 decimal place.

7 Four boys built a dinghy. Two boys spent twice as much time building it as the other two. If altogether the time spent to build the boat was 192 h, how much time did each boy spend?

8 The number of pages in one book is 60 more than 5 times the number of pages in another. If together there are 300 pages, how many pages are in each book?

9 Each day Melanie earns twice as much as John and John earns $4 more than Mary Rose. If after one day they earned a total of $28, how much did each student earn?

10 The sum of my age and my daughter's age is 50 years. In 30 years, 3 times my age increased by my daughter's age will be equal to 242 years. How old are we today?

11 This hockey season the Raiders won twice as many games as they lost and tied 7 games less than they won. If they played 78 games, how many did they win?

12 The Swedish Connection scored 144 goals. If Johann scored 5 times as many goals as Swelm and Swelm scored 2 less than twice as many as Hann, how many goals were scored by each player?

13 A sum of $1500 was invested, part at 8% and part at 12%. If the interest received in one year is $152 how much was invested at 12%?

14 In a rectangle the length is 3 m more than the width. The length doubled and increased by 2 m is the same as the width multiplied by 4 and then decreased by 24 m. Find the dimensions of the rectangle.

15 During last season the Blues Lacrosse team lost 3 times as many games as they won. They also tied 2 fewer games than they won. If the season had 78 games, how many games were won, lost or tied?

Did you know that the game of lacrosse was originally played as training for warfare by the Indians of North America? The head of the stick in this game was called la crosse (in French) because it resembled a bishop's cross. Subsequently, the game became known as lacrosse.

16 In 10 years my age will be 5 times my age 6 years ago. How old will I be next year?

17 I paid my bill in dimes. If I had paid using quarters, I would have needed 12 fewer coins. How much was my bill?

18 Three students compared their marks on an algebra test (as usual). Nora had 50 less than twice as many marks as Brian had. Alan had 16 marks less than Brian. If together they had 198 marks, what were the marks?

PSP 19 In order to break even, the Ticket Committee had to sell at least 200 tickets at $8.00 each for each of three performances. On Thursday evening 112 people attended and on Friday evening 185. Saturday evening was a sell-out with 275 attending. How much money did the Ticket Committee make or lose?

Math Tip

To solve any problem, you must understand *each* word of the problem.
▶ Make a list of all the new words you have met in this chapter.
▶ Make a list of all the new *math* words you have met in this chapter. Provide a simple example of your own to illustrate each word.

5.15 PSP Problem Solving: Using Strategies

To solve the following problems, you need to decide on a strategy. Refer to your list of strategies you have placed into your *Problem Solving Plan* PSP

As in your earlier work, you need to know the answers to these two questions:

I What information am I asked to find?

II What information am I given?

PSP	Problem Solving Plan

Step A: Understand the problem.
  • What are you asked to find?
  • What are you given?

Step B: Decide on a strategy.

Step C: Apply the strategy. Do the work.

Step D: Check your solution.

Step E: Write a final statement.

5.15 Exercise

B 1 Jackie cleared out her jewelry box and found earrings that were either complete pairs, single earrings or broken pairs of earrings. If she counted 55 earrings, how many pairs did she have that were not broken?

2 (a) There are 10 chairs in a square room. They are to be placed along the walls so that the same number of chairs is along each wall. How would you do it?
   (b) What assumption(s) did you make?

3 A figure is made from matchsticks. Remove only 2 matchsticks so that only 2 squares are formed.

4 The value of SAILING is 118. What is the value of CAPTAIN?

5 Margie is a physicist, Rose Mary is a linguist and Shirley is a mathematician. They are married to Alex, Frank and John, but not in that order.
   ▶ Shirley does not like John.
   ▶ Rose Mary is married to John's brother.
   ▶ Alex is married to Rose Mary's sister.
   Who is married to whom? (Assume that married people like each other!)

Practice and Problems: Review

1   Which of the values is the solution to the equation? Use your calculator.
   (a) $3.2x - 6.8 = 6$ $4, 3$ (b) $3p - 4.1 = -19.1$ $-4, -5$
   (c) $12.5w + 2.2w = 44.1$ $5, 3$ (d) $6.8a - 8.6 = 2.5a$ $2, -2$

2   Solve and verify. The variables represent rational numbers.
   (a) $w - 3 = -2$ (b) $14 - k = 3$ (c) $-2p = 36$
   (d) $x \div 7 = -6$ (e) $2x - 12 = x + 3$ (f) $6m = 9 + 3m$
   (g) $5n - 18 \leq 3n$ (h) $-3 = 3(x + 2)$ (i) $3(4y - 20) > 3y + 75$

   (j) $6.5(x - 3) = 2.4(3 - x)$ (k) $\dfrac{x}{8} - \dfrac{3}{2} \geq -\dfrac{1}{4}$

   (l) $\dfrac{2}{3}(p - 2) = p + 5$ (m) $\dfrac{1}{3}(6y - 9) = \dfrac{1}{2}(8y - 4)$

3   Brian read $(2n - 3)$ pages yesterday and $(4n + 1)$ pages today. If he read
   94 pages altogether, how many did he read each day?

4   (a) One number is 3 more than another. If the sum of the numbers is 13,
       find the numbers.
   (b) Find three consecutive numbers whose sum is 87.

5   Do you know how many horses are on a polo team? Solve the problem
   to find the number. Six times the number increased by 8 is equal to the
   product of 7 and the number.

6   Pamela is twice as old as Andrea. Copy
   and complete the chart to show their
   present ages and their ages 3 years
   from now.

	Present age	Age in 3 years
Andrea	k	?
Pamela	?	?

7   Use the information from the previous question. The sum of the girls' ages
   in 3 years will be 27 years. Find each girl's present age.

8   The perimeter of a rectangular plot is 114 m. If the length is 3 m less than
   three times the width, find the dimensions.

PSP   9   Freddy shared his lottery winnings with his family. He kept $1800. He
   gave $\frac{1}{3}$ of the remainder to his parents. His two brothers split an amount
   that was half as much as his parents received. His sister received $400
   more than his brothers. How much did Freddy win in the lottery?

Practice Test

1   Solve and verify. The variables represent rational numbers.

(a) $20 = 7k + 6$
(b) $\dfrac{x}{4} - 1 = \dfrac{x}{5}$
(c) $\dfrac{3}{2}y - 3 \geqq 3$

(d) $5(y + 2) = 17$
(e) $3m - 12 = -18$
(f) $4m + 11 = 6m - 5$

(g) $5x + 8 - x = 18$
(h) $-12 \leqq 3(2y - 1)$

(i) $4(y - 2) = 3(y + 1)$
(j) $7x + 3 - 2x = 23$

(k) $2(x - 3) + 3 < 15 - x$
(l) $2y - 5 - (y - 3) = 7$

(m) $3(x - 2) + x = 2(x + 1)$
(n) $5(2y - 1) - 3(4y - 6) = 7$

2   Find the root of each equation. Check your answer.

(a) $3.6k + 9.3 = 34.5$
(b) $6.4g - 3.8 = 53.8$
(c) $2.5r - 9.1 = 6.9$

3   Bernice scored $(3k - 2)$ goals and $(k + 3)$ assists. If her total number of goals and assists was 21, find the number of goals she scored.

4   One number is 7 less than another. If the sum of the two numbers is 39, find the numbers.

5   Rita has two more dimes than quarters. If she has $3.35 altogether, how many of each type of coin does she have?

6   Vicky invested $4500; part at 12% and the rest at 8%. Find the amount invested at each rate if $463 was earned after the first year.

7   Greg has 3 more nickels than dimes and 2 more quarters than dimes. If he has $3.45 altogether, how many coins of each type does he have?

8   Rejean is a year older than Gilbert. Twice the sum of their ages 4 years ago was 42 years. Find the present age of each boy.

9   A rectangle is 5 cm longer than twice its width. The width of another rectangle is 3 cm less than the width of the first rectangle and its length is 6 cm more than 3 times its width. If the perimeters are equal, find the dimensions of both rectangles.

10   Tara invested $5000; part of it at 6.5% and the rest at 8%. If the total interest earned in one year was $370, find the amount invested at each rate.

11   Peter had a pocketful of dimes. Charlene had the same amount in quarters, but had 15 fewer coins. How much money did Peter have?

6 *Measurement: Concepts, Formulas and Applications*

Concept of perimeter, formulas for area, writing formulas, areas of composite shapes, regular polygons, calculating surface area, relationships for volume, volume of prisms and cylinders, formulas for volume, pyramids, cones, spheres, applications, strategies for problem solving

Introduction

Many decisions are based on measurement. A manufacturer makes decisions about the amount of material needed in packaging. An engineer makes decisions about constructing foundations and erecting buildings. Solutions to problems in the space program and astronomy use measurement skills and concepts.
Skills with equations and formulas provide a foundation for solving problems in measurement.

In each situation shown in the photographs, measurement played an important role. What aspects of measurement do you recognize in each of the photographs?

6.1 Concepts of Perimeter

The distance around a figure is called its **perimeter**. The perimeter, P, in kilometres, of the figure is given by

$$P = 4.6 + 3.8 + 3.2 + 2.8 + 7.8 + 6.6$$
$$= 28.8$$

The perimeter is 28.8 km.

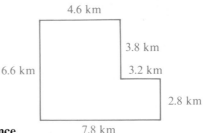

The perimeter of a circle is called its **circumference**.

You have already used formulas to calculate the perimeters of shapes such as the following.

Rectangle
$P = 2l + 2w$

Square
$P = 4s$

Circle
$C = 2\pi r$ or
πd

When solving problems involving circles, use $\pi \doteq 3.14$. If your calculator has a $\boxed{\pi}$ key, use it. However, remember that the $\boxed{\pi}$ key provides more digits than you need to express your final answers.
Round all answers to measurement problems to 1 decimal place unless indicated otherwise.

PSP

Example
The radius of a bicycle wheel is 36.25 cm.
(a) Calculate the circumference of the bicycle wheel.
(b) How many full turns would the wheel make in 1 km?

Solution
(a) Use $C = 2\pi r$, $r = 36.25$ cm, $\pi \doteq 3.14$.
$$C \doteq 2(3.14)(36.25)$$
$$C = 227.65 \text{ (to 2 decimal places)}$$
The circumference of the wheel is
227.7 cm to 1 decimal place.

> Use the π key on your calculator to do the calculation. Compare your answer with the answer shown.

(b) Use 1 km = 1000 m
$$= 100\ 000 \text{ cm}$$
227.7 cm is the length of 1 turn.

1 cm is the length of $\dfrac{1}{227.7}$ turn.

100 000 cm is the length of $\dfrac{1}{227.7} \times 100\ 000$ turns or 439 turns.

Thus the bicycle wheel makes 439 turns in 1 km.

6.1 Exercise

A 1 Calculate the perimeter of each figure.

(a)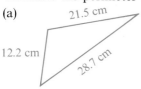

(b)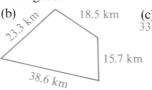

(c)

2 Copy and complete the table for each circle.

	radius (r)	diameter (d)	circumference (C)
(a)	40.0 cm	?	?
(b)	165.0 cm	?	?
(c)	?	8.6 m	?
(d)	?	18.2 km	?

3 Which figure has the greatest perimeter?

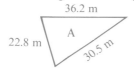

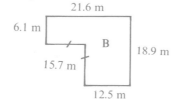

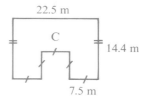

4 Find the measure of the unknown sides of each figure. Then calculate the perimeter of each figure.

(a)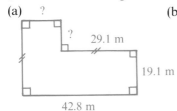

(b)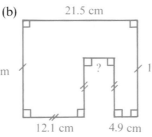

(c)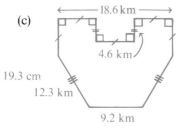

5 You know that the perimeter of a square is found by using $P = 4s$. Use the same principle to find the perimeter of each of the following regular polygons.

(a)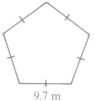

9.7 m

(b)

7.25 cm

(c)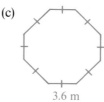

3.6 m

B 6 A baseball diamond is really a square. If its perimeter is 420 m, calcula⌐
the length of each side.

7 Find the perimeter of a square courtyard if each side measures 12.6 m.

8 Each garden is enclosed by a fence. Wire fencing costs $6.58/m. Calculate
the cost of fencing each garden.

(a)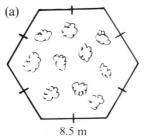

8.5 m

(b)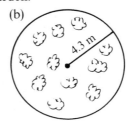

4.3 m

(c)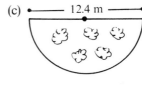

12.4 m

9 For each tire, ▶ calculate the circumference.
▶ calculate the number of turns the tire makes in 1 km.

(a) A compact car has tires 69.5 cm in diameter.

(b) An earth mover has tires with a radius 1.62 m.

(c) The world's largest tire has a diameter of 4.33 m.

10 To make jumps at night, parachutists place flares around a circular target.
Flares are placed 2.90 m apart. About how many flares are required if the
diameter of the target is 11.1 m?

11 A satellite travels 230.5 km above Earth's surface. Calculate the distance
travelled in one orbit. The radius of Earth is about 6400 km.

12 (a) The amount of fencing needed to enclose a square field is 368 m. Find
the length of one side of the field.

(b) One side of a rectangular field is 48.6 m. The perimeter is 169.6 m.
Calculate the measures of the other sides.

(c) A triangular vegetable garden has two sides that measure 3.68 m each.
The perimeter measures 10.96 m. Calculate the measure of the other side.

13 The label placed around a can is 31.5 cm in length.
(a) What is the diameter of the can?   (b) What assumption(s) did you make?

14 The first Ferris wheel, named after George Ferris, had a diameter of 76.3 m.
(a) Calculate the circumference.
(b) If the wheel made one turn every 4 min, how fast was the wheel
turning?

PSP 15 What is the least number of games that must be played in order to
determine a winner in a singles badminton tournament involving 27
players? After each game, the player who loses is out of the tournament.

6.2 Applications with Area

You have used various methods of developing the formulas for calculating area. For example, you used the following steps to find the area of rectangles and other figures.

▶ You first counted the number of square units.

Area = 20 square units

▶ You used numerical examples to develop a formula.

Area = length × width

Then you used symbols to express the relationship.

$A = l \times w$

▶ You then applied these results to calculate the area.

6.9

3.9

$A = 6.9 \times 3.9$
$A = 26.9$
(to 1 decimal place)

The formula for calculating the area, A, of each figure shown below is given.

Rectangle
$A = l \times w$

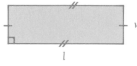

w

l

Square
$A = s^2$

s

Parallelogram
$A = bh$

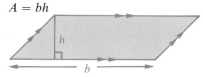

h

b

Triangle
$A = \frac{1}{2}bh$

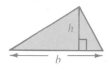

h

b

Trapezoid
$A = \frac{1}{2}(a + b)h$

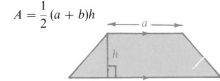

a

h

b

Circle
$A = \pi r^2$

r

You combine the use of these formulas with your other skills in **PSP** mathematics to solve problems.

Example

The prices of two popular pizza sizes are shown.

(a) Calculate the cost per square centimetre to the nearest hundredth of a cent for each pizza.

(b) Based on your results in (a), what conclusion can you make?

A $6.20

32.0 cm
diameter

B $12.90

45.0 cm
diameter

Solution

(a)

Pizza A	Use your calculator.

Pizza A	Pizza B

Pizza A

diameter, $d = 32.0$ cm
radius, $r = 16.0$ cm
$A = \pi r^2$
$\doteq 3.14(16.0)^2$
$= 803.84$
$\doteq 803.8$
803.8 cm^2 of pizza costs \$6.20.

1 cm^2 costs $\dfrac{620}{803.8}$ or 0.77¢/cm^2.

Pizza B

diameter, $d = 45.0$ cm
radius, $r = 22.5$ cm
$A = \pi r^2$
$\doteq 3.14(22.5)^2$
$= 1589.625$
$\doteq 1589.6$
1589.6 cm^2 of pizza costs \$12.90.

1 cm^2 costs $\dfrac{1290}{1589.6}$ or 0.81¢/cm^2.

(b) Based on the calculations, a larger pizza is not necessarily the better buy when considering cost per square centimetre.

6.2 Exercise

A   Estimate your answers first. Use your calculator to find your answers.

1   Calculate the area of each figure.

(a) 8.7 m, 3.9 m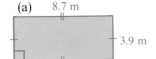

(b) 2.9 cm

(c) 12.8 cm, 5.5 cm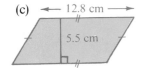

(d) 13.2 m, 6.1 m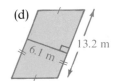

(e) 1.9 m, 1.4 m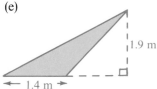

(f) 28.1 cm, 45.7 cm

(g) 9.6 m, 24.7 m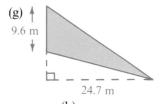

(h) 5.1 m, 4.8 m, 13.3 m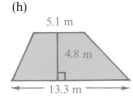

(i) 3.1 cm, 2.2 cm, 7.5 cm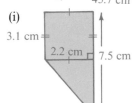

(j) 6.2 m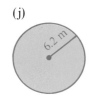

(k) 9.8 cm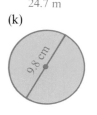

2   Find the unknown dimension in each figure.

(a) ? , $A = 21.0$ cm^2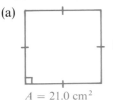

(b) 5.2 cm, ? , $A = 33.8$ cm^2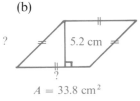

(c) ? , 6.4 m, $A = 20.48$ m^2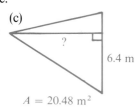

(d) ?. , $A = 271.6$ m^2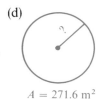

B 3 The height of a parallelogram measures 16.5 cm and the area is 465.3 cm². Calculate its base.

4 The base of a triangle is 10.5 cm. The height is 30.8 cm. Calculate its area.

5 The diameter of a circular disc is 14.8 cm. Calculate the area of the disc.

6 Calculate the radius of a circular garden with area 120.7 m².

7 A credit card measures 8.5 cm by 5.5 cm. Find the area of the card.

8 A patrol aircraft can observe a distance of 15.2 km in all directions. Calculate the area of coverage by the plane.

9 The tail of a modern jet is a triangle with base 8.2 m and area 35.26 m². Calculate the height of the tail.

10 One event at the Olympic Games is the discus throw.
(a) The discus is circular with a radius of about 10.8 cm. Calculate its area.
(b) The discus is thrown by the competitors from a circle with diameter about 2.75 m. Calculate the throw area.

11 A wall is 6.2 m in length and 2.7 m in height and is to be wallpapered. Each roll of wallpaper is 0.68 m in width.
(a) How many metres of wallpaper need to be purchased to cover 4 walls?
(b) What assumption did you make? *PSP*

12 (a) Use the program to calculate the areas of the circles in this section.
(b) If the radius of a circle grows by 1 unit, how does the area of the circle grow? Revise the program to help you explore this.

```
10 PRINT "AREA OF A CIRCLE"
20 INPUT "THE RADIUS IS"; R
30 LET A = 3.14 * R ↑ 2
40 PRINT "THE AREA IS"; A
50 END
```

PSP **13** A backyard has dimensions 16.3 m by 14.5 m and is to be sodded with new grass. How many strips of sod are required, if each strip has dimensions 40.0 cm by 150.0 cm?

PSP **14** Thirty police officers form a straight line barrier along part of a parade route. If the distance between each police officer was increased by 1 m, only 24 police officers would be needed. What was the original space between police officers? List any assumptions you made.

C 15 (a) A rectangle has an area of 96.0 cm². How many different rectangles can you construct with whole number measures for the sides?
(b) A triangle has an area of 42 cm². How many different triangles can you construct with whole number measures for the base and the height?

You can write a formula to calculate the area, A, of the shaded region.

PSP You often need to use more than one formula.

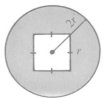

Area of circle	Area of square	Area of shaded region
$A = \pi(2r)^2$	$A = r^2$	$A = 4\pi r^2 - r^2$
$= 4\pi r^2$		

16 Write a formula in terms of the given variables to calculate the area of each shaded region.

(a)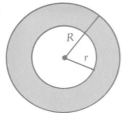

(b)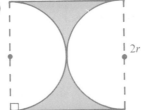

(c)

17 The total area, A, of the shaded region is given by $A = 2\pi R^2 + 2\pi r^2$.

(a) Calculate the area if $R = 4.1$ m and $r = 2.8$ m.

(b) By how much does the area in (a) increase if each radius is increased by 1.0 m?

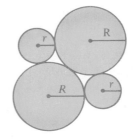

18 Calculate the area of each shaded region.

(a)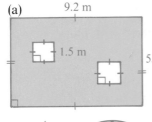

(b)

(c)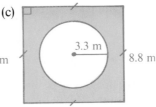

(d)

(e)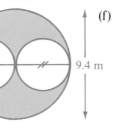

(f)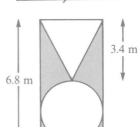

6.3 Areas: Composite Shapes

Some shapes are composed of two simpler shapes. For example, the area of shape **P** is found by adding the areas of **Q** and **R**.

PSP Remember: To solve some problems, you often need to think of a simpler problem.

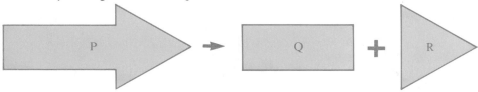

6.3 Exercise

A 1 The shape shown is composed of two simpler shapes.
   (a) Find the area of each simpler shape.
   (b) What is the area of the original shape?

9.6 m   11.5 m

B Review the formulas for finding areas.

2 Calculate the area of each shape.

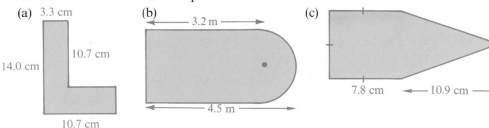

(a) 3.3 cm
10.7 cm
14.0 cm
10.7 cm

(b) 3.2 m
4.5 m

(c) 7.8 cm   10.9 cm

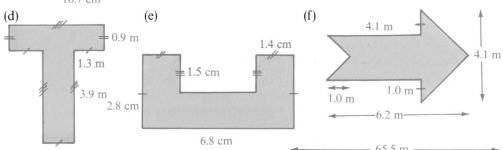

(d) 0.9 m
1.3 m
3.9 m
2.8 cm

(e) 1.4 cm
1.5 cm
6.8 cm

(f) 4.1 m
4.1 m
1.0 m
1.0 m
6.2 m

3 A playing field is shown in the diagram.
   (a) Calculate the area of the playing field.
   (b) A fence placed around the field cost $3.20/m. Calculate the total cost.

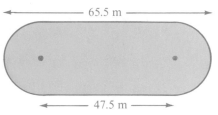

65.5 m

47.5 m

Area of Regular Polygons

Regular polygons are also composed of other shapes whose area formulas you know.

Regular Pentagon

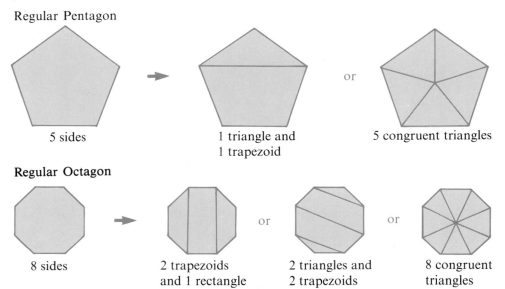

| 5 sides | 1 triangle and 1 trapezoid | or | 5 congruent triangles |

Regular Octagon

| 8 sides | 2 trapezoids and 1 rectangle | or | 2 triangles and 2 trapezoids | or | 8 congruent triangles |

In any regular polygon, one composition of shapes is consistent—congruent triangles with a side of the regular polygon as the base.

4 (a) How many congruent triangles does the regular hexagon shown consist of?

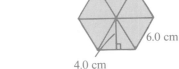

(b) What is the measure of each base of the triangles?

(c) What is the height of each triangle?

(d) What is the area of each triangle?

(e) What is the area of the regular hexagon?

(f) What is the formula for calculating the area of a regular hexagon?

5 Write a formula for calculating the area of a regular polygon of n sides.

6 Calculate the area of each regular polygon.

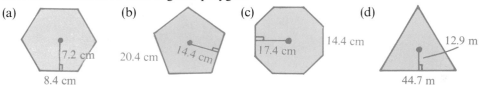

(a) 7.2 cm 8.4 cm

(b) 20.4 cm 14.4 cm

(c) 17.4 cm 14.4 cm

(d) 12.9 m 44.7 m

6.4 Calculating Surface Area

The skills you have used to calculate area are used to determine the surface area of various solids.

Rectangular Prism

To calculate the surface area of a rectangular prism, calculate the area of each **face** or surface. First draw a **net** or diagram showing all the faces. Decide which faces are congruent.

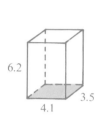

faces A, C
$A = lw$
$\quad = 6.2 \times 4.1$
$\quad = 25.42$

faces B, D
$A = lw$
$\quad = 6.2 \times 3.5$
$\quad = 21.7$

faces E, F
$A = lw$
$\quad = 4.1 \times 3.5$
$\quad = 14.35$

PSP Drawing a diagram to help you solve a problem is an important strategy.

Surface Area $= 2(25.42) + 2(21.7) + 2(14.35)$
$\quad\quad\quad\quad = 50.84 + 43.4 + 28.7$
$\quad\quad\quad\quad = 122.94$

The surface area is 122.9 cm^2 to 1 decimal place.

Square Pyramid

To find the surface area of a pyramid, draw a net showing all the faces and decide which faces are congruent.

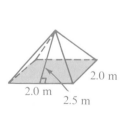

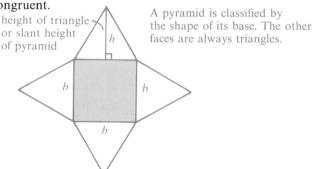

height of triangle or slant height of pyramid

A pyramid is classified by the shape of its base. The other faces are always triangles.

Surface Area = Area of square base + 4(Area of triangular face)
$$= b^2 + 4\left(\frac{1}{2}bh\right)$$

You find the surface area.

Cylinder

Again consider the net. The curved surface of the cylinder is a rectangle. The length is the circumference of the circular base or $2\pi r$ and the width is the height of the cylinder.

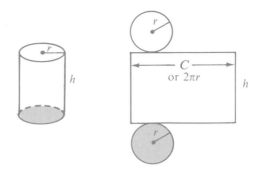

Surface Area = 2(Area of circular base)
             + Area of rectangle
$$= 2\pi r^2 + Ch$$
$$= 2\pi r^2 + 2\pi rh$$

Cone

Once again, consider the net. The curved surface or lateral face is a sector of a circle with radius s, the slant height of the cone. Thus the area of the sector is a fraction of the larger circle.

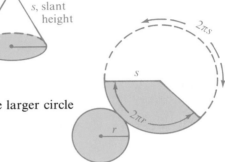

Surface Area = Area of circular base
             + fraction of the Area of the larger circle
$$= \pi r^2 + \frac{2\pi r}{2\pi s}(\pi s^2)$$
$$= \pi r^2 + \pi rs$$

Sphere

Often you need to think of a problem **PSP** from a different point of view. For example, to remember the formula for the surface area of a sphere, you can interpret the surface area as follows.

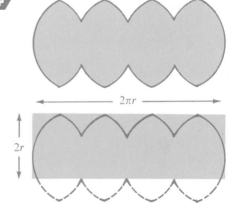

The net of a sphere is similar to the flattened peel of a quartered orange. If the peel were cut and fitted as shown, the net would approximate a rectangle. The length is the circumference or $2\pi r$ and the width is the diameter or $2r$. Thus by interpreting the diagram as above,

Surface Area $= 2\pi r \times 2r$
$$= 4\pi r^2 \qquad \text{Try this with an orange!}$$

PSP Often a model is used to help you remember or do mathematics.

6.4　Exercise

A 1　Each edge of a cube is 20.0 cm.
(a) How many faces are there?
(b) What is the shape of the faces?
(c) What is the area of each face?
(d) What is the surface area of the cube?

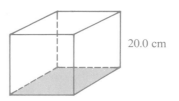

20.0 cm

2　The measures of a rectangular prism are shown.
(a) Draw a net.　(b) Identify the congruent faces.
(c) Find the area of the different faces.
(d) Find the surface area of the prism.

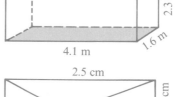

4.1 m
2.3 m
1.6 m

3　The measures of a triangular prism are shown.
(a) Draw a net.　(b) Identify the congruent faces.
(c) Find the area of each face.
(d) Find the surface area of the prism.

2.5 cm
0.8 cm
1.5 cm
2.0 cm

4　The measures of a square pyramid are shown.
(a) Draw a net.　(b) Find the area of the base.
(c) Find the area of each triangular face.
(d) Find the surface area of the pyramid.

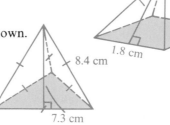

2.4 cm
1.8 cm

5　The measures of a triangular pyramid are shown.
(a) Draw a net.
(b) How many congruent faces are there?
(c) Find the area of each face.
(d) Find the surface area of the pyramid.

8.4 cm
7.3 cm

6　Apply the appropriate formula to calculate the surface area of each solid.

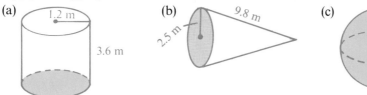

(a) 1.2 m 　 3.6 m
(b) 9.8 m 　 2.5 m
(c) 1.4 m

B　When solving problems, remember to estimate the answers and then **PSP** calculate. Ask yourself if your answers are reasonable.

7　A can has a radius of 8.0 cm and a height of 12.0 cm.
(a) Calculate the surface area of the can.
(b) Calculate the dimensions of the label needed for the can.

8 The dimensions for a tent are shown.

(a) How much material is needed to construct the tent?

(b) What assumption did you make? **PSP**

9 (a) A stereo speaker is made in the shape of a cone.
A nylon material is used to cover the speaker.
Calculate the amount of material needed.

(b) How much more material would you need if the radius
of the base of the speaker were increased by 1 cm?

10 (a) The surface area of a square pyramid is 126.8 cm². If the
length of the base is 4.3 cm, calculate the slant height.

(b) The area of the lateral face of a cone is 33.2 cm². If the slant height
is 4.6 cm, find the radius.

11 (a) By estimating, arrange the solids in order from least to greatest surface area.

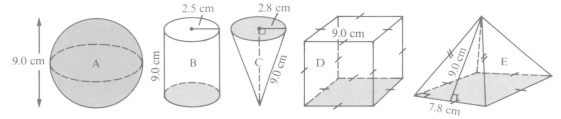

(b) Check your estimate in (a) by calculating the surface areas.

12 Use the computer program
to find the area of
a sphere for R = 6.5 cm.
Choose other input values
of your own.

```
10 PRINT "SURFACE AREA OF A SPHERE"
20 INPUT "THE RADIUS IS"; R
30 LET S = 4 * 3.14 * R ↑ 2
40 PRINT "THE SURFACE AREA IS"; S
50 END
```

PSP 13 To construct a closed container, 500 cm² of tin is provided.

(a) Design a cube and a cylinder so that they have the same surface area.

(b) What are the dimensions of the shapes you constructed?

PSP 14 If 6 pumps can drain 13 200 L of water in 4 h, how many litres can
3 pumps drain in 3 h?

C 15 (a) If the slant height of a cone is doubled, by what percent is the area
of the lateral face changed?

(b) If the radius of a cone is doubled, what change occurs in its surface area?

(c) If the radius of a cylinder is doubled, how does the curved face
change? How does the area of its base change?

6.5 Volume: Prisms and Cylinders

Very often in mathematics, there are different strategies which can be used to solve the same problem. Also a method you develop for one situation can often be applied to other situations.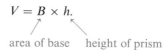

Step 1: If you examine the formula for the volume of the rectangular prism, you will see that the formula could be written as

$$V = l \times w \times h.$$

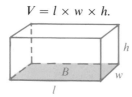

Step 2: You can interpret the formula in a different way. If the area of the base, B, is written as

$$B = l \times w,$$

then the volume formula can be rewritten as

$$V = B \times h.$$

area of base   height of prism

You can then extend the strategy to calculate the volume of *any prism* using the area of the base and the height.

To calculate the volume of any **prism**, you use this principle.

$$V = B \times h$$

$V = B \times h$ $V = B \times h$ $V = B \times h$

The above strategy for finding volume also applies to finding the volume of a **cylinder**.

volume = area of base × height
$$V = B \times h$$
$$V = \pi r^2 \times h$$
$$V = \pi r^2 h$$

6.5 Exercise

A Check whether your answers are reasonable. Round your answers to 1 decimal place.

1 Find the volume of each solid.

(a)
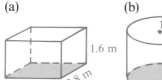
1.6 m
2.6 m
2.8 m

(b)
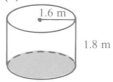
1.6 m
1.8 m

(c)
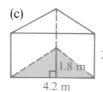
2.6 m
1.8 m
4.2 m

(d)
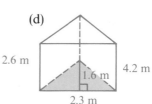
2.6 m
1.6 m
4.2 m
2.3 m

2   The dimensions of a prism are shown.
    (a) What is the shape of the base?
    (b) Find the area of the base.
    (c) Find the volume of the prism.

3   The dimensions of a solid are shown.
    (a) How is the solid related to a cylinder?
    (b) What is the volume of the solid?

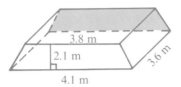

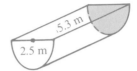

4   Find the missing measure for each cylinder.

	V	r	h
(a)	?	2.1 cm	4.6 cm
(b)	26.1 m³	1.9 m	?
(c)	1143.2 cm³	?	15.8 cm

B 5   (a) A well is dug 28.6 m deep with a radius of 1.3 m. Calculate the amount of earth removed.
      (b) What assumption did you make? **PSP**

6   A circular pool with sides 1.6 m high has a radius of 4.0 m.
    (a) Calculate the volume of water in the pool.
    (b) What assumption did you make? **PSP**

7   Cement pillars that support bridges often are cylindrical.
    (a) Calculate the volume of one pillar if the height of a pillar is 12.3 m and the radius is 0.5 m.
    (b) Calculate the mass of a pillar if 100.0 cm³ of concrete has a mass of 0.51 kg.

8   A large cubical tank whose side measures 4.6 m is filled. How much liquid will be left in the tank if it is used to fill a cylindrical tank with a radius 2.2 m and a height of 4.6 m?

9   An aquarium is 40.3 cm long, 20.1 cm wide and 14.6 cm deep.
    (a) Calculate the number of litres of water it will hold when full.
    (b) The aquarium is filled so that the water is 3.2 cm from the top. Calculate how much water is in it. (Remember: 1 cm³ = 1 mL)

10 The basement of an apartment building is being excavated. The dimensions of the basement are 30.2 m by 15.8 m by 3.2 m.
    (a) What is the volume of the earth removed for the basement?
    (b) If a haulage truck can carry 23.8 m³ of earth each trip, how many trips need to be made to remove all the earth?

11 It is fortunate that when water freezes, it expands. Otherwise, all creatures in the water would be frozen. Water increase in volume by 10% when it freezes.

(a) Calculate the volume of water in a full cylindrical storage tank with radius 24.3 cm and height 115.3 cm.

(b) Calculate the volume of ice obtained in (a) when the water is frozen.

12 A concrete pillar has the shape shown. Calculate its volume.

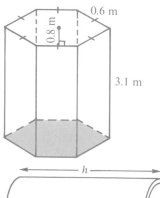

PSP 13 (a) Devise a method to calculate the volume of one leaf of this book.

(b) What is the volume of one leaf of this book?

PSP 14 A cylinder has its radius halved and its height doubled. What change occurs to the volume?

C 15 (a) Find a formula for the volume of the material used to construct the concrete pipe.

(b) Use your formula to find the volume for $R = 1.8$ m, $r = 1.7$ m and $h = 3.2$ m.

16 (a) Find the volume of concrete required to make a pipe if the outside radius is 2.6 cm, the inside radius is 1.5 cm and the length is 3.3 m.

(b) Find the length of a concrete pipe with a volume of 16.6 m³, inside radius 1.4 m and outside radius 1.9 m.

17 (a) Find the amount of concrete used for a pipe 4.65 m long if the outside radius is 0.63 m and the inside radius is 0.54 m.

(b) If 100 cm³ of concrete has a mass 0.51 kg, find the mass of the pipe.

Calculator Use

Refer to Question 15. The formula used to calculate the volume V is given by $V = \pi R^2 h - \pi r^2 h$.

▶ Use the calculator steps shown to calculate the volume when $R = 1.8$ m, $r = 1.7$ m and $h = 3.2$ m.

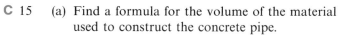

▶ Can you design a more efficient procedure on your calculator for doing these calculations? Remember: Formulas provide an opportunity to use a calculator to solve problems. PSP

6.6 PSP Problem Solving: Volume Relationships

Often mathematics is developed by making comparisons. For example, are the volumes of these solids related?

▶ The areas of the bases are equal.　　▶ The heights are equal.

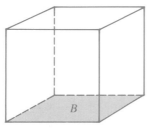 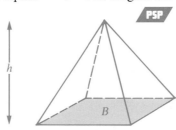

PSP Often to solve a problem, you need to interpret the problem from a different point of view.

To develop a formula for finding the volume of a pyramid, you can think of the pyramid as being made up of layers as shown below. By calculating the volume of the layers, you can approximate the volume of the pyramid.

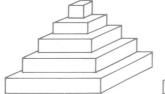 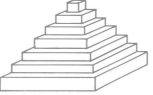 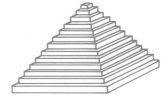

6.6 Exercise

Volume Formula: Pyramids

B 1 (a) Find the volume of each solid by calculating the volume of the stack of layers. The length of each layer decreases by an amount equal to h.

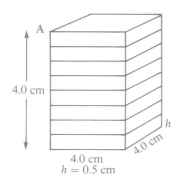 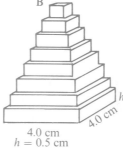 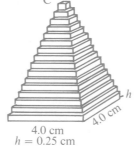 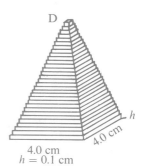

A

4.0 cm

4.0 cm
h = 0.5 cm

B

4.0 cm
h = 0.5 cm

C

4.0 cm
h = 0.25 cm

D

4.0 cm
h = 0.1 cm

(b) Which solid, B, C or D, best approximates the volume of a pyramid?

(c) Write a formula that you think gives the volume of a pyramid.

2 Often a model can be used to help develop a formula for the volume of a solid.

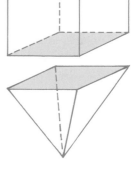

Step 1: Use cardboard to construct each shell as shown. Choose dimensions that are suitable.

Step 2: Fill the prism shell with rice or some other suitable material.

Step 3: By pouring, determine how many pyramid shells can be filled by using a full prism shell of material.

Step 4: Based on your results in Step 3, write a formula to relate the volume of a pyramid to the volume of the corresponding prism.

Volume Formula: Cones

3 (a) Find the volume of each solid by calculating the volume of the stack of layers. The radius of the base is 4.0 cm. The radius of each layer decreases by an amount equal to h.

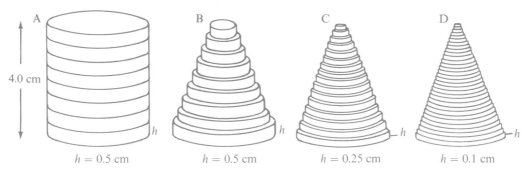

A	B	C	D
$h = 0.5$ cm	$h = 0.5$ cm	$h = 0.25$ cm	$h = 0.1$ cm

(b) Which solid, B, C or D, best approximates the volume of a cone?

(c) Write a formula that you think gives the volume of a cone.

4 Use the suggested models to devise an experiment to develop a formula for the volume of a cone.

Step 1: Use stiff paper to construct each shell. Choose dimensions that are suitable.

Step 2: Fill the cylindrical shell with rice or other suitable material.

Step 3: By pouring, determine how many conical shells can be filled by using a full cylindrical shell of material.

Step 4: Based on your results in Step 3, write a formula to relate the volume of a cone to the volume of the corresponding cylinder.

6.7   Formulas for Volume

In the previous section, you experimented to find the formulas
for the volume of a pyramid and the volume of a cone.

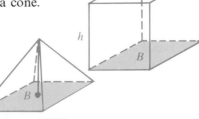

Volume of a pyramid
For a prism and a pyramid with the same base
and the same height, you found the relationship

$$\text{volume of pyramid} = \frac{1}{3} \text{ volume of prism.}$$

Thus if the volume of a prism is $V = Bh$, then
the volume of a pyramid is

$$V = \frac{1}{3}Bh.$$

PSP Often the results of an
experiment will suggest a
formula, a mathematical
relationship among the
measures.

Volume of a cone
For a cylinder and a cone with the same base
and the same height, you found the relationship

$$\text{volume of cone} = \frac{1}{3} \text{ volume of cylinder.}$$

Thus if the volume of a cylinder is
$V = \pi r^2 h$, then the volume of a cone is

$$V = \frac{1}{3}\pi r^2 h.$$

Volume of a sphere
It can be shown using
advanced mathematics that
the volume of a sphere is

$$V = \frac{4}{3}\pi r^3.$$

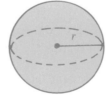

PSP Can you design an
experiment to show
that the formula for
a sphere is reasonable?

Example   Sand is stored in a cone-shaped pile. If the height of the cone is
12.8 m and the diameter of the base is 14.6 m, calculate the amount
of sand to the nearest cubic metre.

Solution   Use $V = \frac{1}{3}\pi r^2 h$, $h = 12.8$, $r = 7.3$, $\pi \doteq 3.14$.

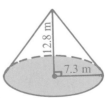

$$V \doteq \frac{1}{3}(3.14)(7.3)^2(12.8)$$

$$V \doteq 713.9 \text{ (to 1 decimal place)}$$

The amount of sand is 714 m³ to the nearest cubic metre.

6.7 Exercise

A Remember: You can use the value of π directly from a calculator with a $\boxed{\pi}$ key.

1 Apply the appropriate formula to find the volume of each solid.

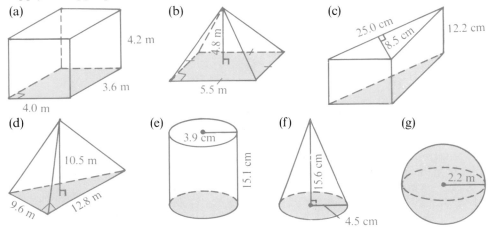

(a) 4.2 m, 3.6 m, 4.0 m

(b) 4.8 m, h, 5.5 m

(c) 25.0 cm, 8.5 cm, 12.2 cm

(d) 10.5 m, 9.6 m, h, 12.8 m

(e) 3.9 cm, 15.1 cm

(f) 15.6 cm, 4.5 cm

(g) 2.2 m

B Remember: Check whether your answers are reasonable. **PSP**
Make an estimate.

2 (a) Find the volume of a cone with height 3.78 cm and with radius 1.65 cm.
(b) Find the volume of a cone 4.2 m in diameter and 6.3 m high.
(c) Find the volume of a pyramid 11.3 m high with a rectangular base measuring 6.9 m by 2.9 m.
(d) A baseball has a radius of 3.58 cm. What is its volume?

3 (a) Find the volume of a spherical tank if the radius is 3.8 m.
(b) If $1 \text{ L} = 1000 \text{ cm}^3$, find the capacity in litres of the tank in (a).

4 (a) By estimating, arrange the solids in order from least to greatest volume.
(b) Check your estimates in (a) by calculating the volumes.

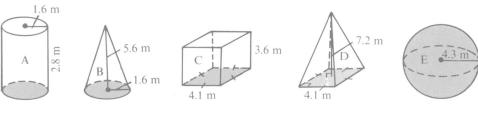

A: 1.6 m, 2.8 m

B: 5.6 m, 1.6 m

C: 3.6 m, 4.1 m

D: 7.2 m, 4.1 m

E: 4.3 m

5 Find the missing measure of each cone.

	V	r	h
(a)	?	1.6 cm	3.2 cm
(b)	51.7 m³	2.8 m	?
(c)	56.1 cm³	?	2.9 cm

6   Sulphur is stored in a conical pile. Calculate the volume of the pile, if the height is 14.2 m and the diameter is 34.4 m.

7   Find the missing measures.

(a)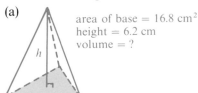
area of base = 16.8 cm²
height = 6.2 cm
volume = ?

(b)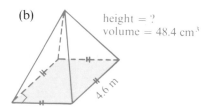
height = ?
volume = 48.4 cm³
4.6 m

8   A funnel is cone-shaped with a radius 1.53 cm and a height of 2.26 cm. Calculate how much the funnel will hold if filled.

9   Which container holds more, the hemisphere (half of a sphere) or the cone?

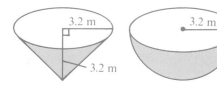
3.2 m   3.2 m
3.2 m

PSP 10   A glass is in the shape of a cylinder and it is completely full of milk. How can you drink exactly one half of the milk without making any measurements?

PSP 11   Read these facts carefully to solve this problem. You may only read the problem *once*! Read it and then look away!

You are the pilot of a jet which flies at 300 km/h. The jet makes 2 stops of 1 h each. The total distance travelled is 1200 km. Use the clues carefully.

(a) How long did the trip take?   (b) What is the pilot's name?

C 12   (a) A billiard ball has a diameter of 5.25 cm. Ivory has a density of 2.00 g/cm³. Calculate the mass of a billard ball made of ivory.

(b) A tennis ball used in international competition has a diameter of 6.75 cm. Calculate its volume.

(c) Which ball has the greatest cross-sectional area? By how much is it greater?

13   (a) The thickness of an orange peel is 0.6 cm. If the diameter of the orange is 8.5 cm, calculate what volume of the orange is peel.

(b) What percent of the volume of the orange is the volume of the peel?

14   A cone has its radius halved and its height doubled. What change occurs to the volume?

6.8 Volume: Composite Solids

Some solids are composed of two simpler solids. For example, the volume of solid A is found by adding the volumes of solids B and C.

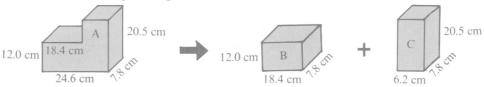

6.8 Exercise

Remember the formulas for finding volume.

A 1 (a) Calculate the volumes of solid B and solid C above.

(b) What is the volume of solid A?

B 2 Calculate the volume of each solid.

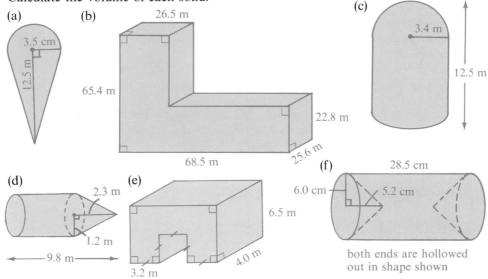

(f) both ends are hollowed out in shape shown

Computer Use

▶ Design a program to find the volume of a solid like the one in Question 2(c).

▶ Design another program to explore the effect on the volume of the solid of increasing the radius by 1 unit. What observation can you make for the above and other solids? Are they all affected in the same way?

6.9 Problem Solving: Using Strategies

To solve problems successfully, you need to develop skills that help you plan how to start. Often a key question from your list provides you with a clue to a particular strategy.

▶ Can I solve a simpler problem?

▶ Do I understand the meaning of all the words in the problem?

▶ Is a strategy for solving the problem immediately evident?

▶ Should I draw a diagram?

▶ Do I need to use a formula? an equation? . . .

Remember: To solve problems, you need a plan that helps you. **PSP**

6.9 Exercise

B To answer these questions, you may need to interpret the questions from a different point of view. The answer you provide must answer the question asked!

1 How much dirt can be removed from a hole that measures 2.3 m by 4.5 m by 6.3 m? Express your answer to 1 decimal place.

2 A bag of 310 coins are unearthed at an archeological dig. The coins are a historic find and are dated 230 B.C. After careful examination of the coins, the team leader concludes that the coins are counterfeit. How did the team leader come to this conclusion?

3 Toothpicks are used to construct Roman numerals. The following statement is not true. Move one toothpick to make the statement true.

4 Golf balls are manufactured at a rate of 50 balls every 15 min. They are sold in packages of 3. How many packages can be produced during an 8-h production shift?

5 115 players participate in an International Chess Tournament. After each game the losing player drops out of the tournament. How many games need to be played to declare a winner for the entire tournament?

6 Twenty-five tomato plants can be placed in a garden such that the distance between adjacent plants is 1 m. How many plants are needed if the distance between adjacent plants is doubled? What assumption(s) did you make?

Practice and Problems: Review

1   The perimeter of each figure is shown. Find the measure of each unknown side.

(a) 15.4 cm, ? cm, P = 43.8 cm

(b) ? m, P = 22.8 m

(c) 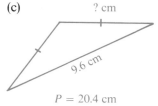 ? cm, 9.6 cm, P = 20.4 cm

2   Find the cost of carpeting a rectangular room with dimensions 3.5 m and 4.5 m if the carpet costs \$32.95/m². What assumption did you make?

3   Find the area of each region.

(a) 1.6 cm, 6.4 cm

(b) 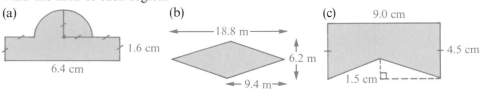 18.8 m, 6.2 m, 9.4 m

(c) 9.0 cm, 4.5 cm, 1.5 cm

4   Find the surface area of a church steeple with the shape of the square pyramid shown.

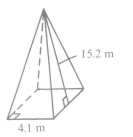

15.2 m

4.1 m

5   What is the surface area of a beach ball with a radius of 18.0 cm?

6   Redwood trees in California have been known to grow to have diameters of 8.6 m.
(a) Calculate the circumference of such a tree.

PSP (b) How many "average" students could be placed end to end around such a tree?

7   (a) Which can has the greatest volume?

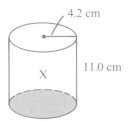 4.2 cm, 11.0 cm, X

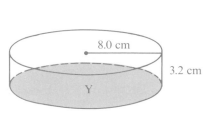 8.0 cm, 3.2 cm, Y

 2.2 cm, 40.0 cm, Z

(b) One of the cans in (a) is a standard size used by many manufacturers. Which one do you think it is? Why do you think it is used?

Practice Test

1 Find the cost of fencing a yard with the shape and dimensions shown in the diagram if the fencing costs $18.50/m.

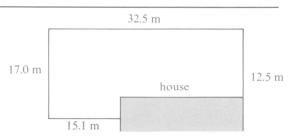

2 Find the number of square tiles with sides 15.0 cm needed to cover a rectangular floor area with dimensions 3.8 m and 2.6 m.

3 Find the area of the shaded part of each rectangular region

(a)

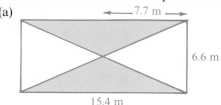

(b)

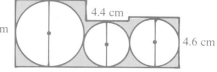

4 Rank each solid from least to greatest

(a) surface area

(b) volume.

5 The surface area of a cone is 398.0 cm³ and its radius is 6.5 cm. What is its slant height?

6 A piece of cheese is in the form of a triangular prism. Find its volume.

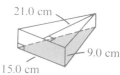

7 What is the volume of the tent shown in the diagram?

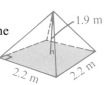

8 What is the volume of the cone-shaped pile of sand shown in the diagram?

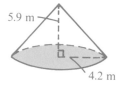

9 A semi-circular arch is made of concrete and painted red.

(a) What is the volume of concrete?

(b) What is the surface area that is painted?

7 Using Exponents: Properties and Polynomials

Applying the laws of exponents, meaning of x^0 and x^{-1}, using scientific notation, equations and exponents, simplifying expressions with monomials, binomials and trinomials, multiplying and dividing polynomials, finding common factors, applications, problem solving skills and strategies

Introduction

In modern-day technology, the time it takes for some events to happen is measured in milliseconds and microseconds. The intricate circuitry in microcomputing requires the use of numbers in exponential form. Thus your skills with exponents are used to write numbers in *scientific notation*.

In this chapter, the process of developing mathematics is again illustrated.

Step A: In your earlier work you used numerical examples to explore patterns with exponents. You observed that

$$2^3 \times 2^2 = 2^5.$$
$$8 \times 4 = 32$$

Step B: You then extended the pattern to a more general result for exponents.

$$x^3 \times x^2 = x^5$$
$$(x \times x \times x)(x \times x) = (x \times x \times x \times x \times x)$$

Step C: You then applied your results to perform calculations involving exponents.

Step D: In this chapter, you will extend your results with exponents to give meaning to x^0 and x^{-1}. Then you will apply these skills to solve problems involving scientific notation and to simplify algebraic expressions with exponents.

It takes only milliseconds for a computer in a control room to calculate many outputs. Microcircuits are used in the flight of a jet and in the launch of a space vehicle. These microcircuits have been designed to work with very small numbers expressed in scientific notation.

7.1 The Laws of Exponents

To develop the laws of exponents, you must understand the vocabulary of exponents.

$$\text{power} \left\{ x^3 \begin{matrix} \leftarrow \text{exponent} \\ \leftarrow \text{base} \end{matrix} \right.$$

x^3 is a power and represents repeated multiplication.

$$x^3 = \underbrace{x \times x \times x}_{3 \text{ factors}}$$

x^3 is said to be in **exponential form**.

When you are looking for patterns and developing mathematics, you need to use definitions carefully. In your earlier work with exponents, numerical examples suggested various laws of exponents. Thus you combine the use of a definition and numerical examples to develop the laws of exponents.

multiplication

The definition of a power is used to complete the example.

$$x^3 \times x^2 = \underbrace{x \times x \times x}_{3} \times \underbrace{x \times x}_{2}$$
$$= x^5$$

The example suggests the generalization
$$x^m \times x^n = x^{m+n},$$
$$m, n \in N.$$

division

The definition of a power is used again.

$$\frac{x^5}{x^3} = \frac{x \times x \times x \times x \times x}{x \times x \times x}$$
$$= x^2$$

The example suggests the generalization
$$\frac{x^m}{x^n} = x^{m-n},$$
$$m, n \in N.$$

power

The law of multiplication is used to complete these examples.

$$(x^3)^2 = x^3 \times x^3 \qquad (x^4)^3 = x^4 \times x^4 \times x^4$$
$$= x^{3+3} \qquad\qquad\quad = x^{4+4+4}$$
$$= x^6 \qquad\qquad\qquad = x^{12}$$

The examples suggest the generalization
$$(x^m)^n = x^{mn},$$
$$m, n \in N.$$

power of a product

The law of multiplication is used again.

$$(xy)^2 = (xy)(xy) \qquad (xy)^3 = (xy)(xy)(xy)$$
$$= x^{1+1}y^{1+1} \qquad\qquad = x^{1+1+1}y^{1+1+1}$$
$$= x^2y^2 \qquad\qquad\quad = x^3y^3$$

The examples suggest the generalization
$$(xy)^n = x^ny^n,$$
$$n \in N.$$

power of a quotient

Which exponent law is used to complete these examples?   The examples suggest the generalization

$$\left(\frac{x}{y}\right)^2 = \left(\frac{x}{y}\right)\left(\frac{x}{y}\right) \qquad \left(\frac{x}{y}\right)^3 = \left(\frac{x}{y}\right)\left(\frac{x}{y}\right)\left(\frac{x}{y}\right)$$

$$= \frac{x^2}{y^2} \qquad\qquad\qquad = \frac{x^3}{y^3}$$

$$\left(\frac{x}{y}\right)^n = \frac{x^n}{y^n}, \ n \in N.$$

Skills with these laws are needed throughout your study of mathematics. You can use the laws of exponents to simplify expressions, as shown in the following example.

Example   Simplify.   (a) $\dfrac{(xy)^5}{x^3}$ (b) $\dfrac{(mn)^2(m^2n)^3}{m^2n}$

Solution   (a) $\dfrac{(xy)^5}{x^3} = \dfrac{x^5y^5}{x^3}$ Power of Product

$$= x^2y^5 \quad \text{Division}$$

(b) $\dfrac{(mn)^2(m^2n)^3}{m^2n} = \dfrac{(m^2n^2)(m^6n^3)}{m^2n}$ Power of Product

$$= \dfrac{m^8n^5}{m^2n} \qquad \text{Multiplication}$$

$$= m^6n^4 \qquad \text{Division}$$

7.1 Exercise

A Remember: If you need to check your understanding of any of the laws of exponents, use a numerical example.

1 Use a numerical example to illustrate each of these laws.
   (a) $x^m \times x^n = x^{m+n}$ (b) $x^m \div x^n = x^{m-n}$ (c) $(x^m)^n = x^{mn}$
   (d) $(xy)^m = x^m y^m$ (e) $\left(\dfrac{x}{y}\right)^m = \dfrac{x^m}{y^m}$

2 Simplify. Which law did you use?
   (a) $(2^2)(2^3)$ (b) $(3^2)(3^3)$ (c) $(5^2)(5)(5^3)$ (d) $(a^2)(a^3)$ (e) $(b^2)(b^3)$

3 Simplify. Which law did you use?
   (a) $2^5 \div 2^2$ (b) $\dfrac{3^5}{3^2}$ (c) $5^4 \div 5^3$ (d) $\dfrac{a^7}{a^3}$ (e) $b^5 \div b^2$

4 Simplify. Which law did you use?
   (a) $(2^2)^2$ (b) $(3^2)^3$ (c) $[(-3)^2]^2$ (d) $(a^2)^3$ (e) $(b^3)^3$

5   Simplify. Which law did you use?

(a) $(mn)^2$　　　(b) $(pq)^3$　　　(c) $(st)^5$　　　(d) $(2x)^3$　　　(e) $(3a)^2$

6   Simplify. Which law did you use?

(a) $\left(\dfrac{a}{b}\right)^2$　　　(b) $\left(\dfrac{c}{d}\right)^3$　　　(c) $\left(\dfrac{a}{c}\right)^4$　　　(d) $\left(\dfrac{m}{2}\right)^3$　　　(e) $\left(\dfrac{y}{3}\right)^2$

B   Refer to the laws of exponents. Can you state them using only words?

7   Simplify each expression. Which law did you use?

(a) $\dfrac{2^5}{2^3}$　　　(b) $(m^4)(m^3)$　　　(c) $(xy)^2$　　　(d) $(m^3)^2$　　　(e) $\left(\dfrac{m}{n}\right)^3$

(f) $\dfrac{a^5}{a^3}$　　　(g) $(x^5)(x^4)$　　　(h) $\left(\dfrac{a}{b}\right)^5$　　　(i) $(ab)^5$　　　(j) $(x^5)^3$

8   Simplify each of the following. Which laws did you use?

(a) $(x^3)(x^2)$　　　(b) $(a^4)(a^2)$　　　(c) $(a^5)(a)$　　　(d) $(t^3)(t^2)(t)$

(e) $(m^2)(m^3)(m^5)$　　　(f) $(b^2)(b^3)(b)$　　　(g) $(ab)(a^2b)$　　　(h) $(ab)(ab)(ab)$

9   Simplify each of the following.

(a) $(x^2)^3$　　　(b) $(a^3)^2$　　　(c) $(m^5)^3$　　　(d) $(y^5)^2$　　　(e) $(y^2)^5$

(f) $(2^3)^2$　　　(g) $(2 \times 3)^2$　　　(h) $(2^2)^3$　　　(i) $(ab^2)^2$　　　(j) $(ab^2)^3$

(k) $(x^3y^2)^2$　　　(l) $(x^5y^3)^3$　　　(m) $(xy^3)^4$　　　(n) $(y^3z^2)^6$　　　(o) $(y^5z^3)^2$

10   Write each of the following without brackets.

(a) $\left(\dfrac{x}{y}\right)^3$　　　(b) $\left(\dfrac{a}{b}\right)^4$　　　(c) $\left(\dfrac{xy}{k}\right)^3$　　　(d) $\left(\dfrac{x^2}{y}\right)^3$　　　(e) $\left(\dfrac{x^4}{y^3}\right)^2$

(f) $\left(\dfrac{xy}{p}\right)^2$　　　(g) $\left(\dfrac{m^3n}{k^2}\right)^5$　　　(h) $\left(\dfrac{x^2y}{mn^2}\right)^3$　　　(i) $\left(\dfrac{-ab}{c}\right)^3$　　　(j) $\left(\dfrac{-a^2b}{c}\right)^2$

11   Simplify each of the following.

(a) $\dfrac{x^9}{x^6}$　　　(b) $\dfrac{x^3}{x^2}$　　　(c) $x^8 \div x^4$　　　(d) $\dfrac{2^5}{2^3}$　　　(e) $\dfrac{10^5}{10^2}$

(f) $\dfrac{3^{10}}{3^8}$　　　(g) $\dfrac{x^4y}{x^2}$　　　(h) $\dfrac{3x^2y^5}{x^2y^2}$　　　(i) $\dfrac{-2x^5y^3}{x^2y^2}$　　　(j) $\dfrac{x^5y^5}{xy^5}$

PSP   12   What are the missing numbers?

C   13   Use $a = -2$, $b = -1$ and $c = 4$. Find the value of each of the following.

(a) $\dfrac{a^5}{a^2}$　　　(b) $(b^3)^2$　　　(c) $\dfrac{(c^2)^3}{c^5}$　　　(d) $\dfrac{a^3b^3}{ab}$　　　(e) $\dfrac{(ab)^3}{a^2b}$

7.2 **PSP** Problem Solving: What If . . . x^0, x^{-1}?

Earlier you developed the laws of exponents for exponents that are natural numbers. An important question in developing mathematics is "*What if . . . ?*" For example, *what if* numbers other than the natural numbers, such as zero or negative integers, are used as exponents?

Exponent Laws

Multiplication	$x^m \times x^n = x^{m+n}$
Division	$x^m \div x^n = x^{m-n}$
Power	$(x^m)^n = x^{mn}$
Power of Product	$(xy)^m = x^m y^m$
Power of Quotient	$\left(\dfrac{x}{y}\right)^m = \dfrac{x^m}{y^m}$

Compare these results, $x \neq 0$.

Use the definition.

$$\frac{x^3}{x^3} = \frac{x \times x \times x}{x \times x \times x} = 1$$

Use the division law.

$$\frac{x^3}{x^3} = x^{3-3} = x^0$$

— Compare. $x^0 = 1$ —

$$\frac{x^3}{x^5} = \frac{x \times x \times x}{x \times x \times x \times x \times x} = \frac{1}{x^2}$$

$$\frac{x^3}{x^5} = x^{3-5} = x^{-2}$$

— Compare. $x^{-2} = \dfrac{1}{x^2}$ —

To extend your work with exponents, you need to give a meaning to powers with zero and negative exponents. The examples above suggest these generalizations.

$$x^0 = 1 \qquad x^{-m} = \frac{1}{x^m}$$

Example Simplify (a) $(2^2)^{-1}$ (b) $\dfrac{x^{-2}(xy)^4}{x^0}$

Solution (a) $(2^2)^{-1} = 4^{-1}$
$$= \frac{1}{4}$$

(b) $\dfrac{x^{-2}(xy)^4}{x^0} = \dfrac{x^{-2}x^4y^4}{x^0}$
$$= \frac{x^{-2+4}y^4}{1}$$
$$= x^2y^4$$

7.2 Exercise

A Remember: What does a negative exponent mean?

1 Use the law $x^m \div x^n = x^{m-n}$.

(a) Simplify. ▶ $\dfrac{x^2}{x^2}$ ▶ $\dfrac{y^3}{y^3}$ ▶ $\dfrac{2^5}{2^5}$

Which exponent law is shown?

(b) Simplify. ▶ $\dfrac{x^2}{x^3}$ ▶ $\dfrac{y^3}{y^6}$ ▶ $\dfrac{2^3}{2^4}$

Which exponent law is shown?

2 Evaluate.

(a) $2°$ (b) $10°$ (c) 10^{-2} (d) 5^{-2} (e) 2^{-3}

3 Express each power with a positive exponent.

(a) 3^{-1} (b) 4^{-1} (c) 2^{-3} (d) $\dfrac{1}{2^{-1}}$ (e) $\dfrac{1}{3^{-2}}$

Simplify.

4 (a) $(-3)^2$ (b) $(3)^{-2}$ (c) $-(3)^{-2}$ (d) $(-2)^3$ (e) $-(-3)^2$

B   Refer to the laws of exponents to simplify each of the following.

5 Simplify.

(a) 3^0 (b) $2x^0$ (c) $(2x)^0$ (d) $\dfrac{4}{x^0}$ (e) $\dfrac{(3x^0)(4y)^0}{3}$

6 Write each of the following with the denominator 1.

(a) $\dfrac{2}{x}$ (b) $\dfrac{3}{x}$ (c) $\dfrac{8}{x^2}$ (d) $\dfrac{m}{n^3}$ (e) $\dfrac{2t}{x^2}$ (f) $\dfrac{ab}{n}$

7 Write each of the following using only positive exponents.

(a) x^{-2} (b) $3x^{-1}$ (c) ax^{-3} (d) $-2n^{-1}p$ (e) $(2n)^{-2}$

8 Find the value of each of the following.

(a) 2^0 (b) $(2^2)(2^3)$ (c) $\dfrac{3^2 \times 3^2}{3^4}$ (d) $\dfrac{10^5 \times 10^8}{(10^3)^4}$

(e) 2^{-1} (f) $(-2)^2 \div 4^{-2}$ (g) 5^{-2} (h) $\dfrac{1}{4^{-2}}$

(i) $\dfrac{8^0 2^3}{2}$ (j) $(-3)^0$ (k) $(2^4)^0$ (l) $4^2 \div 4^{-2}$ (m) $3^5 \div 3^2$

(n) $\dfrac{1}{2^{-1}}$ (o) -2^{-3} (p) $2^{-2} \div 2^2$ (q) $\left(\dfrac{2}{3}\right)^{-1}$ (r) $3^{-3} \times 3^5$

9 Simplify. Write your answers so that the denominator is 1.

(a) $\dfrac{x^3y^2}{x^4y}$ (b) $\dfrac{a^6}{a^3}$ (c) $\dfrac{xy^3}{4y^5}$ (d) $\dfrac{y^2z^5}{y^5}$ (e) $\dfrac{x^3y}{x^2y^3}$ (f) $\dfrac{a^4b^2}{ab}$ (g) $\dfrac{a^6b^3}{a^2b^5}$ (h) $\dfrac{a^3b^2}{a^5b}$

PSP **10** (a) If $A = 6$, $B = 2$ and $C = 1$, find the value of $\dfrac{A + B^{A-BC}}{B}$.

(b) Use the digits 1, 2 and 6 in any order but use each one at most three times. What is the maximum value of the expression in (a)?

C **11** Write each of the following in the form x^a.

(a) $x^{2m}x^{2n}x^{m-n}$ (b) $x^{m-n}x^{m+2n}$ (c) $x^{2m}x^{-m}x^{m+2}$ (d) $x^{a-b}x^{b+a}x^{2a}$

7.3 Simplifying Expressions: Order of Operations for Exponents

The steps of the solutions to your problems in mathematics must follow a proper order. Also you must understand the meanings of symbols. For example, you can use the laws of exponents to evaluate expressions containing exponents by following these steps in order.

Example 1   Evaluate $\left(\dfrac{x^2y}{xy}\right)^{-1}$ for $x = 2$ and $y = 3$.

Solution   **PSP** Think: • Which laws of exponents do I need to use?
               • What does a negative exponent mean?

Step 1: Simplify.

$$\left(\frac{x^2y}{xy}\right)^{-1} = x^{-1}$$

Think: $\dfrac{x^2y}{xy} = x$

$$= \frac{1}{x}$$

Step 2: Substitute.

Since $x = 2$, $\dfrac{1}{x} = \dfrac{1}{2}$.

Thus $\left(\dfrac{x^2y}{xy}\right)^{-1} = \dfrac{1}{2}$ for $x = 2$ and $y = 3$.

Often in your study of mathematics, skills from one part are combined with previously learned skills from another part to solve new problems. In the following example, skills with exponents are combined with your earlier work with the order of operations. You also need to use your skills with rational numbers.

> **Rules for the Order of Operations**
> ▶ Perform the operations in brackets ( ) first.
> ▶ Then calculate the powers. Namely, find the value of expressions involving exponents.
> ▶ Then do each multiplication or division in the order it appears.
> ▶ Then do each addition or subtraction in the order it appears.

Example 2   (a) $2^{-3} + 3^{-2}$ (b) $4^{-1} \div 6^{-2}$

Solution   (a) $2^{-3} + 3^{-2} = \dfrac{1}{2^3} + \dfrac{1}{3^2}$

$$= \frac{1}{8} + \frac{1}{9}$$

$$= \frac{9}{72} + \frac{8}{72}$$

$$= \frac{17}{72}$$

(b) $4^{-1} \div 6^{-2} = \dfrac{1}{4} \div \dfrac{1}{6^2}$

$$= \frac{1}{4} \div \frac{1}{36}$$

$$= \frac{1}{4} \times \frac{36}{1}$$

$$= 9$$

7.3   Exercise

A Review the laws of exponents.

1   Evaluate.   (a) 5^0 (b) 3^{-2} (c) $\dfrac{1}{2^{-2}}$ (d) $\left(\dfrac{1}{10}\right)^{-1}$ (e) $\left(\dfrac{2}{3}\right)^{-1}$

2   Simplify. Read carefully.   (a) -2^{-3} (b) $(-2)^{-3}$ (c) $(-2)^3$

B Express your answers in simplest form. ▰**PSP**▱

3   If $x = -1$ and $y = 2$, evaluate each expression. Remember to simplify first.

(a) $\dfrac{x^2 y}{x}$ (b) $\dfrac{(xy)^2}{x^3}$ (c) $\dfrac{(x^2 y)^3}{y^{-1}}$ (d) $\left(\dfrac{x^3 y^2}{xy^2}\right)^3$ (e) $-(x^2 y)^{-1} \div (xy)^2$ (f) $\dfrac{-x^3 y^0}{(xy)^2}$

4   Express each power with a positive exponent. Then simplify.

(a) $2^0 + 3^0$ (b) $2^{-1} + 3^{-1}$ (c) $3 + 2^{-1}$ (d) $3^0 + 3^{-1}$ (e) $(-3)^{-2}$

(f) $\left(\dfrac{1}{2}\right)^{-1} \left(\dfrac{2}{3}\right)^{-1}$ (g) $2^3 \times 2^{-3}$ (h) $2^2 \times 3^{-2}$ (i) $\left(-\dfrac{4}{3}\right)^{-1}$ (j) $(-2)^3$

5   Evaluate each of the following.

(a) $2^{-2} + 2^{-2}$ (b) -4^{-3} (c) $(-3)^{-3}$ (d) $3(2^{-1} + 3^{-1})$

(e) $\dfrac{1}{2^{-1}} + \dfrac{1}{3^{-1}}$ (f) $2^{-1} + \dfrac{1}{3^2}$ (g) $\left(\dfrac{3}{4}\right)^2$ (h) $\left(\dfrac{2}{3}\right)^{-3}$

6   Simplify each of the following.

(a) $\dfrac{2^{-1} - 3^{-1}}{3}$ (b) $\dfrac{4}{2^{-1} + 3^{-1}}$ (c) $\dfrac{3^2 + 2^{-1}}{3^{-1}}$ (d) $(3^2 \div 3^{-2})^{-1}$

(e) $(2^3 \div 2^2)^{-2}$ (f) $(2^{-1} + 3^{-1})^{-1}$ (g) $(2^3 + 3^2)^{-1}$ (h) $\left(\dfrac{3^{-2}}{2^{-3}}\right)^{-1}$

7   Simplify. Arrange the expression values in order from least to greatest.

(a) $\left(\dfrac{-4^2 - 3^{-2}}{4^2 - 5^{-3}}\right)^0$ (b) $-[-4^2 - 4^{-2} - (-4)^{-2}]$ (c) $\dfrac{3^{-1} + 2^{-1}}{3^{-2} + 2^{-2}}$ (d) $\dfrac{2^{-2} + 3^{-1}}{6^{-1}}$

8   If $x = -2$, $y = -3$, $a = 2$ and $b = 1$, find each value.

(a) a^2 (b) a^{-2} (c) b^0 (d) $(ab)^2$ (e) $(ab)^{-2}$ (f) $-(ab)^{-2}$

(g) $y^{-1} + b^a$ (h) $x^2 + y^{-1}$ (i) $(ab)^x$ (j) $\left(\dfrac{ab}{xy}\right)^{-1}$ (k) $\dfrac{x^2 y}{x}$ (l) $x^{-1} + y^{-1}$

▰**PSP**▱ 9   Refer to the diagram. What letter will complete the diagram?

```
?  R  I  M
R  O  D  E
I  D  E  A
M  E  A  ?
```

7.4 Scientific Notation

Did you know that the sun is a star? The nearest star other than the sun is Proxima Centauri, (Proxima suggest closeness). It is about 40 200 000 000 000 km away. To write such large numbers in a more compact and convenient form, scientists use **scientific notation**. To write a number in this form, it is expressed as a product of a number between 1 and 10 and a power of 10.

Thank Goodness For Zeroes

If you've ever read any information about the universe, you will know that without the humble zero you would have difficulty expressing measures. For example, when talking about distances in this vast universe, scientists use the term light-year, which is

9 500 000 000 000 km.

Compare this large number with the diameter of the average nucleus

0.000 000 000 000 01 cm

or the mass of an electron

0.000 000 000 000 000 000 000 000 904 g.

With all these zeroes needed in order to write measurements, you probably might begin to wonder if there isn't a simpler way.

$$40\ 200\ 000\ 000\ 000 = 4.02 \times 10^{13}$$

This number is between 1 and 10.

The exponent 13 names the place value of the original number. In this case, the decimal has been moved 13 places to the left.

To express small numbers in scientific notation, you use the same procedure.

The diameter of an electron is

$$0.000\ 000\ 000\ 000\ 435 \text{ cm} = 4.35 \times 10^{-13} \text{ cm}$$

This number is between 1 and 10.

The exponent -13 names the place value of the original number. In this case, the decimal has been moved 13 places to the right.

To express a number written in scientific notation in decimal notation, you reverse the steps, as shown in the example.

Example   Write each number in decimal form.
(a) 9.6×10^{15} (b) 8.35×10^{-12}

Solution   (a) $9.6 \times 10^{15} = 9\ 600\ 000\ 000\ 000\ 000$

The exponent shows that the decimal point has been moved 15 places to the left.

Reverse this step. Move the decimal point 15 places to the right.

(b) $8.35 \times 10^{-12} = 0.000\ 000\ 000\ 008\ 35$

Decimal point has been moved 12 places to the right.

Thus, move the decimal point 12 places to the left.

Some calculators have an exponent key. The calculator converts a number in scientific notation to a decimal number. Check your calculator for this feature. Refer to the *Calculator Use* at the end of the next section.

7.4 Exercise

A Check whether your answers are reasonable.

1 Find the exponent in each of the following.

(a) $4630 = 4.63 \times 10^?$ (b) $498 = 4.98 \times 10^?$ (c) $0.003\ 45 = 3.45 \times 10^?$

2 Find the missing values of n.

(a) $46\ 900 = n \times 10^4$ (b) $3890 = n \times 10^3$ (c) $0.000\ 896 = n \times 10^{-4}$

B 3 Write each number in decimal notation.

(a) 6.4×10^2 (b) 3.06×10^3 (c) 6.37×10^{-2} (d) 9.3×10^{-3}

4 Write each number in scientific notation.

(a) 486 000 (b) 9 320 000 (c) 0.000 453 (d) 0.001 35

5 Write each number in decimal form.

(a) 6.36×10^3 (b) 3.21×10^{-4} (c) 4.21×10^5 (d) 4.08×10^{-8}

6 On a calculator display, the number 48 600, converted to scientific notation, looks like this. Write each number in decimal form.

4.86   04

The number is between 1 and 10.� means 10^4

(a) 3.86 03 (b) 9.32 −03 (c) 4.04 −02 (d) 5.98 06

7 Write each number as it would appear in scientific notation on a calculator display.

(a) 986 600 (b) 0.000 493 (c) 0.000 000 12 (d) 3 900 000

8 A computer uses the form shown at the right to display 1250 in scientific notation. Write each number in decimal form.

1.25 + E03

The number is between 1 and 10.⏌ means 10^3

(a) 6.83 + E02 (b) 9.25 − E03 (c) 2.02 − E05 (d) 4.51 + E06

9 Write each number as it would appear in scientific notation on a computer printout.

(a) 28 600 (b) 0.000 321 (c) 0.003 45 (d) 69 600 000

PSP 10 Refer to the diagram. Construct a figure that will complete the diagram. Justify your answer.

    ?

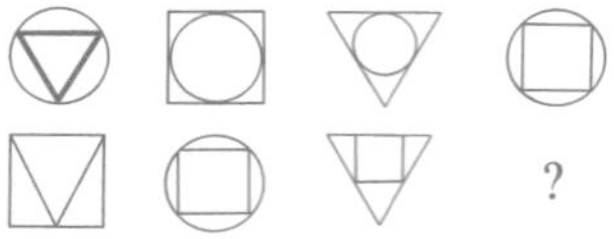

7.5 Using Scientific Notation

In astronomy you often use rounded numbers. For example, the satellite travelled 402 000 000 000 km. However, you do not know the accuracy of the measurement. To show the accuracy, you use the appropriate number of significant digits.

$$4.02 \times 10^{11} \text{ km}$$

These three digits are called **significant digits.**

The chart shows the use of significant digits and scientific notation.

Measure	Accuracy	Scientific notation	Significant digits
0.48 km	nearest 100th	4.8×10^{-1}	4, 8
480 km	nearest 10	4.8×10^{2}	4, 8
480.0 km	nearest 10th	4.800×10^{2}	4, 8, 0, 0
0.048 km	nearest 1000th	4.8×10^{-2}	4, 8
0.004 80 km	nearest 100 000th	4.80×10^{-3}	4, 8, 0

This column shows the significant digits.

Using scientific notation, you write the numbers between 1 and 10.

When zeroes are used as placeholders, they do not indicate significant digits.

480

This zero is a placeholder.

0.004 80

These zeroes are placeholders.

This zero is not a placeholder. It is a significant digit.

The more significant digits used to express a measure, the more accurate is the measure.

When you multiply and divide numbers resulting from measurement, you need to round the answer to the same accuracy as the measure with the least accuracy.

Example Calculate. $\dfrac{4.5 \times 10^{12} \times 3.82 \times 10^{-2}}{4.8 \times 10^{3}}$

Solution

$$\dfrac{4.5 \times 10^{12} \times 3.82 \times 10^{-2}}{4.8 \times 10^{3}} = \dfrac{4.5 \times 3.82}{4.8} \times \dfrac{10^{12} \times 10^{-2}}{10^{3}}$$

$$= 3.581 \times 10^{12+(-2)-3}$$

$$= 3.6 \times 10^{7}$$

7.5 Exercise

A Remember: Express your answers to the least accuracy of the measures used.

1. Write each of the following in scientific notation. The number of significant digits is shown in the brackets.
   - (a) 2300 (3)
   - (b) 2300 (4)
   - (c) 15 000 (2)
   - (d) 0.85 (2)
   - (e) 0.0085 (2)
   - (f) 12 034 (4)
   - (g) 48 000 (3)
   - (h) 0.000 096 0 (3)

2   Calculate. Round your answer to the appropriate accuracy.
(a) $(4.6 \times 10^4)(8.96 \times 10^3)$ (b) $(2.8 \times 10^4)(4.9 \times 10^{-3})$ (c) $(4.32 \times 10^2) \div (2.1 \times 10^3)$

B   ▶ Express the numbers in scientific notation. Then calculate.
▶ Use significant digits to express your final answer.

3   Calculate a value for each.

(a) $\dfrac{68\ 000\ 000\ 000 \times 49\ 000\ 000\ 000}{603\ 000\ 000\ 000\ 000}$

(b) $\dfrac{48\ 000 \times 0.000\ 000\ 002}{0.000\ 000\ 000\ 48}$

4   The diameter of a human red blood cell is 0.000 079 mm. How many would it take, laid end to end, to make a length of 1 m?

5   The mass of a hydrogen atom is 1.66×10^{-24} g. Find the mass of 1 500 000 hydrogen atoms.

6   A microsecond means 0.000 001 s. How many microseconds are there in an hour? a year?

7   A hummingbird has a mass of about 0.0019 kg. The mass of a proton is 0.000 000 000 000 000 000 002 g. How many protons would be equivalent to the mass of a hummingbird?

8   (a) Change each word into a math word by doing the following.
▶ Change one of the letters to a different letter.
▶ Keep the order of the letters the same.

chore   attitude   cute   prize   date

(b) Add two other words to the list.

C 9   A faucet drips at a rate of 1 drop every 5 s. One drop of water is about 0.08 mL. About 30 000 homes have a leaky faucet.
(a) Calculate the total amount of water wasted in all the homes in a year.
(b) A container has a circular base 1.1 m in diameter. What would be the height of the container needed to hold the water in (a)?

Calculator Use

Refer to the manual of your calculator. Is there a calculator key that transforms a number in scientific notation to a decimal number? Look for a key marked as ⎡EXP⎤. To multiply $2.8 \times 10^3 \times 6.8 \times 10^5$, use these calculator steps.

⎡C⎤ 2.8 ⎡EXP⎤ 3 ⎡×⎤ 6.8 ⎡EXP⎤ 5 ⎡=⎤

Try calculations with scientific notation using a calculator.

7.6 Exponents and Equations

To solve equations involving exponents you need to apply the following property.
▶ If two powers are equal and the bases are like, then the exponents are equal.
▶ If $a^m = a^n$, then $m = n$. $5^2 = 5^x$ means $x = 2$.

Example Solve. $2^{3n} = 4^{n-2}$

Solution

$2^{3n} = 4^{n-2}$ Think: $(2^2)^{n-2} = 2^{2(n-2)}$
$2^{3n} = (2^2)^{n-2}$ $= 2^{2n-4}$
$2^{3n} = 2^{2n-4}$

Since the powers are equal and
the bases are like bases,
the exponents are equal.

$$3n = 2n - 4$$
$$3n - 2n = -4$$
$$n = -4$$

Check:
L.S. $= 2^{3n}$ R.S. $= 4^{n-2}$
$= 2^{3(-4)}$ $= 4^{(-4)-2}$
$= 2^{-12}$ $= 4^{-6}$
                   $= (2^2)^{-6}$
                   $= 2^{-12}$
L.S. $=$ R.S.

PSP Always check in the original equation.

7.6 Exercise

A 1 (a) For $10^x = 10^3 \times 10^4$, write the right side with a single base.
(b) Find the value of x.

2 (a) What is the first step of the solution of each equation?

A $3^x = \dfrac{3^5}{3^2}$ B $2^x = (2^3)^2$

(b) Solve the equations.

3 (a) Why are the exponents of $3^2 = 3^{2x-4}$ equal?
(b) Write an equation and solve for x.

B 4 For each equation, ▶ identify the law of exponents you need to use.
▶ then solve the equation.

(a) $2^n = 2^3 \times 2^3$ (b) $5^y = (5^2)^3$ (c) $\dfrac{3^6}{3^x} = 3^2$ (d) $(3^2)^3 = 3^{x+1}$

5 Solve each equation and verify your solutions.

(a) $2^3 = 2^{x+1}$ (b) $2^{5x} = 2^{3x+6}$ (c) $4^{3x-1} = 2^4$ (d) $3^{6x-2} = 9^{x+1}$
(e) $2^{3x} = 2^{2x+4}$ (f) $3^{4x+2} = 3^{2x+6}$ (g) $6^{4y-3} = 6^{y-12}$ (h) $5^{3a+5} = 5^{5a+1}$
(i) $10^{2x+1} = 10^{3x-8}$ (j) $4^x = 2^6$ (k) $9^2 = 3^{2x}$ (l) $2^{3x+2} = 4^{x-1}$

7.7 Multiplying Monomials

To help you learn new skills, vocabulary or concepts, look for similarities between what you are learning and what you already know. Ask

► How are they alike?
► How are they different?

To find the product of two monomials, $(3m)(2n)$, think of an area.

Area = sum of the areas of the rectangles
$$= mn + mn + mn + mn + mn + mn$$
$$= 6mn$$

Area $= (3m)(2n)$

The example suggests
$$(3m)(2n) = 6mn.$$

This is the numerical (number) coefficient. This is the literal (letter) coefficient.

To find the product of monomials, you also need to use your skills with exponents. Examine how the following product is simplified.

$(2a^2)(3a^3) = 6a^5$ $\qquad$ Think: $(2a^2)(3a^3) = 2 \times a^2 \times 3 \times a^3$

Thus $(2a^2)(3a^3) = 6a^5$
$$= 2 \times 3 \times a^2 \times a^3$$
$$= 6 \times a^5$$

Multiply the numerical coefficients. Multiply the literal coefficients.

The examples above suggest a pattern for multiplying monomials. **PSP**

To multiply monomials, ► multiply the numerical coefficients.
$\qquad\qquad\qquad\qquad$ ► multiply the literal coefficients.

Example Find each product.

(a) $(3a)(4ab)$ $\qquad$ (b) $(-3y^2)(4y^3)$

PSP Be sure you understand the meaning of each word.

Solution (a) $\quad (3a)(4ab)$ Think:
$\qquad\qquad = 12a^2b \qquad 3 \times 4 = 12$
$\qquad\qquad\qquad\qquad a \times ab = a^2b$

(b) $\quad (-3y^2)(4y^3)$ Think:
$\qquad = -12y^5 \qquad (-3)(4) = -12$
$\qquad\qquad\qquad\qquad (y^2)(y^3) = y^{2+3}$
$\qquad\qquad\qquad\qquad\qquad\quad = y^5$

7.7 Exercise

A Remember: To simplify means to express in simplest form.

1 Find each product.
   (a) $(m^3)(m^5)$ (b) $(x^4)(x^3)$ (c) $(p^2)(p^4)$ (d) $(y^6)(y^3)$

2 Simplify.
   (a) $2(-3m)$ (b) $3(-5b)$ (c) $-2(-3k)$ (d) $-3(-3n)$ (e) $-5(-2r)$

B To multiply monomials, you need to know the products of integers.

3 Find each product.
   (a) $(3x)(-2y)$ (b) $(-3y)(3y)$ (c) $(-6m)(-2n)$ (d) $(3ab)(-2a)$
   (e) $(2x^2)(3x^2)$ (f) $(-2y^3)(4y^2)$ (g) $(-4m^3)(-2m^3)$ (h) $(3a)(-2a^3)$
   (i) $(2x^2y^2)(-3x^2)$ (j) $(-6a^3)(3a^2b^2)$ (k) $(3ab^2)(-2ab)$ (l) $2a^3(-3a)^2$

4 Simplify.
   (a) $(4a)(-7a)$ (b) $-2m(-6y)$ (c) $-3x^2(-2xy)$ (d) $2a^2(-3a)$
   (e) $-3x^4y(2x^2)$ (f) $(-4x)(-3x^3)$ (g) $(-3xy)(0)$ (h) $-3(xy^3)^3$

5 Find the square of each monomial.
   (a) $3y$ (b) $2m^2$ (c) $-3ab$ (d) $4x^2y$ (e) $-3x^2y^3$

6 Find the value of the following. Use $a = -2$ and $b = 3$.
   (a) $(2a)(3b)$ (b) $(-3a)(2b)$ (c) $(3ab)(a^2)$ (d) $(2a)(-3ab^2)$ (e) $(6ab)(-2ab)$

7 Find the following products.
   (a) $(2a)(5b)(-3c)$ (b) $(-m)(5n)(-p)$ (c) $(-3s)(-t)(-v)$
   (d) $(-x^2)(2xy)(3y^2)$ (e) $(2a^3b)(-a^4)(-5b)$ (f) $(6s^4)(-2st^2)(-t^3)$

8 Simplify each of the following. Use your calculator.
   (a) $(3.2x^4)(1.5x)$ (b) $(0.9ab)(-3.7a^2b)$ (c) $(2.8mn)(-0.5m^2)$
   (d) $(4.1p^2q)(-0.3pq^2)$ (e) $(2.2xy)(-1.1x^2y^3)$ (f) $(-0.3x)(-4.8x^3)$

9 Find the value of each expression for $x = 3.6$ and $y = -1.9$. Use your calculator.
   (a) $(3x)(-2y)$ (b) $(-5x^2)(2y)$ (c) x^2y^2
   (d) $(-x^2)(3y)$ (e) $(-3.5x^2)(-4.2y)$ (f) $(0.6x)(1.2y^2)$

10　Use your calculator.

(a) $(2.1a)(0.5b)(-3.2c)$　　　　　　(b) $(1.1m)(-1.5n)(0.5p)$

(c) $(-3.5s)(-1.3t)(-1.7v)$　　　　(d) $(-1.1x)(2.7xy)(3.2y)$

(e) $(2.25ab)(-1.50b)(5.01a)$　　　(f) $(6.71s)(-2.12st)(-1.85t)$

 11　An octahedron has eight faces. On each face a shape is placed. Different views of the octahedron are shown.

(a) Which face is opposite △?　　(b) Which face is opposite ○?

From Math History

Can you cut a strip of paper that has only one side and one edge? August Ferdinand Möbius created a strip of paper that has only one side and one edge. To this day it bears his name and is called the **Möbius strip**.

▶ Construct a Möbius strip by following these steps.

Step 1: Cut a strip of paper.

Step 2: Put a half twist in it.

Step 3: Connect the ends.

▶ Start anywhere on the strip and draw a line along its length until you are back to where you started. The Möbius strip has only one side!

▶ Cut along the line you drew. Do you get two strips? How many edges does the resulting paper have?

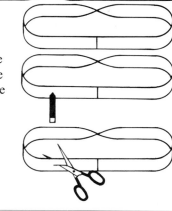

Math Tip

A useful skill in mathematics is to translate from mathematics to English without using any symbols. Can you express these laws of exponents in words?

$$a^m \times a^n = a^{m+n} \qquad a^m \div a^n = a^{m-n} \qquad (a^m)^n = a^{mn}$$

$$(ab)^m = a^m b^m \qquad a^0 = 1 \qquad a^{-1} = \frac{1}{a}$$

Applications: Expressions for Area

If the sides of a rectangle are defined by variable
expressions, then the sides have
different measures depending on the values assigned.

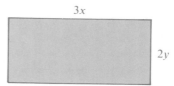

		length	width	area	perimeter
x	y	$3x$	$2y$	$6xy$	$6x + 4y$
1	1	3	2	6	10
2	1	6	2	12	16
3	2	9	4	36	26

Thus as different values of x and y are used, the area and the perimeter of
the rectangle vary.

12 (a) Find an expression for the area of each rectangle.

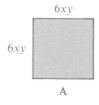

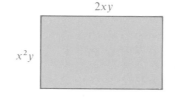

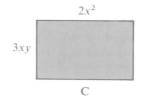

(b) Find an expression for the perimeter of each rectangle in (a).

13 Refer to the previous question.
(a) Find the area and perimeter of each rectangle for $x = 8$ and $y = 2$.
(b) Which rectangle has the greatest area?
(c) Which rectangle has the greatest perimeter?

14 (a) Find an expression for the area of rectangle ABCD.

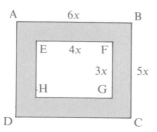

(b) Find an expression for the area of rectangle EFGH.
(c) Use expressions in (a) and (b) to find an expression for the shaded region.
(d) Find the area of the shaded region for $x = 2$ and $x = 10$.

7.8 Multiplying Polynomials by Monomials

Earlier you multiplied monomials by constants. In the previous section you multiplied monomials by monomials. You can now combine these skills to learn new skills for multiplying a polynomial by a monomial.

Example 1   Expand.   (a) $3p(2p^2 - 5)$ (b) $-2xy^2(5x^2 + y)$

Solution   (a) $3p(2p^2 - 5)$ Think: $3 \times 2 = 6$ $3 \times (-5) = -15$
                     $= 6p^3 - 15p$ $p \times p^2 = p^3$ $p \times 1 = p$

             (b) $-2xy^2(5x^2 + y)$ Think: $-2 \times 5 = -10$ $-2 \times 1 = -2$
                     $= -10x^3y^2 - 2xy^3$ $x \times x^2 = x^3$ $x \times 1 = x$
                                                       $y^2 \times 1 = y^2$ $y^2 \times y = y^3$

             What property of exponents are you using?

Example 2   Expand and then find the value of $3x^2y(x^2 - xy)$ for $x = -2$ and $y = -1$.

Solution   *Step 1:*   Simplify.
                          $3x^2y(x^2 - xy) = 3x^4y - 3x^3y^2$

             Step 2:   Substitute $x = -2$ and $y = -1$.
                          $3x^4y - 3x^3y^2 = 3(-2)^4(-1) - 3(-2)^3(-1)^2$
                                      $= 3(16)(-1) - 3(-8)(1)$
                                      $= -48 + 24$
                                      $= -24$

7.8 Exercise

A 1   Multiply each of the following.
   (a) $(3x)(2y)$ (b) $(3x)(-2y)$ (c) $(2x)(3x)$ (d) $(2x)(-3x)$
   (e) $(-x)(-3x^2)$ (f) $(-3x)(-2y)$ (g) $(12a)(4a^2)$ (h) $(-x^2y)(xy^3)$

   2   Expand.
   (a) $-3(x^2 - x + y)$ (b) $-2(xy + z)$ (c) $-9(a - 2b + c)$
   (d) $4(2p - 3q)$ (e) $5(m - 3n)$ (f) $-2(x^2 + xy - y^2)$
   (g) $-4(5a - 3a^2)$ (h) $3(p - 5q + q^2)$ (i) $-4(x^2 - xy - y^3)$

B 3   Find each product.
   (a) $-3x(x - y)$ (b) $-2m(m + n)$ (c) $4x^2(x - xy)$
   (d) $6a(3a - 2b)$ (e) $m^2n(3m + 2n)$ (f) $-6y(-3x^2 + 2y^2)$

4   Expand each of the following.
   (a) $5xy(x + xy - y)$ (b) $-2p(p^2 - p + q)$ (c) $2x(x^2 - 3x - 1)$
   (d) $-3a(a^2 - 2a - 1)$ (e) $-2m(m^2 - 3mn + n^2)$ (f) $-a^2(2a - 3b + c)$

5   Expand and then evaluate each expression for $p = -1$ and $q = -3$.
   (a) $4(p - 2q)$ (b) $-2p(p^2 - q)$ (c) $-p^2q(p + q)$
   (d) $p^2(2p - 3q)$ (e) $2(p + q - pq)$ (f) $4p(-2 - q)$

6   Expand and simplify. Remember to collect like terms.
   (a) $2x^2 + 3(x^2 + 2)$ (b) $3p - 2(p - 5)$ (c) $6 - 3(a - 6)$
   (d) $-16x^2 - x(x + 4)$ (e) $25mn - 2m(n - 6)$ (f) $3y - 3y(3 - y)$

7   Expand and evaluate each expression for $y = -2$.
   (a) $3y + 2(y + 1)$ (b) $2y^2 - 3y(y - 1)$ (c) $4(2y^2 - 3 + 4y^2)$
   (d) $-y(3y - 2) - 5y^2$ (e) $-2y(y + 1) - 3y^2$ (f) $2y - 3y(y - 1)$

8   Expand. Use your calculator when appropriate.
   (a) $0.5x(x - y)$ (b) $1.5(a - 2.4b)$ (c) $0.9p^2(p^2 - 1.1p)$
   (d) $3.2m(m^2 - 1.6m)$ (e) $1.4x(x^2 - 0.5x + 2.2)$ (f) $-0.6k(k^2 - 2.1k + 3.2)$

9   Expand and then evaluate for $x = 1.5$ and $y = -0.6$. Use your calculator
   when appropriate.
   (a) $x^2(x + y)$ (b) $x^2y(x + xy - y)$ (c) $3x(x - y^2)$
   (d) $-2y(y + x^2)$ (e) $-xy(x - y + xy)$ (f) $-3y(x + y - x^2)$

10 Which one does
    not belong?
    Give reasons for
    your answer.

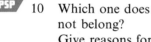

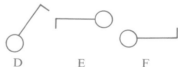

A   B   C   D   E   F

Computer Use

Often before you use a computer, you need to use your mathematics
to make decisions. For example, to calculate many values of an
expression arising in a problem, you might first simplify the expression.

$3y^2 + 2y - 2(y^2 + 2y) - 3$
$= 3y^2 + 2y - 2y^2 - 4y - 3$
$= y^2 - 2y - 3$

```
10 PRINT "EXPLORE VALUES"
20 LET Y = 1
30 LET F = Y ↑ 2 - 2 * Y - 3
40 PRINT "THE VALUE OF Y IS"; Y
50 PRINT "THE VALUE OF
      EXPRESSION IS"; F
60 LET Y = Y + 1
70 IF Y < 11 THEN GOTO 30
80 END
```

▶ What is the program at the
  right designed to do?
▶ Modify the program to find values
  of F for integer values of Y such
  that $-10 \le y \le 10$. What do you notice about the values of F?

7.9 Dividing Monomials

When you multiplied monomials, you combined your skills with integers and your skills with exponents. You can apply these same skills to the division of monomials. Compare the steps in multiplying monomials with the steps in dividing monomials.

$$\frac{50yk}{25k} = 2y$$

PSP Think: Divide the numerical coefficients. Then divide the literal coefficients.
$$\frac{50}{25} = 2, \frac{yk}{k} = y$$

$$\frac{-25a^5b^2}{-5a^2b} = 5a^3b$$

PSP Think: $\frac{-25}{-5} = 5,$
$$\frac{a^5}{a^2} = a^3, \frac{b^2}{b} = b$$

The examples above suggest a pattern for dividing monomials.

To divide monomials, ▶ divide the numerical coefficients.

▶ divide the literal coefficients.

Example 1   Divide.   (a) $\dfrac{-18a^2b}{6ab}$ (b) $\dfrac{-25a^4b^3}{-5a^2b}$

Solution   (a) $\dfrac{-18a^2b}{6ab} = -3a$ Think: $-18 \div 6 = -3$
$$a^2 \div a = a$$
$$b \div b = 1$$

(b) $\dfrac{-25a^4b^3}{-5a^2b} = 5a^2b^2$ Think: $(-25) \div (-5) = 5$
$$a^4 \div a^2 = a^2$$
$$b^3 \div b = b^2$$

To evaluate expressions, simplify first and then evaluate.

Example 2   Find the value of $(16m^3n^2) \div (2m^2n)$ for $m = -1$ and $n = 3$.

Solution   *Step 1:* Simplify
$$\frac{16m^3n^2}{2m^2n} = 8mn$$

Step 2: Substitute $m = -1$ and $n = 3$.
$$8mn = 8(-1)(3)$$
$$= -24$$

7.9 Exercise

A Review the steps for dividing monomials.

1   Find each quotient.
   (a) $m^5 \div m^4$ (b) $x^4 \div x^3$ (c) $y^2 \div y$ (d) $p^3 \div p^3$

2　Find each quotient.

(a) $\dfrac{3y^3}{y^2}$　　　　(b) $\dfrac{-6x^2}{2x}$　　　　(c) $\dfrac{15a^5}{-5a^2}$　　　　(d) $\dfrac{9m^3}{-3m^2}$

B 3　Simplify each of the following.

(a) $\dfrac{9xy}{3x}$　(b) $\dfrac{12x^2y}{4x^2}$　(c) $\dfrac{4a^2}{a^2}$　(d) $\dfrac{-7m^3}{-7}$　(e) $\dfrac{-y^3}{y^3}$　(f) $\dfrac{8x^2y^2}{8y^2}$　(g) $\dfrac{25x^2y^2}{5xy}$　(h) $\dfrac{-m^3y^2}{y^2}$

4　Simplify each of the following. How many can you do mentally?

(a) $\dfrac{27mn}{9n}$　　(b) $\dfrac{16ab}{-8a}$　　(c) $\dfrac{-8ab}{-4b}$　　(d) $\dfrac{36mn}{-6m}$　　(e) $\dfrac{-32bc}{4b}$　　(f) $\dfrac{-16ab}{-2ab}$

(g) $\dfrac{100m^2n}{-10m}$　(h) $\dfrac{-27x^2y^3}{-9y^2}$　(i) $\dfrac{-24a^3b}{6a^3}$　(j) $\dfrac{-3a^2}{a^2}$　(k) $\dfrac{-6m^3}{-2m^2}$　(l) $\dfrac{8m^5}{-4m^4}$

5　Simplify each of the following.

(a) $(18pq) \div (9q)$　　　　(b) $(24rs^2) \div (-6r)$　　　　(c) $(-12m^2n) \div (2mn)$

(d) $(36p^3q) \div (6pq)$　　　　(e) $(48mn^2) \div (-24m)$　　　　(f) $(16a^2) \div (-4a)$

6　Find the value of each expression for $a = 3$ and $b = -2$.

(a) $\dfrac{12ab}{4a}$　　　　(b) $\dfrac{16ab^2}{-4a}$　　　　(c) $\dfrac{-64a^2b}{-4b}$　　　　(d) $\dfrac{-32a^2b}{16ab}$

PSP　7　What is the next number in the pattern　0　3　12　27　48? Justify your answer.

PSP　8　I have \$85 in bills. I have two thirds as many fives as tens. I have one fifth as many twos as the total number of fives and tens and only half as many ones as twos. How many of each bill do I have?

C 9　Find an expression for the unknown side of each rectangle.

(a)

(b)

(c)

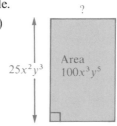

From Math History

Imagine working with algebra without using variables. Diophantus, an ancient Greek, was an innovative mathematician because of his use of a *symbol* to represent an *unknown quantity*. Diophantus wrote his theories on unknown quantities in a book called *Arithmetica*. Diophantus is remembered in history for the solutions of Diophantine equations, which are so named in his honour.

▶ Find out how these equations differ from the equations you have studied.

▶ Research information about the life of Diophantus.

Multiplying and Dividing Monomials

When you multiply or divide monomials in an expression, you do the operations in the order they appear. However, before you multiply or divide, you can first simplify the expression as shown.

$$\left(\frac{6x^2y}{-4xy}\right)\left(\frac{2x^3y}{-3y}\right)$$

$$= \left(\frac{\overset{1}{\cancel{6}}\overset{2x}{\cancel{x^2}}\overset{1}{\cancel{y}}}{\cancel{-4xy}}\right)\left(\frac{\overset{1}{\cancel{2x^3}}\overset{1}{\cancel{y}}}{\cancel{-3y}}\right) \quad \begin{array}{l}\text{Simplify before}\\ \text{you multiply.}\end{array}$$

$$= x^4$$

$$\left(\frac{-6a^2b}{4x^2}\right) \div \left(\frac{9ab}{-2x}\right)$$

$$= \left(\frac{-6a^2b}{4x^2}\right)\left(\frac{-2x}{9ab}\right) \quad \begin{array}{l}\text{Multiply by the multiplicative}\\ \text{inverse of } \dfrac{9ab}{-2x}, \text{ namely } \dfrac{-2x}{9ab}.\end{array}$$

$$= \left(\frac{\overset{-1}{\cancel{-6}}\overset{a}{\cancel{a^2}}\overset{1}{\cancel{b}}}{\cancel{4x^2}}\right)\left(\frac{\overset{-1}{\cancel{-2x}}\overset{1}{}}{\cancel{9ab}}\right) \quad \begin{array}{l}\text{Simplify before}\\ \text{you multiply.}\end{array}$$

$$= \frac{a}{3x}$$

---

10 Find each product.

(a) $\left(\dfrac{3x^2}{2y}\right)\left(\dfrac{-2y}{3}\right)$

(b) $\left(\dfrac{x}{3m}\right)\left(\dfrac{-3m}{-y}\right)$

(c) $\left(\dfrac{3a^2}{5a^2}\right)\left(\dfrac{-10b}{4b^3}\right)$

(d) $\left(\dfrac{6}{x^2y}\right)\left(\dfrac{x^3y^2}{x}\right)$

(e) $\left(\dfrac{-24k^2}{45}\right)\left(\dfrac{-9}{15k}\right)$

(f) $\left(\dfrac{-3x^2y}{4a^2}\right)\left(\dfrac{-5a}{9xy}\right)$

11 Simplify each of the following.

(a) $\left(\dfrac{2x}{-5}\right) \div \left(\dfrac{x^2}{-10}\right)$

(b) $\left(\dfrac{x^2}{4}\right) \div \left(\dfrac{20x^2y}{-16}\right)$

(c) $\left(\dfrac{6x^2k}{-7xy}\right) \div \left(\dfrac{-7k}{3y}\right)$

(d) $\left(\dfrac{4x^2}{2y^2}\right) \div \left(\dfrac{-x^3}{4y}\right)$

(e) $\left(\dfrac{3a^2b}{6a}\right) \div \left(\dfrac{3ab}{-9a}\right)$

(f) $\left(\dfrac{5x}{-4a^2}\right) \div \left(\dfrac{10x^2}{2a}\right)$

12 Simplify.

(a) $\left(\dfrac{-4x^2}{y^2}\right)\left(\dfrac{y^3}{-8x}\right) \div \left(\dfrac{y}{2x}\right)$

(b) $\left(\dfrac{3a}{-b}\right)\left(\dfrac{b^2}{6a}\right)\left(\dfrac{b}{-a}\right)$

(c) $\left(\dfrac{-10a^2}{b}\right)\left(\dfrac{-b^2}{5a}\right) \div \left(\dfrac{b}{2a}\right)$

(d) $\left(\dfrac{-x}{4k}\right)\left(\dfrac{-5}{3x}\right)\left(\dfrac{12k}{x}\right)$

(e) $\left(\dfrac{-16m^3}{n}\right)\left(\dfrac{-1}{4m^2}\right) \div \left(\dfrac{-n^2}{4m}\right)$

(f) $\left(\dfrac{8s}{t}\right)\left(\dfrac{t}{-8s^2}\right) \div \left(\dfrac{-t}{s}\right)$

13 Simplify each expression if $x = \dfrac{-5a}{4b}$ and $y = \dfrac{-2a}{3b}$.

(a) xy

(b) x^2

(c) y^2

(d) $x \div y$

7.10 Dividing Polynomials by Monomials

In your study of mathematics, you apply your previous skills and strategies to develop new skills and strategies.

You know that division is the inverse operation of multiplication. Thus

$$3a(2a - 3b) = 6a^2 - 9ab \text{ means } \frac{6a^2 - 9ab}{3a} = 2a - 3b.$$

This suggests a method of dividing a polynomial by a monomial.

$$\frac{6a^2 - 9ab}{3a} = \frac{6a^2}{3a} - \frac{9ab}{3a}$$

$$= 2a - 3b \longleftarrow \text{This result is the same as the result above.}$$

The example above suggests a method of dividing a polynomial by a monomial.

To divide a polynomial by a monomial, divide each term of the polynomial by the monomial.

As before, simplify first before evaluating.

Example   Evaluate $\dfrac{15x^2 - 10x}{5x}$ for $x = -1$.

Solution   *Step 1:* Simplify.

$$\frac{15x^2 - 10x}{5x} = \frac{15x^2}{5x} - \frac{10x}{5x}$$

$$= 3x - 2$$

Step 2: Substitute $x = -1$.

$$3x - 2 = 3(-1) - 2$$
$$= -3 - 2$$
$$= -5$$

7.10 Exercise

A Review the laws of exponents.

1   Simplify each of the following.

(a) $\dfrac{6y}{3} + \dfrac{18}{3}$

(b) $\dfrac{8m}{2} + \dfrac{16}{2}$

(c) $\dfrac{6ab}{3a} + \dfrac{-9a}{3a}$

(d) $\dfrac{20xy}{4x} + \dfrac{16x}{4x}$

(e) $\dfrac{8m^2}{-2m} + \dfrac{6m}{-2m}$

(f) $\dfrac{24y^3}{4y} + \dfrac{16y^2}{4y}$

2   Divide each of the following.

(a) $\dfrac{3y + 18}{3}$

(b) $\dfrac{4y - 16}{2}$

(c) $\dfrac{-16y - 4}{-4}$

(d) $\dfrac{-6y + 3}{-3}$

(e) $\dfrac{48 - 8y}{8}$

(f) $\dfrac{6ab - 12ac}{a}$

(g) $\dfrac{16xy - 8x}{2x}$

(h) $\dfrac{25mn - 10m}{-5m}$

B Express your answers in simplest form.

3 Simplify each of the following.

(a) $\dfrac{12ax + 16x}{4x}$ (b) $\dfrac{-25my + 10xy}{-5y}$ (c) $\dfrac{6x^2 - 9x^3}{-3x}$ (d) $\dfrac{-12ay^2 - 16ay}{-4ay}$

(e) $(-48ax^2 + 24ay^2) \div (-12a)$ (f) $(-75mn^2 - 50m^2n) \div (-25mn)$

4 Evaluate each of the following expressions for $x = -2$, $y = -3$ and $a = -1$.

(a) $\dfrac{6xy + 2x^2y^2}{-2xy}$ (b) $\dfrac{6x^2y - 3xy^2}{3xy}$ (c) $\dfrac{-12ax - 18ay}{-6a}$

5 Simplify each of the following.

(a) $\dfrac{3x + x^2 - 4x^3}{x}$ (b) $\dfrac{2k - k^2 + 8k^3}{k}$ (c) $\dfrac{9x^3 + 6x^2 - 15x}{3x}$

(d) $\dfrac{-4y^2 + 2y - 2xy}{-2y}$ (e) $\dfrac{xy^2 - x^2y^2 - x^2y}{xy}$ (f) $\dfrac{a^3b - 2a^2b - ab^2}{-ab}$

(g) $(6x^2y - 4xy^2 + 10x^2y^2) \div (-2xy)$ (h) $(9a^2m^2 - 6am^2 - 18a^2m) \div (-3am)$

6 The perimeter of an equilateral triangle is $(12x^2y + 3x)$ units.
(a) Find an expression for the length of each side.
(b) Find the length of each side if $x = 2$ and $y = 5$.

7 The expression for the perimeter of a square is $(16x^2y - 12xy)$ units.
(a) Find an expression for the length of each side.
(b) Use $x = 2$ and $y = 3$ to find the length of each side and the perimeter.
(c) How could you check your answer in (b)?
(d) Find the area of the square when $x = 2$ and $y = 3$.

 8 The digit 3 is used 3 times to make 0 as shown. $0 = (3 - 3) \div 3$
(a) Use the digit 3 three times to make each number from 1 to 4.
(b) Can you use the digit 3 three times to make other numbers less than 10?

Math Tip

To solve a problem, whether it is in mathematics or another discipline, you must understand the meaning of each word that occurs.

▶ Make a list of the new math words you have learned in this chapter. Provide an example of your own to illustrate each word.

▶ Place any new problem solving strategies you have acquired in your *Problem Solving Plan* **PSP** .

7.11 Using Monomial Denominators

In arithmetic, operations are performed on numbers. In algebra, operations are performed on algebraic expressions. The skills you learned in arithmetic extend to skills in algebra. How are the following alike? How are they different?

Arithmetic $\dfrac{3}{5} + \dfrac{1}{5} = \dfrac{4}{5}$ *Algebra* $\dfrac{x}{5} + \dfrac{y}{5} = \dfrac{x+y}{5}$

When the denominators are alike, you can add or subtract the numerators. If the denominators are not alike, you need to find a common denominator as shown.

Example 1   Simplify. $\dfrac{x+3}{3} - \dfrac{3(x-1)}{4}$

Solution $\dfrac{x+3}{3} - \dfrac{3(x-1)}{4} = \dfrac{4(x+3)}{12} - \dfrac{9(x-1)}{12}$ Remember: You need to obtain an equivalent expression. Thus for each expression, multiply numerator and denominator by the same number.

$$= \dfrac{4(x+3) - 9(x-1)}{12}$$

$$= \dfrac{4x + 12 - 9x + 9}{12}$$

$$= \dfrac{-5x + 21}{12}$$

Example 2   Simplify. $\dfrac{5}{3x^2} - \dfrac{x+5}{3x^2}$

Solution $\dfrac{5}{3x^2} - \dfrac{x+5}{3x^2} = \dfrac{5 - (x+5)}{3x^2}$ Since the denominators are like monomials you can subtract the numerators as shown.

$$= \dfrac{5 - x - 5}{3x^2}$$

$$= \dfrac{-x}{3x^2}$$

$$= \dfrac{-1}{3x} \qquad x \neq 0$$

PSP Always check whether you can express your answer in a simpler form.

7.11 Exercise

A 1 Simplify.

(a) $\dfrac{4t}{2} + \dfrac{6t}{2}$ (b) $\dfrac{6y}{3} - \dfrac{3y}{3}$ (c) $\dfrac{8p}{2} - \dfrac{3p}{4}$ (d) $\dfrac{5s}{6} - \dfrac{3s}{2}$ (e) $\dfrac{9k}{3} + \dfrac{8k}{4}$

2 Simplify.

(a) $\dfrac{y}{4} + \dfrac{y+6}{3}$

(b) $\dfrac{p+3}{3} - \dfrac{4}{9}$

(c) $\dfrac{x-3}{2} - \dfrac{5}{3}$

3 (a) What is your first step in simplifying the expression $\dfrac{2(x-3)}{4} + \dfrac{x+5}{5}$?

(b) Simplify the expression in (a).

4 (a) What is your first step in simplifying the expression $\dfrac{y-3}{3} - \dfrac{2(y+5)}{4}$?

(b) Simplify the expression in (a).

B Be sure to express your answer in simplest form.

5 Simplify.

(a) $\dfrac{2y}{2} - \dfrac{3y}{4} + \dfrac{3y}{2}$

(b) $\dfrac{3a}{2} + \dfrac{5a}{3} + \dfrac{3a}{6}$

(c) $\dfrac{3p}{2} - \dfrac{5p}{4} + \dfrac{2p}{5}$

6 Simplify.

(a) $\dfrac{3}{2a} + \dfrac{4}{2a}$

(b) $\dfrac{5}{3x^2} - \dfrac{2}{3x^2}$

(c) $\dfrac{3x}{2a} + \dfrac{5x}{2a}$

(d) $\dfrac{-4}{3x^2} + \dfrac{4+2x}{3x^2}$

(e) $\dfrac{6-y}{2y^2} - \dfrac{3+y}{2y^2}$

(f) $\dfrac{6}{m^2} - \dfrac{2(3-m)}{m^2}$

7 Simplify.

(a) $\dfrac{3x-1}{2} + \dfrac{x-6}{4}$

(b) $\dfrac{3y-2}{6} - \dfrac{y+6}{3}$

(c) $\dfrac{8x-3}{8} + \dfrac{x-3}{4}$

(d) $\dfrac{2m-3}{3} - \dfrac{5(3m+6)}{2}$

(e) $\dfrac{3(x-1)}{4} - \dfrac{2(x-2)}{3}$

(f) $\dfrac{3(k+2)}{5} + \dfrac{5(2k-3)}{2}$

8 Evaluate each expression. Use $x = 1$.

(a) $\dfrac{3x-2}{4} - \dfrac{2(x-5)}{5}$

(b) $\dfrac{5(x-1)}{3} + \dfrac{x-3}{2}$

(c) $\dfrac{2(x-1)}{3} - \dfrac{3(x+1)}{2}$

9 Which expression has the greater value if $x = 1$ and $y = -1$?

(a) $\dfrac{3(x-y)}{2} - \dfrac{2(x+y)}{3}$

(b) $\dfrac{2(3x-2y)}{3} - \dfrac{3(2x-3y)}{2}$

 10 Two congruent (same shape and size) squares are shown. Place 4 line segments in the diagram and create 10 congruent squares.

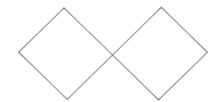

7.12 Working Backwards: Common Factors

Just as multiplying and dividing are inverse operations, expanding and factoring are inverses. Compare the following.

Multiplying $(5ab)(3a) = 15a^2b$ Dividing $\dfrac{15a^2b}{3a} = 5ab$

Expanding $3x(x + y) = 3x^2 + 3xy$

factors   terms

Factoring $3x^2 + 3xy = 3x(x + y)$

The factors of $3x^2$ are 3, x and x.
The factors of $3xy$ are 3, x and y.
The factors common to each term are 3 and x. Thus the **greatest common factor** of $3x^2 + 3xy$ is $3x$.

To factor a polynomial with common factors,

▶ find the greatest common factor of the terms.

▶ divide each term by the greatest common factor.

Example 1   Factor.   (a) $25x^3 + 50x^2$ (b) $4a^2b + 12ab^2 - 16ab^3$

Solution   (a) $25x^3 + 50x^2$ (b) $4a^2b + 12ab^2 - 16ab^3$
              $= 25x^2(x + 2)$ $= 4ab(a + 3b - 4b^2)$

Check by expanding.

Factoring can reduce the number of calculations needed to evaluate an expression.

Example 2   Evaluate $6ab^2 - 6a^2b$ for $a = -1$ and $b = 2$.

Solution   *Step 1:* Factor.
              $6ab^2 - 6a^2b = 6ab(b - a)$

   Step 2: Substitute $a = -1$ and $b = 2$.
              $6ab(b - a) = 6(-1)(2)[(2) - (-1)]$
              $= (-12)(3)$
              $= -36$

The steps shown in Example 2 are a more efficient procedure. Evaluate **PSP**
$6ab^2 - 6a^2b$ without first factoring. Compare the number of calculations.

7.12 Exercise

A Review the meanings of common factor and greatest common factor.

1 Find the greatest common factor of each of the following.
(a) $3y$, 18
(b) 48, $-8y$
(c) $-16y$, -4
(d) $6ab$, $-12ac$
(e) $-12ab$, $16ab$
(f) $6x^2$, $-9x^3$
(g) $16a^2$, $-12a$
(h) $-25a^2b$, $20ab^2$
(i) ax^2, $2bx^2$, $3cx^2$
(j) x^3, $-8x^2$, $+16x$
(k) a^3b, $-2a^2b$, $-ab^2$
(l) $6x^2y$, $-4xy^2$, $10x^2y^2$

B Remember: Check your answers by expanding.

2 Find each missing factor.
(a) $6 + 8x = (?)(3 + 4x)$
(b) $2\pi r + 4\pi = (?)(r + 2)$
(c) $6y - 12y^2 = (6y)(?)$
(d) $4y^3 - 8y^2 = (4y^2)(?)$
(e) $6x^2y - 4xy^2 + 10x^2y^2 = (-2xy)(?)$
(f) $9a^2m^2 - 6am^2 - 18a^2m = (-3am)(?)$

3 Factor each of the following.
(a) $6 - 12x$
(b) $5x^2 - 3x$
(c) $9y - 12x$
(d) $5xy - 3xy^2$
(e) $2x^2 - 6x$
(f) $a^2 - 2a$
(g) $4ab - b^2$
(h) $4y^2 - 16$
(i) $28a^2 - 14ab$
(j) $36mn - 25m^2n^2$
(k) $6x^2 - 12x + 15$
(l) $5m^3 - 25m^2 + 15$
(m) $50a^2 + 75ab + 25b^2$
(n) $10x^3y^3 + 20x^2y^2 - 10xy$

4 Evaluate each of the following for $x = -1$ and $y = 3$.
(a) $3xy - 24x$
(b) $12x^2 - 8xy$
(c) $6y - 12y^2$
(d) $4x^3 - 8x^2$
(e) $5x^3y - 5xy^2$
(f) $6x^2y - 12x^3y^2$
(g) $3xy - 6y^2$
(h) $12x^2 + 24x^2y$
(i) $12x^3y - 18x^2y^2$

5 Factor.
(a) $6a - 12a^2 + 15a$
(b) $ab^2 + 6a + 8a$
(c) $2k^2 - 3k^3 + 8k^4$
(d) $x^3y - 2x^2y^2 - xy^3$
(e) $5b - 25b^2 + 15b$
(f) $10ab + 20a^2b^2 - 10ab$
(g) $-4y^2 + 2y - 2xy$
(h) $x^2y - x^2y^2 - xy^2$
(i) $9x^2 - 12xy - 6y^2$

6 Find a common factor and then simplify.
(a) $\dfrac{2x^2y + 3xy^2}{xy}$
(b) $\dfrac{4xy - 24y^2}{4y}$
(c) $\dfrac{6x^3y + 12x^3y^2}{6x^3y}$
(d) $\dfrac{5x^4y - 35xy^3}{5xy}$
(e) $\dfrac{-12x^3y^2 - 18x^2y^3}{6x^2y^2}$
(f) $\dfrac{3x^4 + 6x^3 + 9x^2}{3x^2}$

7.13 **PSP** Problem Solving: Using Strategies

Refer to your *Problem Solving Plan* **PSP**
Record any questions, statements,
strategies, etc. that you have recently
learned in the appropriate place in
your *Problem Solving Plan* **PSP**

Then solve the following problems. After
you have a solution for each problem,
look over your work.

▶ Does your solution answer the
original problem you were asked to
solve?

▶ Are there other solutions to the
problem?

▶ Place in your *Problem Solving Plan*
any strategies, questions, statements,
features of the problem, etc. that
will assist you later to solve problems
you have not met before.

PSP | Problem Solving Plan

Step A: Understand the problem.
  • What are you asked to
    find?
  • What are you given?

Step B: Decide on a strategy.

Step C: Apply the strategy.
Do the work.

Step D: Check your solution.

Step E: Write a final statement.

7.13 Exercise

1 Find the next number for the pattern: 5, 6, 11, 17. Justify your answer.

2 Toothpicks are used to construct Roman numerals.
The statement shown at the right is not true.
Move two toothpicks to make the statement true.

3 Refer to the diagram.
How many squares can you find?

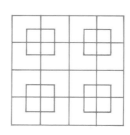

4 You are given tape and a piece of
cardboard 12 cm by 8 cm.

(a) Construct a box with a top with volume 24 cm³.
How much cardboard will you have left?

(b) Is it possible to construct a box with a larger
volume than in (a)? Justify your answer.

(c) Is it possible to construct a box with a smaller volume than in (a)?
Justify your answer.

(d) What are the dimensions of a box with the maximum volume using all
the cardboard?

Practice and Problems: Review

1   Express each as a single power.

(a) $(3^2)(3^4)$ (b) $(x^4)(x)$ (c) $(a^3)(a^3)$ (d) $3^6 \div 3^2$ (e) $m^5 \div m$

(f) $c^5 \div c^3$ (g) $(2^2)^3$ (h) $(x^3)^2$ (i) $(a^3)^5$

2   Simplify. Express your answer with positive exponents.

(a) $\dfrac{8(x^2)^2}{2x}$ (b) $\dfrac{12c^3x^2}{-3cx^5}$ (c) $(-2a^0b^{-3})^2$ (d) $-5(a^2b)^0(b)^{-2}$

3   Evaluate for $a = -3$, $b = -2$ and $c = -1$.

(a) $a^2 - b^2$ (b) a^b (c) c^{ab} (d) $(a^{-1} + b^c)$

4   Write each number in scientific notation.

(a) 850 000   (b) 3 450 000   (c) 0.000 125   (d) 0.003 904

5   (a) Light travels at about 300 000 km/s. Write this in scientific notation.

(b) Write the number of seconds in 1 h in scientific notation.

(c) Use the results of (a) and (b) to find the distance light travels in 1 h in scientific notation.

6   Solve each equation.

(a) $3^{2x+3} = 3^{3x-2}$ (b) $10^{5-2x} = 10^{4x-7}$ (c) $4^{x+1} = 2^{5+x}$

7   Find each product.

(a) $(4a)(2a)$ (b) $6ac(-2a)$ (c) $(d)(d^2)$ (d) $k^3(-2k^4)$

(e) $-n(-3n^2)$ (f) $-y^2(-2y^3)$ (g) $p^2(2pq)$ (h) $x(x^3y)$

8   Find each product.

(a) $3d(-2d)$ (b) $-2k^3(-3k)$ (c) $-4(2r - 3)$ (d) $3f(2f - 5w)$

9   Simplify the following.

(a) $\dfrac{15x}{3}$ (b) $\dfrac{15y^2}{y}$ (c) $\dfrac{24x^2}{6x}$ (d) $\dfrac{-12x^2y}{3xy}$ (e) $\dfrac{-8h^2k^2}{-4hk}$ (f) $\dfrac{3m^2y}{-m^2}$

10   Simplify.

(a) $\dfrac{4n + 12}{4}$ (b) $\dfrac{6k - 18}{-3}$ (c) $\dfrac{4ab - 8ac}{-a}$ (d) $\dfrac{4mn - 8m}{4m}$

11   Factor the following.

(a) $9 - 12y$ (b) $5ab - 3b^2$ (c) $5x^2y - xy + y^2$

(d) $2p^2q - 4pq + 8q^2$ (e) $3k^2 - 9k + 12k^4$ (f) $3m^2n^2 - 9m^3n^3$

Practice Test

1   Simplify. Express your answers in exponential form.
   (a) $(2^3)(2^2)$ (b) $(n^4)(n)$ (c) $3^6 \div 3^2$ (d) $q^7 \div q^2$ (e) $(3^2)^3$
   (f) $(m^3)^4$ (g) $(2t)^3$ (h) $(ac)^2$ (i) $(2k^4)^3$ (j) $(3x^2)^3$

2   Evaluate.
   (a) 5^0 (b) 2^{-4} (c) $\dfrac{1}{3^{-2}}$ (d) $-3^{-1} + 3^{-2}$ (e) $(4^0 - 2^{-1}) \div \dfrac{2}{3}$

3   Evaluate. Use $p = -\dfrac{2}{3}$ and $q = \dfrac{1}{2}$.
   (a) $p^2 - q^{-1}$ (b) q^{-2} (c) $(pq)^{-1}$ (d) $p^{-1} \div q$

4   Write each number in scientific notation.
   (a) 4 500 000   (b) 0.000 029   (c) 0.000 000 392

5   Write each number in decimal form.
   (a) 5.2×10^7 (b) 1.95×10^{-3} (c) 2.8×10^{-7}

6   The mass of gold in water is 0.000 000 5 g/m³. How much gold is in 48 × 10⁶ m³ of water?

7   Solve each equation.
   (a) $2^{4x-2} = 2^{3x+1}$ (b) $5^{7x-4} = 5^{4-x}$ (c) $3^{4x+2} = 9^{-2-x}$

8   Find each product.
   (a) $-3x(4xy)$ (b) $7g(-3gk)$ (c) $4d(9 - 2d)$ (d) $-2p^2(7p - 1)$

9   Evaluate each expression for $x = 4$ and $e = 3$.
   (a) $2(x - 2e) - 4(3e - 2x)$ (b) $2e(e - 3x) - 3e(e + 2x)$

10   Simplify.
   (a) $\dfrac{24h}{-3}$ (b) $\dfrac{36x^3}{-4x}$ (c) $\dfrac{-12g + 8gk}{-4g}$ (d) $\dfrac{15pq^2 - 9p^2q}{3pq}$

11   Find an expression for the area.
    Calculate the area for $x = 3$ and $y = 4$.

$3y$

$2x - 1$

12   Factor the following.
    (a) $5x^2 - 15x$ (b) $9a^2b - 12b$ (c) $2x^5 - 4x^3 - 8x^2$

Cumulative Review (4–6)

1   Simplify.
   (a) $(a - b) + (3a - 2b) - (a - b)$ (b) $(2x - 3y) - (x - 5y) - 3x$
   (c) $2y + 3(y - 2)$ (d) $8 - 4(y - 6)$
   (e) $-6(3 - y) - 2y$ (f) $3y + (3 - y) - 4(y + 1)$
   (g) $-4(m - 2) + 3(m - 3)$ (h) $2p - 3q + 2p - 6q - (2p + 3q)$
   (i) $3(x - 2) - 2(x - 5) + 3(x - 6)$ (j) $-2(a + b) - 3(a - b)$

2   Simplify each expression. Which are equivalent?
   (a) $4(3x - 2y) - 2(x - y)$ (b) $-2(2x - 3y) + 8x$
   (c) $-(-2x + 3y) - (y - 2x)$ (d) $12x - 2(x + 3y)$

3   Find the value of each expression for $a = -2$ and $b = -3$.
   (a) $3a + 4b - 2a - 6b$ (b) $3(2a - b) - 4(a - 6b)$

4   Solve and verify.
   (a) $3m + 4m - 5 = 9$ (b) $8k - 3 = 6k - 8$ (c) $(k - 9) - (k + 7) = 4k$

   (d) $2y + 3 \geq 17$ (e) $p - 1 = \dfrac{2}{3}p + 7$ (f) $\dfrac{3}{4}x - 2 = \dfrac{1}{2}x + 5$

   (g) $0.6x - 1 = 10 - 0.4x$ (h) $25 < 5m - 2m + 1$ (i) $0.75a - 3 = 0.25a + 1 - 0.5a$

5   (a) Express the formula $d = \left(\dfrac{u + v}{2}\right)t$ in terms of u.

   (b) Express the formula $y - a = m(x - b)$ in terms of x.

6   A number is doubled and increased by 6. The same result is obtained when the number is increased by 30. Find the number.

7   John is presently 12 years older than Bill. In 10 years, twice John's age will be equal to 3 times Bill's age. How old are they today?

8   The length of a rectangle is 2 cm less than 5 times the width. If the perimeter is 44 cm, find the dimensions.

9   $1400 is invested for a year, part at 6% and part at 9%. If the total interest received is $120, how much is invested at each rate?

10 The diameter of a long-playing record is 30.1 cm.
   (a) Calculate the distance around the outside edge of the record.
   PSP (b) Calculate the distance covered by the needle on a turntable playing a record that is 20 min long.

8 *Geometry: Constructions and Properties*

Language of geometry, developing properties, properties of polygons, using constructions, parallel lines and their properties, developing strategies in mathematics, types of thinking, relations with circles, applications, strategies for problem solving

Introduction

The history of mathematics is an exciting display of the achievement of many minds that have developed a language of mathematics, a language of geometry, as well as an important foundation of skills and strategies. Read the *From Math History* about Euclid, a Greek mathematician, included in Section 8.3. He organized geometry in a logical way and did it so well that now, when mathematicians think of geometry, they think of Euclid. However, the skills and strategies for applying geometry have gone beyond Euclid. You will study the skills and concepts of different types of geometry, which we refer to as geometries.

▶ In **plane geometry** you will study relations and properties among geometric shapes. You will study these in Chapters 8 and 9.

▶ In **co-ordinate geometry** you will locate points and figures on the plane, and learn important strategies and skills. You will learn about solving problems using co-ordinate geometry in Chapter 10.

▶ In **transformational geometry** you will study the properties and applications of translations, reflections, rotations and dilatations. Refer to this study in Chapter 14.

Examples of the importance of geometry occur everywhere. The stamps below show just a part of the influence of geometry on us.

8.1 Language of Geometry: Vocabulary

To study geometry you need to learn the precise meanings of special words. Some basic ideas such as point, line, plane and space are difficult to define. They are said to be **undefined**.

The **point** is the building block of geometry. It is undefined, but you can illustrate a point by drawing a model or diagram.

In your previous work in geometry, you learned certain words and their symbols. You can use symbols to write your work more compactly.

line	ray	line segment	angle
$\overleftrightarrow{AB}$ or $\overleftrightarrow{BA}$	$\overrightarrow{AB}$	$\overline{AB}$ or $\overline{BA}$	$\angle B$ or $\angle ABC$ or $\angle CBA$

The vertex is written in the middle.

A standard unit, the **degree**, is used for measuring angles. A degree is $\dfrac{1}{360}$ of a complete turn or rotation.

You use a protractor to measure angles.

Special vocabulary is also used to describe the way in which pairs of lines are related.

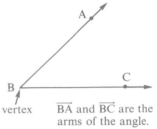

$\overrightarrow{BA}$ and $\overrightarrow{BC}$ are the arms of the angle.

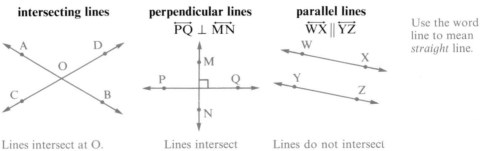

intersecting lines	**perpendicular lines** $\overleftrightarrow{PQ} \perp \overleftrightarrow{MN}$	**parallel lines** $\overleftrightarrow{WX} \parallel \overleftrightarrow{YZ}$	Use the word line to mean *straight* line.

Lines intersect at O.   Lines intersect at right angles   Lines do not intersect

Two figures that are frequently used in your study of geometry are the circle and the triangle. How are they alike? How are they different?

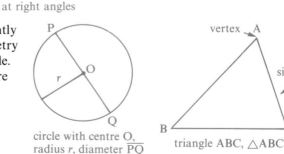

circle with centre O, radius *r*, diameter $\overline{PQ}$ triangle ABC, $\triangle ABC$

8.1 Exercise

A 1 List two things from the world around you that illustrate each word.
(a) point (b) line (c) angle (d) ray (e) line segment

2 From the diagram, name.
(a) two lines (b) two rays
(c) two line segments (d) two angles

3 Use a set of compasses to construct each of the following circles.
(a) radius 5 cm (b) diameter 8 cm (c) radius 2.8 cm

4 (a) Name every line segment (b) Name every angle
in this diagram. in this diagram.

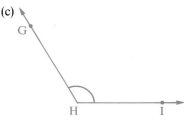

5 Use a protractor to measure each of the following angles.
(a) (b) (c)

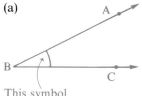 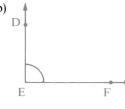

This symbol
indicates the angle.

6 The measure $x°$ of each angle is shown. Write a definition for each angle.
(a) acute (b) right (c) obtuse (d) straight (e) reflex

$0° < x° < 90°$ $x° = 90°$ $90° < x° < 180°$ $x° = 180°$ $180° < x° < 360°$

7 Measure the angles in the diagram and name.
(a) two acute angles
(b) two right angles
(c) one straight angle
(d) one obtuse angle
(e) one pair of intersecting lines
(f) two pairs of perpendicular line segments

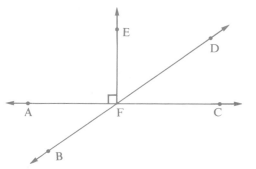

B 8 Each diagram illustrates angles with special names. Write a definition for each type of angle.

(a) 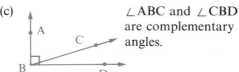 ∠ABC and ∠CBD are adjacent angles.

(b) 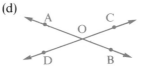 ∠ABD and ∠DBC are supplementary angles.

(c) 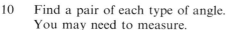 ∠ABC and ∠CBD are complementary angles.

(d)  ∠AOD and ∠COB are vertically opposite angles.

Questions 9 to 10 relate to this diagram.

9 Name.
(a) two lines that intersect
(b) two lines that seem to be parallel
(c) three points that are collinear
(d) two lines that are perpendicular

10 Find a pair of each type of angle. You may need to measure.
(a) supplementary   (b) complementary
(c) adjacent   (d) vertically opposite

PSP **11** Find a pattern in the letters.   T   F   S   E   T   T   F
What is the next letter in the pattern? Give reasons for your answer.

C 12 How many degrees are in each of the following?
(a) complement of 60°   (b) quarter turn   (c) supplement of 130°
(d) half turn   (e) complement of 20°   (f) supplement of 40°

13 Draw and classify each angle.   (a) 125°   (b) 60°   (c) 230°   (d) 90°

From Math History

Some people who have made advances in mathematics have never received credit for their contributions because they did not write them down. For instance, the pattern about polyhedra that you will study in the next section was probably known at least as early as 225 B.C. René Descartes knew the pattern for polyhedra but like others before him, he failed to record it to let others know. In 1752 Leonard Euler stated the formula and *wrote it down*. The formula, although offically called the Euler-Descartes formula, is today more commonly called the Euler formula.

Next time you want credit, *write it down*.

8.2 Working with Polygons: Special Names

Often in the study of mathematics, special names are used to describe figures.

A **polygon** is a simple closed figure that is constructed from line segments. The word polygon is formed from two Greek words, *poly* meaning many and *gonia* meaning angle.

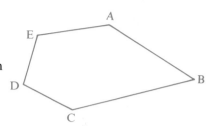

Polygons are classified according to the number of sides they have.

▶ A *triangle* is a polygon with 3 sides.
▶ A *quadrilateral* is a polygon with 4 sides.

Other names used to refer to polygons are pentagon (5 sides), hexagon (6 sides), septagon (7 sides) and octagon (8 sides).

 The words used in mathematics as well as in English have been constructed in a special way.

Triangles can be classified according to their special properties.

These special names are related to the measures of the sides.

Type of triangle	Special property
Scalene	No sides are equal.
Isosceles	Two sides are equal.
Equilateral	Three sides are equal.

These special names are related to the measures of the angles.

Types of triangle	Special property
Acute	All angles are acute.
Right	One angle is 90°.
Obtuse	One angle is obtuse.
Equiangular	All angles are equal.

Quadrilaterals can also be classified according to their special properties.

Type of quadrilateral	Special property
Square	All sides are equal. All angles equal 90°.
Rectangle	Opposite sides are equal. All angles equal 90°.
Parallelogram	Both pairs of opposite sides are equal and parallel.
Rhombus	All sides are equal.
Trapezoid	One pair of opposite sides is parallel.
Kite	Two pairs of adjacent sides are equal.

A polygon is said to be a *regular* polygon if

▶ all sides have equal measures.   ▶ all angles have equal measures.

Regular
pentagon

Regular
hexagon

Regular
octagon

8.2   Exercise

A Record any new words and their meanings in your vocabulary list.
Provide a diagram to illustrate the meaning of each word.

1   What polygons are used to construct each of the following?

(a)   (b)   (c)   (d)

2   These triangles are classified by their sides. Classify each triangle and write
a definition for it.

(a) 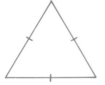   (b)   (c)

3   These triangles are classified by their angles. Classify each triangle and
write a definition for it.

(a) 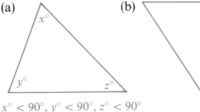   (b)   (c) 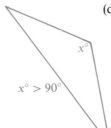   (d)

B 4 Classify each quadrilateral and write a definition for it.

(a)

(b)

(c)

(d)

(e)

(f)

5 Which triangles appear to be
(a) acute?
(b) obtuse?
(c) right?

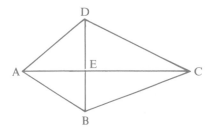

6 A chart can be used to relate the properties of quadrilaterals. Any quadrilateral in the chart also has the properties of the one above it. (A square is a rectangle.)

Give reasons for each statement.

(a) A rhombus is a parallelogram.
(b) A rectangle is not a square.
(c) A square is a parallelogram.

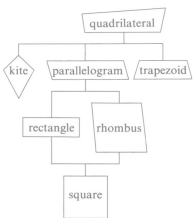

PSP 7 The following are scrambled math words.
Unscramble them to find the math words.

(a) ganel
(b) mobrush
(c) raquse
(d) tacbrust
(e) lumpylit
(f) tencerp

C 8 Use the chart given for Question 6. Which of the following statements are true? Which are false? Why?

(a) A square is a rectangle.
(b) A rectangle is a parallelogram.
(c) A rectangle is a trapezoid.
(d) A parallelogram is a rhombus.
(e) A square is a rhombus.
(f) A rhombus is a parallelogram.

Often to solve a problem you need to do some preliminary constructions.
A **polyhedron** is a 3-dimensional object with flat surfaces called **faces**.
Polyhedra is the plural of polyhedron.

A **net** is used to construct a pyramid.

A **shell** is formed from the net.

Fill the shell with material to obtain a **solid**.

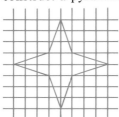
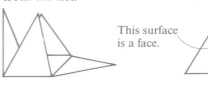
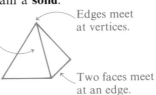

This surface is a face.

Edges meet at vertices.

Two faces meet at an edge.

How are the numbers of edges, faces and vertices of polyhedra related?

9 A square-based pyramid and a square-based prism are shown.

(a) How are the polyhedra alike?

(b) How are they different?

10 The meaning of "regular" is extended to regular polyhedra. The net and name for each one is shown.

▶ Make a larger copy of each net.   ▶ Construct each regular polyhedron.

(a) 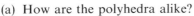   (b)   (c)

Regular tetrahedron

Regular hexahedron

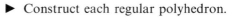

Regular octahedron

(d)   (e)

Regular dodecahedron

Regular icosahedron

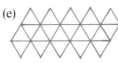

11 (a) Use the polyhedra in the previous question. Copy and complete the chart.

Type of polyhedron	Number of vertices, V	Number of faces, F	Number of edges, E

(b) Examine the results in the chart. How do V, F and E seem to be related?

(c) Test which of the following relationships are true for the results in your chart.

(i) $V - F = E + 2$ (ii) $V + F + 2 = E$

(iii) $V - F = E - 2$ (iv) $V + F = E + 2$

8.3 **PSP** Problem Solving Strategy: Using Experiments

Your first step in solving any problem is to answer these two key questions:

  I What information am I asked to find?
II What information am I given?

Then choose a strategy to help you solve the problem. One possible strategy is to *carry out an experiment*.

In science, you carry out experiments in order to make discoveries. Many of these discoveries have important applications in your everyday living. Similarly, you can carry out experiments in geometry.

When you come to a conclusion, and you have based your conclusion on guesswork, then you are making a **conjecture**. Conjectures are used very often in the study of mathematics. In fact, you probably use conjectures in your everyday living without realizing it. In mathematics, conjectures often lead to the development of new concepts, skills and strategies.

PSP	Problem Solving Plan
Step A:	Understand the problem.
	• What are you asked to find?
	• What are you given?
Step B:	Decide on a strategy.
Step C:	Apply the strategy. Do the work.
Step D:	Check your solution.
Step E:	Write a final statement.

8.3 Exercise

A 1 Four different triangles are drawn.

(a) Measure the angles.

(b) Copy and complete the table.

Triangle	Measure			Sum
	∠A	∠B	∠C	
1	?	?	?	?
2	?	?	?	?
3	?	?	?	?
4	?	?	?	?

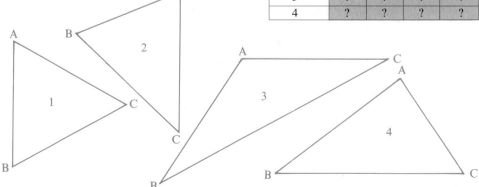

2   Use the results in the previous question.
    (a) What do you notice about the sum of the angle measures?
    (b) Round the sums on the chart to the nearest 10°. What do you notice about your answers?

  B Keep an updated list of the properties of geometric figures as you learn them.

3   (a) Draw three scalene triangles of your own choice.
    (b) Find the sum of the angle measures of each triangle to the nearest 10°. What do you conjecture?

4   (a) Draw three isosceles triangles of your own choice.
    (b) Find the sum of the angle measures of each triangle to the nearest 10°. What do you conjecture?

5   (a) Draw any three different triangles of your own choice. Cut them out.
    (b) Tear off the corners and fit them as shown.
    (c) Based on your results, make a conjecture about the sum of the angles of △ABC.

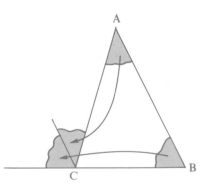

6   Using your results from the previous questions, write a conclusion about the sum of the angles of a triangle.

7   For the square drawn, $\overline{AC}$ and $\overline{BD}$ are called **diagonals**.
    (a) Measure $\overline{AC}$ and $\overline{BD}$. What do you notice?
    (b) Draw another square. Measure the diagonals. What do you conjecture?
    (c) Repeat (b) for another square.
    (d) Based on your results, write a conclusion about the diagonals of a square.

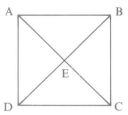

8   Do you think the following statement is true?
"The diagonals of a rhombus intersect at right angles".
    (a) Draw a rhombus. Check whether the statement is true.
    (b) Draw another rhombus. Check whether the statement is true.

PSP 9 Remember: To solve some problems you need to think of a simpler problem. How many triangles are in the diagram?

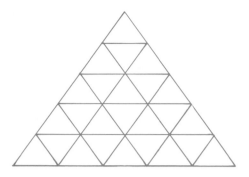

C 10 Each of the following statements is a conjecture.
▶ Draw figures to check whether the statement may be true.
▶ Place any new words in your vocabulary list.
(a) The diagonals of a rectangle intersect at right angles.
(b) The opposite angles of a rhombus are equal.
(c) The diagonals of a rhombus are equal.
(d) The opposite angles of a parallelogram are equal.
(e) The diagonals of a kite are perpendicular to each other.

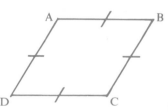

∠ABC and ∠ADC are opposite angles.

From Math History

Often, people who study mathematics attempt to compile bodies of mathematical knowledge. Euclid, one of the best known mathematicians of Greece, achieved a remarkable feat. Up until the 6th century B.C., the known facts of geometry were not organized. Euclid wrote *The Elements*, thirteen books that dealt not only with geometry but also with number theory and algebra. They comprised a comprehensive work on geometry and included sections on proportions, properties of numbers, as well as solid geometry. In *The Elements*, Euclid systematically arranged both his work and that of others.

With the advent of printing, the first printed edition of *The Elements* appeared in Venice, and the books reached more and more people who were then influenced by this publication. Euclid's *The Elements* has been used as a text for over 2000 years.

8.4 Using Reasoning: Developing Properties

Inductive reasoning

In science, experiments are completed, results are collected and conclusions are written. This procedure has led to many important discoveries.

A scientist performs a particular experiment a number of times and notices that the same result is obtained each time. For example, if all conditions remain the same, each time water is heated to 100°C it begins to boil. The scientist studies these results and writes a probable conclusion, namely, water boils at 100°C (under the same conditions as the experiments). This is called a **conjecture** or **hypothesis**.

This method of reasoning, in which particular cases are used to arrive at a probable conclusion, is called **inductive reasoning**.

Much of your earlier work with geometry has been inductive. For example, by measuring the angles of a triangle you found that the sum of the angles was 180°. Your probable conclusion is that the sum of the angles of *any* triangle is 180°. You can show the same result by folding the angles, as shown in the diagram.

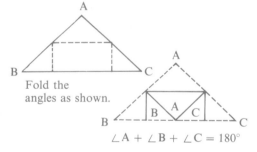

Fold the angles as shown.

$\angle A + \angle B + \angle C = 180°$

Deductive reasoning

By experiment you learned that the sum of the angles of any triangle is 180°. You can use this probable conclusion to learn some new information. For example, a quadrilateral is drawn and you are able to **deduce** new information, as shown in the diagram, by following a logical series of steps. This method of reasoning, in which new information is deduced from conjectures, is called **deductive reasoning**.

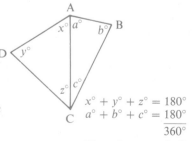

$$x° + y° + z° = 180°$$
$$a° + b° + c° = 180°$$
$$\overline{ 360°}$$

Thus the sum of all measures of the angles in quadrilateral ABCD is 360°.

8.4   Exercise

A Questions 1 to 4 explore the properties of geometric figures. Make a list of the properties you learn.

1   (a) Measure the vertically opposite angles formed by the intersecting lines given at the right.

(b) What do you notice about your results in (a)?

(c) Draw another pair of intersecting lines and measure the vertically opposite angles. What do you notice about your results?

(d) Use your results above and write a probable conclusion.

(e) What type of reasoning did you use to write your conclusion, inductive or deductive?

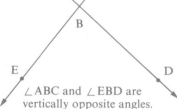

∠ABC and ∠EBD are vertically opposite angles.

2   An **isosceles triangle** is a triangle with two congruent sides.

(a) Measure the angles of the isosceles △ABC.

(b) What do you notice about your results in (a)?

(c) Draw another isosceles triangle and measure the angles again. What do you notice about your results?

(d) Use your results above to write a probable conclusion.

(e) What type of reasoning did you use, inductive or deductive?

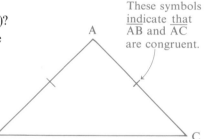

These symbols indicate that AB and AC are congruent.

3   In △ABC and △DEF certain angles are marked congruent.

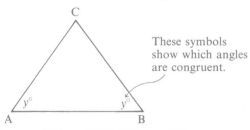

These symbols show which angles are congruent.

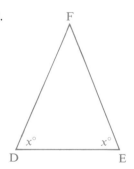

(a) Measure $\overline{AC}$ and $\overline{BC}$; $\overline{DE}$ and $\overline{DF}$.

(b) Draw another triangle with two equal angles. Measure the sides opposite the equal angles.

(c) What do you notice about your results in (a) and (b)?

(d) Use your results to write a probable conclusion.

(e) What type of reasoning did you use?

4   An **equilateral triangle** is a triangle with three
    congruent sides.

    (a) Measure the angles of the equilateral △ABC
        and △DEF.

    (b) Draw another equilateral triangle. Measure the
        angles. What do you notice about your results?

    (c) Use your results to write a probable
        conclusion.

    (d) What type of reasoning did you use?

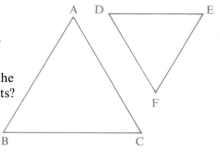

B Review the meaning of each word that occurs in these exercises.

5   In each diagram, name the angles that are congruent. Justify your answer.

    (a)   (b)   (c)

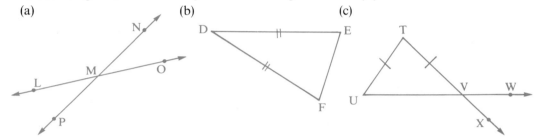

6   For △ABC certain angles are given special names.

    (a) Measure and find the sum of
        ∠ABC and ∠BAC.

    (b) Measure ∠ACD.

    (c) What do you notice about your
        answers in (a) and (b)?

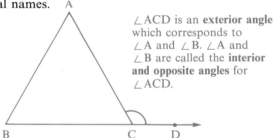

∠ACD is an **exterior angle**
which corresponds to
∠A and ∠B. ∠A and
∠B are called the **interior
and opposite angles** for
∠ACD.

7   Draw any triangle and an exterior angle.

    (a) Measure the two interior and opposite angles and find their sum.

    (b) Measure the exterior angle corresponding to the two interior and
        opposite angles you measured.

    (c) What do you notice about your answers in (a) and (b)?

8   Use your results in Questions 6 and 7 to write a probable conclusion
    about how exterior and corresponding interior and opposite angles are
    related. Are you using inductive or deductive reasoning?

9   Refer to the diagram.
    (a) Why is $\angle ABC = \angle ACB$?
    (b) Why is each true? $\angle ABD + \angle ABC = 180°$
                            $\angle ACB + \angle ACE = 180°$
    (c) Use the results in (a) and (b). Show that $x° = y°$.
    (d) Did you use inductive or deductive reasoning?

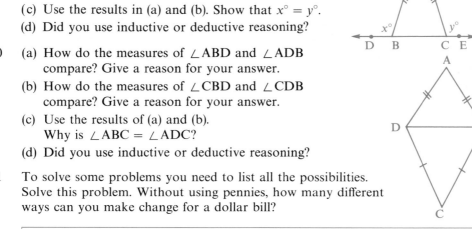

10 (a) How do the measures of $\angle ABD$ and $\angle ADB$
        compare? Give a reason for your answer.
    (b) How do the measures of $\angle CBD$ and $\angle CDB$
        compare? Give a reason for your answer.
    (c) Use the results of (a) and (b).
        Why is $\angle ABC = \angle ADC$?
    (d) Did you use inductive or deductive reasoning?

PSP 11 To solve some problems you need to list all the possibilities.
    Solve this problem. Without using pennies, how many different
    ways can you make change for a dollar bill?

Math Tip

It is important to list the properties of triangles you found in this section.
Show a diagram to illustrate each property.

▶ If two lines intersect, the vertically opposite angles have equal measures.

▶ The angles opposite the equal sides of an isosceles triangle have equal
measures.

▶ The sides opposite the equal angles in an isosceles triangle have equal
measures.

Calculator Use **PSP**

To solve a problem, you need to organize the steps you do carefully. To
use a calculator, you also need to organize your steps carefully. The flow
chart will help you organize your work to do calculations or to solve problems.

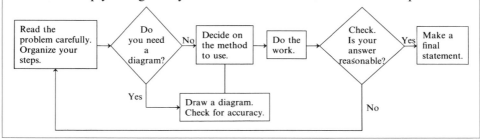

8.5 **PSP** Problem Solving Strategy: Using Algebra in Geometry

Very often you can combine skills in one branch of mathematics with skills in another branch of mathematics. For example, to solve problems about figures, you can combine your skills in deductive thinking with your skills in algebra. Thus you can use the conclusions you have already drawn about angles, along with your skills in equations, to deduce more information as shown in the following example.

Example 1   Find the measure of $\angle C$.

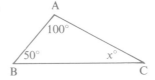

Solution   Use the conjecture that the angle sum of a triangle is $180°$.

$$\angle A + \angle B + \angle C = 180°$$
$$100° + 50° + x° = 180°$$
$$x° = 180° - 150°$$
$$x° = 30°$$

Thus $\angle C = 30°$.

Another skill you can use, along with your deductive skills, is translating English to mathematics as shown in the next example. **PSP**

Example 2   The supplement of an angle is $3°$ more than twice the angle. Find the angles.

Solution   Let x represent the number of degrees in the angle. Then $2x + 3$ represents the number of degrees in the supplement of the angle.

PSP Remember: You can use an equation to solve a problem.

$$x + (2x + 3) = 180$$ The sum of supplementary
$$3x + 3 = 180$$ angles is $180°$.
$$3x = 177$$ Supplement of $59°$ is $121°$
$$x = 59$$ and $2 \times 59 + 3 = 121°$.

The two angles are $59°$ and 121 .

8.5 Exercise

A Give a reason for each of your answers.

1 Find the missing measures.

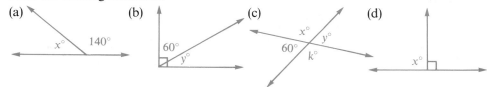

(a)   (b)   (c)   (d)

2 Find the missing measures in each triangle.

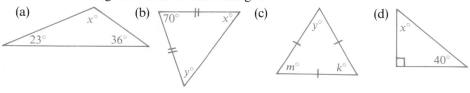

(a)   (b)   (c)   (d)

3 (a) One angle is twice the size of another as shown. Use the diagram. Find the measures of the angles.

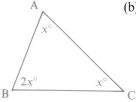

(b) One angle is 30° greater than another as shown. Use the diagram. Find the measures.

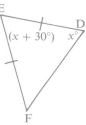

B To help you solve problems, sketch a diagram.

4 Find the missing measures in each figure. Justify your answers.

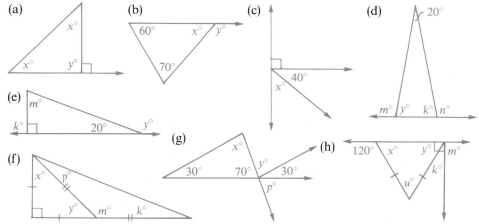

(a)   (b)   (c)   (d)

(e)   (g)   (h)

(f)

5 Two angles are supplementary. One angle is 15° greater than the other. Find the measures.

6 (a) One angle is twice the size of another. If their sum is 180°, find their measures.

   (b) One angle is 3° more than twice the smaller. If their sum is 90°, find their measures.

7 (a) Two angles are supplementary. If they differ by 38°, find their measures.

   (b) The complement of an angle is 2° less than 3 times the measure of the angle. Find the measure of the complement.

   (c) The supplement of an angle is 6° more than twice the angle. Find their measures.

8 (a) Two angles of a triangle are 72° and 30°. Find the other angle.

   (b) What type of triangle is it?

9 In △ABC, ∠B is three times the size of ∠A, and ∠C is four times the size of ∠A. Find the angles.

10 In △ABC, ∠A is 15° more than twice ∠B, and ∠C is equal to the sum of ∠A and ∠B. Find the angles.

PSP 11 Make a copy of the diagram. Can you trace your drawing without lifting your pencil and without going over any line segment twice?

C 12 Find each missing measure. Give reasons for your answers.

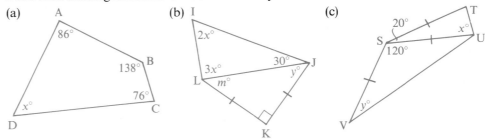

(a)
(b)
(c)

8.6 Parallel Lines and Their Properties

How do each of the following remind you of parallel lines?

▶ railway tracks   ▶ boards in a fence   ▶ floors of a building

Two lines in the same plane that never meet are called **parallel lines**. A **transversal** is a line that intersects any two or more lines. In this section, you will work primarily with transversals that intersect parallel lines.

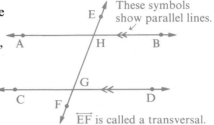

These symbols show parallel lines.

$\overleftrightarrow{EF}$ is called a transversal.

In the diagram $\overleftrightarrow{AB}$ and $\overleftrightarrow{CD}$ are parallel. You can write $\overleftrightarrow{AB} \parallel \overleftrightarrow{CD}$.

In each of the following diagrams, a transversal intersects parallel lines. Special pairs of angles are named as follows.

| **Alternate angles** | **Corresponding angles** | **Interior angles on the same side of the transversal.** |

8.6 Exercise

A This exercise investigates properties of special pairs of angles which are related to parallel lines.

1. What type of angle is shown by each pair of angles?

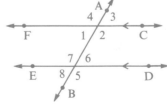

  (a) 1, 8   (b) 1, 6   (c) 1, 7   (d) 2, 5

  (e) 3, 6   (f) 4, 7   (g) 2, 6   (h) 2, 7

2. In the diagram name a pair of each.

  (a) alternate angles

  (b) corresponding angles

  (c) interior angles on the same side of the transversal

  (d) vertically opposite angles

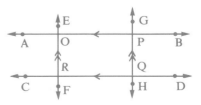

B Questions 3 to 5 are based on the diagram below.

3 (a) Choose a pair of alternate angles and measure them. What do you notice about their measures?

(b) Choose a different pair of alternate angles and measure them. What do you notice this time?

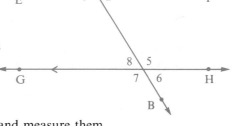

(c) Write a probable conclusion about alternate angles.

4 (a) Choose a pair of corresponding angles and measure them. What do you notice about their measures?

(b) Choose a different pair of corresponding angles and measure them. What do you notice this time?

(c) Write a probable conclusion about corresponding angles.

5 (a) Choose a pair of interior angles on the same side of the transversal $\overrightarrow{AB}$. Measure them and find the sum of the angles. What do you notice?

(b) Choose a different pair of interior angles and measure them. Find their sum. What do you notice this time?

(c) Write a probable conclusion about interior angles on the same side of the transversal.

PSP 6 One night, Peter finished reading his novel on page 300. The total number of digits used to number the pages he had read that day was 625. On what page did Peter start reading that day?

C 7 For each diagram, a transversal intersects parallel lines.

(a) Name the alternate and corresponding angles.

(b) Which angles are equal?

(c) Which angles are interior angles on the same side of the transversal?

(d) Which angles have a sum of 180°?

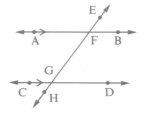

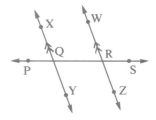

In your earlier work you investigated these two properties about the isosceles triangle. These two results illustrate an example of **converse statements**.

In an isosceles triangle, the angles opposite the equal sides are equal.

In △ABC, if $\overline{AB} = \overline{AC}$, then $\angle B = \angle C$.

In an isosceles triangle, the sides opposite the equal angles are equal.

In △ABC, if $\angle B = \angle C$, then $\overline{AB} = \overline{AC}$.

In the previous pages, you explored and discovered these properties for parallel lines:

> When a transversal intersects two or more parallel lines
> I alternate angles formed are equal.
> II corresponding angles formed are equal.
> III interior angles on the same side of the transversal are supplementary.

In the following questions you will explore the converses of the properties of parallel lines above.

8   Each diagram illustrates one property of parallel lines. Name the property.

(a)   (b)   (c)

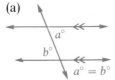
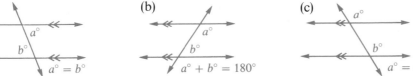
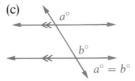

9   Construct the following diagrams. Which lines would meet if they were extended indefinitely? Which would not?

(a)   (b)   (c)   (d)   (e)

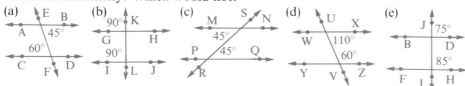
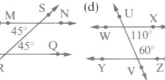

10   A transversal intersects two lines as shown at the right. For which of the following statements do you think the lines will be parallel?

(a) $\angle 4 = \angle 5$ (b) $\angle 6 + \angle 5 = 180°$ (c) $\angle 7 = \angle 4$

(d) $\angle 1 = \angle 3$ (e) $\angle 8 < \angle 3$ (f) $\angle 8 = \angle 5$

(g) $\angle 3 = \angle 6$ (h) $\angle 6 > \angle 3$ (i) $\angle 6 + \angle 4 = 180°$

8.7 Applying Properties: Parallel Lines

In the previous section you used deductive reasoning to discover the
properties of parallel lines and transversals, as well as the converses of
the properties.

Properties of parallel lines	Converses of the properties

Properties of parallel lines

If two parallel lines are
intersected by a transversal, then

A alternate angles are equal.
B corresponding angles are
equal.
C interior angles on the same
side of the transversal are
supplementary.

Converses of the properties

When two lines are intersected by a
transversal

CA If the alternate angles formed by
the transversal are equal, then the
lines are parallel.
CB If the corresponding angles formed
by the transversal are equal, then
the lines are parallel.
CC If the interior angles on the same
side of the transversal are
supplementary, then the lines are
parallel.

Now you can combine the properties of parallel lines and the properties
of the angles of a triangle with your skills in solving equations as shown
in the following example.

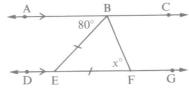

Example 1 Find the measure of $\angle$ BFE.

Solution Since $\overrightarrow{AC} \parallel \overrightarrow{DG}$, then $\angle ABE = \angle BEF = 80°$.
Also, since $\triangle EBF$ is isosceles, then $\angle EBF = \angle BFE = x°$,
And $\angle BEF + \angle EBF + \angle BFE = 180°$.

Thus $80° + x° + x° = 180°$
$$2x° = 180° - 80°$$
$$x° = 50°$$

Thus $\angle BFE = 50°$.

You also need to use your language skills to solve some word problems
by first translating from English to mathematics.

Example 2 $\overrightarrow{AB} \parallel \overrightarrow{CD}$ and $\overrightarrow{EF}$ is a transversal that intersects $\overrightarrow{AB}$ and $\overrightarrow{CD}$ at G
and H, respectively. The interior angle on the same side of the
transversal as $\angle AGH$ is twice the size of $\angle AGH$. Find the
measure of each of these interior angles.

Solution

Let $x°$ represent the measure of $\angle AGH$. Then $2x°$ represents the measure of the other interior $\angle CHG$. Since you know that $\overleftrightarrow{AB} \parallel \overleftrightarrow{CD}$, with transversal $\overleftrightarrow{EF}$, then $\angle AGH$ and $\angle CHG$ are supplementary.

Think: Draw a diagram.

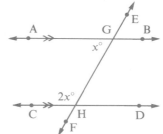

Thus $x° + 2x° = 180°$

$$3x° = 180°$$
$$x° = 60°$$

Thus $\angle AGH = 60°$
and $\angle CHG = 120°$.

PSP Always make a concluding statement when completing your solution.

8.7 Exercise

A Give a reason for each step in your answer. **PSP**

1 Find the value of x in each of the following.

(a)
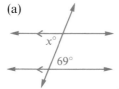

(b)
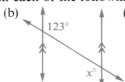

(c)
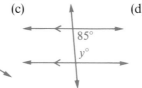

(d)
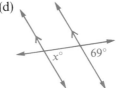

2 Find lines or line segments that are parallel.

(a)
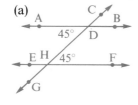

(b)
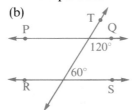

(c)
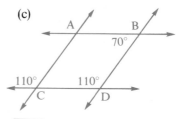

B Remember: Always justify each step of your solution. **PSP**

3 Find lines or line segments that are parallel in each of the following.

(a)
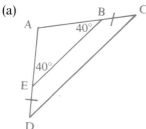

(b)
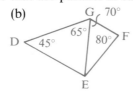

(c)
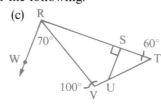

4 Find the value of each variable in the following.

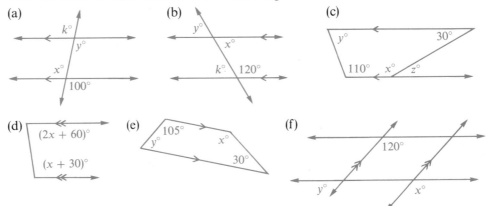

(a)

$k°$
$y°$
$x°$
$100°$

(b)

$y°$
$x°$
$k°$ $120°$

(c)

$y°$
$30°$
$110°$ $x°$ $z°$

(d)

$(2x + 60)°$
$(x + 30)°$

(e)

$105°$
$y°$ $x°$
$30°$

(f)

$120°$
$y°$ $x°$

5 One angle of a parallelogram is three times the measure of the exterior angle adjacent to it. Find the measure of each angle.

6 In a triangle, one angle is 35° more than a second angle. A third angle is 35° more than the first angle. Find the measure of each angle.

7 Use the diagram at the right.
   (a) Why is $a° = b°$?   (b) Why is $c° = d°$?
   (c) Why is $c° + e° + a° = 180°$?
   (d) How would you use the results in (a), (b) and (c) to show that $e° + d° + b° = 180°$?
   (e) What property about triangles have you deduced?

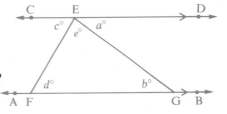

8 A car dealer can order a model of a car with choices of 7 different colours, 4 different types of interiors and 3 different types of motors. How many different cars of this model can the dealer order?

C 9 Find the value of each variable.

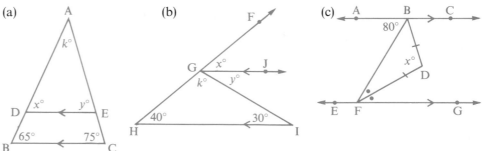

(a)

A
$k°$
$x°$ $y°$
D E
$65°$ $75°$
B C

(b)

F
G $x°$
$k°$ $y°$ J
$40°$ $30°$
H I

(c)

A B C
$80°$
$x°$
D
E F G

8.8   Constructions for Geometry

Two thousand years ago the Greeks used a straightedge and compasses to construct figures. Their interest in geometry has influenced design in art and architecture throughout the world.

Six basic constructions allow you to solve problems in geometry, to construct figures and to create designs.

▶ To copy a given angle
▶ To bisect a given angle
▶ To construct a perpendicular to a line at a point on the line
▶ To construct a perpendicular to a line from a point not on the line
▶ To construct the right or perpendicular bisector of a line segment
▶ To construct a line parallel to a given line through a point not on the given line

In the exercise, you will explore how to perform these basic constructions using a straightedge and compasses and using other techniques such as paper folding and transparent mirrors.

8.8   Exercise

A Use a transparent mirror for Questions 1–3.

1   (a) Draw a line segment 6 cm in length.
    (b) Find the midpoint by reflecting the line segment onto itself.
    (c) Describe how you did this.

2   (a) Draw a line segment 5 cm in length.
    (b) Use the mirror to form an obtuse angle by reflecting the line segment.
    (c) Draw the other arm of the angle.

3   Repeat the previous question, but this time draw an acute angle.

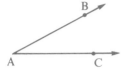

| To copy a given angle. |

B 4 Use these steps to make a copy of ∠ BAC using a straightedge and compasses.

Step 1 Step 2 Step 3 Step 4

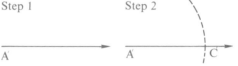
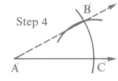

(a) Explain the steps followed in copying an angle.
(b) Draw an acute angle. Use the steps above to copy the angle.
(c) Draw an obtuse angle. Use the steps above to copy this angle.

5 Draw an acute angle. Use a protractor and a straightedge to copy this angle.

6 Draw an obtuse angle. Use tracing paper and a straightedge to copy this angle.

| To bisect a given angle. |

7 Use these steps to bisect ∠ BAC using a straightedge and compasses.

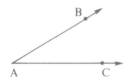

Step 1 Step 2 Step 3

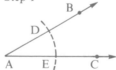
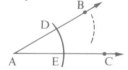
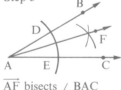

$\overrightarrow{AF}$ bisects ∠ BAC

(a) Explain the steps followed in bisecting an angle.
(b) Draw an acute angle. Use the steps above to bisect the angle.
(c) Draw an obtuse angle. Use the steps above to bisect this angle.

8 Draw an acute angle on a separate sheet of paper. Bisect this angle by folding the sheet of paper.

9 (a) Draw an obtuse angle. Bisect the angle by using a transparent mirror.
(b) Describe the steps you went through in (a).

To construct a perpendicular to a line at a point on the line.

10 Use these steps to construct a perpendicular at
    O using a straightedge and compasses.

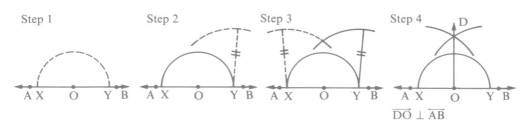

Step 1   Step 2   Step 3   Step 4

$\overrightarrow{DO} \perp \overrightarrow{AB}$

(a) Explain the steps followed in constructing a perpendicular at O.

(b) Draw any line and mark a point on it. Construct a perpendicular to the point.

11 Draw any line segment on a separate sheet of paper and mark a point on it. Locate the perpendicular to the line at that point by folding the sheet of paper.

12 Draw any line segment and mark a point on it. Use a transparent mirror to construct the perpendicular at the point.

To construct a perpendicular to a line from a point not on the line.

13 Follow these steps to draw the perpendicular,
    $\overrightarrow{PD}$, from the point P to $\overleftrightarrow{AB}$
    using a straightedge and compasses.

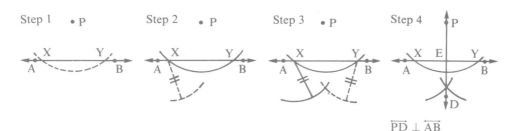

Step 1   • P   Step 2   • P   Step 3   • P   Step 4

$\overrightarrow{PD} \perp \overleftrightarrow{AB}$

(a) Explain the steps followed in constructing $\overrightarrow{PD}$ perpendicular to $\overleftrightarrow{AB}$.

(b) Draw any line and a point not on the line. Construct a perpendicular to the line from the point.

14 Use grid paper to draw a perpendicular to a line from a point not on the line.

15 Use the set square from a geometry set to draw a perpendicular to a line from a point not on the line.

16 (a) Draw any line segment and a point not on the line. Use a transparent mirror to draw a perpendicular to the line from the point.

(b) Describe the steps you went through in (a).

To construct the right or perpendicular bisector of a line segment.

---

17 Follow these steps to draw the right bisector $\overleftrightarrow{CD}$ of $\overline{AB}$ using a straightedge and compasses.

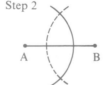

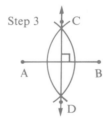

$\overleftrightarrow{CD} \perp \overline{AB}$ and $\overleftrightarrow{CD}$ bisects $\overline{AB}$

(a) Explain the steps followed in constructing $\overleftrightarrow{CD}$, the right bisector of $\overline{AB}$.

(b) Draw any line segment. Use the steps above to draw the perpendicular bisector of the line segment.

18 Draw any line segment on a separate sheet of paper. Construct the perpendicular bisector of the line segment by folding the paper.

19 (a) Draw any line segment. Use a transparent mirror to construct the perpendicular bisector of the line segment.

(b) Describe the steps you went through in (a).

20 (a) Compare the methods used to construct a right or perpendicular bisector of a line segment with those used to bisect an angle.

(b) Explain how the construction of the perpendicular bisector of a line segment is a special case of the construction of the bisector of an angle.

> To construct a line parallel to a given line through a point not on the given line.

21 Use these steps to draw $\overleftrightarrow{EF}$ parallel to $\overleftrightarrow{GH}$ through a point, P, not on the given line using a straightedge and compasses.

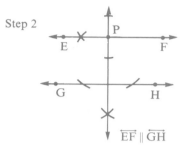

(a) Explain the steps followed in constructing a line through P parallel to $\overleftrightarrow{GH}$.

(b) Upon what property of parallel lines is this construction based?

(c) Draw any line and mark a point not on it. Construct a line through this point parallel to the line. P •

22 These steps show another method for constructing a line parallel to a given line $\overleftrightarrow{GH}$ through a point P, not on $\overleftrightarrow{GH}$.

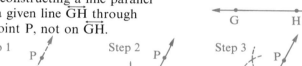

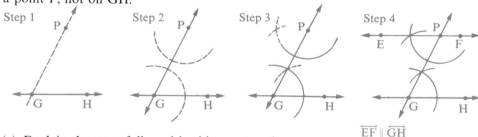

(a) Explain the steps followed in this construction.

(b) Upon which property of parallel lines is this construction based?

(c) Draw a line. Mark a point not on the line. Use the steps above to construct a line through the point and parallel to the line.

23 Use grid paper to draw a line parallel to a given line through a point not on the given line.

C 24 (a) Draw any line. Mark a point not on the line. Use a transparent mirror to construct a line through the point and parallel to the line.

(b) Describe how to construct a line parallel to a given line through a point not on the given line by using a transparent mirror.

8.9 Applications: Using Constructions

In the previous section you used a variety of techniques to carry out the six basic constructions. In this section, you will use those constructions to draw triangles and special angles.

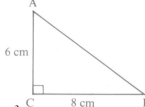

Example 1   Use the sketch to draw △ABC with ∠C = 90°, $\overline{AC}$ = 6 cm and $\overline{CB}$ = 8 cm.

Solution

Step 1
Construct $\overrightarrow{CD}$.
Mark B so that $\overline{CB}$ is 8 cm.

Step 2
Extend $\overrightarrow{DC}$. Construct a perpendicular at C.

Step 3
Mark A on the perpendicular so that $\overline{CA}$ is 6 cm. Join A and B.

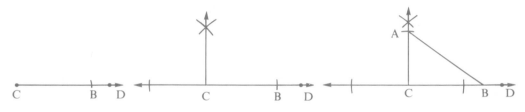

Example 2   Construct an angle of $22\frac{1}{2}°$.

Solution

Step 1
Construct
∠ABC = 90°.

Step 2
Bisect ∠ABC, thus constructing ∠DBC = 45°.

Step 3
Bisect ∠DBC, thus constructing ∠EBC = $22\frac{1}{2}°$.

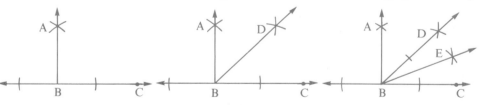

8.9 Exercise

A To do accurate constructions, use a sharp pencil. Label your diagrams carefully.

1 (a) Draw an acute angle.   (b) Make a copy of this angle.
   (c) Construct an angle twice the size of the angle in (b).

2 (a) Draw an obtuse angle.
   (b) Make a copy of this angle. Use a technique different from the one you used in the previous question.
   (c) Construct an angle twice the size of the angle in (b).
   (d) Use a transparent mirror to bisect this angle.

B 3 The measures of two angles are shown. Construct angles that have the following measures.

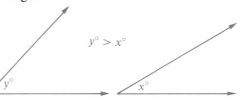

   (a) 2x   (b) 2y   (c) x + y
   (d) y − x (e) 2(x + y) (f) 2y − x

4 Rough sketches of triangles are shown. Make an accurate construction of each triangle.

(a)
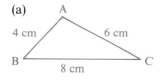

(b)
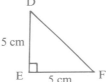

(c)

(d)
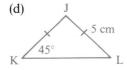

(e)
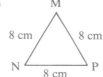

(f)
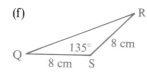

5 (a) Construct an equilateral triangle so that one side measures 8.5 cm.
   (b) Use the same method that you used in (a) to construct an angle of 60°.
   (c) Use your previous work. Construct an angle that measures 30°, 15°.

PSP 6 How many three-digit whole numbers have a middle digit of 1?

PSP 7 The sum of the squares of two consecutive even integers is 340. Find the integers.

C 8 Use only a straightedge and compasses. Construct each angle.

   (a) 45° (b) 120° (c) 105° (d) 165° (e) $67\frac{1}{2}^{\circ}$ (f) 225°

9 Use only a transparent mirror and a straightedge to construct each angle.

   (a) $22\frac{1}{2}^{\circ}$ (b) 135° (c) 75° (d) $157\frac{1}{2}^{\circ}$ (e) 150° (f) 315°

Applications: Designs in Business

Designs and logos are used by companies and advertisers so that people, when they see the logo, may think of their product.

A    B

10 Which shapes are used to construct each of the logos above?

11 Based on your impression of what the logo reminds you of, suggest in what type of business each company might be involved.

12 (a) Which constructions are used to create logo A above?

(b) Make a larger copy of the logo.

13 (a) Which constructions are used to create logo B above?

(b) Make a larger copy of the logo.

14 Which basic constructions have been used to construct each of the following?

(a) 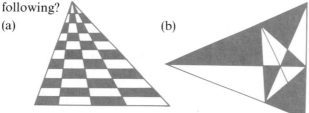   (b)   (c)

15 Identify which basic constructions have been used to construct each logo below. Make a larger copy of each logo. (Choose your own measures.)

(a)   (b)    (c)   (d)   (e)

16 Use the impression created by each logo in the previous question to suggest the nature of the business each company does.

17 All of the basic constructions were used to create this design. Can you find them all? Construct a copy so that $\overline{AB} = 16$ cm and $\overline{CD} = 8$ cm.

8.10   Relations with Circles

In earlier sections you explored the properties of triangles and of parallel lines when crossed by a transversal. The same strategy can be used to explore properties of circles. You will follow the same steps as you did in exploring and applying the properties of other geometric figures. **PSP**

8.10   Exercise

A   To work with circles you need to review the meanings of special words. Add new words to your vocabulary list.

1   The centre of a circle is marked by O. Match each definition with the part of the circle that it describes. Use the diagrams to help.

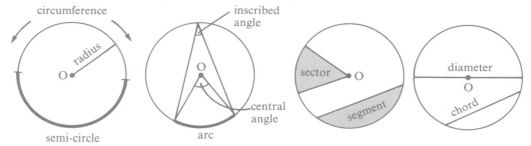

The inscribed angle and the central angle are **subtended** on an arc.

(a) the perimeter or distance around the circle

(b) a line segment that joins the centre to any point on the circumference

(c) half of the circumference   (d) part of the circumference

(e) a line segment joining any two points on the circumference

(f) a chord passing through the centre   (g) a region formed by an arc and two radii

(h) a region formed by a chord and an arc of a circle

(i) an angle formed by two chords as arms and with its vertex on the circumference

(j) an angle formed by two radii as arms and with its vertex at the centre

 Questions 2 to 7 investigate relations about the chords of circles.

B 2   (a) Construct a circle with a radius of 4 cm. Mark the centre O.

(b) Draw any two chords in the circle.

(c) Construct the right bisectors of the chords in (b). What do you notice?

3 (a) Repeat the steps in the previous question for another circle.

   (b) Use your results from (a) to write a probable conclusion about the right bisectors of chords.

4 Two chords are drawn in a circle as shown. Why is it not possible to find the centre using these two chords?

5 (a) Construct a circle with a radius of 6 cm. Mark the centre O.

   (b) Draw any chord in the circle.

   (c) Draw a perpendicular from O to the chord as shown.

   (d) Measure SP and PT. What do you notice?

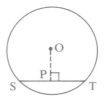

6 (a) Repeat the steps of the previous question for other chords drawn in circles. What do you notice about the measures of $\overline{SP}$ and PT each time?

   (b) Use your results from (a) to write a probable conclusion about the perpendicular drawn from the centre of a circle to a chord.

PSP Writing a probable conclusion is an important skill in problem solving.

7 To find the distance $\overline{OD}$ of a chord from the centre of a circle, you construct the perpendicular as shown. The distance of the chord $\overline{AB}$ from the centre is $\overline{OD}$.

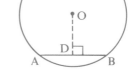

   (a) Draw two congruent chords in a circle with centre O.

   (b) Find the distance from the centre O to each chord. What do you notice?

   (c) Repeat (a) and (b) for other chords and circles. What do you notice each time about the distances from the centre to the chords?

   (d) Use your results from (c) to write a probable conclusion about congruent chords in a circle.

 Questions 8 to 13 explore relations between inscribed angles and central angles.

8 (a) Construct a circle diagram like the one shown.

   (b) Measure $\angle ABC$ and $\angle AOC$. What do you notice about their measures?

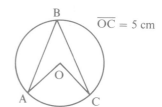

9 (a) Construct any circle and repeat the steps of the previous question.

   (b) Use the results from (a) to write a probable conclusion about the inscribed angle and its corresponding central angle.

10　(a) Construct a circle diagram like the one shown.

　　(b) Measure ∠ABC and ∠ADC. What do you notice?

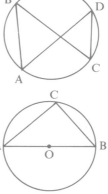

11　(a) Construct any circle and repeat the steps of the previous question.

　　(b) Use the results from (a) to write a probable conclusion about angles inscribed on the same arc.

12　(a) Construct a circle with radius 6.5 cm.

　　(b) Draw the angle subtended by the diameter as shown.

　　(c) Measure ∠ACB. What do you notice?

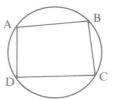

13　(a) Repeat the steps of the previous question for any circle. What do you notice?

　　(b) Use your results from (a) to write a probable conclusion about the inscribed angle subtended by the diameter.

PSP　Questions 14 to 16 explore relations about inscribed quadrilaterals.

14　Quadrilateral ABCD is inscribed in the circle. ∠A and ∠C are called **opposite angles**.

　　(a) Construct a circle with diameter 9 cm.

　　(b) Draw any quadrilateral in the circle.

　　(c) Measure a pair of opposite angles and find their sum. What do you notice?

　　(d) Measure the other pair of opposite angles and find their sum. What do you notice?

15　(a) Repeat the steps of the previous question for any circle and inscribed quadrilateral. What do you notice about the sums of opposite angles each time?

　　(b) Use your results from (a) to write a probable conclusion about the opposite angles of quadrilaterals inscribed in a circle.

PSP 16　The minute hand of a clock is 12 cm long. Find the area swept out by the hand from 08:15 to 10:00.

C 17　The sum of both pairs of opposite angles of a quadrilateral is 180°.

　　(a) Do you think a circle can be drawn through the vertices of the quadrilateral?

　　(b) Test your answer in (a) by using quadrilaterals with the above property.

　　(c) Construct a rectangle with sides 6 cm and 8 cm. Construct a circle to pass through all vertices.

8.11 **PSP** Solving Problems about Circles

In the previous section, you used inductive reasoning to find the following properties of circles.

In a circle
▶ the perpendicular drawn from the centre to a chord bisects the chord.
▶ the right bisectors of chords pass through the centre.
▶ chords of equal length are the same distance from the centre.
▶ chords that are the same distance from the centre are equal in length.
▶ the measure of the central angle is twice that of the inscribed angle on the same arc.
▶ inscribed angles drawn on the same arc have equal measures.
▶ the inscribed angle subtended by the diameter is a right angle.
▶ the opposite angles of an inscribed quadrilateral are supplementary.

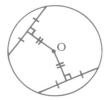  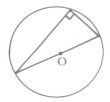

$$x° + y° = 180°$$

You can use these properties and your earlier skills in algebra to find missing measures as shown in the following example.

Example Find the missing measures. Give reasons for your answers.

(a) 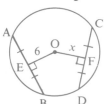 (b) 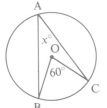 (c)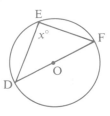

Solution

(a) Equal chords are the same distance from the centre.
$\overline{OE} = \overline{OF}$
$x = 6$

(b) The central angle is twice that of the inscribed angle.
$\angle BOC = 2\angle BAC$
$2x = 60$
$x = 30$

(c) The inscribed angle subtended by the diameter is 90°.
$\angle DEF$ is subtended by diameter $\overline{DF}$.
$x = 90$

A 1   In your own words, write the property displayed by each circle diagram.

(a) 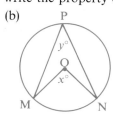   (b) 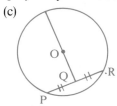   (c)   (d)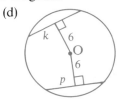

B   For each of your answers indicate the circle property used.   **PSP**
Check whether your answer is reasonable.

2   Find the missing measures in each of the following.

(a) 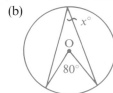   (b)   (c) 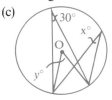   (d)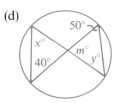

3   Find the missing measures. All linear measures are in centimetres.

(a) 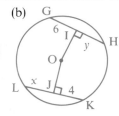   (b)   (c) 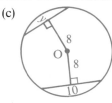   (d)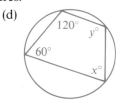

4   Find the missing measures.

(a) 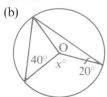   (b)   (c) 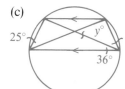   (d)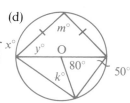

5   Find the missing measures. All linear measures are in centimetres.

(a)   (b) 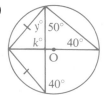   (c)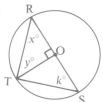

6   All of these letters have a property in common.   **B E I**

The letter M does not share this property, but
the letter H does. What are two other letters
that share the property? Justify your answer.

C 7 $\overline{AB}$ is a diameter of the
circle with centre O. Find
the value of $x° + y°$.

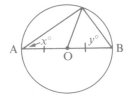

8    $\overline{ST}$ is a diameter of the circle with centre O. Find the
following measures. All linear measures are in
centimetres.

(a) $\angle SPO$ (b) $\angle OPQ$ (c) $\angle OQT$ (d) $\overline{OP}$ (e) $\overline{PQ}$

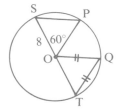

Calculator Use

The formula to calculate the area, A,
of a circle is given by $A = \pi r^2$.

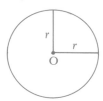

The formula to calculate the area, A,
of an ellipse is given by $A = \pi ab$.

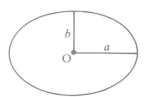

▶ How do the above formulas seem to be related?
▶ Calculate the area of an ellipse when $a = 12.86$ and
$b = 9.65$.

Math Tip

To solve a mathematics problem or a problem from elsewhere, you must
fully understand the meaning of each word that occurs in the problem.

▶ Make a list of the new math words you have learned. Provide an
example of your own to illustrate each word.
▶ List any new problem solving strategies you have acquired and place
them in your *Problem Solving Plan* .

8.12 PSP Problem Solving: More Than One Way

When you solve a problem, you can draw on past experiences to decide on an appropriate strategy. When you think of the problem from a different perspective, another strategy may then seem more readily applicable. Always try to search for an alternative solution, even after you have solved the problem.

In particular, suppose you wanted fo find the exact position of the centre of a circle. Two different strategies for doing so are based on the two following properties of a circle.

A	In a circle, the inscribed angle subtended by the diameter is a right angle.

B	In a circle, the right bisector of a chord passes through the centre of the circle.

You can use the two results above to find the centre of a circle using different strategies.

Strategy A
Find two diameters. Their intersection is at the centre, O, of the circle.

Strategy B
Draw two chords. Construct the right bisector of each. Their intersection is at the centre, O, of the circle.

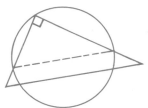 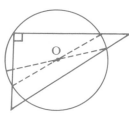 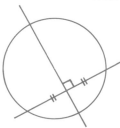 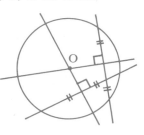

8.12 Exercise

A 1 (a) Trace any circular shape.
  (b) Use strategy A. Find the centre of the circle.
  (c) Use strategy B. Find the centre of the circle.

2 (a) Use a can. Trace the base. (b) Find the centre of the base of the can.

3 Describe a method of finding the exact centre of a circular garden.

8.13   **PSP**   Problem Solving: Using Strategies

In solving a problem, it is important that you know the answers to these two questions.

    I   What information am I asked to find?
   II   What information am I given?

Once you clearly understand the answers to these questions, decide on a strategy to solve the problem. Refer to the list of strategies from your *Problem Solving Plan* **PSP**   Solve the following problems.

PSP   Problem Solving Plan

Step A: Understand the problem.
   • What are you asked to find?
   • What are you given?

Step B: Decide on a strategy.
Step C: Apply the strategy. Do the work.
Step D: Check your solution.
Step E: Write a final statement.

8.13   Exercise

B **1**   Jackson has 4 pairs of pants and 7 shirts. How many different combinations of outfits can he wear?

   2   Suppose you could type five digits every second. About how long would it take you to type the number given by the answer to 3^{3^3}?

   3   To solve some problems, you need to research to obtain further information. Solve this problem. What is the average diameter of the planets and the sun in our solar system?

   4   Each of these letters has a property in common.   M   T   H
The vowel E does not share this property, but the vowel A does.
What are two other letters that share the property? Justify your answer.

   5   The sum of the squares of three consecutive integers is 365.
Find the integers.

   6   How many triangles are in the diagram?

   7   A two-digit number is equal to 4 times the sum of its digits. Find the number.

Practice and Problems: Review

1   Find the complement and the supplement of 75°.

2   Draw an example of (a) an acute triangle that is isosceles.

                       (b) a quadrilateral with 2 right angles and an obtuse angle.

3   Name pairs of congruent angles. Give reasons for your answers.

    (a) 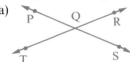   (b) 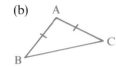   (c)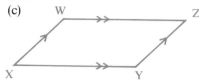

4   Find the missing angle measures.

    (a) 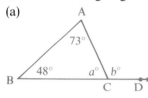 (b) 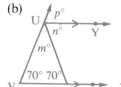 (c) 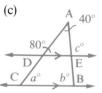 (d)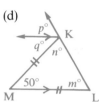

5   Make an accurate construction of the following figures. Measure the remaining angles.

    (a) 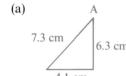   (b) 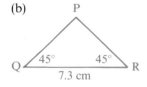   (c)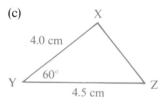

6   Construct an angle of each degree measure.

    (a) $22\frac{1}{2}^{\circ}$ (b) 120°   (c) 225°   (d) 75°

7   (a) Construct a circle with radius 7 cm. Mark the centre O.

    (b) Draw ∠AOC where A and C are points on the circle.

    (c) If B is a point on the circle, compare the measures of ∠ABC and ∠AOC.

8   Find the variable angle measures. O is the centre.

    (a) 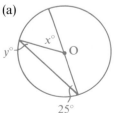   (b) 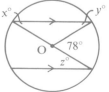 (c) 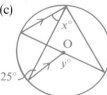   (d)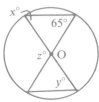

Practice Test

1   From the diagram, identify

   (a) a ray   (b) a line segment

   (c) a line   (d) a pair of parallel lines

   (e) an acute angle   (f) an obtuse angle

   (g) a pair of supplementary angles

   (h) a pair of vertically opposite angles

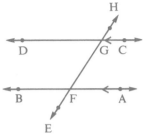

2   Name pairs of congruent angles.

   (a) 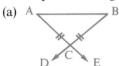   (b) 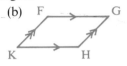   (c)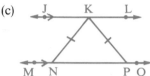

3   (a) Draw any obtuse angle. Then copy it.

   (b) Bisect the copy made in (a).

4   Draw a line segment 10 cm long.

   (a) Locate a point on the line segment and construct a perpendicular at that point.

   (b) Locate a point above the line segment and construct a perpendicular from that point.

   (c) Construct the perpendicular bisector of the line segment

   (d) Locate a point below the line segment and construct a line parallel to the line segment through the point.

5   Construct an equilateral triangle with sides each 6.5 cm.

6   Find the measures indicated by variables. O is the centre of each circle.

   (a) 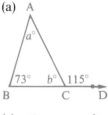 (b) 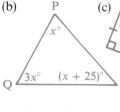 (c)   (d)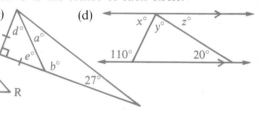

   (e) 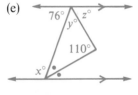 (f) 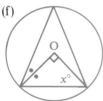 (g) 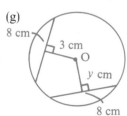 (h)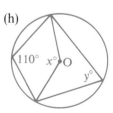

9 *The Nature of Geometry*

Using triangle properties, constructing quadrilaterals, conditions for building triangles, developing strategies, concept of congruence and similarity, applying skills to geometric problems using indirect measurement, essential vocabulary of geometry, applications, strategies for problem solving

Introduction

In any branch of mathematics that you study, certain aspects of doing mathematics recur. The diagram to the right outlines an important aspect of problem solving that provides a useful foundation for success.

As you continue to study mathematics, you will begin to recognize and appreciate that the process of studying each different branch of mathematics has a familiar pattern. In fact, this pattern applies to a variety of other disciplines that you will study as shown below.

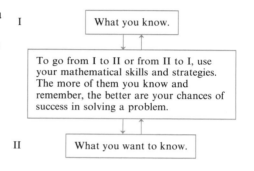

Studying Geometry

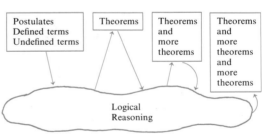

Studying Mathematics

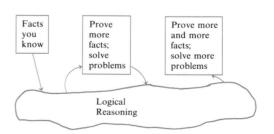

9.1 ◢PSP◣ Problem Solving: What If . . . ?

Often in the pursuit of knowledge, new information is obtained by asking the question, "What if . . . ?"

In geometry, you can ask many "What if . . . ?" questions.

▶ What if you construct the bisectors of all the angles of a triangle?
▶ What if you construct all the right bisectors of the sides of a triangle?

In Chapter 8, you performed the following basic constructions.

▶ To copy a given angle
▶ To bisect a given angle
▶ To construct a perpendicular to a point on a line
▶ To construct a perpendicular to a line from a point not on the line
▶ To construct the right or perpendicular bisector of a line segment
▶ To construct a line parallel to a given line through a point not on the given line

You can use the basic constructions to explore "What if . . . ?" questions. For example, what if you construct the bisectors of all of the angles of a triangle?

Example   (a) Construct the bisectors of all the angles of any △ABC.
           (b) What do you notice?

Solution   (a)

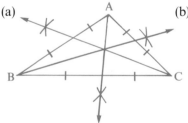

(b) The bisectors of the angles of △ABC intersect at the same point.

Using the basic constructions, you can investigate other "What if . . . ?" ◢PSP◣ questions. Throughout the exercise, you will use inductive reasoning to help you write probable conclusions related to triangles.

9.1 Exercise

A Review the six basic constructions before beginning the exercise. Remember to list any new words that you learn in your vocabulary list.

1   (a) Draw any △PQR. Construct the bisectors of the angles of △PQR. What do you notice?
    (b) Write a probable conclusion about the bisectors of the angles of a triangle.

B Once you have completed the exercise, make a list of the geometric properties you have learned.

2 (a) A perpendicular bisector of one side of △ABC is drawn. Copy this diagram onto a sheet of paper and construct the perpendicular bisectors of the other sides of △ABC.

   (b) What if you extend the perpendicular bisectors until they meet? What do you notice?

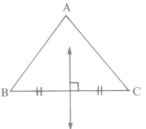

3 Repeat the steps in the previous question for each of the following types of triangles.

   (a) acute   (b) obtuse   (c) right

4 Use your results from the two previous questions to write a probable conclusion about the perpendicular bisectors of the sides of a triangle.

5 For each triangle shown, $\overline{BD}$ is an **altitude**.

   (a) Write a definition for the altitude of a triangle.

   (b) How many altitudes can be drawn for a triangle?

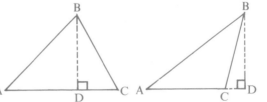

6 (a) Draw any acute triangle.   (b) Construct all the altitudes of the triangle.
   (c) What do you notice about the three altitudes?

7 Repeat the steps in the previous question for each of the following types of triangles.

   (a) obtuse   (b) right

8 Use your results from the two previous questions to write a probable conclusion about the altitudes of a triangle.

9 The median, $\overline{AD}$, of △ABC is shown.

   (a) Write a definition for the median of a triangle.

   (b) How many medians can be drawn for a triangle?

   (c) How would you use the right bisector of $\overline{BC}$ to help you draw the median $\overline{AD}$?

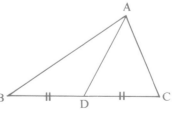

10 (a) Draw an acute triangle.   (b) Construct the median of each side.
    (c) What do you notice about the medians?

11   Repeat the steps in the previous question for each of the following types
     of triangles.
     (a) obtuse   (b) right

12   Use your results from the two previous questions. Write a probable
     conclusion about the medians of a triangle.

13   The vertical angle for an isosceles triangle is shown.
     (a) Construct an acute isosceles triangle.
     (b) Bisect the vertical angle.
     (c) Construct the altitude from the vertical angle of the triangle.
     (d) What do you notice about your results in (b) and (c)?
     (e) Repeat steps (b) and (c) for an equilateral triangle. What do
         you notice?

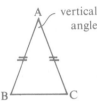

14   (a) Construct an equilateral triangle.
     (b) Construct the right bisector of one of the sides.
     (c) Extend the right bisector. What do you notice?
     (d) Construct all the right bisectors. What do you notice?

 15   (a) For a sphere, A represents the number of square units of surface area
     and V represents the number of cubic units of volume. Decide whether
     the value of A can ever equal the value of V.
     (b) The radius of the sphere in (a) is increased in value. How is the value
     of $\dfrac{A}{V}$ affected?

Calculator Use

You have seen earlier how a calculator can be used to study interesting
patterns. For example, how does the value of $\left(1 + \dfrac{1}{n}\right)^n$ change as n becomes
greater and greater?

▶ Calculate $\left(1 + \dfrac{1}{99}\right)^{99}$. Use the steps shown.

                                        Output

$\boxed{C}\,1\,\boxed{\div}\,99\,\boxed{+}\,1\,\boxed{=}\,\boxed{y^x}\,99\,\boxed{=}$?

▶ As n increases in value, what value does the expression $\left(1 + \dfrac{1}{n}\right)^n$
approach? Try $n = 999, 9999, 99\,999$ and so on.

9.2 Applying Geometric Properties

In the previous section you investigated some "What if . . . ?" questions related to triangles. By using the basic constructions, you found these properties of triangles.

The bisectors of the angles of a triangle intersect at the same point R. They are concurrent. R is called the **incentre**.

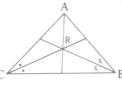

The altitudes of a triangle are concurrent and meet at the point P. P is called the **orthocentre**.

The perpendicular bisectors of the sides of a triangle are concurrent and meet at point Q. Q is called the **circumcentre**.

The medians of a triangle are concurrent and meet at the point G. G is called the **centre of gravity**.

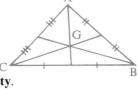

These properties can be extended and used to solve problems. **PSP**

9.2 Exercise

A Review the basic constructions before you begin. Add all the new vocabulary you learn to your vocabulary list. **PSP**

1 (a) Draw any △ABC.
   (b) Bisect each angle of △ABC. Label the incentre D and the points of intersection of the sides and the bisectors E, F and G.
   (c) Construct a circle with centre D and radius $\overline{DE}$. This circle is called the **inscribed** circle.
   (d) What do you notice about the circle?

2 Repeat the steps in the previous question for another triangle. What do you notice?

3 (a) Draw any △LMN.
   (b) Construct the perpendicular bisector of each side. Label the circumcentre O.
   (c) Construct a circle with centre O and radius $\overline{OL}$. This circle is called the **circumcircle**.
   (d) What do you notice about the circle?

4 Repeat the steps in the previous question for another triangle. What do you notice?

B   You must decide which construction is needed to complete each question.

5 (a) Draw a large triangle.
   (b) Construct the medians of this triangle.
   (c) Cut out the triangle and suspend it from its centre of gravity. What do you notice?
   (d) Suspend the triangle from points other than the centre of gravity. What do you notice?

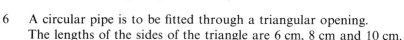

6 A circular pipe is to be fitted through a triangular opening. The lengths of the sides of the triangle are 6 cm, 8 cm and 10 cm.
   (a) Construct the triangle.
   (b) Find the radius of the largest pipe that will fit through a hole with this triangular shape.

7 Find the diameter, to 1 decimal place, of the largest pipe that fits through each of the following triangular openings.

(a)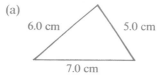

(b)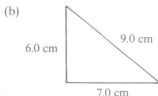

8 Three sentries are placed at the positions A, B and C. Where should a fourth sentry, D, be placed so that D is the same distance from A, B and C?

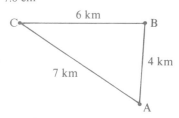

 9 Some letters have a horizontal line of symmetry. $--\mathbf{B}-\mathbf{E}--\mathbf{X}-\mathbf{O}--$

The words shown also have a horizontal line of symmetry. $\mathbf{BE} \qquad \mathbf{BOX}$

   (a) What is the longest word that you can make that has a horizontal line of symmetry?
   (b) Write a sentence that has a horizontal line of symmetry.

C 10 Towns X and Y are 10 km apart. Towns Y and Z are 12 km apart. Towns X and Z are 14 km apart. Where should a hot-air balloon be released so that its departure point is the same distance from each town?

9.3 Constructing Triangles: Using Properties

As in your earlier work, to solve a problem or do a construction, you need to know the answers to these two important questions. **PSP**

I What am I asked to do?   II What information am I given?

Once you answer these questions, a useful next step is to *draw a sketch*. The sketch is then used to plan the steps of the construction.

Example   Construct $\triangle ABC$ where $\angle B = 45°$, $\overline{BC} = 4$ cm and $\angle C = 30°$. Use only a straightedge and compasses.

Solution

Step 1: Draw a sketch and record the given **PSP**   *Step 2:* Draw $\overline{BC} = 4$ cm. information.

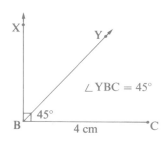

$\overline{BC}$ is a contained side.

Step 3: To obtain an angle of 45° you can bisect a right angle. Thus construct $\overrightarrow{BX} \perp \overline{BC}$ at point B. Then construct $\overrightarrow{BY}$, the bisector of $\angle XBC$.

Step 4: To obtain an angle of 30° you bisect an angle of 60°. Thus construct equilateral $\triangle ZBC$ with $\angle ZCB = 60°$. Now construct $\overrightarrow{CW}$, the bisector of $\angle ZCB$. Label point A, the point of intersection of $\overrightarrow{CW}$ and $\overrightarrow{BY}$. Thus $\triangle ABC$ is the required triangle.

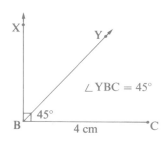

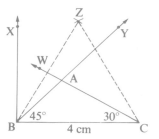

9.3 Exercise

A Review the basic constructions. Remember: Sort the given information by recording it on a sketch. **PSP**

1 Construct each angle without using a protractor.

(a) 90°   (b) 45°   (c) 60°   (d) 30°   (e) $22\frac{1}{2}°$ (f) 135°

B 2 (a) Draw a sketch of △CEF given ∠CEF = 90° and $\overline{CE} = \overline{EF} = 8$ cm.
   (b) How would you classify △CEF?   (c) Construct the triangle.
   (d) Without measuring, predict the measures of ∠ECF and ∠EFC.
   (e) Measure ∠ECF and ∠EFC. How close are your measures to your predictions?
   (f) Find the orthocentre of the triangle.

3 (a) Draw a sketch of △PQS given ∠QPS = 60° and $\overline{PQ} = \overline{PS} = 5$ cm.
   (b) Construct △PQS.
   (c) What should the measure of ∠Q and ∠S be? Measure to check.

4 ▶ Construct each triangle using only a straightedge and compasses.
   ▶ Measure the remaining parts of each triangle.
   ▶ Compare your measures with those of other students.
   (a) △CEF, ∠CEF = 60°, $\overline{CE} = 5$ cm, $\overline{EF} = 4$ cm
   (b) △PST, ∠PST = 75°, ∠PTS = 45°, $\overline{ST} = 6$ cm
   (c) △GHJ, $\overline{GH} = \overline{HJ} = 8.0$ cm, $\overline{GJ} = 6.5$ cm

5 (a) Find the orthocentres for the triangles in Question 4.
   (b) Find the centres of gravity for the triangles in Question 4.

6 (a) Construct △PQS so that ∠QPS = 90°, $\overline{PQ} = 4$ cm and $\overline{PS} = 3$ cm.
   (b) Inscribe a circle in △PQS.   (c) Construct the median from Q to $\overline{PS}$.

7 (a) Construct an equilateral triangle whose sides measure 4.5 cm.
   (b) Construct the circumcircle for the triangle in (a).

8 (a) Construct △ABC so that ∠C = 90° and $\overline{CB} = 4$ cm. The hypotenuse is 8 cm.
   (b) Find the orthocentre of the triangle. What do you notice?
   (c) Construct the median $\overline{CD}$ from ∠C to $\overline{AB}$. What do you notice about $\overline{CD}$ and $\overline{CB}$?

9 Analyze each design to decide how it was constructed. Then construct a copy of the design.
   (a)   (b)   (c)

9.4 Constructing Quadrilaterals

To construct quadrilaterals, you use the same steps that you used earlier to construct triangles.

Step 1: Draw a sketch of the figure you wish to construct.

Step 2: Record the given information on the sketch.

Step 3: Decide on the steps you will follow to plan the actual construction.

Example   Construct a quadrilateral ABCD so that $\angle CAD = 45°$, $\angle BAC = 30°$, $\overline{AC} = 5$ cm and $\overline{AB} = \overline{AD} = 4$ cm.

Solution   Draw a sketch. Record the given information on your sketch.   ![PSP]   Do the accurate construction using a ruler and protractor.

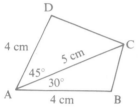

It is often useful to start with a known side placed horizontally.

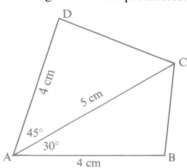

9.4 Exercise

A 1 (a) Construct the square shown in the sketch.

(b) Measure $\overline{DB}$ and $\overline{AC}$. What do you notice about their measures?

2 (a) Construct the rectangle shown by the sketch.

(b) Measure the diagonals $\overline{DF}$ and $\overline{GE}$. What do you notice?

3 (a) Construct the quadrilateral shown in the sketch.

(b) Classify the quadrilateral you have drawn.

(c) $\angle A$ and $\angle C$ are called opposite angles. Measure them. What do you notice?

(d) Measure $\angle D$ and $\angle B$. What do you notice?

B   Make a sketch to organize the given information.   ![PSP]

4 (a) Construct a rhombus with sides of 8 cm and one angle measuring 60°.

(b) Measure pairs of opposite angles. What do you notice?

5   (a) Construct a parallelogram with sides of 4.5 cm and 6.5 cm and one angle 60°.

    (b) Measure pairs of opposite angles. What do you notice?

6   Construct parallelogram KLMN so that $\overline{MN} = 4.5$ cm, $\overline{LM} = 6$ cm and $\angle LMN = 120°$.

7   (a) Construct quadrilateral DEFH so that $\overline{DE} = 6$ cm, $\overline{EF} = 8$ cm, $\angle DEF = 45°$, $\overline{ED} \parallel \overline{FH}$ and $\overline{EF} \parallel \overline{DH}$.

    (b) Find the area of the quadrilateral in (a).

8   To solve some problems you must try all the possibilities. How many different shapes can you make using 5 square tiles, where at least one side of each tile must touch an adjacent tile, as shown in the two possible shapes given at the right?

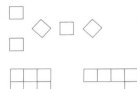

C 9   (a) Construct a parallelogram with sides of 8 cm and 6 cm and one angle 75°.

    (b) Bisect each side of the parallelogram in order to locate the midpoints of the sides.

    (c) Bisect each angle and extend each bisector to intersect a side of the parallelogram. What do you notice?

10   Repeat the steps of the previous question for a parallelogram with sides of 10 cm and 5 cm and one angle measuring 50°.

Math Tip: Vocabulary

You can't do mathematics if you do not understand the meanings of the math words. For each of the following words,

▶ use an example to illustrate that you understand the mean of the word.

▶ if you do not remember the meaning of the word, refer to the index or glossary of this text to search for the meaning of the word.

ray	square	trapezoid	inscribed angle	right triangle
median	kite	concurrent	acute angle	parallelogram
pentagon	bisect	rectangle	straight angle	adjacent angles
hexagon	altitude	right angle	parallel lines	regular polygon
rhombus	diagonal	transversal	obtuse angle	exterior angle

obtuse triangle	isosceles triangle	inscribed circle	equilateral triangle
alternate angles	scalene triangle	complementary angles	intersecting lines

perpendicular lines	corresponding angles	vertically opposite angles
supplementary angles	equiangular triangle	perpendicular bisector

9.5 Conditions for Building Triangles

In the previous sections you used the basic constructions to construct various figures, usually by starting with a sketch. Your sketch provides you with a plan to construct the figure. If each person uses the given information correctly, then the same figure should be constructed. If the given information could be interpreted in different ways, different figures would be obtained.

Earlier you saw that even though a triangle has 6 parts, namely

▶ 3 angles ▶ 3 sides

you do not need to be given all 6 parts in order to construct the triangle. In the following exercise, you will explore how many parts are really needed to construct a triangle. You will also decide whether a unique (only one) triangle can be constructed from the given information.

A blueprint provides the plan for building. Each engineer obtains the same interpretation from reading the blueprint. If it could be interpreted in different ways, errors would be made.

9.5 Exercise

B 1   (a) A sketch with the given information is provided. Construct a triangle.

    (b) Which piece of information on the diagram is not needed?

        ∠ B is called a **contained** or **included** angle with respect to sides $\overline{AB}$ and $\overline{BC}$.

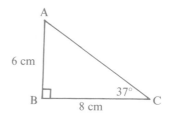

2   (a) A sketch with the given information is provided. Construct a triangle.

    (b) Did you need all the information to do the construction?

        $\overline{BC}$ is called a **contained** or **included** side with respect to the angles B and C.

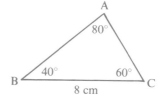

3   (a) A sketch with the given information is provided. Construct the triangle.

    (b) Did you need all the information to do the construction?

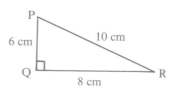

4 (a) Use the information on the diagram. Construct the
       triangle.
   (b) Measure $\overline{AB}$. Compare your answer with those of
        other students. What do you notice?
   (c) Can a unique triangle be constructed from the
        sketch? Give reasons for your answer.

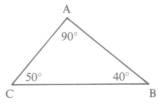

5 Four line segments are sketched at the right.
   (a) Construct triangles with sides as given below.
           ▶ $\overline{AB}, \overline{CD}, \overline{EF}$ ▶ $\overline{CD}, \overline{EF}, \overline{GH}$
   (b) Measure the other parts. Compare your answers
        with those of other students. Are the triangles
        unique?
   (c) Can you construct a triangle with sides: $\overline{AB}, \overline{EF}, \overline{GH}$? Give reasons
        for your answer.
   (d) Choose 3 other segments from which you cannot construct a triangle.
        Give reasons for your choice.

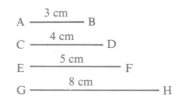

6 (a) Construct the triangle in each sketch.
   (b) List the given information for each
        triangle. What do you notice?
   (c) Based on the information, why is
        △ABC not unique? Give reasons
        for your answer.

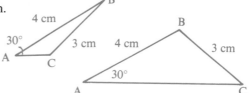

7 Use the information shown on each sketch. List any information you did
   not use to do the construction. For which sketches is it impossible to
   construct a triangle?

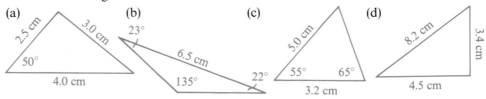

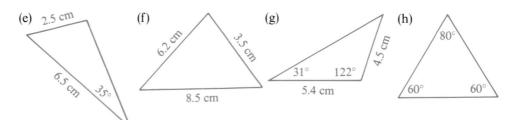

8   Construct each of the following triangles. For which of the following constructions do you obtain
    ▶ only one triangle?   ▶ more than one triangle?   ▶ no triangle?
    (a) △ABC, $\overline{AB}$ = 6 cm, ∠ABC = 30°, $\overline{BC}$ = 5 cm
    (b) △QRA, $\overline{AR}$ = 6 cm, ∠QRA = 30°, $\overline{QA}$ = 5 cm
    (c) △VWX, $\overline{VW}$ = 5 cm, $\overline{VX}$ = 4 cm, ∠VWX = 75°
    (d) △KLM, ∠M = 40°, $\overline{LM}$ = 5 cm, $\overline{LK}$ = 6 cm
    (e) △DEF, $\overline{DF}$ = 8 cm, $\overline{DE}$ = 6 cm, $\overline{EF}$ = 6 cm
    (f) △QRT, $\overline{QR}$ = 3 cm, $\overline{RT}$ = 2 cm, $\overline{QT}$ = 5 cm
    (g) △QVW, ∠VWQ = 45°, $\overline{QW}$ = 7 cm, $\overline{QV}$ = 8 cm
    (h) △RSW, $\overline{RS}$ = 6.0 cm, $\overline{RW}$ = 7.5 cm, ∠RWS = 45°
    (i) △ADF, ∠D = 30°, ∠F = 30°, $\overline{AF}$ = 8 cm
    (j) △AQR, $\overline{AQ}$ = 4 cm, $\overline{AR}$ = 2 cm, ∠AQR = 45°
    (k) △MNP, $\overline{MN}$ = 8 cm, $\overline{MP}$ = 5 cm, $\overline{NP}$ = 9 cm
    (l) △GHI, ∠I = 60°, ∠H = 45°, $\overline{HI}$ = 5 cm
    (m) △SAB, ∠S = 105°, ∠A = 30°, ∠B = 45°

PSP 9   A figure is made from toothpicks as shown. Remove four toothpicks to make five squares.

PSP 10   (a) Is it possible to have a year with no Friday the 13ths? Give reasons for your answer.
    (b) What is the maximum number of Friday the 13ths in one year?

C 11   △ABC can be constructed if you have the measures of *all* of its 6 parts: 3 angles and 3 sides. Which of the following conditions give
    ▶ a unique triangle?   ▶ more than one triangle?
    (a) 3 sides   (b) 2 angles and a side
    (c) 2 sides and the contained angle   (d) 2 angles and the contained side
    (e) 3 angles   (f) 1 angle and 2 sides

12   Refer to your work in the previous question.
    (a) List the conditions you need to construct a unique triangle.
    (b) Construct a triangle with given angle and side measures to illustrate each answer in (a).

9.6 Working with Congruence

In the previous section you saw that when given information about the parts of a triangle, under certain conditions you were able to construct only one triangle. Each triangle constructed had the same shape and size and the corresponding parts were **congruent**. Triangles such as these are called **congruent triangles**.

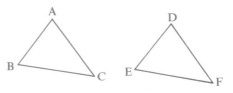

$\triangle ABC$ is congruent to $\triangle DEF$.

corresponding side

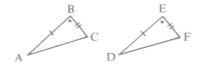

corresponding vertices

If $\triangle ABC \cong \triangle DEF$, then corresponding sides and corresponding angles are congruent.

Sides	Angles
$\overline{AB} \cong \overline{DE}$	$\angle A \cong \angle D$
$\overline{AC} \cong \overline{DF}$	$\angle B \cong \angle E$
$\overline{BC} \cong \overline{EF}$	$\angle C \cong \angle F$

The following sets of conditions are sufficient to construct a unique triangle.

Side Angle Side Relation (SAS)

If two pairs of corresponding sides and the corresponding contained angles of two triangles are congruent, then the two triangles are congruent.

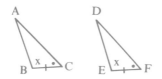

If you know
$\left.\begin{array}{l} \overline{AB} \cong \overline{DE} \\ \angle B \cong \angle E \\ \overline{BC} \cong \overline{EF} \end{array}\right\}$

then you know
$\triangle ABC \cong \triangle DEF$

and you know
$\left\{\begin{array}{l} \overline{AC} \cong \overline{DF} \\ \angle A \cong \angle D \\ \angle C \cong \angle F \end{array}\right.$

Angle Side Angle Relation (ASA)

If two pairs of corresponding angles and the corresponding contained sides of two triangles are congruent, then the two triangles are congruent.

If you know
$\left.\begin{array}{l} \angle B \cong \angle E \\ \overline{BC} \cong \overline{EF} \\ \angle C \cong \angle F \end{array}\right\}$

then you know
$\triangle ABC \cong \triangle DEF$

and you know
$\left\{\begin{array}{l} \overline{AB} \cong \overline{DE} \\ \angle A \cong \angle D \\ \overline{AC} \cong \overline{DF} \end{array}\right.$

Side Side Side Relation (SSS)

If all three pairs of corresponding sides of two triangles are congruent, then the two triangles are congruent.

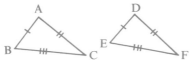

If you know
$\left.\begin{array}{l} \overline{AB} \cong \overline{DE} \\ \overline{BC} \cong \overline{EF} \\ \overline{AC} \cong \overline{DF} \end{array}\right\}$

then you know
$\triangle ABC \cong \triangle DEF$

and you know
$\left\{\begin{array}{l} \angle A \cong \angle D \\ \angle B \cong \angle E \\ \angle C \cong \angle F \end{array}\right.$

Angle Angle Side Relation (AAS)

If two angles of one triangle are equal to two angles of another triangle, then the remaining angles are equal. If two pairs of corresponding angles and one pair of corresponding sides of two triangles are congruent, then the two triangles are congruent.

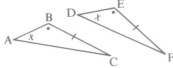

If you know	then you know	and you know
$\angle A \cong \angle D$		$\overline{AC} \cong \overline{DF}$
$\left.\begin{array}{l}\angle B \cong \angle E \\ \overline{BC} \cong \overline{EF}\end{array}\right\}$ $\triangle ABC \cong \triangle DEF$		$\left\{\begin{array}{l}\angle C \cong \angle F \\ \overline{AB} \cong \overline{DE}\end{array}\right.$

Each of these conditions allows you to deduce more information from the given information as shown in the following example.

Example   Two triangles are given.

(a) List the given information.

(b) What information can you deduce?

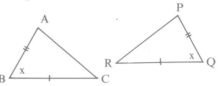

Solution   Match the corresponding vertices.

(a) From the diagram $\overline{AB} \cong \overline{PQ}$

$\qquad\qquad \angle B \cong \angle Q$

$\qquad\qquad \overline{BC} \cong \overline{QR}$

(b) Use SAS. Then $\triangle ABC \cong \triangle PQR$.

The remaining parts are also congruent.

$\qquad\qquad \overline{AC} \cong \overline{PR}$

$\qquad\qquad \angle A \cong \angle P$

$\qquad\qquad \angle C \cong \angle R$

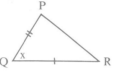

An important aspect of mathematics is to deduce new information from given information.

9.6   Exercise

A To solve problems in geometry, you must learn the symbols of geometry.

1   For each of the congruence relations, name the parts that correspond.

(a) $\triangle DEF \cong \triangle MNP$ (b) $\triangle STP \cong \triangle UVM$ (c) $\triangle PQR \cong \triangle STV$

2   (a) Write the congruence relation to show that the triangles are congruent.

(b) What new information can be obtained because the triangles are congruent?

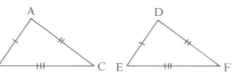

3 (a) Write the congruence relation to show that the triangles are congruent.
   (b) What new information is obtained because the triangles are congruent?

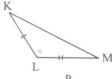

4 (a) Write the congruence relation to show that the triangles are congruent.
   (b) What new information is obtained because the triangles are congruent?

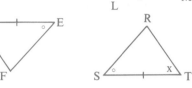

B   To show figures congruent, carefully match the vertices that correspond.

5 For each pair of triangles, what other information is needed for them to be congruent?
   (a)   (b)

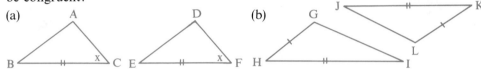

6 (a) $\overline{AD} \cong \overline{AD}$. What other corresponding parts are given as congruent?
   (b) Why are the triangles congruent?
   (c) What other corresponding parts are congruent?

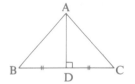

7 Find the missing measures in each of the following.
   (a)   (b)

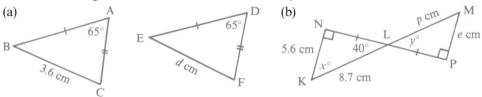

PSP 8 A birthday cake for Wal Nut was baked in the shape shown. Eleven people came to his party. How can you cut the cake into congruent pieces so that each person gets the same amount of cake?

C 9 Find the missing measures.

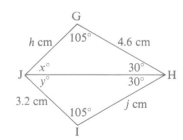

9.7 PSP Problem Solving: Deducing Information

The work you do in the different branches of mathematics is often alike. For example, to solve problems about geometry you can use many of the strategies you have used earlier in other branches of mathematics. Your first step is to answer these two important questions:

I What information am I asked to find?
II What information am I given?

Then you can use one of these strategies to write the given information.

▶ using diagrams
▶ looking for clue words
▶ organizing your work
▶ recording information accurately
▶ using the *Problem Solving Plan* PSP

PSP	Problem Solving Plan

Step A: Understand the problem.
  • What are you asked to find?
  • What are you given?

Step B: Decide on a strategy.

Step C: Apply the strategy. Do the work.

Step D: Check your solution.

Step E: Write a final statement.

In your earlier work, by drawing rhombi (plural of rhombus) and making measurements, you found that the opposite angles of a rhombus are congruent. You can now use the congruence relation for triangles to deduce this information.

Example ABCD is a rhombus. Show that $\angle D = \angle B$.

Solution You are given the rhombus ABCD. Join $\overline{AC}$. In $\triangle ADC$ and $\triangle ABC$,

$$\left.\begin{array}{c} \overline{AD} \cong \overline{AB} \\ \overline{DC} \cong \overline{BC} \\ \overline{AC} \cong \overline{AC} \end{array}\right\} \text{what you know}$$

$\triangle ADC \cong \triangle ABC$ (SSS) ⟵ Reason why the triangles are congruent.

Thus $\angle D \cong \angle B$.

Use SSS, ASA and SAS as symbols to show compactly why you write that two triangles are congruent. As long as everyone understands what the symbols represent, they will convey the same meaning.

Earlier you found useful properties about geometric figures that can be used to deduce new information. For example,

The angle sum of a triangle is 180°.

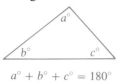

$a° + b° + c° = 180°$

If two lines intersect, the vertically opposite angles are equal.

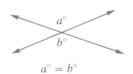

$a° = b°$

In an isosceles triangle, the angles opposite the equal sides are equal.

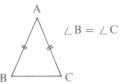

$\angle B = \angle C$

If two lines are parallel, then
$$a° = b°$$
$$b° = c°$$
$$b° + d° = 180°$$

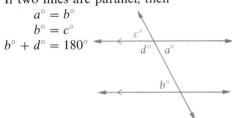

If a transversal meets two lines, then the two lines are parallel if
$$c° = b°$$
or $a° = b°$
or $b° + d° = 180°$

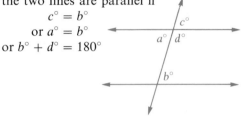

By carefully interpreting the given information and using the geometric facts, you can deduce new information about angles, sides and polygons.

Example 2   Show that $\angle B \cong \angle E$.

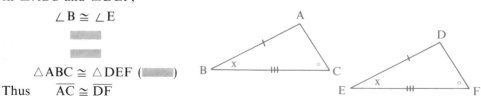

Solution   In $\triangle ABC$ and $\triangle DEC$,

$\overline{AC} \cong \overline{DC}$	(given)
$\overline{BC} \cong \overline{EC}$	(given)
$\angle ACB \cong \angle DCE$	(vertically opposite angles)
$\triangle ABC \cong \triangle DEC$	(SAS)

Thus $\angle B \cong \angle E$ (property of congruent triangles)

9.7   Exercise

A List the given information from each diagram accurately.   PSP

1   Complete the missing steps to show why $\overline{AC} \cong \overline{DF}$.
In $\triangle ABC$ and $\triangle DEF$,

$\angle B \cong \angle E$

▭

▭

$\triangle ABC \cong \triangle DEF$ (▭)

Thus $\overline{AC} \cong \overline{DF}$

2 Complete the missing steps to show why ∠M ≅ ∠O.
In △MNP and △ONP,

$$\overline{MN} \cong \overline{ON}$$

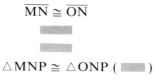

△MNP ≅ △ONP ( )

Thus ∠M ≅ ∠O

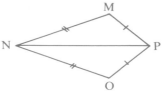

3 Use the method above to record your reasons why ∠B ≅ ∠E in △ABC and △DEF.

4 From the diagrams, which pairs of angles are congruent? Give reasons for your answers.

(a)

(b)
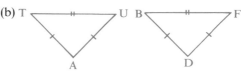

(c)
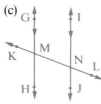

(d)
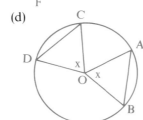

(e)
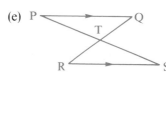

5 Refer to each diagram. Which pairs of line segments are congruent? Give reasons for your answers.

(a)
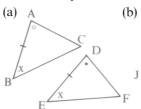

(b)
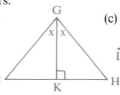

(c)

(d)
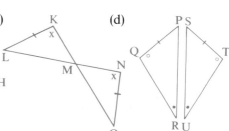

B Give reasons for your answers. **PSP**

6 From the diagram, why is
(a) $\overline{AO} \cong \overline{BO}$?   (b) ∠OAE ≅ ∠OBE?
(c) △AOE ≅ △BOE?   (d) $\overline{AE} \cong \overline{BE}$?
What is the measure of ∠AEO?

7   From the diagram, why is

   (a) $\triangle ADC \cong \triangle CBA$?   (b) $\angle DCA \cong \angle BAC$?

   (c) $\angle DAB \cong \angle BCD$?   (d) $\overline{AB} \| \overline{DC}$?

8   In isosceles $\triangle ABD$, the vertical angle has been bisected
   as shown. Use the diagram to show why

   (a) $\overline{BC} \cong \overline{DC}$.   (b) $\angle ACB \cong \angle ACD$.

9   (a) From the diagram, if $\angle EFH \cong \angle GFH$, what is the
      measure of $\angle EFH$?

   (b) How can you use the result in (a) to show why
      $\angle BCA = 90°$ in the previous question?

10 (a) From the diagram, why is $\angle ACB \cong \angle ECD$?

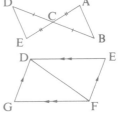

   (b) Use the result in (a) to show that $\overline{AB} \| \overline{DE}$.

11 A diagonal of a parallelogram is drawn. Explain why

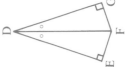

   (a) $\triangle FGD \cong \triangle DEF$.   (b) $\angle G \cong \angle E$.

   (c) $\overline{GF} \cong \overline{ED}$.   (d) $\overline{DG} \cong \overline{FE}$.

12 (a) Which vertices in the diagram correspond?

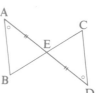

   (b) Deduce that $\angle DFE \cong \angle DFG$.

   (c) Deduce that $\triangle DEF \cong \triangle DGF$.

13 Refer to the diagram.

   (a) List the given information.

   (b) Show why $\overline{AB} \| \overline{CD}$.

   (c) Show why $\triangle EAB \cong \triangle EDC$.

   (d) Show why $\overline{AB} \cong \overline{DC}$.

C 14   (a) X is any point on the bisector of   (b) Q is any point on the perpendicular
        $\angle ABC$. Show that $\overline{DX} \cong \overline{EX}$.   bisector of $\overline{XY}$. Show that $\overline{XQ} \cong \overline{YQ}$.

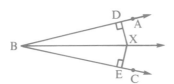
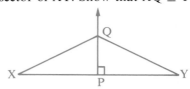

   (c) What relationships are suggested by (a) and (b)?

9.8 Exploring Properties of Similar Triangles

► These stamps have the same shape and size. They are congruent.

► A stamp is enlarged as shown. These stamps have the same shape but are different in size. They are similar.

In the exercise you will explore the properties of similar triangles.

PSP A useful strategy to explore properties in mathematics is to do experiments.

9.8 Exercise

B 1 In the diagram △ABC and △DEF are similar.

(a) Measure the angles. Which angles correspond? What do you notice about your results?

(b) Measure each side of the triangle. Copy and complete the chart. What do you notice about the results?

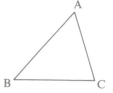
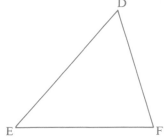

Measure to the nearest tenth of a centimetre.		Calculate. Round to 1 decimal place.
$\overline{DE}$ = ?	$\overline{AB}$ = ?	$\dfrac{\overline{DE}}{\overline{AB}}$ = ?
$\overline{DF}$ = ?	$\overline{AC}$ = ?	$\dfrac{\overline{DF}}{\overline{AC}}$ = ?
$\overline{EF}$ = ?	$\overline{BC}$ = ?	$\dfrac{\overline{EF}}{\overline{BC}}$ = ?

2 A triangle is enlarged on a grid as shown. △ABC is similar to △PQR, $\overline{PQ}$ is a measure on the enlarged triangle. $\overline{AB}$ is the corresponding measure on the original triangle.

(a) List the corresponding angles. Measure the corresponding angles. What do you notice?

(b) Calculate the ratios of the corresponding sides. What do you notice?

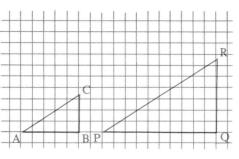

3   If two triangles are similar what is true about

    (a) corresponding angles?   (b) the ratios of the corresponding sides?

4   (a) Construct two different triangles whose angles measure 30°, 60° and 90°.
    (b) Measure the corresponding sides in centimetres to 1 decimal place.
    (c) Calculate the ratios of corresponding sides to 1 decimal place. What
        do you notice?
    (d) Repeat steps (a) to (c) for other triangles.

5   Repeat the steps in the previous question for two different triangles whose
    angles measure 75°, 45° and 60°.

6   Use your results from the two previous questions. Complete the statement.
    If two triangles have corresponding angles that are congruent, then
    the triangles are ▒▒▒ and the ratios of the corresponding sides are ▒▒▒.

7   (a) Construct $\triangle ABC$ similar to $\triangle DEF$ with $\overline{AB} = 4$ cm, $\overline{BC} = 6$ cm,
        $\overline{AC} = 8$ cm, $\overline{DE} = 2$ cm, $\overline{EF} = 3$ cm and $\overline{DF} = 4$ cm.
    (b) Calculate the ratios of corresponding sides. What do you notice?
    (c) Measure the corresponding angles. What do you notice?

8   $\triangle PQR$ has measures, $\overline{PQ} = 3$ cm, $\overline{RP} = 4$ cm and $\overline{QR} = 5$ cm.
    (a) Double the lengths of the sides of $\triangle PQR$. Construct the new $\triangle P'Q'R'$.
    (b) Measure the corresponding angles. What do you notice?

9   A grid is used to construct two
    triangles so that the ratios of
    corresponding sides are equal.
    (a) Measure the sides to check that
        the ratios of the corresponding
        sides are equal.
    (b) Measure the corresponding angles.
        What do you notice?
    (c) Repeat steps (a) and (b) for other
        triangles.

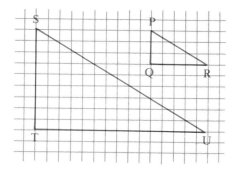

10   Use your results in Questions 7 to 9. Complete the statement.
    If the ratios of the corresponding sides of two triangles are equal,
    then the triangles are ▒▒▒ and the corresponding angles are ▒▒▒.

PSP 11   At the zoo there were one-horned Asian rhinos and African giraffes
    with two horns. If there were 51 horns and 72 eyes, how many of each
    type of animal were there at the zoo?

9.9 [PSP] Problem Solving: Similar Triangles

In your study of mathematics you use Steps A, B and C many times.

Step A   *Step B*   *Step C*

Learn a new skill or concept.	Practise the skill.	Apply the skill to solve problems.

$\triangle$ABC is similar to $\triangle$DEF

$\triangle$ABC $\sim$ $\triangle$DEF

The symbol means *is similar to.*

In your work with similar triangles, you follow these steps again.

You found the following properties for similar triangles.

▶ Corresponding angles are congruent.

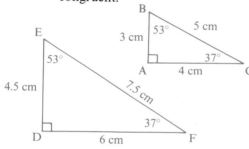

▶ The ratios of the measures of corresponding sides are equal.

In $\triangle$ABC   In $\triangle$DEF

$\overline{AB}$ = 3 cm $\overline{DE}$ = 4.5 cm $\dfrac{\overline{DE}}{\overline{AB}} = \dfrac{4.5}{3} = 1.5$

$\overline{BC}$ = 5 cm $\overline{EF}$ = 7.5 cm $\dfrac{\overline{EF}}{\overline{BC}} = \dfrac{7.5}{5} = 1.5$

$\overline{AC}$ = 4 cm $\overline{DF}$ = 6 cm $\dfrac{\overline{DF}}{\overline{AC}} = \dfrac{6}{4} = 1.5$

Example 1   Find the lengths of the unknown sides of $\triangle$DEF.

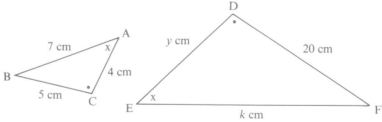

Solution   Since $\angle$A $\cong$ $\angle$E and $\angle$C $\cong$ $\angle$D, then $\angle$B $\cong$ $\angle$F.
(Angle sum of triangle is 180°.)
Thus $\triangle$ABC $\sim$ $\triangle$EFD.

Thus $\dfrac{\overline{DE}}{\overline{CA}} = \dfrac{\overline{DF}}{\overline{CB}}$ and $\dfrac{\overline{EF}}{\overline{AB}} = \dfrac{\overline{DF}}{\overline{CB}}$

$\dfrac{y}{4} = \dfrac{20}{5}$ $\dfrac{k}{7} = \dfrac{20}{5}$

$y = 16$ $k = 28$

Thus $\overline{DE}$ = 16 cm and $\overline{EF}$ = 28 cm.

Similar triangles are used to solve practical problems about measurement.

Example 2   From the diagram, find
the height of the tree.
$\overline{AC} = 20$ m
$\overline{EC} = 4$ m

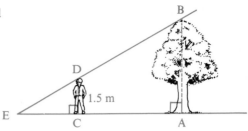

Solution   Let h, in metres, represent   Think of two triangles. Match the vertices.
the height of the tree.
From the diagram

$$\angle E \cong \angle E$$
$$\angle DCE \cong \angle BAE \text{ (Both are 90°.)}$$
Thus $\angle EDC \cong \angle EBA$ (Angle sum of
triangle is 180°.)

Since all corresponding angles are congruent, then

$$\triangle EBA \sim \triangle EDC,$$
$$\frac{\overline{BA}}{\overline{DC}} = \frac{\overline{EA}}{\overline{EC}} \qquad \text{Use } \overline{AC} = 20 \text{ m}$$
$$\frac{h}{1.5} = \frac{24}{4} \qquad \qquad \overline{EC} = 4 \text{ m}$$
$$\overline{AE} = 24 \text{ m}$$
$$h = 9$$

Thus the height of the tree is 9 m.

PSP Remember to check
your answer in the
original word problem.

9.9   Exercise

A Check whether your answers are reasonable. Round answers to 1 decimal
place when necessary.

1    $\triangle ABC$ and $\triangle DEF$ are similar. List the information you know about the triangles.

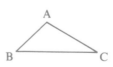
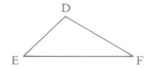

2    $\triangle PQR$ and $\triangle VWT$ are similar.
Find the missing values by
solving each equation.

(a) $\dfrac{y}{8} = \dfrac{12}{4}$ (b) $\dfrac{x}{5} = \dfrac{12}{4}$

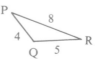
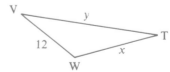

3 For each pair of similar triangles find the values of the variables.

(a) $\triangle ABC \sim \triangle DEF$ (b) $\triangle LMN \sim \triangle PQR$ (c) $\triangle QST \sim \triangle ABC$

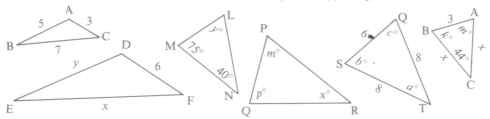

4 To show similar triangles more clearly, the triangles can be redrawn separately.

(a) Which angles are congruent?

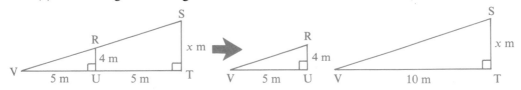

(b) Use $\dfrac{x}{4} = \dfrac{10}{5}$ to solve for x. (c) What is the measure of $\overline{ST}$?

B Remember: The sides opposite corresponding angles are corresponding sides.

5 Each equation is written to find the measures of missing sides. Solve for x.

(a) $\dfrac{x}{3} = \dfrac{20}{6}$ (b) $\dfrac{x}{8} = \dfrac{35}{40}$ (c) $\dfrac{x}{4} = \dfrac{16}{12}$ (d) $\dfrac{x}{52} = \dfrac{5}{26}$ (e) $\dfrac{x}{4} = \dfrac{34}{20}$

6 For each diagram,
► identify which triangles are similar. ► find the values of the variables.

(a) (b) (c)

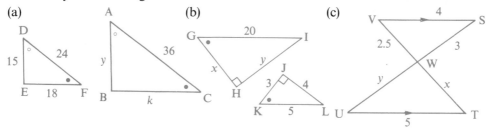

7 Refer to the diagram.
(a) Find the measure of $\overline{AD}$.
(b) Write an equation to find $\overline{AC}$.
(c) What is the measure of $\overline{AC}$?

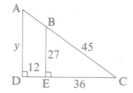

8   Shadows were used to calculate
    the height of the tree.
    (a) Why is $\angle ABC \cong \angle DEF$?
    (b) Find the height of the tree.

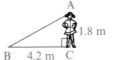

9   To calculate the height of a building, $\overline{AE}$,
    the measurements shown at the right
    were made. How tall is the building?

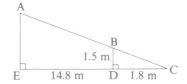

10 The diagram shows the rise of a road
    for the distance called the run.
    (a) If a road rises 2.6 m for every 8.5 m
        of run, calculate the rise for a run
        of 100.0 m.
    (b) A ramp rises 12.6 cm for every
        65.3 cm travelled horizontally. If
        the end of the ramp is 2.3 m high,
        calculate the run of the ramp.

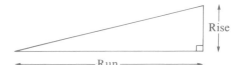

11 During take-off, a jet climbs (rises)
    10 m for a horizontal distance of 60 m.

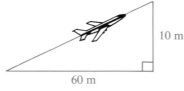

    (a) Calculate the height of the jet after
        it has travelled 1 km horizontally.
    (b) What assumption did you make in
        (a) to obtain your answer?

12 A ladder, $\overline{AD}$, is placed against a house as shown. A
    fence, $\overline{EC}$, is 2.3 m high. Calculate the distance of the
    foot of the ladder from the fence, if the fence is 4.6 m
    from the wall.

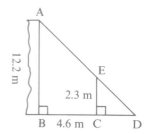

13 For a prime number between 1 and 100,
    ▶ the sum of the digits is divisible by 8.
    ▶ the product of the digits is less than 10.
    (a) What is the prime number?
    (b) Can you find more than one answer?

9.10 Using Indirect Measurement

You can use your knowledge of congruent and similar triangles to find the measure of inaccessible distances. To do so, you need to

▶ make a plan.

▶ combine your skills in geometry with your skills in equations. **PSP**

Example   To find the width of the river, the measurements given in the diagram were made. Find the width of the river.

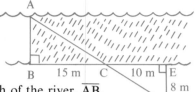

Solution   Let w, in metres, represent the width of the river, $\overline{AB}$.

$\angle ABC \cong \angle DEC$ (Why?)

$$\frac{\overline{AB}}{\overline{DE}} = \frac{\overline{BC}}{\overline{EC}}$$

PSP You can use a proportion to solve some problems.

$$\frac{w}{8} = \frac{15}{10}$$

$$w = 12$$ Thus the width of the river is 12 m.

9.10 Exercise

A Round all answers to 1 decimal place as necessary.

1   To find the length of a pond, the measurements given in the diagram were made.

   (a) Which triangles are similar? Why?

   (b) Complete the equation $\dfrac{\overline{CA}}{\overline{CB}} = \dfrac{\blacksquare}{\blacksquare}$ for finding the length.

   (c) Let l, in metres, represent the length, and solve for l.

   (d) What is the length of the pond?

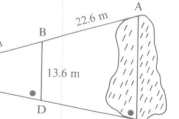

B Draw a diagram if one is not given. Record the given information on the diagram. **PSP**

2   To measure the width of a river, the measurements given in the diagram were made. Find the width of the river.

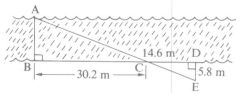

3   To find the distance from one dock to another, the measurements given in the diagram were made. Find the distance between dock A and dock B.

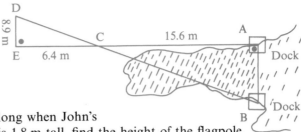

4   A flagpole's shadow is 15.5 m long when John's shadow is 3.6 m long. If John is 1.8 m tall, find the height of the flagpole.

5   The length of the shadow of a monument is 26.8 m when the length of Marnie's shadow is 6.8 m. If Marnie is 1.6 m tall, calculate the height of the monument.

6   The length of the shadow of a metre stick is 3.6 m. Find the height of a tree, if its shadow length is 26.3 m.

7   How long will the shadow of a pole 15.6 m high be if George is 1.7 m tall and casts a shadow of 3.8 m?

C 8   To measure the width of a lake, a point X was located so that it was the vertical angle of an isosceles triangle. The distances $\overline{XY}$ and $\overline{XZ}$, from X to the points on the opposite sides of the shore, measured 4.5 km. The length of the line $\overline{MN}$ joining the midpoints of $\overline{XY}$ and $\overline{XZ}$ was 3.0 km. Find the width, $\overline{YZ}$, of the lake. (Hint: Which diagram in the exercise does this most closely resemble?)

9   Use indirect measurement to calculate the width of
(a) a street or road.   (b) a building.

Computer Use

▶ Try the program shown.

```
10 PRINT "HOW IS SURFACE AREA RELATED TO VOLUME?"
20 FOR R = 1 TO 10
30 V = 4/3 * 3.14 * R ↑ 3
40 A = 4 * 3.14 * R ↑ 2
50 D = A/V
60 PRINT "THE RADIUS IS"; R; "THE VOLUME IS"; V;
   "THE SURFACE AREA IS"; A; "THE RATIO A/V IS"; D
70 NEXT R
80 PRINT "WHAT DO YOU NOTICE ABOUT THE RATIO OF A TO V AS THE
   RADIUS R INCREASES IN VALUE?"
90 END
```

▶ What problem does the program explore?
▶ Based on the output of the program, what conclusion, if any, can you make?

9.11 Skills with Scale Diagrams

A scale diagram may be an enlargement or a reduction. For example, this diagram of a part of a cell is an enlargement and this map is a reduction.

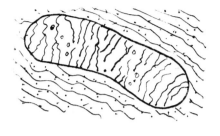

Scale 35 000:1

Scale 1:16 600 000

The scale for the part of a cell indicates that the diagram is 35 000 times as large as the actual part is. The map scale indicates that 1 cm on the map represents 16 600 000 cm (or 166 km) of actual distance.

Example   Use the map to find the actual distance from A to B.

Solution   Let x, in centimetres, represent the actual distance from A to B. By measuring $\overline{AB}$ on the map, you can find $\overline{AB} = 3.0$ cm.

$$\text{map} \longrightarrow \frac{1}{16\ 600\ 000} = \frac{3.0}{x} \longleftarrow \text{map}$$
$$\text{actual} \longleftarrow \text{actual}$$

$$x = 3.0 \times 16\ 600\ 000$$
$$= 49\ 800\ 000$$
$$49\ 800\ 000 \text{ cm} = 498 \text{ km}$$

Thus the actual distance from A to B is 498 km.

9.11 Exercise

A Round your answers to 1 decimal place unless indicated otherwise.

1   The scale on a map is 1 cm represents 15 km. Find the actual distance for each distance measured on the map.

    (a) 8 cm   (b) 6.5 cm   (c) 18.2 cm

2   The scale on a map is 1:10 000. Find the distance, in centimetres, on a map for each actual distance.

    (a) 150 m   (b) 500 m   (c) 1.5 km

3 The scale on a diagram is 1:50.

(a) On the diagram, the distance is measured as 4.5 cm. What is the actual length on the object?

(b) An actual length on the object is 20 cm. What is the distance shown on the scale diagram?

B Check your answers. Are they reasonable? **PSP**

4 A scale diagram of one end of a curling rink is shown. Calculate.

(a) the diameter of the large circle

(b) the length of the hog line

(c) the length of the centre line

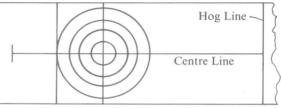

1 mm:15 cm

5 (a) The length of a cafeteria is 40 m. On a diagram the length is shown by 15 cm. What is the scale ratio of the diagram?

(b) The width of an irrigation pond is 28 m. Calculate its length on a diagram if the scale 1:250 is used.

(c) On a map the scale used is 1 cm represents 10.5 km. For a camping trip, Michelle walked a distance of 65.2 km. How many centimetres on the map would represent her walk?

6 A photo can be thought of as a scale diagram. The boat in the photo is shown by a scale 1:60. Estimate.

(a) the height of the mast

(b) the length of the boat

7 On a map of Canada, the scale used is 1 cm represents 37.4 km. The distance measured between two cities is shown. Copy and complete the table.

	City	City	Actual distance	Distance on map
(a)	Edmonton	Sudbury	?	82.4 cm
(b)	London	Regina	2853 km	?
(c)	Saint John	Montreal	?	25.1 cm
(d)	Victoria	Winnipeg	2337 km	?

8   Use an appropriate scale to make a scale drawing of each of the following.
   (a) your classroom   (b) your bedroom
   (c) another room in your home

PSP 9   Often to solve a problem you need to change   916   Hint: 234 *does not* have
   your point of view. The addition question   906   + 727 the same
   shown has an unusual property.   619   property.
   (a) What is this unusual property?   818
   (b) Create another addition question   + 808
      that has the same property.

C 10   The record wing span of the wandering albatross is 3.6 m. What scale
   would you use to fit the bird horizontally on a page of this book?

11   The height of the North African ostrich is about 2.7 m. What scale would
   you use to fit the bird on this page vertically?

From Math History

Often different people are intrigued by the same problem and work at its
solution. Pierre de Fermat (1601–1665) worked with numbers as a hobby. He
found many interesting relationships between numbers but left them for other
people to prove. For example, he said that any prime number that can be
written in the form $4n + 1$, where n is a whole number, is the sum of two
whole numbers squared. (17 is a prime that can be written in the form $4n + 1$
where $n = 4$, and $17 = 16 + 1$). Thus Fermat posed the question whether

$$\underset{\text{a prime number}}{\underbrace{4n + 1}} = x^2 + y^2, \text{ where } n, x \text{ and } y \text{ are whole numbers.}$$

Leonard Euler eventually proved that this relationship is indeed true for any
prime number.

Pierre de Fermat also said that, for any whole numbers x, y, z, the following
inequality always holds.

   $x^n + y^n \neq z^n$ where n is an exponent greater than 2.

Again, he left no proof. But the problem was picked up by Sophie Germain
(1776–1831). Germain enjoyed mathematics and educated herself at home.
(At that time, because she was female, she was not allowed to go to school,
although in time she became a respected mathematician.) She proved that
$x^n + y^n \neq z^n$ for any prime number less than 100. To this day, no one has ever
proved the inequation for all numbers.

9.12   PSP   Problem Solving: Using Strategies

The more problems you try to solve, the more opportunities you will have to apply the strategies you have accumulated in your *Problem Solving Plan*   PSP . To solve the following problems, you need to decide which strategies to use. Refer to the list of strategies you have placed in your *Problem Solving Plan*   PSP . Remember there are two general types of problems.

I   You recognize the strategy needed to solve the problems. Then solve the problem.

II You do not recognize the strategy needed to solve the problem. Refer to your   PSP   list to get ideas for strategies to try.

PSP Problem Solving Plan
Step A: Understand the problem.   • What are you asked to find?   • What are you given?
Step B: Decide on a strategy.
Step C: Apply the strategy. Do the work.
Step D: Check your solution.
Step E: Write a final statement.

9.12   Exercise

B 1 Some letters, like the ones shown, have a vertical line of symmetry.

M T H O

H   T

O   O

          M

The words shown also have a vertical line of symmetry.

(a) What is the longest word that you can make that has a vertical line of symmetry?

(b) Write a sentence that has a vertical line of symmetry.

2 An example of a pair of twin primes is the pair 3, 5. Another pair is 17, 19. How many pairs of twin primes are there from 1 to 100?

3 What is the least number divisible by all of 1, 2, 3, . . . , 9 and 10?

4 The numbers 9 to 17 inclusive are used to fill in the circles. Place the numbers so that each triple (?—?—?) has the same sum.

5 What is the least positive integer that, when multiplied by 18, gives a perfect cube?

6 How many different shapes can you make using 6 square tiles where at least one side of each tile must touch an adjacent tile, as shown in the two shapes given below?

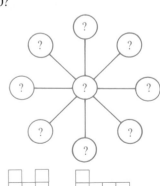

Practice and Problems: Review

1   Match each centre with the construction used to locate it.
   (a) circumcentre   (i)   angle bisectors
   (b) centre of gravity   (ii) altitudes
   (c) incentre   (iii) right bisectors
   (d) orthocentre   (iv) medians

2   Perform the required construction and locate each centre in Question 1.

3   (a) Which of the centres in Question 1 have special circles?
   (b) Construct the circles on your diagrams from Question 2.

4   Construct △GDW with $\overline{GD}$ = 5 cm, $\overline{DW}$ = 4 cm and ∠D = 45°. Measure
   the remaining parts.

5   Illustrate each of the following with an example of your own.
   (a) SAS   (b) ASA   (c) SSS   (d) AAS

6   Use the diagram.
   (a) Why is $\overline{AC} \cong \overline{DC}$?
   (b) Why is ∠A ≅ ∠D?
   (c) How are $\overline{AB}$ and $\overline{DE}$ related?

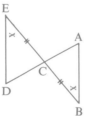

7   △ABC has measures $\overline{AB}$ = 8 cm, $\overline{BC}$ = 6 cm, $\overline{AC}$ = 10 cm, △DEF has
   measures $\overline{DE}$ = 4 cm, $\overline{EF}$ = 3 cm, $\overline{DF}$ = 5 cm.
   (a) Write the ratio of corresponding sides if △ABC ~ △DEF.
   (b) What is the scale ratio?
   (c) What do you know about the measures of corresponding angles?

8   Find the height of
   the clothes line pole
   using the measures
   of the shadows.

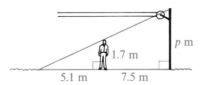

9   The scale on a map of Canada is 1:13 000 000.
   (a) The distance on the map between North Bay and Sudbury is 1 cm.
       What is the actual distance?
   (b) The distance between Edmonton and Vancouver is 820 km. What will
       be the distance between these two places on the map?

Practice Test

1 (a) Draw a right triangle. (b) Construct the altitudes.
   (c) Where is the orthocentre?

2 (a) Draw an obtuse triangle that is isosceles.
   (b) Construct the bisectors of the angles. (c) Construct the incircle.

3 Use an example to illustrate whether or not each statement is a true
   condition for the construction of a unique triangle.
   (a) The measures of 3 sides are known.
   (b) The measures of 3 angles are known.
   (c) The measures of 2 sides and the contained angle are known.
   (d) The measures of 2 angles and the contained side are known.
   (e) The measures of 2 angles and any side are known.

4 (a) Draw a sketch of △XYZ in which ∠XYZ = 45°, $\overline{XY}$ = 8 cm, $\overline{YZ}$ = 6 cm.
   (b) Construct △XYZ.
   (c) Measure the remaining parts of the triangle.

5 (a) Draw a sketch of parallelogram PQRS with sides 5 cm and 3 cm and
       one angle 45°.
   (b) Construct the parallelogram.
   (c) Measure the other angles. What do you notice?

6 Each pair of triangles is congruent. Show why.

   (a) 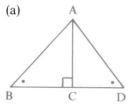 (b) 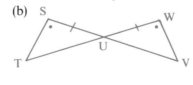 (c)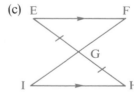

7 The width of a bay was found by
   making the measurements shown in
   the diagram. How wide was the bay
   to 1 decimal place?

   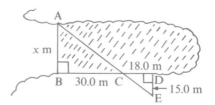

8 Use an appropriate scale to make a
   scale drawing of a rectangular area
   with dimensions 18 m by 24 m.

10 Methods of Co-ordinate Geometry

Vocabulary and concepts, using co-ordinates, graphing relations, representing relations, skills with linear relations, *x*- and *y*-intercepts, concept of slope, distance on the plane, points of intersection, strategies for problem solving

Introduction

There are many similarities and patterns in learning mathematics.

In this chapter you will use the following pattern.

A

> You learned skills with geometry.

B

> You learn new skills with co-ordinates.

> You combine the skills in A and B to learn additional strategies to solve problems.

The principles you learned to solve problems previously are now applied to solve problems involving co-ordinate geometry.

▶ You must understand each skill. You cannot solve a problem about slope if you do not understand the concepts and skills. Use examples of your own to illustrate each new skill or concept.

▶ You must again organize your solutions. Use the steps in the *Problem Solving Plan* **PSP** or your own method of organization.

Co-ordinate geometry plays an important role in many branches of mathematics, as well as in the fields of science, geography and medicine, to name a few.

The navigator on a ship or plane needs to understand the principles of co-ordinate geometry in order to properly arrive at the correct destination.

10.1 Geometry with Co-ordinates

Mathematicians have developed many powerful tools to aid in solving problems. One of them is the number or co-ordinate plane.

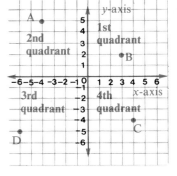

The numbers in an ordered pair such as $(-4, 5)$ are used to locate the position of a point on the grid. The numbers of an ordered pair are the **co-ordinates** of a point.

A dot is used to represent a point. A capital letter names the point.

$$A(-4, 5)$$

horizontal co-ordinate —⌐ └— vertical co-ordinate
(often called **abscissa**)   (often called **ordinate**)

The axes divide the plane into four **quadrants**. The point of intersection of the axes is called the **origin**. Since the variables x and y are often used to show an ordered pair, you name

▶ the horizontal axis as the x-axis.
▶ the vertical axis as the y-axis.
▶ the horizontal co-ordinate as the x-co-ordinate.
▶ the vertical co-ordinate as the y-co-ordinate.

PSP To use the co-ordinate plane, you need to understand the precise, meanings of the words used.

When you draw the points represented by ordered pairs, you are drawing the **graph** of the ordered pairs.

▶ The graph of $(4, -4)$ is shown by the point C.
▶ The graph of $(-6, -5)$ is shown by the point D.

For ordered pairs, if $(x, y) = (2, 4)$, then $x = 2$ and $y = 4$.

Example   The co-ordinates of three vertices of a square are A(3, −3), B(3, 7) and C(−7, 7). Plot the vertices on a number plane. Then find the co-ordinates of the other vertex, D.

Solution   The remaining vertex, D, has co-ordinates $(-7, -3)$.

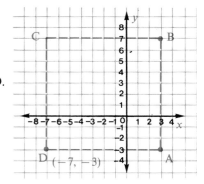

The grid with a horizontal axis and a vertical axis is often called the **Cartesian plane** after the French mathematician René Déscartes who developed many of the results in this branch of mathematics. The geometry studied using co-ordinates is referred to as **co-ordinate geometry**.

10.1 Exercise

A

Questions 1 to 10 are based on the diagram at the right.

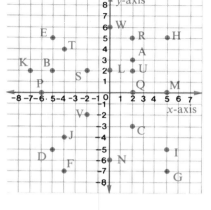

1 Name the co-ordinates of each point.
   (a) U   (b) B   (c) C   (d) V
   (e) G   (f) K   (g) E   (h) N

2 What is the corresponding letter for each ordered pair?
   (a) (2, 3)   (b) (−2, 2)   (c) (−4, −4)
   (d) (5, −5)   (e) (2, 0)   (f) (0, 2)

B 3 (a) Name the co-ordinates of P and Q.
   (b) What property do these points have in common?

4 (a) Name the co-ordinates of W, L and N.
   (b) What property do these points have in common?

5 (a) Name a point that has both co-ordinates negative.
   (b) How many other points can you name for (a)?

6 Name the co-ordinates of the origin.

7 (a) Name a point that has equal co-ordinates.
   (b) How many other points can you name for (a)?

8 (a) Which point is named by (5, −5)?   (b) Which point is named by (−5, 5)?

9 Name the quadrant in which the point named by each ordered pair is found.
   (a) (2, 5)   (b) (−5, 5)   (c) (5, −7)   (d) (−5, 2)   (e) (−4, −7)

10 Name and give the co-ordinates of a point on the boundary of the following.
   (a) 2nd and 1st quadrants   (b) 3rd and 4th quadrants
   (c) 1st and 4th quadrants   (d) 2nd and 3rd quadrants

11 (a) Draw a Cartesian plane and plot the following points. Plot means to locate the points on the Cartesian plane.
   A(1, 7)   B(2, 6)   C(0, 8)   D(−1, 9)   E(−2, 10)
   F(3, 5)   G(−3, 11) H(4, 4)   I(5, 3)
   (b) What do you notice about your graph?
   (c) Name some other points that seem to fit the pattern.

12 (a) Plot these points.

   A(−2, 0)   B(0, 2)   C(1, 3)   D(−3, −1)   E(5, 7)
   F(−4, −2)   G(2, 4)   H(−1, 1)   I(3, 5)

   (b) What do you notice about your graph?
   (c) Name some other points that seem to fit the pattern.

13 These ordered pairs represent a geometric figure.

   A(−1, 2)   B(8, 2)   C(3, −3)   D(−6, −3)

   (a) Plot the points and join them in order.
   (b) What geometric figure have you drawn?

14 These ordered pairs represent a geometric figure.

   A(0, 4)   B(4, 0)   C(0, −4)   D(−4, 0)

   (a) Plot the points and join them in order.
   (b) What geometric figure have you drawn?

15 The co-ordinates of three vertices of a square are

   A(−6, 3),   B(1, 3)   and   C(1, −4).

   Find the co-ordinates of the other vertex, D.

16 The co-ordinates of three vertices of a parallelogram are

   A(−7, −5),   B(3, −5)   and   C(10, 4).

   Find the co-ordinates of the other vertex, D.

 17 (a) Sharon has a 7-L container and a 5-L container. If she has only these
       containers, how can she measure exactly 4 L of water? List any
       assumptions you made.

   (b) The digit 4 is used 4 times to make a value of 4 as shown.

       $4 = 4 + (4 − 4) \times 4$

       Use the digit 4 four times to make the other numbers from 1 to 10.

Math Tip

To solve a problem whether it is in mathematics or another discipline,
you must understand the meaning of each word that occurs.

▶ Make a list of the new math words you have learned thus far in this
   chapter. Provide an example of your own to illustrate each word.
   Continue to add other words from subsequent sections.

▶ List any new problem solving strategies or key questions you
   have acquired and place them in your *Problem Solving Plan*   **PSP**

Writing Coded Messages

18   A message is written using a code based on ordered pairs. The letters of each word are scrambled. You need to unscramble the letters to find the message. The symbol ▶ marks the beginning of each new letter. Follow the instructions carefully.

(a)   ▶ Join $(-9, 10)$ to $(-8, 9)$ to $(-8, 7)$ to $(-9, 6)$ to $(-11, 6)$ to $(-11, 10)$ to $(-9, 10)$.

  ▶ Join $(-3, 10)$ to $(-6, 10)$ to $(-6, 6)$ to $(-3, 6)$. Join $(-6, 8)$ to $(-4, 8)$.

  ▶ Join $(-1, 6)$ to $(-1, 8)$ to $(2, 6)$. Join $(2, 8)$ to $(2, 10)$ to $(-1, 10)$ to $(-1, 8)$ to $(2, 8)$.

  ▶ Join $(4, 6)$ to $(6, 10)$ to $(8, 6)$. Join $(5, 8)$ to $(7, 8)$.

(b)   ▶ Join $(-12, -1)$ to $(-10, 3)$ to $(-8, -1)$. Join $(-11, 1)$ to $(-9, 1)$.

  ▶ Join $(-5, 1)$ to $(-3, 1)$ to $(-3, -1)$ to $(-6, -1)$ to $(-6, 3)$ to $(-3, 3)$ to $(-3, 2)$.

  ▶ Join $(3, 3)$ to $(0, 3)$ to $(0, -1)$ to $(3, -1)$. Join $(0, 1)$ to $(2, 1)$.

  ▶ Join $(5, -1)$ to $(5, 3)$ to $(8, 3)$ to $(8, 1)$ to $(5, 1)$.

(c)   ▶ Join $(-8, -8)$ to $(-8, -4)$.   ▶ Join $(-5, -8)$ to $(-5, -4)$.

  ▶ Join $(-2, -4)$ to $(-2, -6)$ to $(1, -6)$.   ▶ Join $(0, -8)$ to $(0, -4)$.

19   One of the oldest English words is given by the code. What is the word?

  ▶ Join $(-10, 6)$ to $(-7, 6)$ to $(-5, 4)$ to $(-5, 1)$ to $(-6, 0)$ to $(-10, 0)$. Join $(-6, 0)$ to $(-5, -1)$ to $(-5, -4)$ to $(-7, -6)$ to $(-10, -6)$ to $(-10, 6)$.

  ▶ Join $(-4, -6)$ to $(0, 6)$ to $(4, -6)$. Join $(-2, 0)$ to $(2, 0)$.

  ▶ Join $(5, -6)$ to $(5, 6)$ to $(8, 6)$ to $(10, 4)$ to $(10, -4)$ to $(8, -6)$ to $(5, -6)$.

20   The most overworked word in the English language is given by the code. What is the word?

  ▶ $(-5, 4)$ to $(-1, 4)$ ▶ $(-7, -2)$ to $(-7, 1)$ ▶ $(3, -2)$ to $(3, 4)$

  ▶ $(-1, -2)$ to $(-5, -2)$ ▶ $(-11, 1)$ to $(-11, 4)$ ▶ $(-11, -2)$ to $(-7, -2)$

  ▶ $(1, 4)$ to $(5, 4)$ ▶ $(-5, -2)$ to $(-5, 4)$ ▶ $(-5, 1)$ to $(-2, 1)$

  ▶ $(-7, 1)$ to $(-11, 1)$ ▶ $(-11, 4)$ to $(-7, 4)$

21   Half of the longest English palindrome is given in the code. What is the word?

  ▶ Join $(-6, 3)$ to $(-5, 3)$ to $(-4, 2)$ to $(-4, 0)$ to $(-5, -1)$ to $(-6, -1)$ to $(-6, 3)$.

  ▶ Join $(-3, 3)$ to $(-3, -1)$.

  ▶ Join $(-12, -1)$ to $(-12, 3)$ to $(-11, 3)$ to $(-10, 2)$ to $(-11, 1)$ to $(-12, 1)$. Join $(-11, 1)$ to $(-10, -1)$.

  ▶ Join $(-7, -1)$ to $(-9, -1)$ to $(-9, 3)$ to $(-7, 3)$. Join $(-9, 1)$ to $(-7, 1)$.

  ▶ Join $(-2, 3)$ to $(0, -1)$ to $(2, 3)$.

10.2 Graphing Relations

The table of values at the right shows the **relation:** the amount of gasoline consumed at a steady rate.
You can use the ordered pairs to draw a graph of the relation.
To show the amount, V, for any time, you use real numbers to draw the graph.

time taken, t, in hours	amount, V, in litres	ordered pairs
0	0	(0, 0)
1	0.5	(1, 0.5)
2	1.0	(2, 1.0)
3	1.5	(3, 1.5)
4	2.0	(4, 2.0)

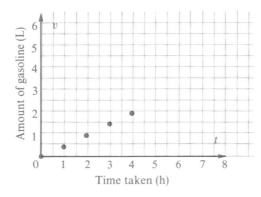

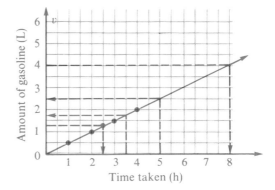

When you choose two known values on a graph and you estimate a value between them, you are **interpolating**.

Example 1   Use the graph shown above.
   (a) Estimate the time it took for 1.25 L to be consumed.
   (b) Estimate the amount of gasoline consumed in 3.5 h.

Solution   (a) Since $V = 1.25$ when $t = 2.5$, it took 2.5 h for 1.25 L to be consumed.
   (b) Since $t = 3.5$ when $V = 1.75$, 1.75 L were consumed in 3.5 h.

When you estimate a value which is beyond the first or the last given value on a graph and your estimate is based on the values given, you are **extrapolating**.

Example 2   Use the graph shown above.
   (a) Estimate the time it took for 4 L of gasoline to be consumed.
   (b) Estimate the amount of gasoline consumed in 5 h.

Solution   Extend the graph and read the values.
   (a) Since $V = 4$ when $t = 8$, it took 8 h for 4 L to be consumed.
   (b) Since $t = 5$ when $V = 2.5$, 2.5 L were consumed in 5 h.

   PSP   When solving a problem, note any assumptions that you make.

10.2 Exercise

A Use a co-ordinate plane to answer the questions.

1 (a) Copy and complete the table of values for the relation $p = 3k$.

k	1	2	3	4	5	6	7	8	9	10
p	3	6								

   (b) Plot the ordered pairs on a graph.
   (c) Extend the graph for $0 \leq k \leq 15$, $k \in R$.

B 2 If you jog at a constant speed of 8 km/h then the distance, d, in kilometres is related to the time taken, t, in hours by $d = 8t$, $t \in R$.
   (a) Make a table of values for $0 \leq t \leq 5$, $t \in W$.
   (b) Plot the ordered pairs on a graph.
   (c) Extend the graph for $0 \leq t \leq 8$, $t \in R$.
   (d) Estimate each distance corresponding to 2.5 h, 5.5 h and 8 h.
   (e) Estimate each time corresponding to 12 km, 36 km and 48 km.

3 An experiment showed the stretch that is the result of adding mass to a spring.

Added mass (g)	5	10	15	20	25	30
Stretch (cm)	1	2	3	4	5	6

   (a) Plot the ordered pairs on a graph.
   (b) Extend the graph for real values of added mass from 0 g to 50 g.
   (c) Estimate each stretch corresponding to 12 g, 40 g and 45 g.
   (d) Estimate each added mass corresponding to 3.5 cm, 5.5 cm and 7 cm.

4 Perform the following experiment.
   (a) Use grid paper and cut out squares with sides of 1 unit, 2 units and so on up to 10 units.
   (b) Inside each square write its area in square units.
   (c) Plot the ordered pairs (length of side, area) on a graph.
   (d) Extend the graph to include real numbers by joining the points.

5 (a) Use your graph in Question 4 to estimate the square root of 24.
   (b) Use the table of square roots on page 489 to find the square root of 24.
   (c) Which answer is easier to obtain?   (d) Which answer is more accurate?

6 (a) Use your graph in Question 4 to estimate $\sqrt{10}$ to 1 decimal place.
   (b) Use a calculator to find $\sqrt{10}$.
   (c) Is your estimate in (a) greater than or less than your value of $\sqrt{10}$ in (b)?

7 Use the graph in Question 4 to estimate each square root. Then use a calculator to find a value of the square root to 1 decimal place.
   (a) $\sqrt{14}$ (b) $\sqrt{32}$ (c) $\sqrt{19}$ (d) $\sqrt{28}$ (e) $\sqrt{7}$ (f) $\sqrt{26}$

Questions 8 to 10 are based on the graph at the right. The graph shows the minimum stopping distance of a car travelling at different speeds.

Speed (km/h)	Reaction Time Distance (m)	Braking Distance (m)	Total Stopping Distance (m)
10	2.1	1.6	3.7
20	4.2	3.4	7.6
30	6.3	5.7	12.0
40	8.4	8.7	17.1
50	10.5	12.4	22.9
60	12.6	17.2	29.8
70	14.7	23.2	37.9
80	16.8	30.7	47.5
90	18.9	39.7	58.6
100	21.0	50.6	71.6
110	23.1	63.4	86.5
120	25.2	78.3	103.5
130	27.3	95.5	122.8
140	29.4	115.3	144.7

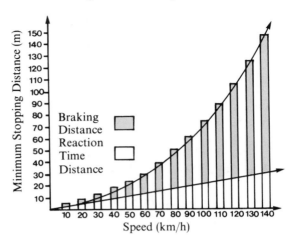

8   What is the minimum stopping distance required for each speed?

(a) 50 km/h   (b) 100 km/h   (c) 75 km/h

9   What is the speed you are travelling at for each minimum stopping distance?

(a) 10 m   (b) 25 m   (c) 50 m

10 You are travelling at 50 km/h. By how much does the minimum stopping distance increase if you increase your speed by each amount?

(a) 10 km/h   (b) 20 km/h   (c) 30 km/h

 11 (a) Change each word into a math word by
       ▶ changing one letter to another letter.
       ▶ keeping the order of the letters the same.

    team   tower   bass   patio   late   grape

    (b) Add two other words to the list.

C 12 A motorbike is 25 m from a wall when the brakes are applied. The distance, d, in metres the motorbike is from the wall after time, t, in seconds is given by $d = 25 - 10\sqrt{t}$.

    (a) Make a table of values for $0 \leq t \leq 7, t \in W$.
    (b) Extend the graph to include real values.
    (c) At what time does the motorcycle hit the wall?
    (d) Create a problem based on the graph. Solve your problem.

10.3 Working with Relations: Graphs

A rectangle is constructed so that the relationship between the sides is that the length is twice the width. In the previous section, you saw how relations could be represented in a number of ways.

▶ in words
The length is twice the width.

▶ in a graph

▶ by an equation
$l = 2w$ where l = length, w = width

▶ in a table of values

w	1.5	2	2.5	3	3.5	4
l	3	4	5	6	7	8

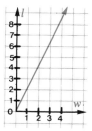

▶ as ordered pairs
(1.5, 3), (2, 4), (2.5, 5), (3, 6), (3.5, 7), (4, 8)

The graph of specific values is only a **partial graph**. In this case, all positive real values of w are possible.

The following are some other ways of representing a relation.

▶ as an arrow diagram

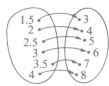

▶ as a relation rule
$w \longrightarrow 2w$

$2w$ represents the length, l.

Example　A relation is given by $p = 5v - 1$, $v \in I$. Use five values to draw an arrow diagram and write a relation rule.

Solution　$p = 5v - 1$　　Relation rule
$v \longrightarrow 5v - 1$, $v \in I$

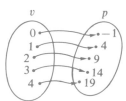

10.3 Exercise

A You must use your substitution skills when working with relations.

1　For the relation $m \rightarrow 2m + 1$, $m \in I$, find the missing value in each of the following ordered pairs.

(a) (0, ?)　　(b) (−1, ?)　　(c) (1, ?)　　(d) (−2, ?)　　(e) (2, ?)

2   For the relation $k \rightarrow 5k^2 - 1$, $k \in I$, find the missing value in each of the
    following ordered pairs.
    (a) $(-1, ?)$ (b) $(-3, ?)$ (c) $(-2, ?)$ (d) $(1, ?)$ (e) $(3, ?)$

3   (a) Draw a graph of the ordered pairs for $y = 2x - 1$, $x \in \{-2, -1, 0, 1, 2\}$.
    (b) Use the same Cartesian plane and draw a graph of
        $y = 2x$, $x \in \{-2, -1, 0, 1, 2\}$.
    (c) Use the same Cartesian plane and draw a graph of
        $y = 2x + 1$, $x \in \{-2, -1, 0, 1, 2\}$.
    (d) Compare the graphs in (a), (b) and (c).

B 4   The graphs of various relations are shown. For each relation,
        ▶ write three additional ordered pairs.
        ▶ write the relation in the form of an equation such as $y = \blacksquare x + \square$, $x \in I$.
    (a)   (b)   (c)

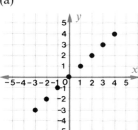   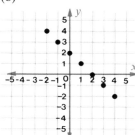   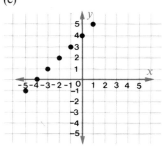

5   A relation is given by $x \rightarrow x^2 - 3$, $x \in R$.
    (a) Find the ordered pairs for $x = -3, -2, -1, 0, 1, 2, 3$.
    (b) Draw a graph of the relation.

C 6   The following graphs represent relations for $x \in R$. Write each relation in
      the form of a relation rule such as $x \rightarrow \blacksquare$.
    (a)   (b)   (c)

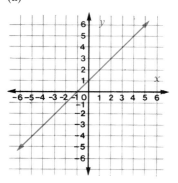   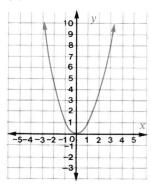   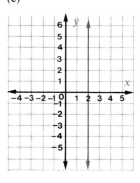

10.4 Linear Relations

In the previous sections, you graphed relations like $x \to 2x + 1$. When you graphed these relations, they formed straight lines. Thus relations like $x \to 2x + 1$ are called **linear relations**.

Table of Values
$x \to 2x + 1$

x	$2x + 1$
-2	-3
-1	-1
0	1
1	3
2	5

The domain is the set of integers.
$x \to 2x + 1, x \in I$

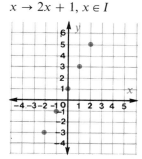

The domain is the set of real numbers.
$x \to 2x + 1, x \in R$

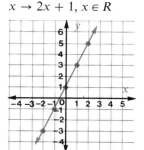

The equation $y = 2x + 1$, $x \in R$ is called the **defining equation** of the relation. It is a first degree equation because the greatest degree of each term is one. An equation such as this is called a **linear equation**. Follow these steps to draw the graph of any linear relation.

▶ Plot at least two points that satisfy the relation.

▶ Plot a third point to check whether the graph is reasonable.

▶ Draw a line through the points.

10.4 Exercise

A All variables represent real numbers.

1   Decide which of the following relations are linear.

(a)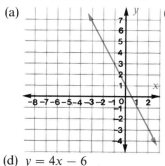

(b)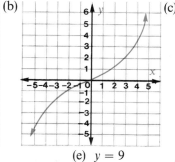

(c)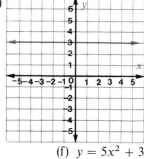

(d) $y = 4x - 6$ (e) $y = 9$ (f) $y = 5x^2 + 3$

2   Which of the given ordered pairs satisfies each equation?

(a) $y = 3x$; A(0, 3) B(2, 6) K(3, 1)   (b) $y = 4x - 1$; C(0, -1) D(-1, 0) L(3, 11)

(c) $y = -2x + 5$; E(0, 5) F(5, 0) M(-5, -5)   (d) $y = -\dfrac{1}{2}x + 4$; I(2, 3) J(-2, -5)

B **3** Draw the graph defined by each equation.

(a) $y = x + 3$, $x \in I$ (b) $y = 2x$, $x \in R$ (c) $y = 2x - 3$, $x \in R$

(d) $y = 3x + 2$, $x \in I$ (e) $y = \dfrac{1}{2}x - 1$, $x \in R$ (f) $y = -\dfrac{1}{3}x + 3$, $x \in R$

4 (a) On the same axes, draw the graphs defined by
$$y = 2x, \quad y = 2x + 1, \quad y = 2x - 1, \quad y = 2x + 2.$$
(b) How are the graphs alike? How are they different?

5 (a) On the same set of axes, draw the graphs defined by
$$y = -2x, \quad y = -2x + 3, \quad y = -2x - 1, \quad y = -2x + 2.$$
(b) How are the graphs alike? How are they different?

6 (a) On the same set of axes, draw the graphs defined by
$$y = x + 3, \quad y = 2x + 3, \quad y = -x + 3, \quad y = -2x + 3.$$
(b) How are the graphs alike? How are they different?

7 (a) On the same set of axes, draw the graphs defined by
$$y = x - 2, \quad y = 3x - 2, \quad y = -2x - 2, \quad y = -x - 2.$$
(b) How are the graphs alike? How are they different?

8 Jennifer works part-time at the Pizza Dome and earns money according to the equation $A = 4.5n$ where A is the amount earned in dollars and n is the number of hours worked.

(a) Copy and complete the chart.

(b) Draw a graph of the relation. Describe the graph.

(c) Estimate how much Jennifer was paid if she worked 2.5 h.

(d) Estimate how long Jennifer worked if she was paid $15.75.

n	A
0	?
1	?
2	?
3	?
4	?

PSP **9** Nine apple trees are planted in the array shown. Design a path using 4 line segments from which all apples can be picked. The paths may cross but not overlap.

C **10** For each of the following relations,
▶ Choose values of the variables and draw a graph. Describe the graph.
▶ Create two problems based on the graph. Solve your problems.

(a) The temperature, T, of the pool in degrees Celsius rose according to the relation $T = 2.5t$, where t is the time in hours.

(b) The cost, C, in dollars of producing brochures is given by $C = 2n + 8$ where n is the number of brochures and 8 is a fixed cost, independent of the number of brochures.

10.5 Intercepts

The graph of $2x - y = -4$ crosses the x-axis at the point A and the y-axis at the point B.

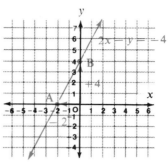

▶ The **x-intercept** is the directed distance from the origin to the point where the graph crosses the x-axis. From the graph, the x-intercept is -2.

▶ The **y-intercept** is the directed distance from the origin to the point where the graph crosses the y-axis. From the graph, the y-intercept is $+4$.

You can also use your skills with algebra to find the values of the x- and y-intercepts.

x-intercept Use $y = 0$ in the equation.

$$2x - y = -4$$
$$2x - (0) = -4$$
$$2x = -4$$
$$x = -2$$

The x-intercept is -2.

y-intercept Use $x = 0$ in the equation.

$$2x - y = -4 \qquad +4 \text{ if you}$$
$$2(0) - y = -4 \qquad \text{think of it as}$$
$$-y = -4 \qquad \text{a directed line}$$
$$y = 4 \qquad \text{segment}$$

The y-intercept is 4.

▶ The co-ordinates of the point A where the graph crosses the x-axis are $A(-2, 0)$.

▶ The co-ordinates of the point B where the graph crosses the y-axis are $B(0, 4)$.

10.5 Exercise

A 1 What are the x- and y-intercepts for each graph?

(a)
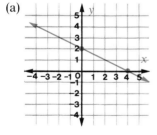

(b)
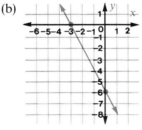

(c)
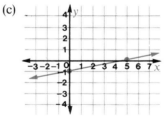

(d)
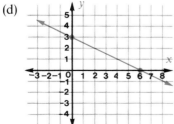

(e)
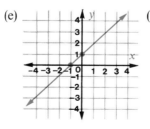

(f)
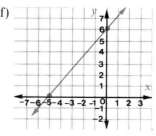

2 What are the co-ordinates of the points at which each graph intersects the axes?

(a) 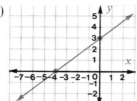 (b) 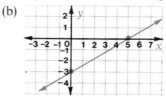 (c)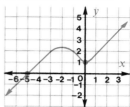

3 (a) Draw the graph of $3x + y = 9$. Label the point N where the graph crosses the x-axis.

(b) What is the value of the x-intercept?

(c) What are the co-ordinates of the point N?

4 (a) Draw the graph of $2y - x = 16$. Label the point M where the graph crosses the y-axis.

(b) What is the value of the y-intercept?

(c) What are the co-ordinates of the point M?

5 (a) Draw the graph of $4x - y = 12$.   (b) What are the values of the intercepts?

(c) What are the co-ordinates of the point where the graph of $4x - y = 12$ crosses each axis?

6 Find the x- and y-intercepts for each line.

(a) $3x - y = 9$ (b) $x + y = 7$ (c) $y = 3x - 6$

(d) $2x + 3y = 6$ (e) $4x - 3y = 12$ (f) $y = \dfrac{1}{2}x + 3$

7 Three sheriffs and three convicts need to get to an island prison using a two-person canoe. A sheriff must always be in the canoe. Is it possible for all six people to get to the island prison? List any assumptions you made.

From Math History

Emmy Noether (1882–1935) was a German mathematician who was barred at first from becoming a full-time student at university and only allowed to attend lectures in languages and mathematics. Eventually, through persistence, she was granted full-time student status and earned her doctorate in mathematics. Then she was barred from holding a position in a university. Again, because of her persistence, her research and her solutions to important problems in mathematics, she eventually received a position at Göttingen University. Emmy Noether had an importance beyond mathematics because she illustrated that if you believe in something, you should persist until you achieve it.

An important strategy in problem solving consists of making predictions and then testing or proving them. Use this problem solving strategy to complete the following.

8   (a) Draw the graph of each relation. $y = 3x + 2$ $y = -x + 2$ $y = \frac{1}{2}x + 2$
       Use the same axes.
    (b) How are the graphs alike? How are they different?
    (c) Predict which of the following would have the same property.

$$y = 2x + 1 \quad y = -\frac{1}{2}x + 2 \quad y = -3x + 2$$

    (d) Test your answer in (c).

9   (a) Draw the graph of each relation. $y = 2x - 3$ $y = \frac{1}{2}x - 3$ $y = 5x - 3$
       Use the same axes.
    (b) How are the graphs alike? How are they different?
    (c) Predict which of the following would have the same property.

$$y = -3x + 1 \quad y = x - 3 \quad y = \frac{3}{2}x + 3$$

    (d) Test your answer in (c).

10 Use your results in the previous questions to answer the following questions. A linear relation is defined by $y = 3x - 2$. Without drawing the graph predict the co-ordinates of the point where the line crosses the y-axis.

11 (a) Draw each pair of graphs.

    A: $y = 3x + 2$ B: $y = \frac{2}{3}x - 1$ C: $y = 2x + 3$

    $y = -\frac{1}{3}x + 1$ $y = -\frac{3}{2}x + 2$ $y = -\frac{1}{2}x - 1$

    (b) Describe the pairs of graphs in (a).

12 (a) Use your results in the previous question. Write a probable conclusion.
    (b) Based on your answer in (a), predict which of the following relations, when put in pairs, would have the same property as those in the previous questions.

    A: $y = 2x - 3$ B: $y = -\frac{1}{3}x + 2$ C: $y = -2x + 3$

    D: $y = -\frac{1}{2}x + 2$ E: $y = 3x - 1$ F: $y = \frac{1}{2}x - 4$

10.6 Finding Slope

When you think of slope in your everyday activities, you might think of steepness.

The track is built with a slope so that racers can hug the track.

A roof slopes so that in winter the snow will slide off.

Often the meaning of a word in mathematics is related to its meaning in everyday activities. For example, the **slope** of a line or a line segment is the measure of its *steepness*.

The slope of $\overline{AB}$ is the ratio of the rise (vertical distance) to the run (horizontal distance).

$$\text{slope} = \frac{\text{rise}}{\text{run}} \qquad \text{slope } \overline{AB} = \frac{3}{4}$$

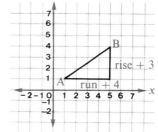

You can find the slope of a line from its graph by choosing two points on the line. Calculate the rise and the run from one point to the other as shown for each line.

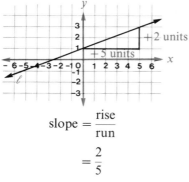

$$\text{slope} = \frac{\text{rise}}{\text{run}}$$

$$= \frac{2}{5}$$

The slope of line ℓ is $\frac{2}{5}$.

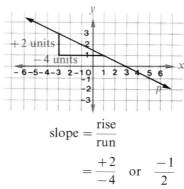

$$\text{slope} = \frac{\text{rise}}{\text{run}}$$

$$= \frac{+2}{-4} \quad \text{or} \quad \frac{-1}{2}$$

The slope of line p is $-\frac{1}{2}$.

You can find the slope by using the relationship.

$$\text{slope} = \frac{\text{difference in } y\text{-co-ordinates}}{\text{difference in } x\text{-co-ordinates}}$$

10.6   Exercise

A Review the meanings of rise, run and slope.

1   For each line, calculate its
▶ rise   ▶ run   ▶ slope.

(a) 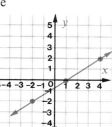   (b) 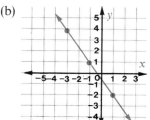   (c)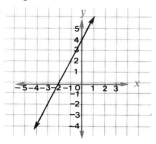

2   (a) The slope of a line segment parallel to the x-axis is zero. Why?
    (b) The slope of a line segment parallel to the y-axis is undefined. Why?

3   (a) If a line has slope $\frac{2}{3}$ and passes through the point (1, 3), describe how
        you would plot a second point to draw the graph.
    (b) If a line has slope $-\frac{4}{5}$ and passes through the point $(-2, 4)$, describe
        how you would plot a second point to draw the graph.

B Be sure to label the axes and the origin properly.

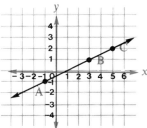

4   Calculate the slope of the line using these pairs
    of points.
    (a) A, B   (b) B, C   (c) A, C
    What do you notice about the slopes you found?

5   Use the results of Question 4.
    (a) Write a probable conclusion about the points on the same line. Points
        on the same line are **collinear**.
    (b) How would you test your probable conclusion in (a)?

6   Determine which sets of points are collinear.
    (a) A(-6, -4),   B(-2, -6),   C(2, -8)   (b) D(-5, 1),   E(0, 3),   F(7, 6)
    (c) J(-5, 3),   K(-1 1),   L(7, -1)   (d) A(-4, 2),   B(-2, 4),   C(0, 6)

7 Draw the graph of each line.

(a) slope $\frac{5}{6}$, point (2, 3)

(b) slope $-\frac{3}{2}$, point $(-4, 3)$

(c) slope 2, x-intercept 3

(d) slope $-\frac{1}{2}$, y-intercept -3

PSP 8 To answer each question, you may need to examine it from a different point of view. The answer you provide must answer the question asked!

(a) How could you have an egg fall 1 m to a concrete floor so that the egg does not break? (You cannot cushion the fall.)

(b) You have probably played sports and worn various types of shoes. For example, if you run or play golf, you often have spikes on your shoes. In lumberjack contests, the participants often use metal tips on their shoes. In what sport are the shoes made entirely of metal?

(c) Jackson walked 1 km south, 1 km east and 1 km north. He discovered that he was exactly in the same position he started from. How is this possible?

C 9 Draw the graph of each of the following. Find their slopes.

(a) $y = 2x$

(b) $y = 2x + 3$

(c) $y = -3x - 1$

(d) $y = 3x - 2$

(e) $y = \frac{1}{2}x$

(f) $y = \frac{-2}{3}x$

Compare each slope you found with the coefficient of x. What do you notice?

10 (a) Predict the slope of each graph defined by the following.

(i) $y = 2x - 3$

(ii) $y = -x + 1$

(iii) $y = -\frac{3}{2}x$

(b) How can you check your answers in (a)?

Computer Use

To find the slopes of many line segments, you can use a computer. The program shown at the right finds the slope between two points $P(x_1, y_1)$ and $Q(x_2, y_2)$.

▶ Run the program for the points $P(4.3, 2.8)$, $Q(6.5, 9.6)$.

▶ Choose other pairs of points from this section. Run the program using these values.

```
10 INPUT X1, X2, Y1, Y2
20 LET Y = Y2 – Y1
30 LET X = X2 – X1
40 IF X < > 0 THEN 70
50 PRINT "THE SLOPE IS UNDEFINED"
60 GO TO 90
70 LET S = Y/X
80 PRINT "THE SLOPE IS"; S
90 END
```

10.7 Calculating Distance on the Plane

The skills you learned previously are applied to solving problems on the Cartesian plane.

To calculate distance on the plane, you apply the Pythagorean property.

$\triangle ABC$ is plotted on the Cartesian plane. To find the length of $\overline{AB}$, you need to know the lengths of the other sides.

In a right triangle
$c^2 = a^2 + b^2$

From the graph, $\overline{BC} = 5$ units and $\overline{AC} = 3$ units. Now use the Pythagorean property to calculate the length of $\overline{AB}$.

$$c^2 = a^2 + b^2 \qquad \text{Use } a = 5, b = 3.$$
$$= (5)^2 + (3)^2$$
$$= 25 + 9$$
$$= 34$$
$$c = \sqrt{34}$$

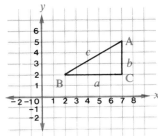

Thus $\overline{AB} = \sqrt{34}$ units or $\overline{AB} = 5.8$ units to 1 decimal place.

10.7 Exercise

A Express your answers to 1 decimal place.

1   To find distance on the plane, you need to find the lengths of vertical and horizontal line segments. Find the length of each line segment.

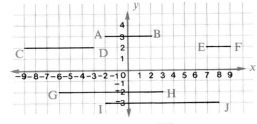

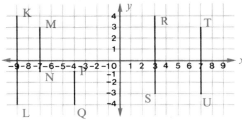

2   Calculate the length of $\overline{AB}$ in each of the following.

(a)

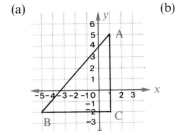

(b)

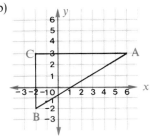

(c)

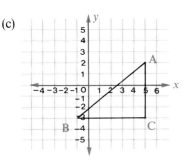

B 3 Find the length of $\overline{AB}$ to 1 decimal place if A(4, 6) and B(−2, 3).

4 Find the length of each line segment for the following end points.
(a) (4, 3), (4, −6)   (b) (3, −2), (6, −2) (c) (2, 3), (5, −7)   (d) (−4, 3), (−6, 2)

5 Which line segment is longer?   ▶ $\overline{AB}$, A(−2, 5), B(5, −2)   ▶ $\overline{CD}$, C(−2, 2), D(4, 8)

6 (a) Construct the triangle with vertices P(−3, 0), Q(−1, −6), and R(3, −2).
(b) Calculate the length of each side.   (c) Classify the triangle.

7 (a) Plot △ABC given by A(−6, −2), B(2, 4) and C(6, −4).
(b) Find the co-ordinates of the midpoint E of $\overline{AB}$ and of the midpoint F of $\overline{BC}$.
(c) Find the length of $\overline{EF}$ and of $\overline{AC}$. What do you notice?
(d) Write a probable conclusion about your results. How can you test the probable conclusion?

8 (a) A rectangle has co-ordinates D(1, 6), E(11, 6), F(11, 2) and G(1, 2). H is the intersection of the diagonals. Plot the rectangle.
(b) Use your diagram to calculate $\overline{DH}$ and $\overline{HF}$; $\overline{GH}$ and $\overline{HE}$.
(c) Write a probable conclusion about the diagonals of a rectangle.
(d) Repeat steps (a) to (c) for a rectangle of your own choice.

 9 Refer to the diagram. How many squares can you find?

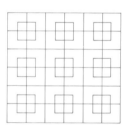

C 10 (a) Plot quadrilateral ABCD given by
A(3, 2)   B(−2, 6)   C(−6, 1)   and   D(−1, −3).
(b) Find the lengths of $\overline{AB}$, $\overline{BC}$, $\overline{CD}$ and $\overline{CA}$.
(c) Is figure ABCD a rhombus or a square?

Computer Use

To find the distance between two points, you can use the program shown at the right.

▶ What are the co-ordinates of the points shown in the program?

▶ Choose values in this section. Use the program to find the distance between the points.

```
10 PRINT "FOR THE FIRST POINT"
20 INPUT "GIVE THE X CO-ORDINATE", X1
30 INPUT "GIVE THE Y CO-ORDINATE", Y1
40 PRINT "FOR THE SECOND POINT"
50 INPUT "GIVE THE X CO-ORDINATE", X2
60 INPUT "GIVE THE Y CO-ORDINATE", Y2
70 REM FIND THE DISTANCE
80 LET D = SQR((X1 − X2) ↑ 2 + (Y1 − Y2) ↑ 2)
90 PRINT "THE DISTANCE IS", D
100 END
```

10.8 Intersecting Graphs

A plane is flying along the line defined by $y = x + 1$.
A ship is sailing along a path defined by the line
$y = -2x + 4$. You can use a graph to find the
co-ordinates of the point where the path of the plane
crosses the path of the ship.

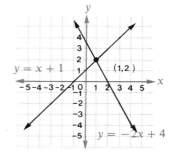

$y = x + 1$

x	y
-1	0
0	1
1	2

$y = -2x + 4$

x	y
-1	6
0	4
1	2

The same pair of co-ordinates
show the point of intersection.

Example (a) What is the point of intersection
of the lines given in the graph?

(b) Verify that the point lies on
both lines by substituting the
co-ordinates into the equations.

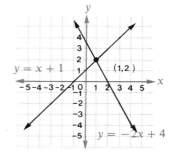

Solution (a) From the graph the point of intersection is $(6, -2)$.

(b) Substitute $x = 6$ and $y = -2$ into the equation of each line.

Use $x + y = 4$.   Use $x - 2y = 10$.

L.S. $= x + y$ L.S. $= x - 2y$
$\quad = (6) + (-2)$ $\quad = (6) - 2(-2)$
$\quad = 4$ $\quad = 10$
$\quad = $ R.S. ✓ $\quad = $ R.S. ✓

10.8 Exercise

A 1 For each graph, ► identify the point of intersection from the graph.
► verify your answer by substituting into the equations.

(a)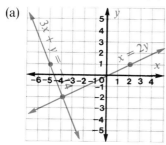

(b)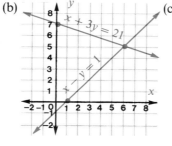

(c)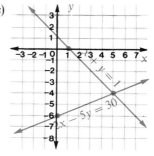

2   (a) Draw the graph of $y = 2x - 1$.
    (b) Draw the graph of $y = 3x - 3$ on the same axes.
    (c) What are the co-ordinates of the intersection point for $y = 2x - 1$
        and $y = 3x - 3$?

B   The domain of all the graphs is the real numbers, $x \in R$.

3   For each pair of equations,
    ▶ draw the graphs.   ▶ find the point of intersection.
    (a) $y = x$ (b) $y = x + 2$ (c) $y = -x$
        $y = -x + 2$ $y = -x + 2$ $y = x - 2$
    (d) $y = x - 2$ (e) $y = -2x - 2$ (f) $y = x + 4$
        $y = \frac{1}{3}x + 2$ $y = -\frac{2}{3}x + 2$ $y = 3x$

4   A ship sails along a path defined by $y = 2x + 4$. A motor boat travels
    along the line defined by $y = -x + 1$. Find the point of intersection
    of the two paths.

5   Two planes are flying along the paths defined by $y = x - 7$ and
    $y = 2x - 16$. An airport is located at the point of intersection of the
    two paths. Find the co-ordinates of the airport.

6   A helicopter is flying on a path defined by $y = \frac{3}{2}x + 3$. A bird is flying on
    a path defined by $y = 3x$. Find the co-ordinates of the point at which
    their paths cross.

 7   Three congruent squares are shown.
    Show how to use one additional
    line segment to form four congruent
    shapes that are not squares.

C 8   Two relation rules show the distance travelled, d, in kilometres after time,
    t, in hours.
        $d = 4t$ $d = 2t + 4$
    (a) Draw the graph of each relation rule on the same axes. Use t for
        the horizontal axis.
    (b) From the graph, at what time, in hours, do the graphs intersect?
        What is the value of d at this time?
    (c) Create a problem based on the graph. Write a solution for the
        problem.

10.9 **PSP** Problem Solving: Using Strategies

To solve a problem, whether in mathematics or another discipline, you need to have some plan so you can effectively use your experiences (whether successful or not), your strategies and your key questions to attempt a solution.

▶ Refer to the strategies in your *Problem Solving Plan* **PSP** . Have you kept your plan up to date? Have you updated your list of math words? Have you provided an example of your own to illustrate each word?

▶ Review the flow chart shown at the right. Use the flow chart to help you plan solutions to the following problems.

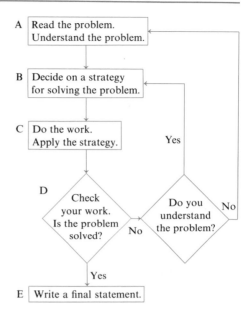

A | Read the problem. Understand the problem.

B | Decide on a strategy for solving the problem.

C | Do the work. Apply the strategy.

D | Check your work. Is the problem solved?

Do you understand the problem?

E | Write a final statement.

10.9 Exercise

B 1 Which one of the following does not belong in the list?

   topin   nile   pareg   gements   lange

2 Fredrik, Erik and Axelito shared 62 Halon Batar (Swedish candies). Axelito had a perfect square more than Erik. Fredrik had a perfect square more than Axelito. How many Halon Batar did each person have?

3 Toothpicks are used to construct Roman numerals. The statement is not true. Move two toothpicks to make the statement true.

4 Use the digits 0, 1, 2, 3, 4, 5, 6, 7, 8, 9 and the operations of addition and subtraction to make the value of the expression equal to 100.

5 I have $243 in paper money. I have 3 times as many $20 bills as $50 bills and half as many $5 bills as $20 bills. If I have 4 times as many $1 bills as $50 bills, how many of each bill do I have?

Practice and Problems: Review

1   One of the newest letters added to the English alphabet is given by the code. What is the letter?
    ▶ Join $(-1, -3)$ to $(1, 2)$ to $(3, 7)$.   ▶ Join $(-5, 7)$ to $(-3, 2)$ to $(-1, -3)$.

2   In an experiment, a spring is stretched by adding mass. The ordered pairs are given as   (mass added, g, amount of stretch, cm).
    (a) Use the data to draw a graph. $(0, 0)$, $(10, 1)$, $(20, 2)$, $(30, 3)$, $(40, 4)$
    (b) Use the graph. About how much mass is added if the stretch is 1.5 cm?
    (c) Use the graph. About how much stretch is there for a mass of 65 g?

3   A relation is given by $x \rightarrow x + 3$, $x \in \{-2, -1, 0, 1, 2\}$.
    (a) Find the ordered pairs for the relation.
    (b) Draw a graph of the relation.

4   (a) Draw the graph of each relation.
        ▶ $y = x + 1$, $x \in I$ ▶ $y = x + 1$, $x \in R$
    (b) How are the relations alike? How are they different?

5   Find the x-intercept and the y-intercept of each line.
    (a) $x + y = 6$ (b) $5x - 2y = 20$ (c) $y = -2x + 8$

6   Draw a graph of each line.
    (a) slope $\dfrac{1}{2}$, point on line $(-1, 4)$ (b) slope $\dfrac{2}{3}$, y-intercept 4

7   Show that $A(-2, 0)$, $B(0, 1)$ and $C(2, 2)$ are collinear.

8   Plot the points for $\triangle ABC$ where $A(1, 0)$, $B(-1, 4)$ and $C(5, 2)$.
    (a) Measure $\angle A$.
    (b) Calculate the measure of $\overline{AB}$, $\overline{BC}$ and $\overline{AC}$.
    (c) Find the area of $\triangle ABC$.

9   Draw the graphs of the pair of equations. Find their point of intersection.
        $y = 2x + 1$ $y = x + 3$

10 A jeep is crossing the desert on a path defined by $y = \dfrac{-3}{2}x + 1$. A camel is travelling on a path defined by $y = -2x$. Find the co-ordinates of the point where their paths cross.

Practice Test

1 (a) Follow these instructions.
        Join $(-8, -7)$ to $(-8, 2)$ to $(-3, -7)$ to $(2, 2)$ to $(2, -7)$.
   (b) What letter of the alphabet have you made?

2 Data are collected for Awajohn's running of the 100-m race.

time in seconds	distance in metres
0	0
1	5
4	20
7	35

   (a) Use the horizontal axis for time and the vertical
        axis for distance. Draw a graph of the data.
   (b) About how long will it take him to run 13 m?
   (c) How far will he run in 9 s?

3 A relation is given by $y = x^2 - 1$ for $x \in R$.
   (a) Find ordered pairs for $x = -3, -2, -1, 0, 1, 2, 3$.
   (b) Draw a graph of the relation.

4 (a) Draw the graph of the linear relations $y = x + 2$ and $y = 2x + 2$
        on the same set of axes.
   (b) How are the relations alike? How are they different?

5 Find the rise, run and
   slope of each line.

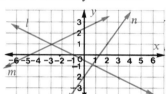

6 Draw a graph of each line.

   (a) x-intercept -3, y-intercept 2   (b) slope $\dfrac{3}{2}$, x-intercept -1

7 Show that $(-2, -2)$, $(1, 0)$ and $(7, 4)$ are collinear.

8 A rectangle has co-ordinates $A(-4, 1)$, $B(-2, 3)$, $C(3, -2)$ and $D(1, -4)$.
   (a) Plot the rectangle.   (b) Find the lengths of the diagonals.

9 Draw the graphs of the pair of equations. Find their point of intersection.
        $y = x + 2$ $y = 3x$

10 Four congruent triangles are shown.
    How many line segments do you need
    to place in the diagram to
    create 10 congruent triangles?

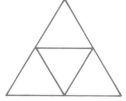

Cumulative Review (7–9)

1 Simplify.

(a) $(4x)(3x^3y)$ (b) $(-2x)(3xy^2)$ (c) $3y(x + xy - y)$ (d) $-4x(x^2 - 7)$

(e) $\dfrac{48x^3y}{-6xy^2}$ (f) $\dfrac{-18x^2y}{-2x^3y}$ (g) $\dfrac{3x^2 - 6x}{-3x}$ (h) $\dfrac{2y^2 - 6y}{-2y}$

2 If $x = 3$ and $y = -2$, find the value of each of the following.

(a) $x^2y + xy^2$ (b) $x^2y \div xy^2$ (c) $x^3 \div x^2$ (d) $(xy)^3 \div x^2y$

3 Solve and verify.

(a) $4^{2x-5} = 8^{x+3}$ (b) $1000^{x+2} = 10^{4x+8}$ (c) $3^{4x+1} = 9^{1+x}$

4 Factor the following.

(a) $12 - 3k$ (b) $15x^2 - 5x$ (c) $4a^2b - 8ab + 16ab^2$

5 Find the missing measures in each figure. Be able to justify your answer.

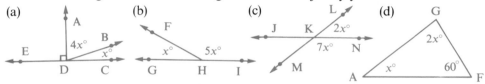

6 Construct the following triangles using a straightedge and compasses.

(a) $\triangle KLM$ where $\angle L = 45°$, $\overline{KL} = 7$ cm, $\overline{LM} = 5$ cm

(b) $\triangle PQR$ where $\angle P = 60°$, $\overline{PQ} = 6$ cm, $\angle Q = 75°$

7 Find the unknown angle measures. O is the centre of each circle.

(a)
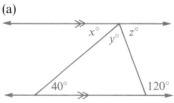

(b) (c)
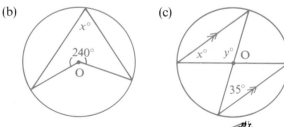

8 To find the height of the tree shown in the diagram, a metre stick $\overline{AB}$ was placed as shown. What is the height of the tree?

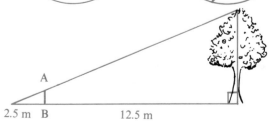

11 *Using Algebra: Percent, Ratio, Rate, Proportion*

Skills with percent, simple and compound interest, applying ratios and rates, equations for proportions, formulas for speed, time and distance, organizing information, thinking visually, applications, strategies for problem solving

Introduction

In your study of mathematics thus far, you have seen many aspects of mathematics and its uses. These aspects include the following.

▶ Understanding the meanings of key words is essential to solving problems.

▶ Many applications in other fields are based on a knowledge of mathematics.

▶ An equation or a formula can be used to solve some problems.

▶ Patterns play an important role in the study of mathematics. Often they suggest strategies for solving problems or developing skills.

▶ Problems essentially fall into two categories.

> *Category I:* problems for which the strategy needed to solve the problem is evident

> *Category II:* problems for which the strategy needed to solve the problem is not evident

▶ The technology of calculators and computers reduces the tedious calculations needed to solve certain problems.

▶ Being organized is key to solving problems. A plan such as the *Problem Solving Plan* **PSP** is a useful, efficient approach to solving problems.

It is essential that the circuit boards in electronic equipment are accurate. For example, passengers on a jet depend on the accuracy of computer circuits for safe takeoff and safe landing. The circuits need to be checked in an organized way.

11.1 Inventory: Percent

Skills with percent are often required not only in
mathematics but also in other studies.
Percent means per hundred and the symbol %
is used to show "parts of one hundred." The
diagram is shaded 25%.

100 equal parts
25 parts shaded

The three basic percent calculations follow.

A Find the percent.

What percent of 2000 is 1500?

Let n be the percent.

$$\frac{n}{100} = \frac{1500}{2000}$$

$$n = \frac{1500}{2000} \times 100 \text{ or } 75$$

Thus 1500 is 75% of 2000.

B Find the percent of the number.

Find 35% of 840.

$$35\% \text{ of } 840 = 0.35 \times 840$$
$$= 294$$

Thus 35% of 840 is 294.

You can use your calculator.

$\boxed{C}\ 840\ \boxed{\times}\ 35\ \boxed{\%}\ 294$

C Find the number.

If 15% of a number is 30, find the number.

15% of the number is 30.

1% of the number is $\frac{30}{15}$ or 2.

100% of the number is 100×2 or 200.

Thus the number is 200.

or   Let n be the number.
15% of the number is 30.

$$\frac{15}{100} = \frac{30}{n} \qquad n = \frac{30 \times 100}{15}$$

$$n = 200$$

When solving problems about percent, you must identify which type of
calculation is required.

Example A survey showed that 26.8%, or 134, of those surveyed use public
transportation to travel to work. How many people were surveyed?

Solution Let x represent the number of people surveyed. 26.8% of the
number surveyed is 134.

$$\frac{26.8}{100} = \frac{134}{x}$$

$$x = \frac{134 \times 100}{26.8}$$

$$x = 500$$ Thus 500 people were surveyed.

PSP Use an equation
to solve the problem.

11.1 Exercise

A Questions 1 to 3 review the relationship among decimals, fractions and percent.

1   Write each percent as a decimal.
   (a) 36%   (b) 4%   (c) 125%   (d) $\frac{1}{2}$%   (e) 9.5%   (f) $11\frac{3}{4}$%   (g) 265%

2   Write each decimal as a percent.
   (a) 0.36   (b) 0.06   (c) 1.46   (d) 0.005   (e) 0.375   (f) 2.5   (g) 0.0001

3   Write each fraction as a percent.
   (a) $\frac{3}{10}$ (b) $\frac{4}{5}$ (c) $1\frac{1}{2}$ (d) $\frac{1}{200}$ (e) $\frac{7}{4}$ (f) $\frac{7}{8}$ (g) $\frac{15}{8}$

4   What percent is
   (a) 40 of 200?   (b) 75 of 225?   (c) 64 of 16?   (d) 32 of 180?

5   Find each percent of a number.
   (a) 15% of 400   (b) 6.2% of 36   (c) 125% of 360   (d) $12\frac{1}{2}$% of 150

6   (a) If 12% of a number is 630, find the number.
   (b) If 0.1% of a number is 96, find the number.
   (c) If 130% of a number is 585, find the number.
   (d) If 7.5% of a number is 27, find the number.

B Use your calculator when appropriate. Remember: The first step is to identify which type of calculation is involved.

7   Find the unknown in each of the following.
   (a) 60% of 120 is x.   (b) 12% of x is 24.   (c) 48 is x% of 960.
   (d) 400 is x% of 2000.   (e) 22.5% of x is 72.   (f) 125% of 4.80 is x.

8   A test result of 80% is considered an A. On one test an A was 52 marks or more. How many marks were possible for the test?

9   Jennifer earned $325 last year working at the Pizza Boat. She spent $165. What percent did she spend?

10   Jeff bought a tennis racquet for $98. If it decreased in value by 25%, by how much did it decrease in value?

11 In a survey, 35% of the students said they would prefer live bands at school dances. That response was given by 63 students. How many students were surveyed?

12 One day at the school cafeteria, 62.5% of the 192 hot meals served were the daily special. How many daily specials were served?

13 Out of 600 first-time home owners, 432 used the financial arrangements of their builder or real estate broker to pay for their homes. What percent is that?

14 The average person is 65% water by mass.
   (a) Allan found that 40.3 kg of his body mass is water. What is his total body mass?
   (b) Leah's mass is 54 kg. How many kilograms of her body is not water?
   (c) How many kilograms of your body mass is water?

15 Read this article.
   (a) How many people were surveyed?
   (b) What percent of people had no preference?
   (c) The third response was: *preferred the later time change.* What percent of people gave this response?

Daylight Savings Time Poll Results
Traditionally on the last weekend in April we set our clocks ahead one hour for Daylight Savings Time. This gives us more daylight in the evening and less in the early morning. On the last weekend in October, we set our clocks back one hour to return to Standard Time. In 1987 Canadians set their clocks ahead 3 weeks earlier than usual. A public opinion poll indicated that 42.5%, or 867, of the people polled preferred the earlier "spring forward"; 792 had no preference.

PSP 16 Nicole bought 2 bags of potato chips which totalled $4.04 including tax. She presented a five-dollar bill for payment. Can she obtain 7 coins as her change? Justify your answer.

C 17 A ring was appraised at $3250. Three years later its value had appreciated (increased) by 8%.
   (a) By what dollar value did it appreciate?
   (b) What was its value 3 years later?

18 An antique car was appraised at $42 500. A year later it had appreciated in value by 6%.
   (a) What percent of $42 500 is its appreciated value?
   (b) Find its appreciated value one year later without first finding how much it had appreciated in value.

11.2 Business Percent: Applications

Percent has many applications in business.

Commission

When you work you can be paid in different ways. You might be paid
▶ a **salary** whereby you receive a fixed amount of money each week (or month).
▶ a **commission** whereby you are paid a percent of your sales per week (or per month).
▶ a **salary and some commission**.

Example 1   Lance sold subscriptions. He received a commission of 12% of the value of the subscriptions he sold. What did he earn after selling $128.00 worth of subscriptions?

Solution   Commission rate is 12% of amount sold.

$$12\% \text{ of } \$128.00 = 0.12 \times \$128.00 \qquad \text{Use your calculator.}$$
$$= \$15.36$$

Thus Lance earned $15.36 for selling $128.00 of subscriptions.

Profit

When you buy something, you pay more for the item than the seller did in order for the seller to make a profit.

> **PSP**
> To solve a problem you must know the meaning of all the words.

$$\text{Profit} = \text{Selling Price} - \text{Cost Price}$$

Example 2   Kay's Stereo buys speakers for $175 a pair and then sells them for $255 a pair. What profit is made on a pair of speakers as a percent to 1 decimal place?

Solution

$$\text{Profit} = \text{Selling Price} - \text{Cost Price}$$
$$= \$255 - \$175$$
$$= \$80$$

Thus the profit on a pair of speakers is $80.
Let x be the percent profit.

$$\frac{x}{100} = \frac{80}{175} \quad\begin{array}{l}\longleftarrow \text{ profit} \\ \longleftarrow \text{ cost price}\end{array}$$

$$x = \frac{80}{175} \times 100 \qquad \text{Use your calculator.}$$

$$x = 45.7 \text{ to 1 decimal place}$$

Thus the profit as a percent is 45.7%.

Discount

Sometimes when you buy something, you save money because a discount has been applied to the price.

Example 3   The price of ski equipment was $382.50, but it was offered at a 25% discount. Find the sale price.

Solution   Discount is 25% of $382.50 = 0.25 × $382.50
$$= \$95.63 \text{ (to the nearest cent)}$$
Sale price = Selling Price − Discount
$$= \$382.50 − \$95.63$$
$$= \$286.87$$

Thus the sale price was $286.87.

Sales Tax

Often when you buy something, you pay sales tax.

Example 4   If the sales tax is 7%, find the total cost of a bicycle selling for $175.50.

Solution

Method 1
Sales Tax = 7% of $175.50
$$= 0.07 × \$175.50$$
$$= \$12.29$$
Total Cost
$$= \text{Selling Price} + \text{Sales Tax}$$
$$= \$175.50 + \$12.29$$
$$= \$187.79$$

Thus the total cost of the bicycle is $187.79.

Method 2
Total Cost = 107% of $175.50
$$= 1.07 × \$175.50$$
$$= \$187.79$$

PSP To successfully solve percent problems, you need to recognize which type of percent calculation is involved. Once you identify the strategy, you only need to record your solution in an organized way.

11.2   Exercise

A Remember: There are only three basic types of percent calculations.

1   For each of the following problems,
   ▶ first identify the strategy to use.   ▶ then solve the problem.
   (a) Alexis earned $10 commission on sales of $200. What percent was the commission?
   (b) Carl earned $4500, or 3%, commission. What was the value of what he sold?
   (c) Bernice earned 5% commission for selling $12 500 worth of T.V. sets. How much did she earn?

2   Identify the type of percent calculation needed for each problem. Then solve.

(a) A profit of $40 was made on an item costing $150. What percent was the profit? What was the selling price?

(b) A profit of 15% was made on the sale of items costing $235. What was the profit? What was the selling price?

(c) A profit of 22%, or $16.50, was made on an item. What was the cost of the item? What was its selling price?

B Refer to your *Problem Solving Plan* **PSP** to organize your written work.

3   For each problem,
▶ what is the first decision you need to make?
▶ solve the problem.

(a) A discount of $33\frac{1}{3}\%$, or $86.25, was offered. What was the original selling price? What was the sale price?

(b) A discount of 20% was offered on an item selling for $79.50. What was the discount? What was the sale price?

(c) A discount of $12 was offered on an item originally selling for $79.99. What percent was the discount? What was the sale price?

4   Which type of percent calculation is each of the following? Solve the problem.

(a) 8% sales tax was paid on an item selling for $69.95. What was the sales tax? What was the total cost?

(b) 5% sales tax, or $6.20, was paid on an item. What was the selling price of the item? What was the total cost?

(c) $37.44 sales tax was paid on an item selling for $312. What percent was the sales tax? What was the total cost?

5   For selling magazines Jeannette is paid 8% commission of the total sales. If she received $14.88 one week, what were her total sales?

6   A set of lawn furniture cost the retailer $285. It is sold for $375.00. What is the profit as a percent?

7   Some televisions were reduced in price to clear space for a new model line. An advertisement announced that there was 40% off with prices ranging from $260.40 to $569.40. What was the range of the original selling prices?

8   A real estate salesperson received $1\frac{1}{2}\%$ commission for a house that sold for $123 000 and a 3% commission for a house that sold for $129 000. What were the earnings for the two houses?

9 Use the provincial sales tax table shown at the right to find the total cost of each item in each province.

(a) radio @ $36.50   (b) coat @ $139.95

(c) record @ $9.49   (d) boots @ $55.98

Sales Tax	Province
12%	Newfoundland
9%	Prince Edward Island
8%	New Brunswick, Quebec, Nova Scotia
7%	Ontario, Saskatchewan
6%	British Columbia
5%	Manitoba
no tax	Alberta

 10 (a) Create a question based on the information given in the table in the previous question. Include information that is *not needed* to solve the problem.

(b) Write a solution for the problem.

 11 (a) Create another question based on the table in Question 9 that *does not have enough* information to solve the problem.

(b) Provide the needed information and write a solution for the problem.

C 12 Use the provincial sales tax table given in Question 9. Identify in which province(s) each item was purchased.

(a) headphones @ $49.95, total cost $53.95

(b) toy @ $29.50, total cost $30.98

(c) paint @ $24.50, total cost for 2, $53.41

(d) wallpaper @ $12.75, total cost for 6, $81.86

13 The original price of a pair of skates was $75.00. Find the total cost if a discount of 15% was applied and the sales tax was 8%.

14 Gino receives a commission of 12% on sales up to $8500 per month and 15% on sales over $8500 per month. Calculate the total amount of commission earned for the following sales: March $7600, April $9600, May $11 500, June $12 600.

Computer Use

In business, a computer is invaluable for doing repetitive calculations. The program at the right calculates the percent of a number.

▶ Choose some input values from this section and try the program.

▶ List ways in which a computer is used in doing calculations in a business setting.

```
10 PRINT "PERCENT OF A NUMBER"
20 INPUT " PERCENT IS"; P
30 INPUT "THE NUMBER IS"; N
40 LET A = 0.01 * P * N
50 PRINT "THE ANSWER IS"; A
60 IF N = 0 GOTO 80
70 GOTO 20
80 END
```

11.3 Consumers and Simple Interest

When you invest money, you are paid interest for the use of your money. When you borrow money, you are charged interest for the privilege.

When you calculate simple interest, you use

$I = Prt$ where I is the interest in dollars
P is the principal (investment or loan) in dollars
r is the rate of interest per year as a percent
t is the length of time in years.

Example 1   Stefan invested \$500 at $7\frac{1}{2}\%$ per annum (year) for 6 months. Find the interest he earned.

Solution   Use $P = 500$, $r = 7\frac{1}{2}\%$ or 0.075 and
$t = \frac{1}{2}$ (6 months expressed as a fraction of a year).

$I = Prt$
$ = 500(0.075)(\frac{1}{2})$
$ = 18.75$ Use your calculator.   **PSP** To solve some problems you need to use a formula.

Thus Stefan earned \$18.75 in interest.

The amount, A, of money to be paid at the end of the loan period or investment period is calculated using

$A = P + I$ where P is the principal and I is the interest earned as above.

What is the amount of the investment in Example 1?

Often you use the interest formula to find one of the other variables.

Example 2   Find the length of time of the investment if \$750 earned \$123.75 in interest when invested at 11% per annum (or 11%/a).

Solution   Use $I = 123.75$, $P = 750$ and $r = 11\%$ or 0.11.

Method 1 $I = Prt$
$123.75 = 750(0.11) \times t$
$123.75 = 82.5t$
$\dfrac{123.75}{82.5} = t$
$1.5 = t$

Method 2 $I = Prt$
$\dfrac{I}{Pr} = \dfrac{Prt}{Pr}$
$\dfrac{I}{Pr} = t$
$\dfrac{123.75}{750(0.11)} = t$
$1.5 = t$

Thus the length of time of the investment was 1.5 years.

11.3 Exercise

A 1 Express each interest rate as a decimal.

(a) 9% (b) $7\frac{3}{4}\%$ (c) $12\frac{1}{2}\%$ (d) $8\frac{1}{4}\%$ (e) $11\frac{3}{4}\%$

2 Express each length of time in years.

(a) 6 months (b) 4 months (c) 4 years 6 months

B Estimate your answers before you calculate. Then check whether your answers are reasonable. **PSP**

3 The rate of interest charged by a bank is $12\frac{1}{2}\%$/a on loans. Calculate the interest paid on each loan.

(a) $270 for 2 years (b) $180 for 6 months (c) $950 for 3 months

4 Find the amount of each investment.

(a) $800 at 10%/a for 6 months (b) $450 at 12%/a for 3 months

(c) $1250 at 9.5%/a for 6 months (d) $960 at $8\frac{3}{4}\%$/a for 9 months

5 Who pays the greater amount of interest? Estimate first.

A: John borrowed $690 for 1 year at 12.5%/a.

B: Lucy borrowed $760 for 9 months at $13\frac{3}{4}\%$/a.

6 Find the principal invested if $21.38 interest was earned after 3 months and the rate was $9\frac{1}{2}\%$/a.

PSP 7 Mara, Nina and Serena are sisters who live in Canada, Germany or France. Use the clues to establish where each sister lives.

▶ Mara does not like Europe. ▶ Nina cannot speak French.

List any assumptions you made.

C 8 Copy and complete the table.

	P	I	r	t
(a)	$650	$78	12%/a	?
(b)	$1200	$51	?	6 months
(c)	?	$46.25	$9\frac{1}{4}\%$/a	3 months

	P	I	r	t
(d)	$500	?	13%/a	6 months
(e)	$950	$19.79	$12\frac{1}{2}\%$/a	?
(f)	$1500	$52.50	?	3 months

11.4 Principles of Compound Interest

In the previous section you used two formulas to solve problems involving simple interest.

If $I = Prt$ and $A = P + I$, then by substitution $A = P + Prt$ and by factoring $A = P(1 + rt)$.

To find the amount of $500 invested for 3 years at 9% per annum, you can use $A = P(1 + rt)$.

$$A = P(1 + rt) \qquad \text{Use } P = 500, r = 9\% \text{ or } 0.09 \text{ and } t = 3.$$
$$= 500(1 + 0.09 \times 3)$$
$$= 500(1.27)$$
$$= 635$$

Thus the amount is $635.

Frequently the interest earned after each interest period is added to the principal. Thus the principal is greater for each interest period. This is called **compound interest**.

 To solve a problem you must understand the meanings of the words used. Be sure you clearly understand the meaning of compound interest.

Example 1 Find the amount of $500 invested for 3 years at 9% per annum compounded annually.

Solution

End of first year	End of second year	End of third year
$A = P(1 + rt)$	$A = P(1 + rt)$	$A = P(1 + rt)$
$= 500(1 + 0.09 \times 1)$	$= 545(1 + 0.09 \times 1)$	$= 594.05(1 + 0.09 \times 1)$
$= 500(1.09)$	$= 545(1.09)$	$= 594.05(1.09)$
$= 545$	$= 594.05$	$= 647.51$

Thus the amount of $500 compounded annually for 3 years is $647.51.

 Be sure to make a final statement. Check your answer in the *original* problem.

Compare the amount when $500 is calculated at compound interest to the amount when $500 is calculated at simple interest as shown above. Which amount would you prefer?

By examining the solution, you notice that P, or $500, has been multiplied by $(1 + r)$, or 1.09, three times. Thus a compact formula for the amount, A, results.

$$A = P(1 + rt)^n \text{ where } P \text{ is the principal, } r \text{ is the rate per compound period}$$
$$\text{and } n \text{ is the number of compound periods.}$$

Example 2   Yvonne borrowed $1500 at 12% per annum compounded annually for 5 years. Find the amount to be repaid.

Solution   Use $P = 1500$, $r = 12\%$ or 0.12 and $n = 5$.

$$A = P(1 + r)^n$$
$$= 1500(1 + 0.12)^5$$
$$= 1500(1.12)^5$$
$$= 2643.51 \text{ (to the nearest cent)}$$

Use your calculator.

$\boxed{C}\,1.12\,\boxed{y^x}\,5\,\boxed{\times}\,1500\,\boxed{=}\,2643.51$

Thus the amount to be repaid is $2643.51.

If you calculated the amount in the previous example using simple interest, the amount to be repaid would be $2400. Compare this with the amount calculated using compound interest.

11.4 Exercise

A Round your answers to the nearest cent.

1   Use your calculator to evaluate each power.
   (a) $(1.11)^3$ (b) $(1.12)^4$ (c) $(1.09)^2$ (d) $(1.045)^6$
   (e) $(1.02)^8$ (f) $(1.085)^3$ (g) $(1.0775)^5$ (h) $(1.055)^6$

2   Find the amount for each investment.
   (a) $2500 at 11% per annum, compounded annually for 3 years
   (b) $675 at 9% per annum, compounded annually for 5 years
   (c) $950 at 7% per annum, compounded annually for 8 years

3   Find the amount for each loan.
   (a) $5000 at 8% per annum, compounded annually for 2 years
   (b) $1780 at 12% per annum, compounded annually for 4 years
   (c) $825 at 10% per annum, compounded annually for 6 years

B Use your calculator in each of the following problems. Be sure to check whether your answers are reasonable.

4   Interest rates are constantly changing. To see the effect of changing interest rates, find the amount after 5 years for each annual interest rate for a principal of $15 000 compounded annually.

   (a) 6%   (b) $9\frac{1}{2}\%$ (c) $11\frac{3}{4}\%$ (d) $15\frac{1}{4}\%$

5 Mark invests $1400 at $12\frac{1}{4}\%$ per annum, compounded annually for 5 years.

    (a) Find the amount.   (b) Find the amount using simple interest.

    (c) How much more is the amount when it is calculated at compound interest?

6 Zarina invested $2500 at $9\frac{3}{4}\%$ per annum, compounded annually for

2 years. She also invested $2000 at $10\frac{1}{2}\%$ per annum, compounded annually

for 5 years. Which investment earned more interest. How much more interest was earned?

 7 A baker needs 300 mL of cream for baking cookies. He only has 500 mL and 175 mL measuring cups. How would the baker proceed to measure out the exact amount of 300 mL of cream?

C 8 (a) If $1000 is invested at 10% per annum, compounded semi-annually (or every half year) for 2 years, you use $A = 1000(1.05)^4$. Explain why $r = 0.05$ and $n = 4$.

    (b) If $500 is invested at 9% per annum, compounded quarterly (or every quarter of a year) for 3 years, you use $A = 500(1.0225)^{12}$. Explain why $r = 0.0225$ and $n = 12$.

9 Use your explanations in the previous question to find the amount for each investment.

    (a) $1450 at $9\frac{1}{2}\%$ per annum, compounded semi-annually for 5 years

    (b) $875 at 11% per annum, compounded quarterly for 2 years

    (c) $2650 at 12% per annum, compounded monthly for 1 year

---

Computer Use

Often to solve problems, you need to understand what symbols mean and how they can be used.

▶ Refer to the program. What does each symbol mean? (You may need to look at a BASIC computer language reference.)

▶ Try the program. Use various inputs for X.

```
10 INPUT X
20 LET M = X ↑ 2 − 8 * X − 12
30 LET A = ABS(M)
40 PRINT X, M, A
50 IF X = 100 THEN 70
60 GOTO 10
70 END
```

11.5 Essential Skills: Ratio, Rate and Proportion

A **ratio** can be used to compare the attendance at the West Ferris Swimming Pool on Monday and Tuesday. A ratio is a comparison of like quantities.

West Ferris Pool	
Day	*Attendance*
Monday	240
Tuesday	360
Wednesday	300
Thursday	390
Friday	370

number of persons that attended on Monday — compared to — number of persons that attended on Tuesday

$$240 : 360$$

The ratio 240:360 is read as "240 is compared to 360". The numbers 240 and 360 are called the **terms** of the ratio. To obtain **equivalent ratios**, multiply or divide both terms by the same number. An equation that shows two ratios are equivalent is called a **proportion**. For example,

$$240 : 360 = 2 : 3$$

The ratio 2:3 is said to be in **simplest form** because the only common factor of both terms is 1. Two-term ratios such as 2:3 can also be written in fractional form as $\frac{2}{3}$.

To compare three numbers, you can write a three-term ratio.

number of persons that attended on Tuesday — number of persons that attended on Wednesday — number of persons that attended on Thursday

$$360 : 300 : 390$$

From the proportion 360:300:390 = 12:10:13, you can write three other proportions using two-term ratios.

$$360 : 300 = 12 : 10 \qquad 360 : 390 = 12 : 13 \qquad 300 : 390 = 10 : 13$$

To find the missing terms of a proportion, you use your earlier skills with equations as shown in the following example.

Example 1   Find the missing terms for $6:5:t = 18:k:6$.

Solution

Step 1:
Find k. Solve the proportion.

$$6 : 5 = 18 : k \quad \text{or} \quad \frac{6}{5} = \frac{18}{k}$$

$$6k = 90$$
$$k = 15$$

Step 2:
Find t. Solve the proportion.

$$6 : t = 18 : 6 \quad \text{or} \quad 6 : t = 3 : 1$$

$$\frac{6}{t} = \frac{3}{1}$$

$$6 = 3t$$
$$2 = t$$

Often you need to compare unlike quantities. A comparison of unlike quantities is called a **rate**. For example,

> Michael jogs 12 m in 2 s or 6 m in 1 s.
> The rate is expressed as 6 m/s.

The number of metres jogged in 1 s is often called the **unit rate**.

Since a rate shows a comparison of quantities expressed in different units, the units must be written as part of the rate, namely 6 m/s.

To solve a problem involving rate, you can use an equation.

Example 2 During the first part of the season Carole scored 72 points in 45 games. At this rate, how many points might she expect to score by the end of the 80 game season?

Solution Let n represent the number of points.

$$\text{Solve } \frac{72}{45} = \frac{n}{80}$$

$$\frac{8}{5} = \frac{n}{80} \quad \begin{array}{l} \longleftarrow \text{ number of points} \\ \longleftarrow \text{ number of games} \end{array}$$

$$640 = 5n$$
$$128 = n$$

Thus the number of points she would expect to score is 128.

To find Carole's unit rate in Example 2, you find how many points are scored in 1 game.

$$72 \div 45 = 1.6 \text{ points per game}$$

11.5   Exercise

A 1 Express each ratio in simplest form.
(a) 4:8   (b) 12:3   (c) 4:8:2   (d) 6:10   (e) 2:4:8   (f) 20:50
(g) 5:10:5   (h) 4:12:8   (i) 100:10   (j) 10:100   (k) 10:6:4   (l) 4:8:16

2 For each of the following express the terms in the same unit. Then write as a ratio in simplest form.
(a) 45 min to 3h   (b) 1 min to 30 s   (c) 1 m to 36 cm   (d) 15 min to 2 h
(e) 3 min to 30 s   (f) 45 g to 1 kg   (g) 4 a to 6 months   (h) 36¢ to $2

3 Write an equivalent ratio for each of the following.
(a) 3:4   (b) 3:8   (c) 5:9   (d) 2:3   (e) 2:3:4
(f) 1:2:1   (g) 4:7   (h) 5:3   (i) 3:10   (j) 1:3:6

B Round your answers, as needed, to one decimal place.

4 Calculate the unit cost (cost for one unit) for each of the following.
(a) 3 L of milk cost $1.83. (b) $42 for 4.5 m of fabric (c) 500 mL of juice cost 89¢.

5 Find the unit rate for each of the following.
(a) 8 goals scored for 20 shots on goal   (b) 35 g of chocolate for 49¢
(c) 12 pages read in 45 min   (d) $59.25 for 15 h work

6 Find the speed as a unit rate for the following.
(a) Jimmy Weismuller swam 100 m in 20 s.
(b) The submarine travelled 132 km in 6 h.
(c) The satellite travelled 60 400 km in 4 h.
(d) The mountain climber went 80 m in 10 min.

7 Find the missing term in each proportion.
(a) $3:2 = x:6$ (b) $15:y = 3:2$ (c) $3:13 = 6:d$ (d) $10:3 = t:15$
(e) $12:15 = 4:w$ (f) $25:b = 5:3$ (g) $q:10 = 2:5$ (h) $2:3 = m:45$

8 Find the missing term in each of the following.
(a) $\dfrac{x}{8} = \dfrac{15}{6}$ (b) $y:15 = 2:6$ (c) $\dfrac{9}{k} = \dfrac{7}{21}$ (d) $\dfrac{14}{7} = \dfrac{9}{t}$

(e) $m:18 = 18:24$ (f) $\dfrac{10}{15} = \dfrac{8}{s}$ (g) $\dfrac{12}{s} = \dfrac{16}{12}$ (h) $4:8 = y:10$

9 Find the missing terms.
(a) $1:k:3 = 2:4:p$ (b) $s:8:r = 3:2:5$ (c) $20:4:m = p:1:5$ (d) $2:1:5 = y:2:s$
(e) $x:9:6 = 1:k:2$ (f) $12:y:m = 4:6:3$ (g) $x:9:m = 2:3:5$ (h) $k:2:10 = 5:1:p$

10 The winner in a school election won by a ratio of 5:4. The loser received 576 votes.
(a) How many votes did the winner receive?   (b) How many votes were cast?

11 The ratio of tickets sold for adults, students and children was 12:8:3.
(a) If 432 adult tickets were sold, how many student tickets were sold?
(b) If tickets cost $1.75 for adults, $1.25 for students and 50¢ for children, how much money was collected?

12 The ratio of lime juice to orange juice in a drink is 3:8.
(a) If 21 L of lime juice are used, how much orange juice is needed?
(b) If 32 L of orange juice are used, how much lime juice is used?
(c) In a 22-L mixture, how much is lime juice?
(d) How much orange juice is used in 55 L of the mixture?

PSP 13 Often you need to use the given information in a creative way to solve a problem. Solve the following problem.

(a) If $a{:}b = c{:}d$, prove that
  • $(a + b){:}b = (c + d){:}d$ • $(a - b){:}b = (c - d){:}d$

(b) Express the mathematical proportions given in (a) in words.

C 14 The record amount of snow that fell in a 24 h period was 1.83 m at Silver Lake, Colorado.

(a) How much snow would have accumulated in a week?

(b) What assumption did you make?

The record snowfall in Canada occurred at Mount Copeland, B.C.: a record 2446 cm fell in 1971–72. The greatest accumulation of snow in one day in Canada was 112 cm, a record held by Ranger Station, Alberta.

15 During a poll, 366 out of 488 drivers were in favour of seat belt legislation.

(a) If 200 more drivers were polled, how many more drivers would you expect to be in favour of seat belt legislation than those against the legislation?

(b) What assumption did you make?

Math Tip

The proportions shown are written in *different* forms but convey the *same* information.

$$x{:}y = a{:}b \qquad \frac{x}{y} = \frac{a}{b}$$

The proportions can be also written in other useful equivalent forms.

$$x{:}a = y{:}b \qquad \frac{x}{a} = \frac{y}{b} \qquad bx = ay$$

$$y{:}x = b{:}a \qquad \frac{y}{x} = \frac{b}{a}$$

$$a{:}x = b{:}y \qquad \frac{a}{x} = \frac{b}{y}$$

Show that the above proportions are equivalent.

11.6 Using Skills with Algebra and Ratio

Earlier you used algebra to solve equations. You can now combine these skills with ratios and rates to solve problems. The diagram illustrates this important nature of using mathematics.

To start a business you need to invest capital (an amount of money). If you are a partner in a business, you receive a share of the profits in proportion to the amount of money or time you invest.

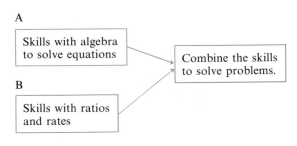

A

> Skills with algebra to solve equations

> Combine the skills to solve problems.

B

> Skills with ratios and rates

For example, skills with ratios and equations can be used to solve many everyday problems. The information in the photograph's caption is needed in order to solve the following problem.

Example   To start a sports equipment business, Sylvia and Gayle invested capital (money) in the ratio 7:5. They agreed to share the profit in the same ratio. If they made $9468 profit last year, how much did each person receive?

Solution   Let $7x$ represent Sylvia's share of the profit in dollars and $5x$ represent Gayle's share in dollars.

Think: Choose variables so that they are in the ratio 7:5. Namely, $7x:5x = 7:5$.

Then $7x + 5x = 9468$
$$12x = 9468$$
$$x = 789$$

Sylvia's profit $= 7x$ Gayle's profit $= 5x$
            $= 7(789)$ $= 5(789)$
            $= 5523$ $= 3945$

Check:
$$\$5523$$
$$+\$3945$$
$$\overline{\$9468} \checkmark$$

Sylvia received $5523 and Gayle received $3945.

In your study of mathematics, you use the same methods and skills many times. An important skill is organizing your written work. Use your *Problem Solving Plan* to help you organize your solutions.

PSP

11.6   Exercise

A Decide on which variables you will use to solve the problem.

1   The substances M and N are mixed in the ratio 3:7 by mass. The mass
    of M in grams is $3y$.
    (a) Write an expression for the mass of N in the mixture.
    (b) The total mass of the mixture is 50 g. Write an equation.
    (c) Solve the equation in (b). Find the mass of each substance in the
        mixture.

2   The number of hours that Robin and Dom worked on a project is in the
    ratio 12:7. Dom worked $7x$ hours.
    (a) Write an expression for the number of hours that Robin worked.
    (b) If the total number of hours worked is 114 h, write an equation.
    (c) How many hours did each person work on the project?

B Be sure to check whether your answer is reasonable. Always verify
    in the original question.   `PSP`

3   There are 250 g of peanuts and 150 g of raisins in a snack mixture.
    (a) What is the ratio of peanuts to raisins?
    (b) What mass of raisins would you expect in 600 g of the snack mixture?

4   For a fruit punch, orange juice, grape juice and lemonade were mixed in
    the ratio 5:4:6 by volume. The volume of orange juice in litres in the
    punch is $5y$.
    (a) Write an expression for the volume of grape juice and the volume of
        lemonade in the fruit punch.
    (b) There are 12 L of punch. Find the volume of orange juice used.

5   The ratio of adult visitors to student visitors at the Science Fair was 2:3.
    (a) If there were 1500 visitors in all, how many were students?
    (b) The admission charges were $3 per adult and $1.50 per student. How
        much money was obtained from admissions?

6   (a) Two numbers are in the ratio of 4:5. If the sum of the numbers is
        162, what are the numbers?
    (b) The sum of two numbers is 2040 and they are in the ratio 11:13. Find
        the numbers.
    (c) The difference between two numbers in the ratio 8:5 is 324. Find the
        numbers.

7 During a trip to Alberta, Brad and Kelly decided to share the expenses in the ratio of 6:5. The total cost of the trip was $511.50. Calculate each person's share.

8 A fertilizer contains 55 kg of nitrogen and 22 kg of potash.
   (a) What is the ratio of nitrogen to potash?
   (b) How much nitrogen is in 728 kg of the fertilizer?

9 A bag of fertilizer for flowering plants contains nitrogen, phosphorus and potash in the ratio 20:5:5. How much of each substance is in a 90-kg bag?

10 The ratio of nitrogen to phosphorus to potash in fertilizers used for fruits and vegetables is 3:10:12. How much of each substance is there in a 100-kg bag?

To obtain prize-winning flowers, you often need fertilizer to supplement the nutrients that occur in the soil.

11 George, Susan and Bruce invested money in the ratio of 4:3:5 to buy and then sell comic books. If they made a profit of $360 in one year, how much profit should each person receive?

12 Three numbers are in the ratio 3:5:6. If their sum is 504, find the numbers.

13 Three numbers are in the ratio 2:5:11. If the greatest number exceeds the sum of the other numbers by 232, find the numbers.

14 The ratio of quarters to dimes to nickels collected in a candy machine is 5:4:1. If there are 280 coins altogether, how many dimes are there?

PSP 15 To solve some problems, you often need to obtain more information. Read the following problem.

> Four shapes are given. If the sun was the size of a volleyball, which of the following would be the size of earth?
> ▶ a baseball   ▶ a pea   ▶ a pingpong ball   ▶ a grain of salt

   (a) What information do you need in order to solve the problem? From what sources can you find such information?
   (b) Solve the problem.

C 16 During a trip to Vancouver, Danny and Michael spent $1169.19.
   (a) Danny and Michael agreed to share the expenses in the ratio 7:4. How much did each pay?
   (b) What percent did Michael pay to 1 decimal place?

Applications: Ratios for Chemicals

Skills in mathematics can be used to solve problems in other subjects such as problems about chemicals.

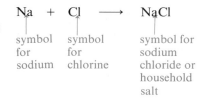

$$Na \ + \ Cl \ \longrightarrow \ NaCl$$

symbol for sodium | symbol for chlorine | symbol for sodium chloride or household salt

▶ In mathematics, relations about numbers are dealt with.

▶ In science, relations about chemicals are studied.

For example, sodium and chlorine chemically combine to form common household salt. A chemist would show the relation as shown to the right.

The study of relations and symbols is helpful to chemists and their work with chemistry. In the questions that follow, the ratios relate to the masses of the substances that combine to form the familiar things mentioned.

17 Salt consists of sodium and chlorine in the ratio 46:71.
   (a) How much chlorine is in a box of common salt whose mass is 150 g?
   (b) What percent of salt is sodium?

18 The basic substances of silicon and oxygen chemically combine in the ratio 7:4 to form sand.
   (a) How much silicon is in 550 kg of sand?
   (b) How much oxygen is in 1000 kg of sand? Express your answer to the nearest kilogram.

19 Hydrogen (H) and carbon (C) chemically combine in the ratio of 3:2 to make moth balls.
   (a) What percent is hydrogen?
   (b) How much carbon is in a mass of 1200 g of moth balls?

20 Laughing gas consists of nitrogen and oxygen in the ratio 7:4. How much oxygen is in 770 kg of laughing gas?

21 Marble consists of calcium, carbon and oxygen in the ratio 10:3:12.
   (a) How much carbon would you find in a 300-kg piece of marble?
   (b) What percent of marble is calcium? oxygen?

22 The alloy (mixture of metals) made for bells consists of copper and tin in the ratio 4:1. How much copper is in a bell that has a mass of 625 kg?

11.7 Skills with Speed, Time and Distance

A snail is concerned with motion and so is a swimmer in shark-infested waters. People have always been interested in data involving time, speed and distance. Some statistics are shown in the newspaper clipping at the right.

The relationship between the time taken, t, speed, v, and the distance travelled, d, can be shown in different ways:

$$v = \frac{d}{t} \qquad d = vt \qquad t = \frac{d}{v}$$

Wow! What records!
How fast is fast? At one time, people believed it was impossible to run 100 m in less than 10 s. But this is no longer so. The list shows a few speed records. How many others can you collect?

- The fastest dog is the greyhound, which can run at 67 km/h.
- Clyde McRae holds the record for the Trans-Canada walk. He walked 6056 km in 96 d.
- The speed reached in a 2-person bobsled is almost 100 km/h.
- The record speed for water skiing is unofficially 206 km/h.

Example 1 Renée jogged 2 km in 30 min.
(a) Find her speed. (b) How far will Renée jog in x hours?

Solution (a) Use $v = \frac{d}{t}$

$v = \frac{2}{0.5}$ Remember: 30 min = 0.5 h

$v = 4$

Renée's speed is 4 km/h.

(b) Use $d = vt$
$d = 4(x)$
Renée will jog $4x$ km in x h.

To compare speeds the same units must be used.

Example 2 Norm rides his bicycle at 5 m/s. Dawn cycles at 16 km/h. Which person is travelling faster?

Solution 5 m/s means in 1 s Norm travels 5 m.
In 60 s Norm travels 60 × 5 or 300 m.
In 60 min Norm travels 60 × 300 or 18 000 m. Use 18 000 m = 18 km.
Thus Norm travels 18 km in 1 h or 18 km/h.
Since Dawn's speed is 16 km/h, Norm is travelling faster.

When you deal with problems about motion, you make certain assumptions such as the speed is uniform. This speed is often referred to as the **average speed**.

11.7 Exercise

A What is meant by the symbols m/s and km/h?

1 A car travels 1800 km in 30 h. What is its average speed?

2 A horse trots 75 km in 5 h. What is its average speed?

3 A rabbit at top speed runs at 55 km/h. At that rate, how long will it take to go 110 km?

4 A plane travels at 800 km/h. How long does it take to travel 2400 km?

5 A ball is thrown and travels at a speed of 15 m/s. How far will it go in 2.2 s?

6 An elevator descends at a rate of 3.5 m/s. How far will the elevator go in 12.8 s?

B Refer to your *Problem Solving Plan* **PSP** to organize your solutions.

7 Copy and complete the table.

	d	v	t
(a)	120 km	20 km/h	?
(b)	154 km	?	4.4 h
(c)	?	70 km/h	8 h

	d	v	t
(d)	1500 m	50 m/s	?
(e)	1200 m	?	10 min
(f)	850 km	100 km/h	?

8 Nancy ran 3.8 km in 55 min. Calculate her speed to 1 decimal place in
(a) kilometres per hour.   (b) metres per second.

9 A car is travelling at 50 km/h. How fast is it going in metres per second to the nearest metre?

10 An elevator descends at the rate of 5.5 m/s. How fast is this in kilometres per hour?

11 Which animal is faster?
▶ a squirrel travelling at 20 km/h   ▶ a dog running at 6 m/s

PSP 12 If 5 whales eat 300 kg of fish in 4 d, how many kilograms of fish could 3 whales eat in 2 d?

PSP 13 John runs 1.5 km each day and he has already run 12 km. Jennifer runs 2 km each day and she has already run 6 km. In how many days will they have run the same distance? List any assumption that you made.

C 14 In the summer of 1987, Ben Johnson ran 100 m in 9.83 s. Calculate his speed in kilometres per hour to the nearest kilometre.

15 At the 1984 Winter Olympics, Gaetan Boucher won a gold medal in the 1500-m speed skating event in 1 min 58.38 s. Calculate his speed in kilometres per hour.

16 Gaetan also won a gold medal in the 1000-m speed skating event in 1 min 18.80 s. Predict how much faster his speed is in this event than in the event in the previous question. Then check your prediction.

From Math History

Albert Einstein (1879–1955) was perhaps one of the most well known scientists of the 20th century. Many of his contributions to mathematics and science go well beyond the grasp of the average person.

Einstein did not begin to talk until he was 3 years old, but he showed a keen curiosity in the happenings in the family's shop that manufactured electrical machinery. He began to develop an ability to understand difficult concepts and by the time he was 12 years of age, he taught himself all that had to be learned about Euclidean geometry.

Although he enjoyed physics, he spent much time on other activities such as playing his violin. This led some to believe that he did not spend enough time on his studies. Eventually he received his doctorate. He was so far ahead of his time in the theories he was publishing that few physicists understood or related to his ideas. In his famous theory of relativity, almost no one understood his reasoning and arguments. He "believed that scientific theories are the free creations of a finely tuned intuition which cannot always be logically connected to experiment." Eventually he was recognized for his theories and became internationally famous in scientific circles. In 1922 he received the Nobel Prize in Physics. Soon everywhere he went he was followed by photographers and reporters. Despite the fame bestowed on him, Einstein remained humble throughout his life, spending his time not only on his scientific work, but also on humanitarian issues. In his honour, a radioactive element was named Einsteinium designated by the symbol Es.

11.8 PSP Problem Solving Strategy: Thinking Visually

To organize the solution to a problem you have often used the *Problem Solving Plan*. You have also learned different strategies to help you solve problems. A few of them are reviewed in the list. Which other problem solving strategies can you add to the list? A diagram often helps you to visualize a problem involving motion and to organize and sort the information.

Often you also need to use variables and your skills with equations as shown in the next example.

> Review your strategies and the questions you need to ask. Here are a few of the strategies.
> ► Checking whether an answer is reasonable by using estimation
> ► Identifying essential information needed to solve a problem
> ► Recording the information on a diagram
> ► Solving the problem by thinking of a simpler problem

Example Linda made a trip by bus and by train. The speed of the bus was 40 km/h and of the train 80 km/h. Linda spent 3 h more on the train than on the bus. If the total distance of the trip was 480 km, how long did she spend on the bus?

Solution Let b, in hours, represent the time spent on the bus.

 Think: Record the information on a diagram.

By bus   By train

A   B   C

speed = 40 km/h   speed = 80 km/h   Think: 3 h more were
time = b h   time = $(b + 3)$ h   spent on the train.
Thus distance = $40b$ km   Thus distance = $80(b + 3)$ km

Remember: $d = vt$

distance by bus + distance by train = total distance

$$40b + 80(b + 3) = 480$$
$$40b + 80b + 240 = 480$$
$$120b = 480 - 240$$
$$120b = 240$$
$$b = \frac{240}{120}$$
$$b = 2$$

Linda spent 2 h on the bus.

11.8 Exercise

A Questions 1 to 5 refer to a trip travelled by car and by bicycle.

1 Copy and complete the diagram.

By car   By bicycle

$v = 50$ km/h, $t = x$ h, $d = ?$ $v = 10$ km/h, $t = (x + 1)$ h, $d = ?$

2 Write an expression for the complete distance travelled.

3 If the total distance travelled was 70 km, write an equation to show this information.

4 Solve the equation in the previous question for x.

5 How far did the car travel?

Questions 6 to 10 refer to a trip travelled by plane and by boat.

6 Copy and complete the diagram.

By plane   By boat

$v = x$ km/h, $t = 12$ h, $d = ?$ $v = 20$ km/h, $t = \dfrac{x}{40}$ h, $d = ?$

7 Write an expression to show the total distance travelled.

8 The total distance travelled was 2500 km. Write an equation to show this information.

9 Solve the equation in the previous question for x.

10 For how long did the boat travel?

B 11 Susan and Marnie lived in different cities 450 km apart. One day they left at the same time and drove towards each other. Susan travelled at 80 km/h and Marnie travelled at 100 km/h. How much time passed before they met?

(a) Copy and complete the diagram. Let x, in hours, represent the time taken to meet.

Marnie   They met here.   Susan

$v = ?, t = ?, d = ?$ $v = ?, t = ?, d = ?$

(b) Use the information in (a) to write an equation.

(c) Solve the equation in (b).

(d) Use your solution in (c) to answer the question.

12 Two planes leave an airport at the same time and fly in opposite directions. One plane flies 150 km/h faster than the other plane. After 3 h they are 1650 km apart. What is the speed of each plane?

(a) Copy and complete the diagram. Let x represent the speed of the slower plane in kilometres per hour.

Slower plane	Airport	Faster plane

$v = ?,\ t = ?,\ d = ?$ $v = ?,\ t = ?,\ d = ?$

(b) Use the information in (a) to write an equation.

(c) Solve the equation in (b).

(d) Use your solution in (c) to answer the question.

PSP 13 To solve problems, you need to try different possibilities and keep track of your attempts. To change SWEET to CANDY, you can only change one letter at a time and the change must result in a word. You do not need to keep the letters in the same order each time. What are the fewest number of steps you need to make the change?

Step 1	SWEET
Step 2	SWEAT
'	'
'	'
'	'
'	'
Step ?	CANDY

From Math History

Archimedes (287–212 B.C.), a Greek mathematician, was considered the greatest mathematician of antiquity. He proposed the problem that the ratio of the volume of a sphere to the volume of the smallest cylinder into which the sphere could be fitted was 2:3.

Refer to the diagram. Prove that the ratio is 2:3.

11.9   PSP   Problem Solving Strategy: Essential Translating

When you are solving word problems involving motion there are certain decisions you must make. First identify which of the following formulas you need in order to solve the problem.

$$v = \frac{d}{t} \qquad d = vt \qquad t = \frac{d}{v}$$

Then the *Problem Solving Plan* will help you organize your solution. You must choose a strategy or a combination of strategies to help you write the equation needed to solve the problem. Some of these strategies are as follows.

- Choose a variable.
- Write expressions for the distance, speed and time.
- Draw a diagram and include the information you are given.

Now you can use the expressions you have written and your diagram to write an equation.

Example   Ron drove to the cottage and back in 10 h. His speed going was 72 km/h, but coming home he drove at 48 km/h. How far is it to the cottage?

Solution   Let x represent the distance to the cottage in kilometres.

Home   Cottage

$v = 72$ km/h, $d = x$ km, $t = \dfrac{x}{72}$ h   Remember: $t = \dfrac{d}{v}$

Home   Cottage

$v = 48$ km/h, $d = x$ km, $t = \dfrac{x}{48}$ h   The distance is the same in both directions.

$$\begin{array}{c} \text{time} \\ \text{going} \end{array} + \begin{array}{c} \text{time} \\ \text{returning} \end{array} = \begin{array}{c} \text{total} \\ \text{time} \end{array}$$

$$\frac{x}{72} + \frac{x}{48} = 10$$

$$144\left(\frac{x}{72}\right) + 144\left(\frac{x}{48}\right) = 144(10)$$

$$2x + 3x = 1440$$
$$5x = 1440$$
$$x = 288$$

Check:
Ron's speed going was 72 km/h.
Thus Ron took $\dfrac{288}{72}$ h or 4 h going.
Ron's speed returning was 48 km/h.
Thus Ron took $\dfrac{288}{48}$ h or 6 h returning.
Ron took 10 h in total.
$4 + 6 = 10$ ✓

Thus the distance to the cottage is 288 km.

11.9 Exercise

A For Questions 1 and 2 answer (a) to (f) to solve the problem.

1 Jennifer and Adrianna live in different towns 54 km apart. They leave at
   the same time and cycle towards each other. Adrianna cycles 2 km/h
   faster than Jennifer. They meet after 3 h. How fast was each girl
   travelling?
   (a) Use x to represent Jennifer's speed in kilometres per hour. Write an
       expression for Adrianna's speed.
   (b) Draw a diagram to represent their trip.
   (c) Use the information in the diagram to write an equation.
   (d) Solve the equation.
   (e) Check your solution in the original problem.
   (f) Use your solution to write a final statement as an answer to the problem.

2 To get to a lake for fishing, Miguel needs to drive by car and by ATV
   (All Terrain Vehicle). Miguel travels at 80 km/h by car and at 15 km/h by
   ATV. He travels three times longer by car. If the total distance is 255 km,
   how much time does he travel by car?
   (a) Use x to represent the time travelled by the ATV in hours. Write
       an expression for the time travelled by car.
   (b) Draw a diagram to represent the trip.
   (c) Use the information in the diagram to write an equation.
   (d) Solve the equation.
   (e) Check your solution in the original problem.
   (f) Use your solution to write a final statement as an answer to the problem.

B To solve the following problems,
   ▶ draw a diagram to represent the trips.
   ▶ write distance, speed and time for each trip using a variable if
     necessary.
   ▶ write an equation and solve it.

3 Two ships leave a port at the same time. One ship sails west at 30 km/h.
   The other ship sails east at 20 km/h. How far apart are the ships after 5 h?

4 A car and a motorcycle left a gas station at the same time and travelled
   in the same direction. The car travelled at 90 km/h and the motorcycle
   at 75 km/h. After 3 h how far apart were they?

5 Two planes leave an airport at the same time and fly in opposite directions. Their speeds differ by 150 km/h. After 4 h the planes are 3000 km apart. How fast is each plane going?

6 At noon two freight trains 600 km apart start toward each other and meet in 6 h. If one train travels 12 km/h faster than the other, how fast is each train going?

7 (a) To go to the cottage Mallory travels 330 km. The trip takes 5 h and for 3 of these hours Mallory is in congested traffic. The speed on the open highway is 40 km/h faster than on the congested highway. How fast are the vehicles on the congested highway going?

  (b) Use the information given in (a) to create another word problem. Write a solution for the problem you have created.

8 A train travelled through a canyon for 3 h and then along a river for 6 h. The total distance travelled was 432 km. If the train went 12 km/h faster along the river, what was its speed through the canyon?

9 (a) A dog sled travelled through a forest for 4 h and then on a frozen lake for 5 h. The total distance of the trip was 114 km. If the dog sled went 12 km/h faster on the lake, what was its speed through the forest?

  (b) Use the information given in (a) to create another word problem. Write a solution for the problem you have created.

10 For a moped excursion everyone was supposed to leave at noon, Sandy arrived 30 min late. If the others travel at 18 km/h, how long will it take Sandy to catch up travelling at 24 km/h?

 11 Read these clues carefully.
  • I have two digits; one odd, one even.
  • My remainders are equal when I am divided by 6 or 8.
  • My digits reversed make me smaller than I am.
  • I am more than half a hundred.
  • I am the least value that satisfies the other clues.
  Who am I?

C 12 On a circular race track, the faster car was averaging 180 km/h. The slower car was averaging 150 km/h. The lap time keeper noticed that the slower car took 1 min longer than the faster car to complete one lap. What was the radius of the race track to the nearest tenth of a kilometre?

11.10 PSP Problem Solving Strategy: Organizing Information

To solve a problem you need to answer these two questions.

More and more people are enjoying the fresh air and exercise of hiking.

  I What information am I asked to find?
II What information am I given?

In the previous section, you used a diagram to help you organize the given information, as well as to help you understand the problem.

Another strategy for organizing the given information is to make a chart. Once the chart is completed, you can compare the given information. Then you can decide which equation to write.

Example

A hike up a mountain and back along the same route took 2 h. Coming down the mountain, the hikers went 1.5 m/s, and going up the mountain they went 0.5 m/s. How far was the hike?

Solution

Let d represent the distance in metres travelled up the mountain. Record the information in a chart.

	d (m)	v (m/s)	t (s)
down the mountain	d	1.5	$\dfrac{d}{1.5}$
up the mountain	d	0.5	$\dfrac{d}{0.5}$

← Think: Use $t = \dfrac{d}{v}$.

time up + time down = total time

$$\frac{d}{1.5} + \frac{d}{0.5} = 7200 \quad\leftarrow\quad \begin{array}{l}\text{The same unit} \\ \text{of time must be used.} \\ \text{2 h} = 7200 \text{ s}\end{array}$$

$$1.5\left(\frac{d}{1.5}\right) + 1.5\left(\frac{d}{0.5}\right) = 1.5(7200)$$

$$d + 3d = 10\ 800$$
$$4d = 10\ 800$$
$$d = 2700$$

distance up = 2700 m
distance down = 2700 m
⎯⎯⎯⎯⎯⎯
5400 m

PSP Check the answer in the original problem.

The distance of the hike was 5400 m or 5.4 km.

You have used charts earlier to record information. In the following exercise, charts help you to relate the given pieces of information.

11.10 Exercise

A To solve the problem answer (a) to (d).

1   Two trains leave stations 350 km apart and travel towards each other. If one train travels at 80 km/h and the other at 60 km/h, how soon will they meet?

	distance (km)	speed (km/h)	time (h)
train A	?	80	t
train B	?	60	t

(a) Let t represent the number of hours for the trains to meet. Copy and complete the chart.

(b) Write an expression to show the sum of the distances travelled by the two trains.

(c) Write an equation involving the total distance travelled.

(d) Solve the equation in (c) and answer the problem.

B For each question, answer the parts to solve the problem.

2   Two campers leave the same camp and jog in opposite directions. If they jog at 2 m/s and 3 m/s respectively, how long will it take before they are 3 km apart?

	distance	speed	time
jogger A	?	?	t
jogger B	?	?	t

(a) Let t represent the number of seconds each camper jogs. Copy and complete the chart.

(b) Write an expression to show the distance Jogger A and Jogger B are apart.

(c) Write an equation involving the distance between the two joggers.

(d) Solve the equation in (c) and answer the question.

3   Lloyd's boat travels at 35 km/h and Melanie's boat at 28 km/h. One hour after Melanie leaves the dock, Lloyd follows. How long will it take for Lloyd to overtake Melanie?

	d	v	t
Lloyd's boat	?	?	t
Melanie's boat	?	?	$t + 1$

(a) Let t represent the number of hours taken by Lloyd to overtake Melanie. Copy and complete the chart.

(b) Write an equation using the expressions for the distances travelled by Lloyd and Melanie.

(c) Solve the equation in (b) and answer the question.

4   Two boats leave the same dock and travel along the same route. The faster boat travels at 22 km/h. After 6 h they are 30 km apart. What is the speed of the slower boat?

	d	v	t
slower boat	?	?	?
faster boat	?	?	?

(a) Let x km/h represent the speed of the slower boat. Copy and complete the chart.

(b) Write an equation involving the distance between the two boats, solve it and answer the question.

5   Dave left camp by motorcycle and travelled 45 km/h. One hour later Joan left from the same camp on her motorcycle and followed Dave at 50 km/h. How long will it take for Joan to catch up with Dave?

	d	v	t
Dave	?	?	?
Joan	?	?	?

(a) Let x h represent the time Joan took to catch up with Dave. Copy and complete the chart.

(b) Write an equation involving the distance travelled by Dave and Joan, solve it and answer the question.

6   Steven's final mark in math is based on 4 tests worth 10% each of the final mark and 2 exams equally weighted for the remainder of the mark. His average on the tests was 72% and he obtained 80% on the two exams. Find Steven's final mark.

Calculator Use

You can use your calculator to answer this question. What do pelicans and the mail have in common? To find the answer to the riddle, do these calculations. Then read the answer on your calculator upside down.

$$\boxed{C}\ 20\ \boxed{x^2}\ \boxed{\times}\ 150\ \boxed{-}\ 3486\ \boxed{+}\ 1204\ \boxed{=}$$

To create a riddle of your own and have the answer appear on the calculator is a challenge.

▶ Analyze why the above answer can be read upside down. Which other letters have the property that they can be read in this way?

▶ Create a riddle of your own with suitable calculations.

Math Tip

▶ If you create a problem of your own, you will have a better understanding of what is needed to solve it.

▶ The more problems you create, the more you understand how problems are created and the better you will be able to solve problems given to you by others.

11.11 PSP Problem Solving: Putting it Together

In the previous section you saw how useful charts are for solving problems about motion. Diagrams were used to help you visualize the given information. Deciding on a strategy from your list of strategies is an essential skill. Putting it all together successfully allows you to solve problems.

Example Pat and Sue canoed upstream and returned to their starting place in 6 h. Going upstream they travelled at 4 km/h. Coming back downstream they went at 12 km/h.

(a) For how many hours did they travel upstream?

(b) How far upstream did they go?

Solution Let x represent the time spent canoeing upstream in hours.

	v (km/h)	t (h)	d (km)
upstream	4	x	$4x$
downstream	12	$6 - x$	$12(6 - x)$

distance upstream = distance downstream
$$4x = 12(6 - x)$$
$$4x = 72 - 12x$$
$$16x = 72$$
$$x = 4.5$$

distance upstream: $4x = 4(4.5)$
$$= 18$$

Check you answer in the original problem.

(a) They travelled upstream for 4.5 h.

(b) They travelled 18 km upstream.

11.11 Exercise

A 1 (a) Complete the chart.

(b) If the slower train travelled 1 h longer than the faster train, write an equation.

(c) Find each distance.

	v (km/h)	d (km)	t (h)
faster train	115	$x + 60$	?
slower train	90	x	?

2 (a) Complete the chart.

(b) If the cycling speed is three times the walking speed, write an equaion.

(c) Find each speed.

	v (km/h)	t (h)	d (km)
walking	?	2	x
cycling	?	3	$143 - x$

B For each of the following questions, use a chart to organize the given information for distances, speeds and times. Then solve the problem.

3 Two cars leave at the same time and travel the same road. One car travels twice as fast as the other. After 6 h the cars are 270 km apart. How fast is each car travelling?

4 Two cyclists leave Hamilton at the same time and travel along Highway 8. One cyclist travels 2 km/h slower than 3 times the other cyclist's speed. After 4 h they are 56 km apart. How fast is each cyclist travelling?

5 Wayne took an hour and a half to cycle to the beach and back. His speed going to the beach was 22 km/h, but coming home was 8 km/h.
(a) How long did it take him to get to the beach?
(b) How far is it to the beach?

6 Sally drove at 70 km/h in the country. While in the city she drove at 50 km/h. She spent 2 h longer in the city than in the country. The distances driven in the city and in the country are the same. Find
(a) how long she drove in the city.   (b) the total length of the trip.

7 Marty cycles 6 km/h faster than he walks. To go to the bowling alley by bicycle he takes 12 min, but he takes 30 min if he walks.
(a) At what speed does he walk?   (b) How far is it to the bowling alley?

8 Two boats leave their ports 486 km apart and steam directly towards each other. If the boats travel at 24 km/h and 30 km/h respectively, how long will it take for them to meet?

9 Karen rides her bicycle 11 km/h faster than she walks. If she cycles for 4 h and walks for 5 h, the total distance she travels is 107 km. Find how fast she walks.

10 If Ken goes to his grandmother's by bus, it takes 45 min less than if he rides his bicycle. If the bus travels at 40 km/h and he rides his bicycle at 15 km/h, how far is it to his grandmother's?

PSP 11 A houseboat can hold 15 children and 5 adults. Alternatively it can hold 4 children and 10 adults. How many children can the houseboat hold with no adults on board?

C 12 For a hockey tournament two buses leave 20 min apart and travel along the same road. The first bus travels at 66 km/h and the later bus, at 77 km/h. How long will it take before the later bus catches up?

Applications: Mathematics for Flying

The actual speed of a plane is affected by the speed of the wind. For example, if a plane is flying at 500 km/h against a headwind of 60 km/h, then the actual speed of the plane is 440 km/h.

plane 500 km/h   headwind 60 km/h

In general, if a plane is flying at V km/h against a headwind of s km/h, then its actual speed is $(V - s)$ km/h. If the plane is flying with a tailwind of s km/h, then its actual speed is $(V + s)$ km/h.

When Orville Wright completed the first successful powered flight, he didn't have to worry about headwinds. He only had to worry about hitting his brother Wilbur who was running alongside the plane.

13 (a) Find the distance travelled in 6 h if the speed of the plane is 650 km/h and the headwind is 45 km/h.
    (b) If the headwind in (a) increases by 15 km/h how much shorter is the distance travelled by the plane?

14 A plane travelled 1834 km against a headwind of 126 km/h. If the time of the trip was 3.5 h, find the speed of the plane.

15 A jet went an average speed of 572 km/h for 4.5 h into a headwind. If the length of the trip was 2304 km, find the speed of the headwind.

16 How long would a flight be if a jet flew 1665 km at 400 km/h into a headwind of 30 km/h?

17 An L1011 and a DC9 leave an airport at the same time. The L1011 flies at 550 km/h against a headwind of 40 km/h. The DC9 flies in the opposite direction. After 2 h the planes are 2000 km apart.
    (a) What is the actual speed of the L1011?
    (b) Let V km/h represent the speed of the DC9. Write an expression for the actual speed of the DC9.
    (c) Copy and complete the chart for the two planes.

	d (km)	v (km/h)	t (h)
L1011	?	?	2
DC9	?	?	2

    (d) Write an equation involving the distances travelled by the two planes.
    (e) Solve the equation in (d) to find the speed of the DC9.

11.12 Problem Solving Strategy: Deciding on a Key Skill

To solve a problem with algebra, often you need to use a key skill. One such skill is percent which is used to solve problems about mixtures.

Did you know that most gold jewelry is not pure gold? Since pure gold is soft, it is mixed with other metals to obtain the necessary hardness. The resulting mixture is called an **alloy**.

Jewellers, cooks, chemists and engineers all, at times, have to solve problems involving mixtures. Their ability to solve problems is based on a clear understanding of percent.

Even to this day, you can see prospectors panning for gold in the far North. The heavy gold sinks to the bottom of the pan, as the lighter gravel is washed away. The rarest form of gold is a nugget.

Example A chemist has 800 g of a 20% hydrochloric acid solution. How much water must be added to make it a 15% solution?

Solution Let x represent the mass of water to be added in grams.

PSP It is helpful to draw a diagram to compare the original situation with the new one.

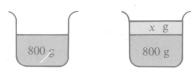

Think: 20% acid ⟶ 80% water
15% acid ⟶ 85% water
mass of water = 80% of 800
$= 0.80(800)$
$= 640$

	Total mass (g)	Mass of water (g)
20% solution	800	640
15% solution	800 + x	640 + x

85% of 15% solution = mass of water in 15% solution

$$85\% \text{ of } (800 + x) = 640 + x$$
$$0.85(800 + x) = 640 + x$$
$$85(800 + x) = 64\,000 + 100x$$
$$68\,000 + 85x = 64\,000 + 100x$$
$$4000 = 15x$$
$$266.6 = x$$

To simplify the equation, multiply *both* sides of the equation by 100.

Thus 270 g of water must be added.

11.12 Exercise

A **1** A gold bar with a mass of 400 g is 35% gold and 65% zinc. A jeweller needs to increase the percent of gold to 48%. How much pure gold needs to be added?

	Total mass of the bar (g)	Mass of pure gold (g)
Original gold bar	400	?
New bar	?	?

   (a) How many grams of pure gold are in the original gold bar?

   (b) Let x, in grams, represent the mass of gold the jeweller needs to add. Copy and complete the chart.

   (c) Use the information in the chart to write an equation.

   (d) Solve the equation in (c). Answer the problem.

2 A chemist has 1620 g of a 5% nitric acid solution. Find how much pure nitric acid must be added to obtain a 10% nitric acid solution.

	Total mass of acid solution (g)	Mass of pure nitric acid (g)
5% solution	1620	?
10% solution	?	?

   (a) How much pure nitric acid is in the original 5% solution?

   (b) Let n, in grams, represent the mass of pure nitric acid to be added to make a 10% solution. Copy and complete the chart.

   (c) Use the information in the chart to write an equation.

   (d) Solve the equation in (c). Answer the problem.

3 A fuel is 60% gasoline and 40% alcohol. To obtain a more efficient fuel, engineers need to increase the alcohol to 55%. How much alcohol needs to be added to 3000 kg of the original fuel?

	Total mass of fuel (kg)	Mass of alcohol (kg)
Original fuel	3000	?
New fuel	?	?

   (a) How much alcohol is in the original fuel?

   (b) Copy and complete the chart. Let y represent the number of kilograms of alcohol to be added.

   (c) Use the information in the chart to write an equation.

   (d) Solve the equation in (c). Answer the problem.

B To solve each of the following problems, use a chart to record the information. Check whether your answers are reasonable. PSP

4 Have you ever seen a white powder on bricks? Muriatic acid is used to remove this powder. How much pure muriatic acid must be added to 1200 g of a 20% solution to make a 40% solution?

5	A public library has a total of 7000 books. At present 20% of the books are non-fiction. How many non-fiction books must be added to the library's collection to increase the percent of non-fiction books to 30%?

6	A cooling system has 25 kg of antifreeze solution in it with a concentration of 15% antifreeze. How much antifreeze needs to be added to the 15% antifreeze solution to increase its strength to 40%?

7	To prepare a household cleaning product, 2 kg of bleach are mixed with 18 kg of water.
	(a) Estimate the bleach as a percent of the cleaning product.
	(b) How much more water needs to be added to reduce the concentration to 4%?

8	The water of the Dead Sea is a solution with a 27% concentration of various salts. It is 6 times as salty as ocean water. To obtain the same concentration as sea water, how much water would you need to add to 100 g of Dead Sea water?

9	Vinegar is a mixture of acetic acid and water. Pickling vinegar is 8% acetic acid. Table vinegar is 5% acetic acid. How much water must be added to 350 g of pickling vinegar to obtain table vinegar?

10	Liquid lye is mixed with water to make a cleaning liquid. Five kilograms of cleaning liquid is 60% lye. How much water must be added to the 60% solution to reduce its strength to 25%?

11	Brine is a solution of water and salt. Thirty kilograms of a brine solution is 8% salt. How much water must be added to the solution to make the solution contain 5% salt?

PSP 12	To solve certain problems, you need to reverse the known procedure. Instead of adding something, you boil or evaporate some of the water to obtain the concentration you want. Use this procedure to solve the following problems.

	(a) Maple syrup is obtained from the species of Maple tree called *acer saccharum*, the sugar maple. Maple sap is 3% pure maple syrup and 97% water. How much water needs to be evaporated from 500 kg of maple sap to make a 30% maple syrup solution?

	(b) A sugar solution is 20% sugar. How much water needs to be evaporated from 100 kg of solution to make the concentration of sugar 50%?

	(c) Les made a 5% salt solution. How much water needs to be evaporated from 30 kg to make the solution 20%?

11.13   **PSP**   Problem Solving: Using Strategies

To solve the following problems, you need to decide which strategy to use. Refer to the list of strategies you have placed in your *Problem Solving Plan* **PSP** .
Remember there are essentially two types of problems.

I You recognize the strategy needed to solve the problem. Then solve the problem.

II You do not recognize the strategy needed to solve the problem. Refer to your **PSP** list to get ideas for strategies to try.

PSP	Problem Solving Plan

Step A: Understand the problem.
- What are you asked to find?
- What are you given?

Step B: Decide on a strategy.

Step C: Apply the strategy.
Do the work.

Step D: Check your solution.

Step E: Write a final statement.

11.13   Exercise

B 1 In a class of 32 students, 16 enjoy science, 20 enjoy math and 4 enjoy neither. How many students enjoy both science and math?

2 The letters of the word **THING** are used to make a nonsense word such as **GINTH**.
(a) How many different five-letter words can you make?
(b) How many of the words make sense?

3 (a) What is the volume of the smallest cube that can be covered with rectangular tiles that measure 27 cm × 36 cm?
(b) How many tiles are required?

4 The difference of the squares of two consecutive even integers is 60. What are the integers?

5 In the *Yellow Pages*, entries under B start on page 70. If 360 digits are used for page numbers before the start of the entries under E, on what page do the entries under E start?

6 Predict the next number for the pattern.   1   3   7   15   31
Justify your answer.

Practice and Problems: Review

1 Find the unknown value.
   (a) 65% of 150 is x.   (b) 25% of x is 17.5.   (c) 45 is x% of 225.
   (d) 125% of 60 is x.   (e) 12.5% of x is 10.   (f) 900 is x% of 150.

2 Find the total cost of an item discounted at 20% of its regular selling price of $189.98 and taxed at 7%.

3 Find the principal invested if $210.38 simple interest was earned after 18 months and the rate was $8\frac{1}{4}$% per year.

4 Find the amount of $5000 borrowed at 9.5% per annum compounded annually for 3 years.

5 Express each ratio in lowest terms.
   (a) 5:15   (b) 24:18   (c) 12:4:8   (d) 12 min to 28 min

6 Find each missing term.
   (a) $3:8 = n:56$ (b) $m:4:10 = 4:2:k$ (c) $5:x:7 = 15:6:y$

7 (a) The sum of two numbers is 132 and their ratio is 5:6. What are the numbers?
   (b) The measures of three angles in a triangle are in the ratio 4:4:1. Find their measures.

8 (a) The Hughes family travelled 205 km in 2.5 h. What was their average speed?
   (b) A jet travels 500 km in y h. What is its average speed?

9 Steve drove his car to the airport at 60 km/h and then caught a plane to Ottawa. The plane flew at an average speed of 500 km/h. Steve's flying time was 5 h more than his driving time. If his total trip was 3620 km, for how many hours was he in the airplane?

10 Larry and Glenda live 435 km apart. They travel towards each other. If Larry travels at 75 km/h and Glenda travels at 70 km/h, how soon will they meet?

11 A 2-kg container of windshield washer fluid has a 15% methyl alcohol concentration. How much methyl alcohol needs to be added to increase the strength to 25%?

PSP 12 The value of HOLIDAY is -115. Based on the value of HOLIDAY, what value might you obtain for VACATION?

Practice Test

1 Marcie bought an antique clock 10 years ago for $300. Today she was offered $1250 for it. By what percent has the value of the clock increased?

2 Dean earned $602.50, or 5%, commission. What was the value of his sales?

3 Joyce bought a coat on sale at $33\frac{1}{3}\%$ off the regular price of $165.50. What was the sale price?

4 Brad invested $2000 at $11\frac{1}{2}\%$ per annum compounded annually for 5 years.
(a) Find the amount.   (b) Use simple interest to find the amount.
(c) How much more is earned when the interest is compounded?

5 Find the missing terms.
(a) $18:8 = 36:y$ (b) $k:10 = 24:60$ (c) $p:8:q = 6:4:10$
(d) $a:18:12 = 2:b:4$ (e) $8:x:y = 12:18:9$ (f) $m:2:10 = 10:1:n$

6 Two numbers are in the ratio $5:3$. If they differ by 12, find the numbers.

7 Hydrogen (H) and carbon (C) are chemically combined in the ratio $3:2$ to make moth balls. How much hydrogen is in 2 kg of moth balls?

8 Brass is made from copper and zinc mixed in the ratio $17:3$. How much zinc is in 100 kg of brass?

9 (a) How far will Jeffrey be in $2k$ hours if he rides his bike at $3k$ kilometres per hour?
(b) How long will it take Vera to run $15d^2$ kilometres at $3d$ kilometres per hour?

10 Diane and Jack travel in the same direction but Jack leaves 1 h before Diane. Jack travels 5 km/h slower than Diane. After 3 h Diane is 5 km ahead of Jack. How fast is each person travelling?

11 A 15-kg solution of vinegar and water is 18% vinegar. How much vinegar needs to be added to increase the strength of the solution to 25%?

Math Tip

To solve a problem whether it is in mathematics or another discipline, you must understand the meaning of each word that occurs in the problem.
▶ Make a list of the new math words you have learned. Provide an example of your own to illustrate each word.
▶ List new problem solving strategies in your *Problem Solving Plan* **PSP**

12 *Polynomials: Products and Factors*

Language and vocabulary, products of binomials, squaring binomials, using patterns, simplifying and substituting, solving word problems, binomials and equations, factoring trinomials, working backwards, difference of squares, organizing skills, factoring quadratic equations, applications, strategies for problem solving

Introduction

In your work you have applied some useful strategies to develop mathematics.

Strategy

Develop Skill A → Combine Skill A and Skill B to develop yet another strategy.

Develop Skill B →

Strategy

Your work with numerical examples → Suggests a more general strategy.

An important characteristic of mathematics is that its strategies and skills can often be applied to solve problems in other fields. Compare the two charts below.

You might use these steps to solve problems using equations.

PSP Problem Solving Plan

Step A: Understand the problem.
  • What are you asked to find?
  • What are you given?

  Read the problem carefully.

Step B: Decide on a strategy.

  Use a variable. Translate to mathematics.

Step C: Apply the strategy. Do the work.

  Solve the equation. Interpret your answer.

Step D: Check your solution.

  Verify your answer in the original problem.

Step E: Write a final statement.

  Answer the original problem.

Can you apply the chart to solve some problems in science, in geography, etc.?

PSP Problem Solving Plan

Step A: Understand the problem.
  • What are you asked to find?
  • What are you given?

  Read the problem carefully.

Step B: Decide on a strategy.

  Use the strategies you have learned.

Step C: Apply the strategy. Do the work.

  Use the strategy to solve the problem.

Step D: Check your solution.

  Verify that you answered the original problem.

Step E: Write a final statement.

  Answer the original problem.

12.1 Multiplying Binomials

In your earlier work, you used models to visualize products.

$$x(x + 2) = x^2 + 2x$$

The product above illustrates the distributive property. You can extend your skills with the distributive property to multiply binomials.

$$\blacksquare(x + 2) = (\blacksquare)x + (\blacksquare)2$$

Use $x + 3$ for $\blacksquare$. Then you obtain

$$(x + 3)(x + 2) = (x + 3)x + (x + 3)2$$
$$= x^2 + 3x + 2x + 6$$
$$\text{factors} \qquad = x^2 + 5x + 6$$
$$\text{terms}$$

To find products of binomials, you can apply the distributive property.

Think of a diagram.

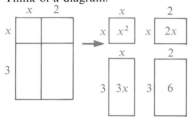

Area is given by $(x + 3)(x + 2)$.

Area is given by $x^2 + 2x + 3x + 6$ $= x^2 + 5x + 6$.

Example Expand and simplify.

(a) $(2y - 3)(3y + 2)$ (b) $(2m + 4)(3m - 2)$

Solution (a) $(2y - 3)(3y + 2)$
$= (2y - 3)3y + (2y - 3)2$
$= 6y^2 - 9y + 4y - 6$
$= 6y^2 - 5y - 6$

(b) $(2m + 4)(3m - 2)$
$= 2m(3m - 2) + 4(3m - 2)$
$= 6m^2 - 4m + 12m - 8$
$= 6m^2 + 8m - 8$

12.1 Exercise

A You can use diagrams to help you understand mathematics. **PSP**

1 (a) To find the product $(x + 4)(x + 5)$, Carol wrote
   $(x + 4)(x + 5) = x(x + 5) + 4(x + 5)$.
   Complete her solution to find the product.

   (b) To find the product, Andy wrote $(x + 4)(x + 5) = (x + 4)x + (x + 4)5$.
   Complete his solution to find the product.

   (c) What do you notice about the answers in (a) and (b)? Why?

2 A diagram is shown for each product of a binomial. Use the diagram to help you expand and simplify each product.

(a)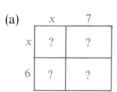

$(x + 6)(x + 7) = ?$

(b)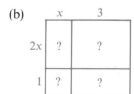

$(2x + 1)(x + 3) = ?$

3 Use a diagram to help you find each of the following products.
  (a) $(x + 3)(x + 6)$ (b) $(y + 5)(y + 7)$ (c) $(a + 4)(a + 4)$
  (d) $(k + 6)(k + 8)$ (e) $(m + 5)(m + 6)$ (f) $(n + 5)(n + 5)$

B 4 Find each product.
  (a) $(x + 1)(x + 5)$ (b) $(a - 4)(a + 3)$ (c) $(m + 5)(m - 8)$
  (d) $(x - 2y)(x - 3y)$ (e) $(k + 5)(k - 1)$ (f) $(6 + x)(8 + x)$

5 Find each product. What do you notice about your answers?
  (a) $(a - 3)(a + 3)$ (b) $(x + 5)(x - 5)$ (c) $(2y + 3)(2y - 3)$
  (d) $(3m + 6)(3m - 6)$ (e) $(6 - 2m)(6 + 2m)$ (f) $(8 - 3x)(8 + 3x)$

6 Find each product.
  (a) $(x + 6)(x + 3)$ (b) $(y + 7x)(y - 9x)$ (c) $(2t - 3)(2t - 3)$
  (d) $(k - 6)(k + 6)$ (e) $(y^2 + 6)(y^2 - 6)$ (f) $(5 + x)(6 - x)$

7 Each binomial involves more than one variable. Expand and simplify.
  (a) $(x + 2y)(3x + y)$ (b) $(2c + 6d)(3c - d)$ (c) $(3a + b)(a + 2b)$
  (d) $(3y - 2x)(2y - 3x)$ (e) $(3y - x)(2y - x)$ (f) $(6k + s)(3k - 2s)$

8 Find an expression for the area of each figure.
  (a)    (b)   (c)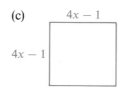

9 A machine pumps $(2x + 1)$ litres every hour. The pump works for $(x - 3)$ hours.
  (a) Find an expression for the amount pumped.   (b) Simplify the expression.

10 The cost of one delivery is $(2y - 3)$ cents.
   (a) Find an expression for the cost of $(y + 3)$ deliveries. (b) Simplify the expression.

PSP 11 Use this result. $(10x + 5)^2 = 100x^2 + 100x + 25$
$$= (x^2 + x)100 + 25$$
$$= x(x + 1)100 + 25$$
   Develop a rule to find these products mentally.
   (a) $25^2 = ?$ (b) $35^2 = ?$ (c) $45^2 = ?$ (d) $55^2 = ?$

C 12 Remember $(x + 1)^2 = (x + 1)(x + 1)$
$$(x + 1)^3 = (x + 1)(x + 1)(x + 1)$$
   (a) Find an expression for each of the following.
       A: $(x + 1)^2$ B: $(x + 1)^3$ C: $(x + 1)^4$ D: $(x + 1)^5$
PSP (b) Use your results in (a). Predict an expression for $(x + 1)^6$. How can
       you check your prediction?

12.2 Square of a Binomial

When the factors of a product are the same, you are able to use exponents.

$(x + 2)^2$ means $(x + 2)(x + 2)$

To find the square of a binomial, you can again use the distributive property.

$$(x + 2)^2 = (x + 2)(x + 2)$$
$$= x(x + 2) + 2(x + 2)$$
$$= x^2 + 2x + 2x + 4$$
$$= x^2 + 4x + 4$$

The square $(x + 2)^2$ can be illustrated by this model.

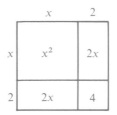

Area of square $= x^2 + 2x + 2x + 4$
So $(x + 2)^2 = x^2 + 4x + 4$

12.2 Exercise

B 1 A diagram is used to illustrate each binomial square. Find A, B and C for each region.

(a) 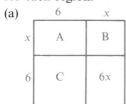 (b) 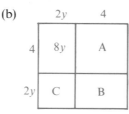 (c)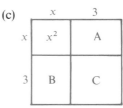

How are the areas for A, B and C used to find an answer for $(x + 6)^2$? $(2y + 4)^2$? $(x + 3)^2$?

2 Use the distributive property to expand each of the following.
(a) $(x + y)^2$ (b) $(m - 3)^2$ (c) $(2y + 6)^2$ (d) $(3 + m)^2$
(e) $(3y - 1)^2$ (f) $(3x - y)^2$ (g) $(3 + 2b)^2$ (h) $(3x + 2y)^2$

3 Find each product. How many can you do mentally?
(a) $(x + 5)^2$ (b) $(y - 6)^2$ (c) $(3 - y)^2$ (d) $(5 + b)^2$
(e) $(m - 3n)^2$ (f) $(2m + 6n)^2$ (g) $(2m - 3n)^2$ (h) $(5x - 2y)^2$

4 Square each binomial.
(a) $(x + 3)$ (b) $(y - 4)$ (c) $(2y + 1)$ (d) $(6 + 3y)$ (e) $(8 - 2x)$

5 For each of the following, which are squares of binomials?
(a) $a^2 + 4a + 4$ (b) $y^2 + 8y + 16$
(c) $x^2 + xy + y^2$ (d) $4x^2 + 4xy + y^2$

12.3 Using Patterns: Products of Binomials

In learning mathematics you often follow the steps shown.

| Learn a concept or skill. | → | Master the concept or skill. Practise. | → | Look for a pattern. | → | Apply the skill or concept to solve problems. |

Apply the distributive property to obtain the binomial product.

$$(y + 4)(y + 5)$$
$$= y^2 + 5y + 4y + 20$$
$$= y^2 + 9y + 20$$

Analyze the answer. Determine how each term was obtained.

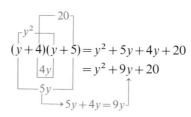

You can use this pattern to help you multiply mentally. Refer to the *Math Tip* at the end of this section.

Step 1: Multiply the first terms in each binomial.

$$(y + 4)(y + 5) = y^2 \ldots$$

Step 2: Multiply the outer terms and then the inner terms. Add the two products.

outer product

$$(y + 4)(y + 5) = y^2 + 9y \ldots \quad \text{Add the terms.}$$

inner product
$$5y + 4y$$

Step 3: Multiply the last terms.

$$(y + 4)(y + 5) = y^2 + 9y + 20$$

12.3 Exercise

A Remember: Think of a pattern to help you find products.

1 Find the missing term of each product.
   (a) $(x + 1)(x + 6) = ? + 7x + 6$
   (b) $(y + 3)(y + 2) = y^2 \ ? + 6$
   (c) $(a - 5)(a + 3) = a^2 - 2a \ ?$
   (d) $(m + 6)(m - 7) = ? - m - 42$
   (e) $(x - 3)(x - 2) = x^2 \ ? + 6$
   (f) $(2 - y)(3 - y) = 6 - 5y \ ?$

2 Find each product. How many can you do mentally?
   (a) $(y - 1)(y - 9)$
   (b) $(2x + 8)(x + 4)$
   (c) $(y + 3)(3y - 5)$
   (d) $(m + 7)(m + 2)$
   (e) $(2a + 4)(3a - 7)$
   (f) $(2y - 6)(y + 3)$
   (g) $(x - 2)(x - 6)$
   (h) $(4x - 2)(x + 7)$
   (i) $(m^2 - 6)(m^2 - 5)$

3 Simplify. Check your work.
   (a) $(t + 6)(t + 4)$
   (b) $(m - 2)(m - 3)$
   (c) $(x - 9)(2x + 1)$
   (d) $(3t + 3)(t - 3)$
   (e) $(x^2 + 8)(x^2 - 3)$
   (f) $(8 + 2a)(1 + a)$

B 4 Expand and simplify.

(a) $(x - 2y)(x + 2y)$ (b) $(3m + 2y)(3m - 2y)$ (c) $(5a - 2b)(5a + 2b)$

What do you notice about the answers? Create two other binomial products that have the same property.

5 Expand and simplify. Which answers are binomials? trinomials?

(a) $(k - 4)(k + 3)$ (b) $(2x + 1)(x + 2)$ (c) $(y + 4)(y - 4)$

(d) $(2y + 3)(2y + 3)$ (e) $(5 + y)(6 - y)$ (f) $(x - 3)(x + 3)$

(g) $(y + 4)(y + 4)$ (h) $(6s + 3)(5s + 3)$ (i) $(2x + 1)(2x - 1)$

(j) $(y + 8)(2y - 8)$ (k) $(6y - 2)(5y + 2)$ (l) $(3 - 2a)(3 + 2a)$

6 Expand each of the following products.

(a) $\left(x + \dfrac{1}{2}\right)\left(x - \dfrac{1}{2}\right)$ (b) $\left(x - \dfrac{1}{2}\right)^2$ (c) $\left(2x + \dfrac{3}{2}\right)^2$ (d) $\left(4x - \dfrac{1}{2}\right)^2$

(e) $(a - 2bc)(a + 2bc)$ (f) $(xy - 3)(xy - 3)$ (g) $(ab - 3)(ab + 3)$

(h) $\left(3x - \dfrac{2}{3}\right)^2$ (i) $\left(2y - \dfrac{5}{2}\right)^2$ (j) $(xy - 3)^2$ (k) $(x^2 + 1)^2$ (l) $\left(\dfrac{1}{2} - p\right)^2$

7 (a) Find the area of a rectangle whose sides in metres measure $3x - 2$ by $4x - 5$.

(b) Find the perimeter of the above rectangle.

(c) What operation did you use to find the area in (a)?

(d) What operation did you use to find the perimeter in (b)?

8 The width of a rectangular pool is $(w - 12)$ metres. The length of the pool is 5 m more than 3 times the width in metres.

(a) Write a variable expression for the length of the pool.

(b) Find the area of the pool. (c) Find the perimeter of the pool.

PSP **9** An apple is 84% water. Once the apple is picked water begins to evaporate from it. If water evaporates at a weekly rate of 4%, what percent of water is in the apple after 6 months? List any assumptions you made.

Math Tip

Think of the diagram shown at the right when you are trying to multiply binomials mentally. The memory aid F O I L may help you.

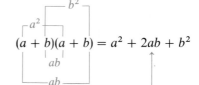

$(a + b)(a + b) = a^2 + 2ab + b^2$

F Multiply first terms. $(a)(a) = a^2$

O Multiply outer terms. $(a)(b) = ab$

I Multiply inner terms. $(b)(a) = ba$ or ab

   Add inner and outer terms. $ab + ab = 2ab$

L Multiply last terms. $(b)(b) = b^2$

12.4 Simplifying Expressions with Binomials

In solving a problem in mathematics, you often simplified **PSP** expressions before doing further calculations. Similarly, before evaluating expressions involving binomials, you simplify expressions. Simplify means to expand and collect like terms.

Example Simplify $(x + 5)^2 + (x - 3)(x - 7)$.

Solution

$(x + 5)^2 + (x - 3)(x - 7)$
$= (x + 5)(x + 5) + (x - 3)(x - 7) \longleftarrow$ Expand both products.
$= (x^2 + 10x + 25) + (x^2 - 10x + 21)$
$= x^2 + 10x + 25 + x^2 - 10x + 21 \longleftarrow$ Collect like terms.
$= 2x^2 + 46$

After you have simplified the expression in the example above, you can evaluate it with fewer calculations.

Use $x = -2$. $2x^2 + 46 = 2(-2)^2 + 46$
$= 2(4) + 46$
$= 8 + 46$
$= 54$

12.4 Exercise

A To simplify expressions, you need to use your skills with finding products of binomials.

1 Expand.
   (a) $(y + 8x)(y - 3x)$ (b) $(3y - 3)(6y - 6)$ (c) $(3k + 9)(5k + 5)$
   (d) $(6y - 2)(6y - 2)$ (e) $(2c + 6)(4c - 4)$ (f) $(3x^2 - 7)(4x^2 + 7)$

2 Complete each solution.
   (a) $2(x - 4)(2x - 3) = 2(2x^2 - 11x + 12)$ (b) $-3(2x - y)(3x + y) = -3(6x^2 - xy - y^2)$
                     $= ?$ $= ?$

3 Simplify each of the following.
   (a) $2(x - 1)(x - 3)$ (b) $3(y - 2)(y + 6)$ (c) $-2(a - 4)(3a + 5)$
   (d) $-3(m - 3)(m - 5)$ (e) $-4(4x - 3)(x + 6)$ (f) $5(5 - y)(4 - y)$

4 Complete each solution.
   (a) $3(x - 1)^2 = 3(x^2 - 2x + 1)$ (b) $-2(2x - 3y)^2 = -2(4x^2 - 12xy + 9y^2)$
               $= ?$ $= ?$

5 Simplify each of the following.
   (a) $2(x - 1)^2$ (b) $3(y + 2)^2$ (c) $-2(8 - a)^2$
   (d) $-3(m + 6)^2$ (e) $3(5 - 2x)^2$ (f) $-y(3y - 2)^2$

B   Remember: Simplify means to expand and collect like terms.

6   Simplify each expression.
(a) $(a - 2)^2 + (a + 2)^2$ (b) $2(a + 1)^2 + (a - 1)^2$
(c) $(x + 1)^2 - (x - 1)^2$ (d) $3(a + 1)^2 - 2(a + 1)^2$

7   (a) To simplify this expression, Alexis wrote
$$2(x - 3)(x - 2) - 3(x - 5)^2 = 2(x^2 - 5x + 6) - 3(x^2 - 10x + 25)$$
$$= ?$$

Why did Alexis use parentheses?
Complete her solution.
(b) Apply the steps in (a) to simplify the following.
(i) $(3 - y)^2 - 2(4 - y)^2$ (ii) $3(x - 1)^2 + 2(x + 1)^2$

8   Simplify each of the following.
(a) $3(x - 2)(x + 4) - 3(x + 4)(x - 2)$
(b) $2(2a - 3)(a + 4) - 2(a + 4)(2a - 3)$
What do you notice about your answers?

9   Simplify each of the following.
(a) $(a + 1)(a + 2) + 3(a + 1)(a - 2)$ (b) $(a - 3)(a - 5) - 2(a - 5)^2$
(c) $2(y - 3)(y + 6) - 3(y + 2)^2$ (d) $2(x - 3)(2x - 3) - 2(x - 5)$
(e) $2(a - 3)(2a - 2) - a(a - 5)$ (f) $2(y - 3)^2 - 3(y + 5)^2$

10   Evaluate. Use $x = -1$ and $y = 3$.
(a) $2(2x + y)^2 - 2(x + 2y)^2$ (b) $(x - y)^2 - 3(x + y)^2$
(c) $3(x - 3y)^2 - 2(x + 2y)^2$ (d) $-2(x - y)^2 + (x - 2y)^2$

PSP 11   (a) Simplify each expression.
A: $(x - 1)^2 - (x - 2)^2$ B: $(x - 2)^2 - (x - 3)^2$
C: $(x - 3)^2 - (x - 4)^2$ D: $(x - 4)^2 - (x - 5)^2$
(b) Use the pattern in (a) to predict the answer to these expressions.
E: $(x - 5)^2 - (x - 6)^2$ F: $(x - 6)^2 - (x - 7)^2$
(c) Without finding the products, what is the simplified expression for
$(x - 25)^2 - (x - 26)^2$?

C 12   (a) Evaluate each expression for $a = -1$. Which has the greatest value?
A: $-3(2a + 1)(a - 1) - 3a(a - 6)$ B: $-2(a + 5)(a - 6) - 3(a + 7)^2$
C: $3(a - 3)(a + 5) - 4(a - 6)(a - 7)$
PSP   (b) Create an expression using binomial products that has a greater
value when $a = -1$ than those in (a).

12.5 PSP Problem Solving: Using Binomials

To solve some word problems, you need to be able to solve equations that involve the products of binomial expressions. To solve equations you use the same principles that you developed earlier. In the following example, your first step is to expand the products.

Example 1

Solve $(x + 4)^2 - (x - 2)^2 = 36$.

Solution

$$(x + 4)^2 - (x - 2)^2 = 36$$
$$x^2 + 8x + 16 - (x^2 - 4x + 4) = 36$$
$$x^2 + 8x + 16 - x^2 + 4x - 4 = 36$$
$$12x + 12 = 36$$
$$12x = 24$$
PSP Check. $x = 2$

PSP Problem Solving Plan

Step A: Understand the problem.
- What are you asked to find?
- What are you given?

Read the problem carefully.

Step B: Decide on a strategy.

Choose a variable and translate.

Step C: Apply the strategy. Do the work.

Solve the equation.

Step D: Check your solution.

Verify the answer in the original problem.

Step E: Write a final statement.

Answer the original problem.

To solve problems involving binomials, organize your solution as you have done with your earlier work. Use the *Problem Solving Plan* to help organize your work.

Example 2 The width of a rectangle is 5 cm less than the length. If the length is increased by 1 cm and the width decreased by 2 cm, the area decreases by 21 cm². Find the dimensions of the original rectangle.

Solution Let x, in centimetres, represent the original width. Then $x + 5$, in centimetres, represents the original length. Then $x - 2$, in centimetres, is the new width and $x + 6$, in centimetres, is the new length.

PSP Think: Use a diagram to organize your thinking.

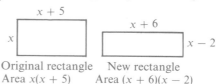

Original rectangle New rectangle
Area $x(x + 5)$ Area $(x + 6)(x - 2)$

Thus the equation is
$$x(x + 5) - (x + 6)(x - 2) = 21$$
$$x^2 + 5x - (x^2 + 4x - 12) = 21$$
$$x^2 + 5x - x^2 - 4x + 12 = 21$$
$$x = 21 - 12$$
$$x = 9$$

Thus the dimensions of the original rectangle are 14 cm by 9 cm.

Check:
Area of original rectangle
    14×9 or 126 cm²
Area of new rectangle
    15×7 or 105 cm²
Difference   21 cm² ✓

12.5 Exercise

A The domain of the variables is the real numbers.

1. (a) What is your first step in solving $(y - 3)(3y - 1) - 3y(y - 5) = 28$?
   (b) Solve the equation. Verify your answer.

2. (a) Find the solution set for $(x + 4)(2x - 5) = 2x(x - 3) - 38$.
   (b) Verify your answer in (a).

3. Solve and verify.
   (a) $3(x + 1)(x + 2) - (3x + 1)(x - 4) = 30$
   (b) $2(y - 3)^2 + 51 = (y + 5)^2 + y^2$
   (c) $(a - 3)^2 = 1 + (a - 1)(a - 2)$
   (d) $25 + 4(a - 3)(a - 5) = (2a - 1)^2$
   (e) $2(m - 3)(2m - 4) = 148 + 4(m - 3)^2$

B To solve some problems, it is helpful to sketch a diagram. **PSP**

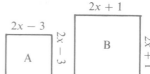

4. When the area of A is increased by 40 square units, the result is equal to the area of B. Find the dimensions of each square.

5. If each side of a square is increased by 6 m, the area increases by 132 m². Find the dimensions of the square.

6. A rectangular backyard is 8 m longer than it is wide. A neighbour's rectangular backyard is 4 m shorter and 3 m narrower and is 82 m² less in area. Find the dimensions of both backyards.

7. If you add the squares of two consecutive integers, the result is the same as twice the square of the lesser and then increased by 25. Find the integers.

PSP 8. Michael and Lesley needed to be at school by 8:30. Lesley's watch was 6 min slow and Michael's watch was 7 min fast. They both thought that they had arrived at school 5 min late.
   (a) What time did they actually arrive at school?
   (b) What was the actual difference in time shown on their watches?

C 9. The width of a rectangular garden is 3 m shorter than the length. A sidewalk 1 m wide is placed as shown. This decreases the area of the garden by 64 m². Find the dimensions of the garden.

Sidewalk ➔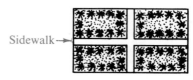

12.6 Factoring Trinomial Squares

When the factors are the same, you often write the product as a square.

$$(a + b)(a + b) = (a + b)^2$$
$$(a - b)(a - b) = (a - b)^2$$

Products such as these are called **trinomial squares**.

To learn to factor trinomials, you need to reverse the procedure. By examining the pattern obtained in expanding trinomial squares, you can develop a method of factoring trinomial squares. Examine the following results.

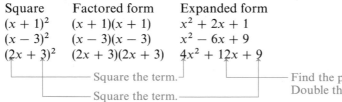

Square	Factored form	Expanded form
$(x + 1)^2$	$(x + 1)(x + 1)$	$x^2 + 2x + 1$
$(x - 3)^2$	$(x - 3)(x - 3)$	$x^2 - 6x + 9$
$(2x + 3)^2$	$(2x + 3)(2x + 3)$	$4x^2 + 12x + 9$

Square the term.
Square the term.

Find the product. $(2x)(3) = 6x$
Double the product. $2(6x) = 12x$

To find the factors of a trinomial square, you need to examine the terms and then work backwards as shown in the following example. Check your work by finding the product.

PSP Working backwards is a helpful strategy to develop mathematics.

Example 1   Factor.   (a) $a^2 + 8a + 16$ (b) $9m^2 - 6m + 1$

Solution

(a) $a^2 + 8a + 16 = (a + 4)^2$

Think: $a^2 = (a)^2$
$16 = 4^2$
$8a = 2(a)(4)$

Check the factors.
$(a + 4)^2 = (a + 4)(a + 4)$
$= a^2 + 8a + 16$

(b) $9m^2 - 6m + 1 = (3m - 1)^2$

Think: $9m^2 = (3m)^2$
$1 = (-1)^2$
$-6m = 2(3m)(-1)$

Check the factors.
$(3m - 1)^2 = (3m - 1)(3m - 1)$
$= 9m^2 - 6m + 1$

Whenever you factor an expression, check first to see if the expression has any common factors as shown in the next example.

PSP The strategies you used to factor trinomial squares are similar to the strategies you used to find factors of other polynomials.

Example 2   Factor $2n^2 + 8n + 8$.

Solution

$2n^2 + 8n + 8$
$= 2(n^2 + 4n + 4)$ 2 is a common factor.
$= 2(n + 2)^2$

12.6 Exercise

A 1 Which of the following are *not* trinomial squares? Why?

(a) $4a^2 + 4ab + b^2$ (b) $a^2 + 20a + 36$ (c) $a^2 + 26a + 25$

(d) $a^2 - 6ab + ab^2$ (e) $x^2 - 8xy + 16y^2$ (f) $4y^2 - 12y + 9$

(g) $x^2 - 5xy + 4y^2$ (h) $4m^2 - 12mn + 9n^2$ (i) $a^2 - 10ab + 9b^2$

(j) $16 + 64y + 64y^2$ (k) $y^2 + y + \dfrac{1}{4}$ (l) $y^2 + \dfrac{5}{4}y + \dfrac{1}{4}$

2 Find the missing value required to make each a trinomial square.

(a) $a^2 + 4a + ?$ (b) $? - 6y + 9$ (c) $4a^2 + ? + 1$

(d) $? - 40y + 16y^2$ (e) $4x^2 + 12xy + ?$ (f) $9a^2 + ? + 4b^2$

B Remember: The first step in factoring is to check for a common factor.

3 Factor the trinomial squares. One cannot be factored.

(a) $y^2 + 4y + 4$ (b) $x^2 - 6x + 9$ (c) $a^2 + 12a + 36$

(d) $m^2 - 10m + 25$ (e) $4y^2 + 4y + 4$ (f) $1 + 4x + 4x^2$

(g) $x^2 - 6xy + 9y^2$ (h) $4x^2 + 4xy + y^2$ (i) $9a^2 - 12ab + 4b^2$

(j) $9 - 24y + 16y^2$ (k) $4a^2 + 12ab + 9b^2$ (l) $9m^2 - 30mn + 25n^2$

(m) $x^2 - 12xy + 36y^2$ (n) $81 - 36y + 4y^2$ (o) $a^2 + a + \dfrac{1}{4}$

(p) $a^4 - 2a^2 + 1$ (q) $1 - 4y^2 + 4y^4$ (r) $y^2 - 3y + \dfrac{9}{4}$

4 Factor each of the following. Check for a common factor first.

(a) $2a^2 + 12a + 18$ (b) $3y^2 - 18y + 27$ (c) $9ax^2 + 12ax + 4a$

(d) $by^2 - 4bxy + 4bx^2$ (e) $4x^3 + 4x^2 + x$ (f) $y^3 - 6y^2 + 9y$

(g) $4a^3 - 4a^2b + ab^2$ (h) $9m^2n - 12mn^2 + 4n^3$ (i) $18a^3 - 48a^2b + 32ab^2$

5 If $x = 3$ and $y = 4$, find the value of each expression.

(a) $x^2 + 2xy + y^2$ (b) $(x + y)^2$

Which answer, (a) or (b), was more easily obtained?

PSP 6 Choose the number 5 and follow the steps shown.

What answer did you get? Why is your result surprising? Try it again but choose a different whole number. Use algebra to show why you always end up with this surprising result.

Steps

Add 12.
Double your answer.
Add your original number.
Divide by 3.
Subtract 8.

12.7 Factoring Trinomials: Known to Unknown

An important method in problem solving is to use the "known" to develop a strategy for solving the "unknown."

| known: Finding products of binomials | unknown: Finding factors of trinomials |

You can learn how to factor trinomials by studying the products of binomials.

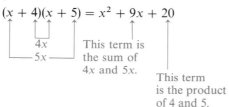

$$(x + 4)(x + 5) = x^2 + 9x + 20$$

$4x$
$5x$
This term is the sum of $4x$ and $5x$.

This term is the product of 4 and 5.

Thus when you want to factor a trinomial you ask this question.

Think:
What two numbers have a sum of 9 and a product of 18?

$$x^2 + 9x + 18$$

The pairs of factors of 18 are
$18 = 1 \times 18$ This pairs of factors
$18 = 2 \times 9$ has a sum of 9.
$18 = 3 \times 6$
Thus $x^2 + 9x + 18 = (x + 3)(x + 6)$

Remember to check your factors by multiplying them to obtain the original trinomial.

Example 1   Factor $x^2 - 12x + 27$.

Solution
Think:
What two numbers have a sum of -12 and a product of 27?

$$x^2 - 12x + 27 = (x \quad ?)(x \quad ?)$$

Think:
Since the product is positive, the two numbers are either both negative or both positive.
$27 = (3)(9)$ or $(-3)(-9)$

Thus $x^2 - 12x + 27 = (x - 3)(x - 9)$

Think:
Since the sum is negative, the numbers are both negative.
$-12 = (-3) + (-9)$

In the next example the signs of the two factors are different. However you ask similar questions to find the product.

Example 2   Factor $y^2 + y - 42$.

Solution   Think:
What two numbers have
a sum of 1 and a product of -42?

$$y^2 + y - 42 = (y \quad ?)(y \quad ?)$$
$$y^2 + y - 42 = (y + 7)(y - 6)$$

Think:
$7(-6) = -42$ and
$7 + (-6) = 1$

The skills for factoring trinomials are important skills in your work with algebra.

12.7   Exercise

A 1   Find two integers with the following properties.

	(a)	(b)	(c)	(d)	(e)	(f)
product	18	12	6	30	18	14
sum	9	-8	7	-13	11	-9

2   Use the results from the previous question to find the missing factors.
(a) $m^2 + 9m + 18 = (m + 6)(?)$ (b) $n^2 - 8n + 12 = (?)(n - 6)$
(c) $c^2 + 7c + 6 = (?)(c + 1)$ (d) $a^2 + 11a + 18 = (?)(a + 2)$
(e) $d^2 - 13d + 30 = (d - 10)(?)$ (f) $y^2 - 9y + 14 = (?)(y - 2)$

3   Find the missing factor.
(a) $m^2 - 11m + 24 = (m - 3)(?)$ (b) $t^2 + t - 2 = (?)(t + 2)$
(c) $p^2 + 11p + 28 = (p + 4)(?)$ (d) $k^2 + 4k - 21 = (k + 7)(?)$
(e) $w^2 + 5w - 24 = (?)(w - 3)$ (f) $z^2 - 3z + 2 = (z - 2)(?)$

B   Remember: Before you factor, check for a common factor.

4   To factor each trinomial, remember to ask
▶ which integers have a product of ▨?   ▶ which integers have a sum of ▨?
(a) $x^2 - 11x + 18$ (b) $y^2 + 6y + 8$ (c) $m^2 + 12m + 27$
(d) $n^2 - 11n + 30$ (e) $25 - 10a + a^2$ (f) $h^2 + 8h + 12$
(g) $t^2 + 6t + 5$ (h) $18 - 9m + m^2$ (i) $m^2 + 9m + 14$
(j) $t^2 - 20t + 96$ (k) $y^2 - 10y + 9$ (l) $d^2 + 13d + 36$
(m) $x^2 - 3x - 10$ (n) $y^2 + y - 6$ (o) $m^2 - m - 2$
(p) $t^2 - 7t - 30$ (q) $x^2 + 13x - 14$ (r) $m^2 + 7m - 18$
(s) $t^2 - 2t - 24$ (t) $y^2 - y - 30$ (u) $x^2 + 3x - 4$

5   Factor each of the following completely.

(a) $k^2 + 4k - 5$ (b) $x^2 + 12x + 35$ (c) $m^2 + 10m - 11$
(d) $x^2 + x - 12$ (e) $y^2 + 10y + 9$ (f) $t^2 + 2t - 48$
(g) $m^2 - m - 42$ (h) $s^2 - 5s - 50$ (i) $t^2 - 9t + 20$
(j) $56 - 15x + x^2$ (k) $x^2 - 12x - 85$ (l) $y^2 + 8y + 15$

6   The factors of the following involve two variables. Find the factors.

(a) $m^2 + 6mn + 8n^2$ (b) $a^2 - ab - 2b^2$ (c) $t^2 + 9tn + 8n^2$
(d) $x^2 - 8xy + 12y^2$ (e) $p^2 - pq - 20q^2$ (f) $b^2 + bc - 20c^2$

7   Factor each of the following. Check for a common factor first.

(a) $2x^2 - 12x + 16$ (b) $y^3 + 14y^2 + 24y$ (c) $2x^2 + 22x + 36$
(d) $4m^2 + 44m - 104$ (e) $x^3 + 8x^2 - 48x$ (f) $a^3 - 12a^2 + 27a$
(g) $3y^2 - 36y + 108$ (h) $2x^2 + 2x - 84$ (i) $b^3 + 24b^2 - 81b$
(j) $3m^2 + 72m - 156$ (k) $2x^2 - 36x + 112$ (l) $x^3 - 2x^2 - 48x$

8   A field has an area in square metres given by the expression $x^2 + x - 6$. If the length in metres is given by $(x + 3)$, find an expression for the width.

9   The length of a trip in kilometres is given by the expression $x^2 + 8x - 20$. If the time taken in hours is given by $(x - 2)$, find an expression for the speed in kilometres per hour.

10   Find the missing values.

	Area (m²)	Length (m)	Width (m)
(a)	$x^2 + 20x + 100$	$x + 10$	?
(b)	$y^2 + 24y - 81$	?	$y - 3$
(c)	$s^2 + 16s + 64$	$s + 8$	?
(d)	$a^2 - 13a + 36$	?	$a - 9$

	Distance (km)	Time (h)	Speed (km/h)
(e)	$y^2 + 5y - 36$	$y - 4$	?
(f)	$y^2 + 15y + 54$	?	$y + 9$
(g)	$k^2 + 10k - 11$	$k - 1$	?
(h)	$y^2 + 4y - 32$	?	$y + 8$

PSP 11   Jackie sent 34 letters to her camp friends in Canada and the United States. It costs 36¢ to send a letter in Canada and 6 more cents to send one to the United States. If Jackie spent $12.90 on stamps, how many letters did she send to each country?

C 12 (a) The trinomial $x^2 + kx + 25$, $k \in I$, has two different binomial factors. What is the value of k? What other values can you find for k?

(b) The trinomial $x^2 + kx - 24$, $k \in I$ has two binomial factors. What is the value of k? What other values can you find for k?

(c) The trinomial $x^2 - kx - 20$, $k \in I$ has two binomial factors. What is the value of k? What other values can you find for k?

12.8 **PSP** Factors of $a^2 - b^2$: Working Backwards

The expression $a^2 - b^2$ is called a **difference of squares**.

square term   square term

To find the factors of $a^2 - b^2$, you again use the strategy of working backwards. By analyzing known examples, you can develop a method of finding the factors of expressions given in the form of a difference of squares.

PSP Working backwards is a useful strategy to develop mathematics.

In finding these products you obtained binomials.

$$(x + y)(x - y) = x^2 - y^2$$
$$(2a + b)(2a - b) = 4a^2 - b^2$$

difference of squares

To factor $x^2 - 9y^2$, you use your earlier work again to help you.

$$x^2 - 9y^2 = x^2 + 0xy - 9y^2$$ Think: What two numbers have a sum of 0 and a product of -9?

$$x^2 - 9y^2 = (x + 3y)(x - 3y)$$ ←—— The two numbers are 3 and -3.
Thus the factors are shown.

To find factors of a difference of squares, first you need to find the terms of each factor and then write opposite signs as shown in the following example.

PSP Remember: You need to ask yourself key questions to solve some problems.

Example   Factor.   (a) $x^2 - 16y^2$ (b) $9a^2 - 25b^2$

Solution   (a) Write each term as a square.
$$x^2 - 16y^2 = (x)^2 - (4y)^2$$
$$x^2 - 16y^2 = (x - 4y)(x + 4y)$$

(b) Write each term as a square.
$$9a^2 - 25b^2 = (3a)^2 - (5b)^2$$
$$9a^2 - 25b^2 = (3a - 5b)(3a + 5b)$$

Think: The signs differ.

12.8   Exercise

A Remember: First write each term as a square, $a^2 - b^2 = (a)^2 - (b)^2$. Then factor.

1   Find the missing values.

(a) $(y - 6)(y + 6) = (y)^2 - (?)^2$

(b) $(x + 5)(x - 5) = (?)^2 - (5)^2$

(c) $(a + 1)(a - 1) = (a)^2 - (?)^2$

(d) $(3a - 1)(3a + 1) = (?)^2 - (1)^2$

(e) $(3a + b)(3a - b) = (?)^2 - (b)^2$

(f) $(2x + 5)(2x - 5) = (2x)^2 - (?)^2$

B   Remember: Before you factor, check for a common factor.

2   Factor each of the following.
    (a) $a^2 - b^2$ (b) $y^2 - x^2$ (c) $a^2 - 4b^2$ (d) $x^2 - 1$
    (e) $4m^2 - 9n^2$ (f) $9k^2 - 16m^2$ (g) $1 - 25y^2$ (h) $16y^2 - 25x^2$
    (i) $2m^2 - 72$ (j) $4t^2 - 25s^2$ (k) $98 - 18m^2$ (l) $36 - x^2$

3   Factor each of the following.
    (a) $3m^2 - 48$ (b) $2x^2 - 128$ (c) $98 - 2y^2$ (d) $75x^2 - 3$
    (e) $-8 + 18m^2$ (f) $50 - 32m^2$ (g) $50y^2 - 2$ (h) $108 - 3m^2$
    (i) $72 - 98y^2$ (j) $ax^2 - 100a$ (k) $m^3 - 36m$ (l) $x^3 - 16x$

4   Factor each of the following. Be careful! One cannot be factored.
    (a) $m^2n^2 - 25$ (b) $x^2y^2 - 4$ (c) $100 - a^2b^2$ (d) $64 - m^2n^2$
    (e) $x^2y^2 - 3^2$ (f) $a^2b^2 - k^2$ (g) $x^2y^2 + 4$ (h) $1 - 25a^2b^2$
    (i) $(mn)^2 - 6m^2$ (j) $(4pq)^2 - 16p^2$ (k) $100m^2 - 64n^2$ (l) $25x^2y^2 - 1$
    (m) $\dfrac{x^2}{9} - 25$ (n) $x^2 - \dfrac{1}{4}$ (o) $(xy)^4 - (xy)^2$ (p) $\dfrac{4x^2}{25} - 64$

PSP 5   Find the numbers for which all these statements are true.
    ▶ I am less than 100 and always even.
    ▶ One more than me is a multiple of 5.
    ▶ When you add all my digits I'm divisible by 3.

C 6   In finding factors you should always check to see whether the factors you obtain are factorable again. Factor each of the following.
    (a) $a^4 - 1$ (b) $16m^4 - n^4$ (c) $16y^4 - 100x^4$ (d) $1 - 16b^4$

7   (a) Find four factors for $x^4 - 5x^2 + 4$.
    (b) Find three factors for $x^4 - 11x^2 + 18$.

Calculator Use

Often procedures in mathematics are invented to work with a calculator. For example, to evaluate this expression use the nested form shown.

$$3x^2 + 2x + 1 = x(3x + 2) + 1$$

You do not need to use the memory of the calculator. Follow these calculator steps for $x = 5.65$.

    $\boxed{C}\ 3\ \boxed{\times}\ 5.65\ \boxed{+}\ 2\ \boxed{=}\ \boxed{\times}\ 5.65\ \boxed{+}\ 1\ \boxed{=}$

Try this procedure to evaluate other expressions given in this section.

12.9 Applications with Factoring

By applying your factoring skills to the solution of problems involving measurement, you can often reduce the amount of work you must do. For example, to calculate the area of the shaded region, you can use the following expression.

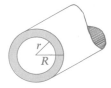

Area of shaded region = Area of large circle − Area of small circle

$$= \pi R^2 - \pi r^2$$
$$= \pi(R^2 - r^2) \qquad \text{π is a common factor.}$$
$$= \pi(R - r)(R + r) \qquad \text{difference of squares}$$

Example   Find the area of concrete on the cross-sectional end of the pipe above to the nearest square centimetre for $R = 52.00$ cm, $r = 48.00$ cm and $\pi = 3.14$.

Solution

Method A: Without factoring

$A = \pi R^2 - \pi r^2$
$\doteq 3.14(52.00)^2 - 3.14(48.00)^2$
$= 8490.56 - 7234.56$
$= 1256$ (to the nearest square centimetre)

Method B: With factoring

$A = \pi(R + r)(R - r)$
$\doteq 3.14(52.00 + 48.00)$
$\times (52.00 - 48.00)$
$= 3.14(100)(4)$
$= 1256$ (to the nearest square centimetre)

Thus the area of concrete on the end of the pipe is 1256 cm² to the nearest square centimetre.

You can use $a^2 - b^2 = (a - b)(a + b)$ and $(a + b)^2 = a^2 + 2ab + b^2$ to calculate mentally.

Calculate   Think:
$21 \times 19 = 399$ $21 \times 19 = (20 + 1)(20 - 1)$
                      $= 20^2 - 1^2$
                      $= 400 - 1$
                      $= 399$

Calculate.   Think:
$32^2 = 1024$ $32^2 = (30 + 2)^2$
                    $= 30^2 + (2)(2)(30) + 2^2$
                    $= 900 + 120 + 4$
                    $= 1024$

With practice, you will improve not only your skills in working with binomials but also your ability to compute mentally.

12.9 Exercise

A 1   Find the missing values. Then find the products mentally.

(a) $22 \times 18 = (20 + ?)(20 - ?)$

(b) $34 \times 26 = (30 + ?)(? - 4)$

(c) $32 \times 28 = (30 + ?)(? - 2)$

(d) $48 \times 52 = (? - 2)(? + 2)$

2 ▶ Write each product in a form similar to that in Question 1.
 ▶ Then calculate.
 (a) 57×63 (b) 27×33 (c) 24×16 (d) 68×72

3 Find the missing values. Then find the answers mentally.
 (a) $22^2 = (20 + ?)^2$ (b) $32^2 = (? + 2)^2$ (c) $43^2 = (40 + ?)^2$
 (d) $68^2 = (? - 2)^2$ (e) $73^2 = (70 + ?)^2$ (f) $62^2 = (? + 2)^2$

4 Find each of the following products.
 (a) 23×17 (b) 36×44 (c) 55×65 (d) 42×38

5 Compute each of the following.
 (a) $36^2 - 34^2$ (b) $48^2 - 45^2$ (c) $96^2 - 4^2$ (d) $75^2 - 25^2$

6 Evaluate each of the following.
 (a) 63^2 (b) 19^2 (c) 29^2
 (d) 97^2 (e) 68^2 (f) 91^2

B For each of the following questions use your skills with factoring to reduce the amount of computation. Use a calculator when appropriate.

7 Evaluate each of the following.
 (a) 88×92 (b) $32^2 - 29^2$ (c) 48^2
 (d) 99×101 (e) 66×74 (f) 38^2
 (g) $80^2 - 20^2$ (h) 49^2 (i) 101^2

8 Find the area of each shaded region to 1 decimal place.
 (a)

OB = 16.0 m
OC = 14.0 m

 (b)
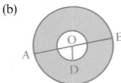
AE = 50.0 cm
OD = 21.0 cm

9 Find the area of each shaded region.
 (a)
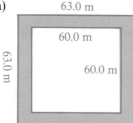
63.0 m
60.0 m
63.0 m
60.0 m

 (b)
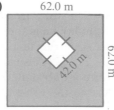
62.0 m
42.0 m
62.0 m

 (c)
100.0 m
100.0 m
60.0 m
20.0 m   20.0 m

10 A square courtyard has a walkway 2.0 m wide. If the enclosed square garden is 42.0 m wide, find the area of the walkway.

2.0 m

11 A circular sidewalk, 1.0 m wide, encircles a garden. Calculate the area of the sidewalk.

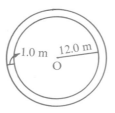

1.0 m   12.0 m
O

PSP 12 Each letter represents a digit. Find the missing digits for each calculation.

(a)   BITE
     + THE
     ──────
      DUST

(b)   TWO
     + FOR
     ──────
      ONE

C 13 (a) Estimate which of the following carries the most water.

A: 1 pipe with a 10-cm diameter
B: 10 pipes each with a 1-cm diameter
C: 1 square pipe with a 10-cm diagonal

(b) Calculate which carries the most water.

Computer Use PSP

The area of a shaded region, A, is given by $A = \pi R^2 - \pi r^2$.

▶ Draw a diagram to illustrate the formula. What do the variables represent?

▶ Write a program in BASIC to calculate the area A.

▶ Use your program. What happens to the area A as the values of R and r increase or decrease by the same amount?

From Math History

Many contributors to mathematics often study more than mathematics in depth. For example, William Thomson (1824–1900) from Scotland, known as Lord Kelvin, was not only a mathematician but a prominent physicist. He was a prodigy in mathematics at an early age and made his first contribution to mathematics when still a teenager. Although he made contributions in mathematics, today he is remembered as the person after whom the Kelvin temperature scale was named. He proposed that no temperature could be below $-273°C$ (Celsius) which was named $0°K$ (Kelvin). Today the temperature for absolute zero, or $0°K$, is known to be $-273.18°C$, which is very close to the value used over a hundred years ago.

It is important to choose the correct skill for solving a problem. You should look for clues that will help you to factor polynomials. For example, the clues you learned in the previous sections will help you identify the factors.

Just as you planned the steps needed to solve a problem, so you must plan the steps needed to factor. Sometimes you need to apply more than one type of factoring.

PSP   Decide on a plan to solve problems.

▶ First find a common factor.

$$2y^2 + 16y + 30 = 2(y^2 + 8y + 15)$$
$$= 2(y + 3)(y + 5)$$

▶ Check whether the factors can be factored again.

$$x^4 - 4x^2 - 45 = (x^2 - 9)(x^2 + 5)$$
$$= (x - 3)(x + 3)(x^2 + 5)$$

12.10   Exercise

B Factor each of the following.

1	$x^2 + 4x$	2	$3a + 6ab$	3	$x^2 - 11x + 28$
4	$x^2 - 2x - 24$	5	$abc + abd$	6	$36x^3 - 9x^2$
7	$y^2 + 5y - 14$	8	$2a^2 - 2$	9	$25x^4 - 16y^4$
10	$y^2 - 16y + 63$	11	$x^2 - 24x + 80$	12	$2x^2 + 4$
13	$3a^2 - 3b^2$	14	$x^2 + 7x + 12$	15	$m^2 - 9m - 10$
16	$x^4 - 13x^2 + 36$	17	$a^2 + 9a + 8$	18	$16x^2 - 8x + 1$
19	$-b^2 - 16a^2$	20	$m^2 + 2m - 8$	21	$a - 4a^2$
22	$2n^2 - 50$	23	$y^2 - 2y - 3$	24	$2x^2 - 8x^2$
25	$-x^2 - 2xy - y^2$	26	$8y^2 - 32$	27	$10x^2 - 10y^2$
28	$-a^2 - 2ab - b^2$	29	$a^2b - b^3$	30	$90x^2 - 1000$
31	$3y^2 - 36y + 36$	32	$x^2 - 144$	33	$a^2 - 64$
34	$m^4 + 5m^2 - 36$	35	$-y^2 + 144$	36	$-48 + 3x^2$
37	$81x^4 - 1$	38	$-24 - 2y + y^2$	39	$3a^2 - 27b^2$
40	$25m^2 - 16n^2$	41	$2n^2 + 6n - 20$	42	$2x^2 - 2x - 24$
43	$4n^2 - 4n - 80$	44	$m^4 - 3m^2 - 4$	45	$2a^3 - 4a$
46	$8x^2 - 24y^2$	47	$a^2 - ab - 56b^2$	48	$b^2 - 15b + 56$
49	$x^3 - xy^2$	50	$5m - 25m^2$	51	$m^4 + 3m^2 - 4$
52	$y^4 - 8y^2 + 16$	53	$10x^2 - 30x + 20$	54	$18x^2 + 9$
55	$x^4 - y^4$	56	$\frac{1}{4}x^2 - x + 1$	57	$x^2 + 3x - 18$
58	$x - xy^2$	59	$2x^2 - 8$	60	$25 - n^2$
61	$y^2 - 10y - 24$	62	$m^2 + 6m - 16$	63	$x^2 + 18x + 32$
64	$36x^2 - 4y^2$	65	$a^3 + 3a^2 - 10a$	66	$x^2 - 21x + 108$
67	$2ax^2 - 8ab^2$	68	$36x^2 - 25y^2$	69	$2y^3 + 8y^2$
70	$3a^2 + 6a + 3$	71	$x^2 - 4y^2$	72	$m^4 - 5m^2 - 36$
73	$1 + 38x + 72x^2$	74	$-(1 - x^4)$	75	$y^4 - 17y^2 + 16$

12.11 Using Factoring: Solving Equations

In your earlier work you solved equations. You can apply your factoring skills to solve quadratic equations such as

$$x^2 - 6x = 0 \qquad x^2 - 6x + 8 = 0 \qquad x^2 - 9 = 0.$$

Each of these equations is of degree 2.

The solution of a quadratic equation is based on the principle,

if $ab = 0$, then either $a = 0$ or $b = 0$.

Example Solve and verify $x^2 - x - 12 = 0$.

Solution
$$x^2 - x - 12 = 0$$
$$(x + 3)(x - 4) = 0$$
$$x + 3 = 0 \quad \text{or} \quad x - 4 = 0 \qquad \text{Use the principle:}$$
$$x = -3 \qquad\qquad x = 4 \qquad \text{If } ab = 0, \text{ then } a = 0 \text{ or } b = 0.$$

Check: For $x = -3$,
$$\text{L.S.} = x^2 - x - 12$$
$$= (-3)^2 - (-3) - 12$$
$$= 9 + 3 - 12$$
$$= 0$$
$$= \text{R.S. } \checkmark$$

For $x = 4$,
$$\text{L.S.} = x^2 - x - 12$$
$$= (4)^2 - (4) - 12$$
$$= 16 - 4 - 12$$
$$= 0$$
$$= \text{R.S. } \checkmark$$

12.11 Exercise

A You need to use your skills with factoring to solve equations.

1   Each equation is factored. What are the roots?
(a) $(x + 5)(x + 2) = 0$
(b) $(x - 3)(x + 2) = 0$
(c) $(x - 5)(x - 3) = 0$
(d) $x(x + 4) = 0$

2   Three values are given for each equation. Which are the roots?
(a) $x^2 + 5x + 6 = 0, \quad 3, -2, -3$
(b) $y^2 - y - 12 = 0, \quad 4, -3, -4$
(c) $x^2 - 16 = 0, \quad 4, -16, -4$
(d) $y^2 - 4y - 5 = 0, \quad 1, -1, 5$

3   One root of each equation is given. Find the other root.
(a) $x^2 + 7x + 12 = 0, \quad -4$
(b) $y^2 - y - 6 = 0, \quad 3$
(c) $m^2 - 5m + 6 = 0, \quad 2$
(d) $k^2 + 3k - 10 = 0, \quad -5$

B Be sure to check your roots. Verify.

4   Factor each expression and then solve.
(a) $x^2 + 9x + 20 = 0$
(b) $y^2 + 7y - 30 = 0$
(c) $m^2 + 6m = 0$
(d) $m^2 - 36 = 0$
(e) $y^2 - 7y + 12 = 0$
(f) $4m^2 - 9 = 0$

5   Solve and verify.
    (a) $y^2 + 11y + 30 = 0$ (b) $m^2 - 2m - 35 = 0$
    (c) $m^2 - 13m + 42 = 0$ (d) $y^2 + 4y - 21 = 0$

6   (a) What is the first step needed to solve the equation $x^2 - 2x = 15$?
    (b) Solve and verify the equation.

7   Solve each equation.
    (a) $x^2 - x = 6$ (b) $y^2 - 2y = 15$
    (c) $a(a - 13) = -42$ (d) $y^2 - 8 = 2y$
    (e) $x(x + 8) = -15$ (f) $21 = x(x - 4)$

8   Solve each equation.
    (a) $x^2 - 2.1x = 0$ (b) $y^2 + 3.6y = 0$
    (c) $2y^2 + 4.4y = 0$ (d) $6.2k - k^2 = 0$
    (e) $y^2 - 3.6y = 0$ (f) $m^2 - 0.6m - 1.6 = 0$

9   One root of each equation is an integer. The other is a decimal.
    ▶ Estimate the roots.   ▶ Then check your estimate.
    (a) $x^2 - 5.1x + 6.3 = 0$ (b) $y^2 + 7.2y + 12.8 = 0$
    (c) $k^2 - 2.5k - 9 = 0$ (d) $x^2 - 2.8x - 11 = 0$

10 For each equation,
    ▶ Decide what the first step is.   ▶ Then solve.
    (a) $y^2 + 0.6y = 2.8$ (b) $x^2 - 4.2x = -3.2$
    (c) $5.4 = m^2 - 1.2m$ (d) $k^2 = 6.1k - 8.2$

PSP 11 To solve some problems, you can begin by thinking of all *possible*
        answers and deciding which ones are *not* correct. Write the years in
        the last two thousand years that reads the same backwards or forwards or
        upside down.

C 12   The following program solves any quadratic equation given in the form
       $Ax^2 + Bx + C = 0$. Try the program using quadratic equations in
       Questions 9 and 10.

```
10 INPUT A, B, C
20 IF A = 0, THEN GOTO 70
30 LET X1 = (−B + SQR(B ↑ 2 − 4 ∗ A ∗ C))/(2 ∗ A)
40 LET X2 = (−B − SQR(B ↑ 2 − 4 ∗ A ∗ C))/(2 ∗ A)
50 PRINT "THE ROOTS ARE"; X1, X2
60 GO TO 10
70 END
```

12.12 PSP Problem Solving: Using Strategies

In solving a problem, it is important that you know the answers to these questions.

I What information am I asked to find?

II What information am I given?

Once you clearly understand the answers to these questions, you need to decide on a strategy to solve the problem. Refer to your list of strategies from your *Problem Solving Plan* PSP .

12.12 Exercise

B 1 A design pattern is made as shown. Draw the next design.

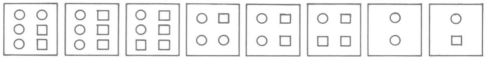

2 (a) If the value for **SKATING** is 108, what is the value of **HOCKEY**?

(b) If the value of **FLOWERS** is 196, what is the value of **GARDEN**?

3 (a) For any prime number, P, show that $P = \left(\dfrac{P+1}{2}\right)^2 - \left(\dfrac{P-1}{2}\right)^2$ is always true.

(b) Use the formula in (a) to show why the prime number 101 is given by $101 = 51^2 - 50^2$.

(c) Write other prime numbers in the above form.

4 If 6 people catch 144 fish in 4 d, how many fish will 2 people catch in 2 d?

5 To solve some problems, you must research needed information. For example, look in any book and you will find an ISBN number which means

International Standard Book Numbering.

What is the significance of how this number **ISBN 0-17-601728-3** is constructed?

> ## Math Tip
>
> To solve a problem, whether it is in mathematics or in another discipline, you must understand the meaning of each word that occurs.
>
> ▶ Make a list of the new math words you have learned. Provide an example of your own to illustrate each word.
>
> ▶ List any new problem solving strategies you have used or learned and place them in your *Problem Solving Plan* PSP .

Practice and Problems: Review

1   Find each product.
     (a) $(a + 3)(a + 2)$ (b) $(a + 3)(a - 2)$ (c) $(a - 3)(2a - 2)$
     (d) $(2c + 1)(c + 3)$ (e) $(x - 3)(2x + 7)$ (f) $(3k - 4)(3k + 4)$

2   Salina worked for $(x - 3)$ hours at an hourly rate of $(x + 5)$ dollars.
     (a) Write an expression to show her earnings.   (b) Simplify the expression.

3   (a) Write an expression for
        the area of the square.
     (b) Simplify the expression.

4   Multiply. How many can you do mentally?
     (a) $(m - 3)(2m + 1)$ (b) $(h + 2)(2h + 3)$ (c) $(2m - 1)(2m + 1)$
     (d) $(3r + 1)^2$ (e) $(7 - y)(4 + y)$ (f) $(5x + 3)(2x - 1)$

5   Expand and simplify.
     (a) $(2a + 1)(a - 3) + (2a - 1)(a + 3)$ (b) $(3x - 1)^2 - 3(x - 4)(x + 3)$

6   Solve and verify.
     (a) $(a - 2)(2a + 3) - (2a + 1)(a - 4) = 10$ (b) $k^2 + 8k + 15 = 0$

7   For what value of t is each of the following a trinomial square?
     (a) $x^2 + txy + 4y^2$ (b) $a^2 - 4ab + tb^2$ (c) $tx^2 + 4xy + y^2$
     (d) $9a^2 - 6ab + tb^2$ (e) $9x^2 - txy + 4y^2$ (f) $ta^2 - 40ab + 25b^2$

8   Factor each trinomial.
     (a) $x^2 + 5x + 6$ (b) $y^2 - 6y - 27$ (c) $x^2 - 12x + 36$
     (d) $y^2 - 11y + 30$ (e) $a^2 + 6ab + 9b^2$ (f) $50p^2 + 20pq + 2q^2$

9   Factor each difference of squares.
     (a) $x^2 - 81$ (b) $4y^2 - 25$ (c) $9a^2 - 16b^2$ (d) $x^2 - 121$
     (e) $p^2 - \dfrac{1}{4}$ (f) $64 - m^2$ (g) $9k^2 - \dfrac{1}{9}$ (h) $16x^4 - 9y^4$

PSP   10   A diagram is used to record the digits from
             1 to 9. Each digit is used once. Use the clues
             below to place all 9 digits in the diagram.

Practice Test

1   Simplify.
    (a) $(p - 5)(p + 2)$ (b) $(w + 3)(w + 4)$ (c) $(k - 7)(k - 9)$
    (d) $(x + y)(x - 3y)$ (e) $(2a - 3)(2a - 3)$ (f) $(5q + 1)(5q - 1)$
    (g) $(7 - b)(5 + b)$ (h) $(3x - 4y)^2$ (i) $(9k - 1)(3k + 2)$
    (j) $(5p + q)(3p - 4q)$ (k) $(4x - 9)(4x + 9)$ (l) $(-9 - x)(7 + x)$

2   Expand and simplify.
    (a) $(x - 3)(x - 2) + 3(x - 2)$ (b) $(y - 4)(y + 5) - 3(y + 2)$
    (c) $(2y - 1)(y - 3) + 3(2 - y)$ (d) $(3x - 2)(x - 5) + (4x - 1)(2x - 3)$
    (e) $3(n + 2)(n + 4) - (n - 1)$ (f) $(x - 4)^2 - 3(x + 6)(x - 2)$
    (g) $(3 - k)(k - 2) + 3(k - 4)(k + 4)$ (h) $2(n - 4)(n + 2) - 2(n - 3)^2$

3   Solve and verify.
    (a) $3k - 4(k + 2) = 5$ (b) $5k - 4(k - 6) = 2(k + 6) - 12$
    (c) $(a + 2)^2 = (a + 5)(a - 3) + 7$ (d) $(x - 3)^2 + (x - 2)(x - 5) = 4$
    (e) $w^2 - 4w - 21 = 0$ (f) $p^2 - 9p + 20 = 0$

4   Two numbers differ by 3 and their squares differ by 75. Find the numbers.

5   Factor fully. Watch for common factors.
    (a) $x^2 + 8x + 15$ (b) $w^2 - w - 30$ (c) $2p^2 + 2p - 4$
    (d) $x^2 - 4y^2$ (e) $m^4 - 5m^2 - 36$ (f) $25x^4 - y^4$
    (g) $4y^2 + 8y - 60$ (h) $a^2 - 12a + 36$ (i) $x^2 + 4x - 5$
    (j) $5x^2 - 20y^2$ (k) $3y^2 - 12y - 63$ (l) $1 + 38y + 72y^2$

6   Find the width of each rectangle.

    (a) $(x + 5)$ m   (b) $(x + 7)$ cm

     $(x^2 + x - 20)$ m^2 | ? m $(x^2 + 9x + 14)$ cm^2 | ? cm

7   Evaluate.
    (a) 52×48 (b) $95^2 - 5^2$ (c) 31^2
    (d) 27×33 (e) $28^2 - 22^2$ (f) 49^2

8   Find the area of each shaded region.

    (a)   (b) $R = 24.0$ cm, $r = 16.0$ cm

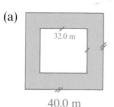

    32.0 m R r

    40.0 m

13 *Statistics and Probability: Applications*

Methods of collecting data, language of statistics, types of samples, organizing data, displaying data, stem-and-leaf plots, circle graphs, bar graphs, histograms, decision making, mean, median and mode, concepts of probability, independent events, data and predictions, simulations, applications, strategies for problem solving

Introduction

Many important decisions are based on gathered data.

▶ How many television shows have good ratings? Which shows will be dropped?
▶ At which intersections should stoplights be placed?

Making sense of data is an important study in many diverse fields such as sports, medicine, business and industry. Important skills include the intelligent interpretion of data and the making of subsequent decisions based on the data. When you work with data, you involve yourself with the branch of mathematics known as statistics. Statistics involves

    A: collecting data
    B: organizing and analyzing data
    C: interpreting data and making inferences, predictions and decisions about data and problem solving.

The graph is a tool for studying statistics. Throughout the chapter various types of graphs and their use-fulness in showing numerical data are illustrated.

In commerce, the accumulation of data and the subsequent organization of data provide a rich base upon which predictions for investments can be made. However the answers you obtain to problems using statistics are often only probably true.

13.1 Collecting Data

Have you ever wondered how
- ▶ weather forecasters are able to predict the weather so closely?
- ▶ scientists are able to predict an abundance of certain fish or wildlife?

People use statistics to answer questions such as those above. **Statistics** is the branch of mathematics that uses these steps.

Step 1: Collect data.
Step 2: Organize data.
Step 3: Interpret data.

The language used in statistics is illustrated by the following example. Inspectors for a battery manufacturer want to check the quality of hundreds of thousands of batteries.

- ▶ The complete set of batteries (or people or things) for which you want data is called the **population**. If the inspectors check each member of the population (in this case each battery), they are said to be taking a **census**. To do this would be impractical because of the time and expense involved.
- ▶ Thus the inspectors could select a **sample** of the batteries and check only those. From the sample (of batteries), information could be obtained that would apply to the entire population (of batteries) provided that the sample was representative of the complete population and randomly selected. In a **random sample** each member of the population has an equal chance of being selected.

Data can be gathered from a sample of the population by a variety of methods.
- ▶ interviews   ▶ questionnaires   ▶ experiments

13.1 Exercise

A 1 List the advantages and the disadvantages of using a census.

2 List the advantages and the disadvantages of using a sample.

3 Would you use a census or a sample to collect data about the following? Give reasons.

(a) the favourite television program of your class

(b) the most popular political leader in the country

(c) the need for subsidized senior citizen housing in a town

(d) the life of lightbulbs in one production run

B Make a summary of what you have learned about collecting data.

4 List the advantages and the disadvantages of each type of interview.
(a) calling on the phone　　　　　(b) going door-to-door
(c) stopping people at shopping centres

5 List the advantages and the disadvantages of each distribution of questionnaires.
(a) sent by mail　　　　　　　　(b) placed in a newspaper
(c) placed with an article that you buy

6 Experiments were conducted to collect information about the effectiveness of air valves. List the advantages and the disadvantages of using experiments (observations and measurements).

7 (a) List the methods of collecting information first-hand that have been considered in this section.
(b) List sources of obtaining information that has already been collected.
(c) List the advantages and the disadvantages of each source in (b).

8 Would you use a census or a sample to collect data to help you answer the following? Give reasons.
(a) You own an apple orchard. Are the apples ready to be picked?
(b) You manufacture parachutes. How many parachutes are defective?
(c) You ordered 8000 ballpoint pens. How many pens are defective?
(d) You purchased 2000 cases of grapes. Are the grapes sweet enough?

9 Which method would you use to collect first-hand data on the following? Give reasons.
(a) the favourite rock group　　　　(b) the quality of cassette tapes
(c) the attitude towards building an expressway
(d) the most popular flavour of soft drink

PSP 10 Peter, Steven and Pitman are brothers who exercise regularly. One lifts weights, another cycles and the third swims. Use the clues to decide which exercise each brother does. List any assumptions you made.
▶ Peter cannot swim.
▶ Steven does not own a bike.
▶ Pitman does not like the outdoors.

Sampling: Stratified and Clustered

There are specialized types of sampling that are used to obtain a sample. Suppose you publish a magazine for tennis players and you want to decide on the types of articles to publish about tennis. The best type of people to poll is tennis players. Thus you would take a sample of only tennis players. If a sample is taken, as described, from a particular part of a population, the sample is said to be **clustered**.

If you are to take a poll across Canada, how should the sample be chosen? The number of people in each province is different. To poll 1000 persons you would select or **stratify** the sample in proportion to the number of people in each province as shown.

percent of people   Saskatchewan 4.1%
number of people in sample   4.1% of 1000 = 41

11   Would you use a census, a random sample, a clustered sample or a stratified sample to do the following?

(a) Evaluate the facilities at a local exercise gym.

(b) Decide who will be the next prime minister.

(c) Check the compression in tanks used for scuba diving.

(d) Test the quality of corn.

12   A sample of 10 000 people from across Canada is needed. The chart shows the percent of the population in each province. How many people should be selected from each province for the sample?

Newfoundland	2.4%	Ontario	36%
Nova Scotia	3.6%	Manitoba	4.3%
New Brunswick	3.0%	Saskatchewan	4.1%
P.E.I.	0.5%	Alberta	8.6%
Quebec	26.5%	British Columbia	10.2%

13   At a camp there are 485 children, 365 teenagers and 75 adults. To determine the entertainment program, opinions are to be selected. If 75 persons are to be interviewed, how many should there be of each?

(a) children   (b) teenagers   (c) adults

14   A manufacturer of hockey sticks wants people's opinions about hockey sticks. From which population should a sample be selected?

(a) people entering a supermarket   (b) people at an ice-hockey arena

(c) people in a movie line-up   (d) readers of a winter sport magazine

13.2 Organizing Data

Once data have been collected, they need to be organized in some way before conclusions can be made. **Tally charts** and **frequency tables** can be used to organize data. Sometimes when the data consist of many different numbers, the data can be grouped into equal divisions or intervals. These equal intervals are referred to as **class intervals**.

Example

The ages of a random sample of movie goers are shown.

```
43 61 60 58 10 30 26 45 11 15
44 32 33 34 26 38 19 17 21 35
24 27 19 17 16 22 15 23 18 16
19 17 46 18 29 45 20 31 17 23
16 25 27 31 18 26 28 14 18 20
```

(a) How many were sampled?

(b) Based on the sample, what percent of the people were less than 20 years old?

Solution

A frequency table is made using 10-year class intervals.

From the data organized in the frequency table answer the questions.

Class Intervals	Tally	Frequency
0–9		0
10–19	卌 卌 卌 IIII	19
20–29	卌 卌 卌	15
30–39	卌 III	8
40–49	卌	5
50–59	I	1
60–69	II	2

(a) number sampled
$$= 0 + 19 + 15 + 8 + 5 + 1 + 2$$
$$= 50$$
There were 50 people in the sample.

PSP It is easier to answer questions when the data are presented in an organized way.

(b) percent under 20 $= \dfrac{\text{number under 20}}{\text{total number}} \times 100\%$

$$= \frac{19}{50} \times 100\%$$

$$= 38\%$$

38% of the people attending were under 20 years of age.

13.2 Exercise

A 1 The following data show the number of hours spent by people in one week on a sport.

5 8 5 9 0 1 0 6 3 1 9 5 0 1 5 4 7 6 1 0 7 1 3 5 4
0 9 6 1 4 2 3 5 0 5 9 2 3 4 2 4 9 2 1 8 5 5 0 9 1

(a) Construct a frequency table without class intervals.

(b) How many people were surveyed?

(c) How many people were actively involved in sports for 3 h? 4 h? 6 h? 0 h?

2 At a tourist resort a record was kept of the masses in kilograms of the fish caught.

1.4 0.5 1.5 5.6 3.4 1.2 0.6 2.2 5.4 2.1 1.9 1.8 2.7 0.6 2.8
4.0 5.3 3.5 2.1 4.4 2.9 1.6 0.7 5.1 1.3 4.0 3.2 1.1 2.4 1.6
3.0 3.8 1.2 0.6 4.4 0.5 0.8 2.7 5.3 0.7 1.9 3.5 4.1 4.9 1.9

(a) Refer to the data. Why is it difficult to answer the question: "How many fish with a mass between 4 kg and 5 kg were caught?"

(b) Copy and complete the frequency table for the data.

(c) Use the frequency table. What is the answer to the question in (a)?

Mass (kg)	Tally	Frequency
0–0.9	?	?
1.0–1.9	?	?
2.0–2.9		

3 (a) Refer to the data in Question 2. What information do you need to answer the question: "What percent of the fish had a mass between 5 kg and 6 kg?"

(b) What is the answer to the question in (a)?

4 (a) Refer to the data in Question 2. The resort owner advertised: "Over half of the fish caught at our resort have a mass of 4 kg or more." Based on the data, would you agree or disagree?

(b) How would you modify the statement so that it is supported by the data?

B 5 The lengths of songs on 5 LP records are recorded in minutes and seconds.

4:13
↗ ↖
minutes seconds

(a) Why is it difficult to answer the question: "What percent of the songs are less than 5 min long?"

The Watch	Cubet	Gloria	Culture	Police
4:08	4:25	7:13	3:39	6:01
3:37	3:01	5:20	5:08	3:03
3:33	3:12	6:46	3:40	5:30
2:56	3:31	3:16	4:33	4:47
4:03	3:26	2:45	4:50	6:37
4:39	4:40	5:48	3:49	7:12
3:44	3:23	6:08	4:03	3:15
4:19	3:46	5:55	4:01	
3:52	3:45	4:12	6:10	
3:20	4:05			

(b) Use 30-s class intervals. Construct a frequency table.

(c) Could you answer the question in (a) more easily by using the frequency table? Give reasons.

(d) Answer the question in (a).

6   (a) Based on the data in the original form in Question 5, why is it difficult to answer the question: "In which class interval do most of the songs fall?

(b) Refer to your frequency table. Answer the question in (a).

(c) What percent of the songs fall within one class interval on either side of the answer in (b)?

7   (a) Use the original data in Question 5. Create a problem based on it.

(b) Use the frequency table. Solve your problem.

8   The time taken in seconds by each student in a class to run 100 m is recorded.

14.7 13.5 13.8 14.3 15.2 14.7 13.1 15.2 14.3 13.6 15.8 14.7
16.3 12.9 15.5 13.7 15.2 16.5 17.3 14.9 13.9 13.4 16.6 15.6
16.3 16.5 15.2 15.7 15.1 16.1 17.8 17.9 12.2 16.5 15.3

(a) Choose an appropriate class interval and construct a frequency table.

(b) What percent of the students take 15 s or more?

(c) What percent of the students take less than 15 s?

PSP 9   What is the last digit of the value of 2^{2222}?

Calculator Use

Use your calculator to do lengthy computations throughout your work in mathematics. For example, a sum E is found using the following pattern.

$$E = 1 + \frac{1}{1} + \frac{1}{1 \times 2} + \frac{1}{1 \times 2 \times 3} + \frac{1}{1 \times 2 \times 3 \times 4} + \cdots$$

Based on the pattern, you can write other terms.

▶ How many terms are needed so that the value of E to 3 decimal places is given by $E = 2.718$?

▶ What is the value of E to 4 decimal places?

Math Tip

In this chapter you will study the steps used in statistics and the process of probability. To solve problems that use data, you will use your computational skills as well as skills from geometry, percent, ratio, graphing and so on. The calculator and the computer are useful tools.

At the annual Pacific Exhibition, a sample of people's ages was taken. The results of interviewing 40 people are shown. It is difficult to use the data as presented to arrive at any observations or conclusions.

34	58	21	63	48	52	23	50	39	21
28	62	52	45	75	12	40	24	45	51
50	37	15	73	42	61	46	54	72	43
40	81	24	53	47	38	68	44	17	30

However squared paper can be used to record the data in a useful form.

▶ A stem-and-leaf plot is begun for the first row of the data.

This square shows the number 52.

The ones digits are called the **leaves**.

The tens digits are called the **stems**.

This branch represents the numbers 21, 23 and 21.

▶ A stem-and-leaf plot is made for all the data.

---

10 Use the data in the stem-and-leaf plot.

(a) How many persons were less than 40 years of age?

(b) What percent of the people interviewed were 30 years or older?

11 The number of super deluxe hamburgers sold each day was recorded over a period of 3 months.

```
55 127   76 23   17   84   20 50 49 60   30 65 66 44 57 99 75 42 110
45  87   66 54 107   51 100 28 59 66   82 77 63 39 52 95 23 81   46
79  34   99 61   98   73 118 22 89 36 101 55 63 61 53 28 84 49   66
52  52 117 31   45 111   85 71 54 36   74 52 80 76 67 94 72 11   58
69 122   70 88   73   48 100 98 89 73 108 14 53 65 17
```

(a) Construct a stem-and-leaf plot for the data.

(b) On how many days were fewer than 50 super deluxe hamburgers sold?

(c) What was the most frequent number sold per day?

(d) On what percent of the days were 100 or more hamburgers sold?

(e) Why would it be difficult to answer the above questions using the data in the given form?

(f) List advantages of recording data as a stem-and-leaf plot to make conclusions.

12 (a) Use your stem-and-leaf plot in Question 11. Create a problem based on it.

(b) Solve the problem created in (a).

(c) List any assumptions you made in obtaining your answer in (b).

13.3 Displaying Data: Solving Problems

So far you have used tally charts, frequency tables and stem-and-leaf plots to display information. Information can also be displayed in other forms.

A **pictograph** uses symbols to represent data.
A pictograph must have
▶ a title
▶ a key or legend
▶ an axis labelled and identified.

Cheerleading Contest Results

A **bar graph** uses bars to represent data. A bar graph must have
▶ a title   ▶ each axis labelled   ▶ each axis identified.
Bar graphs can be drawn in a vertical or horizontal form.

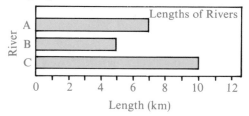

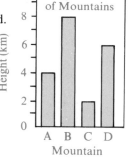

Horizontal bar graphs often show data about lengths, horizontal distances, walking distances and so on. Vertical bar graphs often show data about heights, vertical distances, altitudes and so on.

A **histogram** shows the frequency of data in each class interval. The data from a frequency table is used to draw a histogram. There is no space between the bars.

 PSP   You can use graphs to solve problems.

Class interval	Frequency
0–9	2
10–19	5
20–29	10
30–39	26
40–49	32
50–59	22
60–69	18
70–79	10
80–89	4
90–99	1

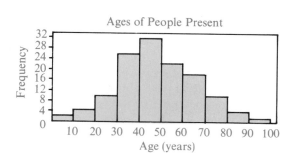

Ages of People Present

13.3 Exercise

A Check whether your answers are reasonable. Round all answers to 1 decimal place when necessary.

1 The number of strikeouts by pitchers displayed. Rena has 12 strikeouts.

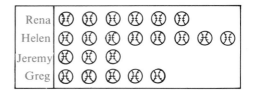

   (a) What information is missing from the graph? Provide it.
   (b) How many strikeouts does each pitcher have?
   (c) What are the advantages and disadvantages of using the pictograph?

2 Sales of different size pizzas are shown.

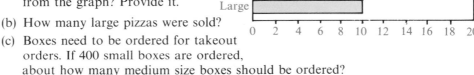

   (a) What information is missing from the graph? Provide it.
   (b) How many large pizzas were sold?
   (c) Boxes need to be ordered for takeout orders. If 400 small boxes are ordered, about how many medium size boxes should be ordered?
   (d) What are the advantages and the disadvantages of using the bar graph?

3 The results of a survey of distances travelled in kilometres by students during the summer vacation are shown by the histogram.

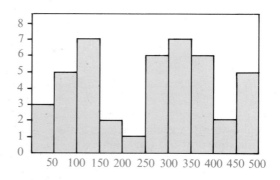

   (a) What information is missing from the graph? Provide it.
   (b) In what ways are histograms and bar graphs similar? different?
   (c) When is it most appropriate to use a histogram to show data?

B By using graphs to display information, you can solve problems and interpret your answers. **PSP**

4 The number of people in each vehicle entering a tourist region was recorded for a period of time.

```
5 3 4 5 7 5 3 4 6 8 3 8 1 7 4 2 4 6   5 3 5 9
5 3 4 5 7 4 2 4 5 9 3 4 6 7 5 4 6 6  10 2 6 7
5 3 6 4 2 5 5 3 6 6 3 4 6 5 6 4 8 5   4 9 6 5
```

   (a) Construct a frequency table. (b) Use the data in (a). Construct a histogram.
   (c) What percent of the vehicles had 5 people in them?
   (d) What percent had two people or fewer?

5   Shelly owns the number of each type of book as shown.

Science fiction	25	Humour	23
Mystery	40	Western	17
Biography	18	Non-fiction	5

(a) Construct a bar graph to show the data.

(b) What percent of the books are biographies?

6   The data show the height in centimetres of the students in a class.

158 169 156 174 180 163 162 159 175 161 174 176 182 173 168 160
177 167 179 181 172 167 170 164 183 157 165 174 169 180 176 168

(a) Organize the data into a frequency table using the class intervals 155–159, 160–164, 165–169 and so on.

(b) Display the data in a histogram.

7   For each set of data,

▶ Decide on the most effective type of graph for displaying the data. Give reasons.

▶ Draw the graph.

▶ Create two questions based on the graph. Then answer the questions.

(a) Methods of Getting to Work in Newfoundland

Driving alone	45%
Driving with passenger	10%
Riding as passenger	20%
Shared driving	5%
Public transportation	4%
Walking	16%

(b) Total Airline Passengers Arriving or Departing

Sydney, N.S.	198 954
Moncton, N.B.	242 158
Victoria International	569 748
Gander International	196 617
Charlottetown, P.E.I.	195 538
Sept Iles, Que.	232 308
Windsor, Ont.	242 158

(c) Exam Marks

55 76 64 72 72 53 62 88 61 71 91 78 64 70 80 66 54 67 81 82 58 96
68 85 63 79 73 67 92 30 75 36 74 51 65 71 68 53 67 42 83 74 75 46
47 70 40 74 77 78 64 85 78 81 88 32 46 73 73 62 59 84 68 71 79 65

PSP 8   Mathematics often appears in many different forms. Read the old English children's rhyme carefully. Then answer the question, "How many were going to St. Ives"?

> "As I was going to St. Ives
> I met a man with seven wives.
> Every wife had seven sacks,
> Every sack had seven cats,
> Every cat had seven kits.
> Kits, cats, sacks and wives
> How many were going to St. Ives?"

C 9   (a) Choose 5 current popular T.V. programs. Conduct a survey of students to find out which T.V. program most students prefer. Organize the data in a frequency table.

(b) Construct a histogram to display the data.

(c) Create a question about your graph. Answer the question.

13.4 Circle Graphs

A **circle** or **pie graph** is used to show data that can be expressed as part
of the whole data. Each piece of data is expressed as a percent of the
total. The percents are then used to calculate the size of the **central angle**
for each sector of the circle graph.

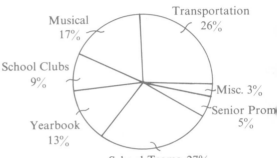

Student Council Budget

Student Council Budget $15 500			
Activity	Amount	Percent	Central angle
Transportation	$4070	26%	→94°
Musical	$2584	17%	61°
School Clubs	$1378	9%	32°
Yearbook	$2066	13%	47°
School Teams	$4176	27%	97°
Senior Prom	$752	5%	18°
Miscellaneous	$474	3%	11°
Total	$15 500	100%	360°

26% of 360° = 93.6° or 94° (to the nearest degree.)

To solve problems, you often need to combine earlier skills. **PSP**

13.4 Exercise

A 1 For each shaded region, ▶ estimate and then measure the central angle.
▶ calculate the percent of the circle that is shaded.

(a) 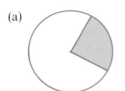 (b) 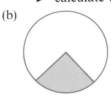 (c) 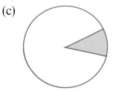 (d)

2 (a) Copy and complete the
chart showing people's
favourite winter sport.

(b) Match the data in the
chart with each region
of the graph.

Sport	Percent of people	Calculation of central angle	Measure of central angle
Skiing	25%	?	?
Hockey	?	0.40 × 360°	?
Snowshoeing	?	?	54°
Curling	20%	?	?
Total	?	?	?

(c) What are the advantages and the disadvantages
of using a circle graph to show the data?

3   A sample of cheese is analyzed. The data obtained
    are shown in the chart

Substance	Mass
Protein	78.4 g
Fat	188.1 g
Water	83.7 g

    (a) Construct a circle graph for the data.
    (b) Based on the data, how much of a 950-g wedge
        of cheese would you expect to be water?

4   (a) The central angle for the washers and dryers in the
        circle graph is 72°. Explain why the washers and
        dryers accounted for 20% of the total sales.
    (b) Measure the central angle for the refrigerators.
    (c) What percent of the total sales did the
        refrigerators account for?
    (d) The total sales last month were $125 060.
        Calculate the amount of sales for
        (i) televisions   (ii) freezers

Monthly Sales

5   A survey was conducted to obtain an answer to the
    question: "When was your home constructed?"

Period	Responses
before 1945	252
1945–1970	540
since 1970	408

    (a) Construct a circle graph to show the data.
    (b) If you did a similar survey in your area, would
        you expect the responses to be similar or different?
        Give reasons for your answer.

6   The blood types of a random
    sample of people were recorded.

Type of Blood	O	A	AB	B
Number of People	661	616	53	121

    (a) Construct a circle graph.
    (b) Based on the data, how many people would you expect to have AB
        blood at a football game with 14 000 in attendance?
    (c) Do your own survey about the blood types. Construct a circle graph.
        How does your graph compare with the one you constructed in (a)?

7   During one hour of radio listening,
    Harriet recorded the following
    information.

Broadcast	Amount of time
News other than sports	6 min 36 s
Sports and sport news	4 min 42 s
Music	28 min 54 s
Commercials	8 min 18 s
Discussions	11 min 30 s

    (a) Construct a circle graph.
    (b) Use your circle graph to create
        two questions. Answer them.

PSP 8 The letters show a pattern. Find the next three letters. Justify your choice.
    (a) T   S   N   T   F   E   (b) A   E   F   H   I   K   L

There are many different graphs that you can use to display data. The type of graph you use depends on the type of data as well as the visual impression you want to make. Each of these graphs displays the same information, but each provides you with a different visual impression.
Each graph shows the area used for each type of crop.

You used these graphs.
▶ pictograph
▶ stem-leaf plot
▶ bar graph
▶ circle graph
▶ histogram

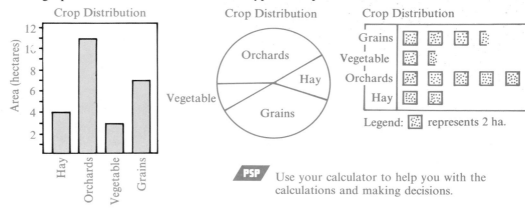

PSP   Use your calculator to help you with the calculations and making decisions.

13.5   Exercise

A   **1**   Pulse rate varies with age as shown in the chart.

      (a) Why would a circle graph not be suitable to display the data?

      (b) Construct a graph of your choice to display the data.

Age (years)	Pulse Rate (beats/min)
Newborn	135
1–9	87
10–19	71
20–59	72
60–69	73
70 plus	75

B   For Questions 2 to 7, display the data in a suitable graph. Use each of the graphs to create and solve two problems.

2

Length of boat (m)	Maximum load (kg)	Approximate number of persons
3	185	2
3.7	260	3
4	335	4
5	440	5

Source—Canadian Coast Guard

3   Calgary Flames 5-Year Record

Number of games
won: 215
lost: 109
tied: 66

4   Black Currant Shortcake Ingredients

100 g flour	100 g maple sugar
100 g butter	450 g black currants
250 g cream	100 g granulated sugar
3 g salt	150 g eggs (2 eggs)

5   Distance (in kilometres) Cycled by Bikeathon Participants

17 20 53 27 29 33 36 19 61 13 28
27 16 54 19 42 56 45   8 15 36 25
47 44 32 12 10 65 31 53 35 30

6   Total Monthly Precipitation (in millimetres)

	J	F	M	A	M	J	J	A	S	O	N	D
Prince George	59	42	32	30	42	58	58	73	56	61	55	54
Saint John	126	114	98	100	103	94	90	100	100	105	145	132
Calgary	17	20	20	30	50	92	68	56	35	19	16	15

7   Average Monthly Sunshine (in hours), September

Kamloops	194	St. John's	145	Prince Rupert	95
Schefferville	101	Sydney	168	Coppermine	69

PSP 8   Make a copy of the figures shown. Which figures can you trace without lifting your pencil?

(a)    (b)    (c)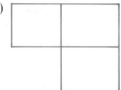

(d)    (e)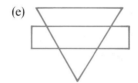

C 9   To answer some questions you need to do research. **PSP**

▶ Collect data to answer the question. Research the information.

▶ Draw a suitable graph to display the data.

▶ Use your graph to answer the original question.

(a) What is the length of time people spend sleeping as teenagers? as adults?

(b) In the Saturday newspaper, what percent of the cartoons are about animals? about people?

(c) How does your rate of breathing change when you perform different activities such as jogging, doing pushups, climbing stairs, reading?

(d) What are the four favourite record albums of the students in your class?

(e) Which of these names is the most appealing?

Fundy National Park (N.B.)	Stoney Wilderness Centre (Alta.)
Liscomb Game Sanctuary (N.S.)	Steele Narrows Historic Park (Sask.)

13.6 PSP Problem Solving: Misusing Data

There are many useful ways to use statistics but, unfortunately, statistics can also be misused. What impressions do you obtain from the information shown by the circle graph?
From the graph, you might quickly conclude that men drivers are worse than women drivers. To interpret the graph accurately and make valid conclusions, you often need more information. For example, are there more men drivers than women drivers? Do men drivers drive more?

Drivers in
Fatal Accidents

13.6 Exercise

A   Often the same information can be drawn on two different graphs and the results appear to be quite different. Look for examples in newspapers of how graphs can be used to distort or misuse data.

1   These graphs have been drawn to show the profit of a company.
   (a) How are the graphs alike? How are they different?
   (b) How much has the profit increased on each graph?
   (c) List any false impressions conveyed by the graphs.

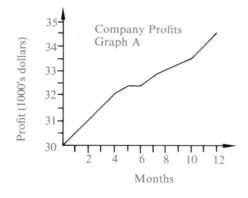

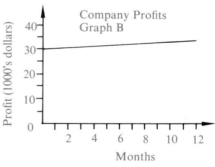

B 2   To show the increase in the number of houses built by a company, the graph at the right is drawn.
   (a) Why are the houses similar?
   (b) How many times as great is the area of house B as the area of house A?
   (c) How many times as many houses were built in the 1970's as in the 1960's?
   (d) List any false impressions conveyed by the graph.

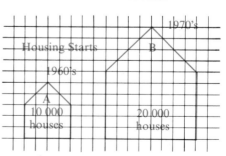

3　For each graph, list the false impressions. How would you change the graph to correct these false impressions?

(a)

(b) Canadian Exports by Destination for 2 years

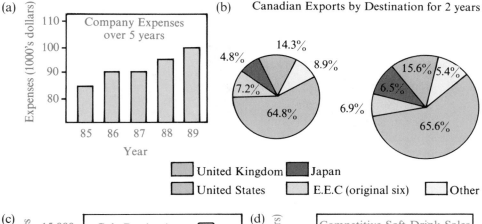

(c)

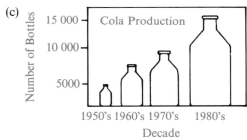

(d)

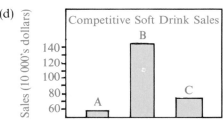

Which company do you think prepared the advertisement?

4　Use the data in the graph. Construct a graph that distorts the information and creates a false impression.

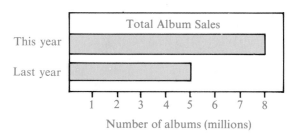

PSP　5　To solve some problems, you need to think of a simpler problem. How many triangles are in the diagram?

C 6　Use newspapers or magazines.

(a) Collect examples of how graphs have been used to create false impressions.

(b) Collect data from newspapers. Construct graphs to create

▶ an accurate impression.　▶ a false impression.

13.7 Mean, Median, Mode

When you determine the mean, the median or the mode of a set of numbers, you obtain a single value which is an indicator of the data. The numbers of the data cluster around this single value. For this reason, these indicators are often referred to as the **measures of central tendency**.

The **average** or **mean** of a set of data is equal to

$$\frac{\text{the sum of all the data}}{\text{the number of pieces of data}}.$$

PSP To do mathematics, you must understand the meanings of the words used.

For an odd number of data, the **median** is the middle number of the data arranged in order from least to greatest.

For an even number of data, the **median** is the average of the middle two numbers.

The **mode** of a set of data is the number that occurs most frequently.

Example

The table shows the amount of rainfall each month.

Month	J	F	M	A	M	J	J	A	S	O	N	D
Rain (mm)	96	84	65	40	10	0	0	8	17	45	55	70

For the data, calculate each measure of central tendency.
(a) mean   (b) median   (c) mode

Solution

(a) mean $= \dfrac{96 + 84 + 65 + 40 + 10 + 0 + 0 + 8 + 17 + 45 + 55 + 70}{12}$

$= \dfrac{490}{12}$

$= 40.8$ (to 1 decimal place)

The mean monthly rainfall is 40.8 mm.

(b) Arrange the data in order from least to greatest.
0, 0, 8, 10, 17, 40, 45, 55, 65, 70, 84, 96

The median is $\dfrac{40 + 45}{2} = 42.5$

The median monthly rainfall is 42.5 mm.

(c) In the rainfall data, 0 occurs most frequently.
The mode of the monthly rainfall is 0 mm.

You often have to decide which measure of central tendency is most representative of the data.

When is the mean the best indicator? The mean is an appropriate measure if there are no extreme values within the data. For example • average gas consumption • annual rainfall • annual snowfall • goals scored on a goaltender • student grade average.	When is the median the best indicator? The median is an appropriate measure if there are a few extreme values, as it is least affected by these. For example • average test marks • attendance records • wages • athlete's competition times	When is the mode the best indicator? The mode is an appropriate measure if the measure of the most characteristic value of a group of data is required. For example • shoe sizes, hat sizes, dress sizes • inventory of T.V. • number of pills in a bottle

13.7 Exercise

A   Use your calculator. Round your answers to 1 decimal place as needed.

1   The mean water depth is 16 m. What effect will each of the following measures have on the mean depth?

(a) 16 m   (b) 20 m   (c) 6 m

2   Which of mean, median or mode values is always a member of the data? Use an example for each to illustrate your answer.

B 3   The number of injuries at the sports complex for the past year is shown.

J	F	M	A	M	J	J	A	S	O	N	D
4	3	3	2	4	6	7	8	2	0	3	0

(a) Which best represents the data, mean, median or mode? Give reasons.

(b) Which measure is least representative of the data?

4   The heights of students in centimetres are given by the following data.

160, 158, 180, 180, 171, 168, 166, 160, 169, 173, 172, 181, 174, 160, 179, 160, 176, 157, 165, 159, 183, 162, 177, 167, 163, 170, 178, 161, 175

(a) Find the mean, the median and the mode.

(b) Which of your results in (a) best represents the data? Give reasons.

5   The points won by a school swim team during the past 8 competitions are shown. 210, 186, 170, 73, 175, 180, 73, 196

(a) Find the mean, the median and the mode.

(b) Which of the measures in (a) best represents the data?

(c) Predict the number of points you would expect the team to obtain in the next swimming competition.

(d) Predict the total number of points you would expect the team to obtain in the next four swimming competitions.

(e) Which answer, (c) or (d), would you expect to be more accurate? Why?

6   (a) In which class interval do
        the most data occur?
    (b) In which class interval do
        the least data occur?

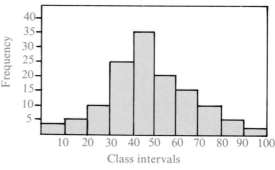

Final Examination Marks

7   (a) Use the histogram in
        Question 6 to predict
        in which *one class* the
        mean might occur.
    (b) Predict in which *classes*
        the mean might occur.
    (c) Which answer, (a) or (b), is more likely to be correct? Why?

8   (a) Describe how the histogram in Question 6 can be used to determine
        in which one class the median occurs.
    (b) Can the histogram be used to determine in which class the mode
        occurs? Explain why or why not.

9   The pulse rate in beats per minute was recorded for a group of people.
        75, 72, 91, 67, 80, 77, 73, 67, 86, 71, 75, 72, 94, 71, 70, 69, 93, 64, 80, 54, 75,
        69, 74, 73, 89, 78, 64, 81, 59, 80, 74, 76, 77, 70, 77, 70, 79, 58, 71, 82, 70, 68,
        77, 81, 71, 70, 78, 63, 74, 75, 56, 83, 69, 77, 53, 73, 68, 84, 59, 86, 78, 57, 78,
        66, 75, 64, 80, 73, 88, 62, 81, 86, 61, 73, 81, 75, 65, 74, 75, 65, 84, 70, 73

    (a) Decide on a class interval for the data and construct a histogram.
    (b) Predict from your histogram the average pulse. How could you check
        the accuracy of your answer?
    (c) What percent of the people had a pulse less than 70?
    (d) What percent of the people had a pulse of 80 or more?
    (e) What do you notice about your answers in (c) and (d)?
    (f) What percent of the people had a pulse in the interval 70–79?

10 Use the data in the previous question.
    (a) If you were to check the pulse rate of the next person you meet,
        predict what it might be.
    (b) If you were to check the pulse rate of the next 20 people, how many
        would you expect to have a rate in the interval 70–79? Give reasons
        for your answer.
    (c) Which of your answers, (a) or (b), do you think is more accurate? Why?

PSP 11 The average of two numbers is 11. When a third number is included the
        average of the numbers is 15. Find the third number.

Applying Calculators: Skills with Means

The properties of numbers can often be used to reduce the amount of work you need to do to obtain answers. For example, to calculate the mean of a set of data you use the following steps.

Calculate the mean of 62, 67, 58, 60, 62.

Step 1
Estimate the mean.   about 60

Step 2
Determine how much each number
is above or below the estimate.

62	67	58	60	62
+2	+7	−2	0	+2

Step 3
Calculate.

$$\text{mean} = 60 + \frac{2 + 7 + (-2) + 0 + 2}{5}$$

$$= 60 + \frac{9}{5}$$

$$= 60 + 1.8$$

$$= 61.8$$

Calculate all answers to 1 decimal place.

12   Use the procedure above to calculate the mean of 26, 25, 18, 21, 19, 23, 27, 20.

13   Use the procedure above to calculate the mean of 58, 67, 52, 69, 55, 48, 42, 51, 68, 49.

14   On small bags of potato chips it states that each contains a mass of 35 g.
In an experiment, the mass of the contents of each of 20 bags was measured and recorded.

     34 36 35 37 36 32 35 34 36 33 31 38 36 35 34 37 33 32 35 37

   (a) Find the mean of the masses recorded.
   (b) Do consumers have a reason to complain about the potato chip manufacturer? Give reasons for your answer.

15   In a class interval frequency table, the individual values are not known.

   (a) Copy and complete the table.
   (b) Calculate the approximate mean for the data.

Class Interval	Frequency	Total for class interval
0–9	2	9
10–19	3	?
20–29	8	?
30–39	5	?
40–49	2	?

   (c) The following are the original data for the frequency table. Calculate the actual mean.

     14 34 2 28 18 21 20 35 47 28
     20 33 11 7 33 23 32 41 29 28

   Think: Middle value of class interval is 4.5.
           Total for interval is 2 × 4.5 = 9.

   (d) Find the difference between the means in (b) and (c). Explain this difference.
   (e) Which method was easier to use?

13.8　Language of Probability

Concepts of probability occur frequently in your everyday life. Probably you have heard of people who predict events.

▶ The weather office predicts rain.

▶ The newspapers predict who will win the elections.

▶ During a holiday weekend, the number of accidental deaths is predicted.

Probability is the branch of mathematics used to help predict **PSP** the **outcomes** of various events. To solve problems involving probability, you need to know the skills and vocabulary.

Probability was first used to solve problems that dealt with games of chance. For example, if you do an experiment and roll a die, there are 6 **equally likely** outcomes: 1, 2, 3, 4, 5 or 6.

A bag contains 10 nickels and 10 dimes. The probability of picking a nickel from the bag is given by a ratio.

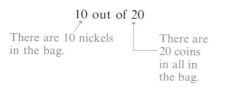

10 out of 20

There are 10 nickels in the bag.

There are 20 coins in all in the bag.

Probability (choosing a nickel)

$$P = \frac{10}{20} \leftarrow \text{number of favourable outcomes} \atop \leftarrow \text{number of possible outcomes}$$

$$P = \frac{1}{2}$$

This number line shows what the probabilities are of taking certain coins from the bag. You can also record the probability as a percent as shown.

There are no quarters in the bag. The probability, P, of choosing a quarter is

$$P = \frac{0}{20}$$
$$P = 0\%$$

The probability, P, of choosing a nickel from the bag is $P = \frac{10}{20}$

$$P = \frac{1}{2}$$
$$P = 50\%$$

The probability, P, of choosing a nickel or a dime is $P = \frac{20}{20}$

$$P = 1$$
$$P = 100\%$$

This is called a **certainty**.

The skills and concepts of probability provide other strategies **PSP** for solving problems.

Example　What is the probability of rolling an even number on a die?

Solution　$P(\text{even}) = \frac{3}{6} \leftarrow \text{number of favourable outcomes} \atop \leftarrow \text{number of possible outcomes}$

You can use two methods to determine the measure of probability.

By Theory:
You decide on the number of favourable outcomes, as you did for choosing a nickel from the bag, and write the probability.

By Experiment:
You actually list the data, as you choose coins from the bag, to see how many nickels or dimes you obtain. Then you write the probability.

13.8 Exercise

A 1   Assign an approximate value, 0 to 1, to show the probability of each event.
   (a) A bottle of soda is dropped on concrete. What is the probability of the bottle remaining intact?
   (b) What is the probability of snow in July in Winnipeg, Manitoba?
   (c) List different events. Describe the probability of each event happening.

2   What is the probability of rolling each number on a die?
   (a) 2   (b) 6   (c) an odd number   (d) 12

3   A bag contains 6 green balls, 9 white balls and 12 blue balls. You are to pick a ball. What is the probability that you will pick the following.
   (a) a white ball   (b) a blue ball   (c) a green ball   (d) a black ball

4   A circle is divided into different regions as shown. Find the following.
   (a) *P*(black)   (b) *P*(red)

B   Express your answers in lowest terms.

5   You tossed a thumb tack 50 times and it landed point up 34 times. What is the probability that the next time the thumb tack will land point up?

6   (a) A coin can land either heads or tails. What is the probability of tossing a head? a tail?
   (b) Toss a coin. Record the number of heads and tails for 100 tosses of the coin. How many times would you expect a head to occur? Write the probability.
   (c) Compare the probabilities you found in (a) and (b). What do you notice?

7   A nickel and dime are tossed. List the different outcomes that can occur. What is the probability of the following outcomes?
   (a) 2 heads   (b) 2 tails   (c) a head and a tail

8 (a) Toss two coins 100 times
       and record your results.

   (b) Compare your results above with
       your answers in Question 7.

Outcome	Occurrence
2 heads	?
1 head and 1 tail	?
2 tails	?

9 You can use a tree diagram to list the
   possible outcomes of tossing 3 coins as
   shown. Based on the diagram, what is
   the probability of the following
   outcomes?

   (a) 3 heads   (b) 2 heads and 1 tail
   (c) 3 tails   (d) 1 head and 2 tails

penny nickel dime penny nickel dime

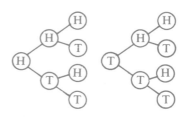

10 (a) Toss three coins 100 times and
       complete the table for each event.

   (b) Use your data. What is the probability
       of the following outcomes?

       (i) 3 heads   (ii) 2 heads and a tail
       (iii) 3 tails   (iv) 1 head and 2 tails

   (c) Compare your answers in (b) with those in Question 9. What do you notice?

penny	nickel	dime	Occurrence
H	H	H	?
H	H	T	?
T	T	H	?
T	T	T	?

11 A box contains 25 dimes, 10 pennies and 15 nickels. If you were to pick one
   coin, what would be the probability that you would pick each of the following?

   (a) a dime   (b) a nickel   (c) a penny

12 If you were to conduct an experiment based on the previous question,
   how many times would you expect to pick a penny for each number of attempts?

   (a) 50   (b) 500

13 A pair of dice is rolled. Copy and
   complete the chart to show the sum
   shown for all possible combinations of
   the roll.

   (a) Explain why the total number of
       possible outcomes when a pair of
       dice is rolled is 36.

   (b) What is the probability of rolling
       a sum of 2? of 7?

   (c) Which sum has the greatest
       probability of occurring? Why?

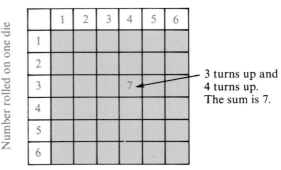

3 turns up and
4 turns up.
The sum is 7.

14 Each word is a scrambled math word. Unscramble them.

   (a) mnea   (b) dome   (c) catittisss   (d) garevae   (e) maples

13.9   PSP   Problem Solving: Strategies

Often there is more than one strategy for solving a problem.

For example, what is the probability of not rolling a 7 with a pair of dice? The chart at the right shows the results of rolling the various sums with a pair of dice.

	1	2	3	4	5	6
1	2	3	4	5	6	7
2	3	4	5	6	7	8
3	4	5	6	7	8	9
4	5	6	7	8	9	10
5	6	7	8	9	10	11
6	7	8	9	10	11	12

The probability of rolling a sum of 7 $= \dfrac{6}{36}$ ← number of favourable outcomes or sums of 7
← number of possible outcomes or sums

The probability of not rolling a sum of 7 $= \dfrac{30}{36}$ ← number of favourable outcomes or sums that are not 7
← number of possible outcomes or sums

In rolling the dice you will roll either a sum of 7 *or* not a sum of 7.

$$P\left(\begin{array}{c}\text{sum of}\\7\end{array}\right) + P\left(\begin{array}{c}\text{not sum}\\ \text{of } 7\end{array}\right) = 1$$

$$\dfrac{6}{36} + \dfrac{30}{36} = 1$$

Probabilities that are related as above are called **complementary**.   PSP   Complementary probabilities provide you with an alternative strategy for finding the probability of an event as shown in the next example.

Example   A bag contains 12 red, 20 blue and 8 black balls. What is the probability that you will not draw a red ball from the bag?

Solution $P\left(\begin{array}{c}\text{not}\\ \text{red}\end{array}\right) = 1 - P(\text{red}) \longrightarrow = \dfrac{28}{40}$

$= 1 - \dfrac{12}{40} \qquad = \dfrac{7}{10}$

13.9   Exercise

A 1   On a production line, 28 defective bolts were found in 1000 randomly selected bolts. Find the probability of each.
(a) a bolt being defective   (b) a bolt not being defective
Find the sum of your answers in (a) and (b).

2   Two dice are rolled. Find the probability of each.
(a) rolling a sum of 5   (b) not rolling a sum of 5
Find the sum of your answers in (a) and (b).

B Remember: Use a tree diagram or a chart to show the possible outcomes.

3 A pair of dice is rolled. Find the probability of each sum.
   (a) a sum greater than 8   (b) a sum less than 10   (c) a sum not less than 9

4 A card is drawn from a deck of 52 playing cards. Find each probability.
   (a) a red card   (b) an ace   (c) not a club
   (d) not a face card   (e) not an even numbered card

5 To decide on the next site for a baseball stadium, the committee placed these names in a box and pulled one from the box.

Estevan	Red Deer	Aylmer	Glace Bay	Wabana
Hamilton	Kamloops	Mississauga	Penticton	

   What is the probability of each of the following?
   (a) Red Deer   (b) not Penticton   (c) not Aylmer or Glace Bay

6 About 42% of the population of Canada has type O blood. What is the probability that the next person you meet will not have type O blood?

7 A bag contains 36 cubes numbered 1 to 36. After you choose one cube from the bag, you place it back in the bag. What is each probability?
   (a) an even number   (b) an odd number   (c) a number greater than 15
   (d) a number less than 30   (e) not a multiple of 3   (f) not a square number

8 A nickel, a dime and a penny are tossed. What is each probability?
   (a) 2 heads and a tail   (b) not 3 heads

9 There are 15 numbers under each letter of the game BINGO.

B	I	N	G	O
1 to 15	16 to 30	31 to 45	46 to 60	61 to 75

   Find each probability.
   (a) The first number called will be "under the G".
   (b) The first number called will not be "under the B".
   (c) The first number called will be an even number "under the N".
   (d) The first number called will not be an odd number "under the I".

PSP 10 To change from the word GRASS to LANES, you change one letter in each line but you must still have a word. You do not need to keep the letters in the same order each time.

   GRASS

   LANES

13.10   Data and Predictions: Probability

The decision to sail a boat depends on the weather forecast. Often a race will be cancelled because of bad weather. In order to inform the competitors of whether a race has been cancelled or not, you need to consider the weather forecast a day ahead. If you are to forecast the weather, it is best to base your forecast on as much information as is available.

PSP The more data you have, the more reliable your solution to a problem.

In the exercise, the collected data are used to calculate probabilities.

13.10   Exercise

B Express your answers in lowest terms.

1   A die is rolled 10 times and the results are recorded in the table.

Number	1	2	3	4	5	6
Occurence	1	1	4	2	1	1

(a) In the next 10 rolls how many times would you expect to roll a 3?

(b) Roll a die 10 times and record the results.

(c) Was your prediction in (a) accurate? Why or why not?

(d) How could you improve your prediction in (a)?

2   After 500 rolls of the die, the data given at the right were gathered. Based on the sample, if the die was rolled 1000 times, estimate how many times you would expect each outcome.

Number	1	2	3	4	5	6
Occurrence	76	78	83	81	86	96

(a) 3   (b) 2   (c) 6

3   When tossing a coin 500 times, 239 heads and 261 tails were tossed. Based on the data, if the coin was tossed 1000 times, estimate how many times you would expect each outcome.

(a) a head   (b) a tail

Based on your results, what is the probability of tossing a head?

4   The following results were obtained by drawing one card from a deck of regular playing cards 100 times. The card drawn was replaced and the deck shuffled after each draw.

Ace	Face Card	2 to 10
8	22	70

Based on the results, if a card is drawn 300 times, estimate how many times you would expect each outcome.

(a) an ace   (b) a face card

5   Three sets of trials of 500 rolls of a die are listed below.

(a) Total each number based on the three trials and find the average per trial.

(b) Use the results of (a) to predict the number of threes in another trial of 500 rolls.

Number	1	2	3	4	5	6
Trial 1	93	93	82	80	93	59
Trial 2	87	81	92	73	74	93
Trial 3	88	77	74	93	90	78
Total	268	?	?	?	?	?
Average per trial	?	?	?	?	?	?

6   Data are given for the range of marks on an exam. You select an exam paper at random. What is the probability of each of the following?

(a) the student passed

(b) the student received over 80

(c) the student did not have a mark in the 61–70 class

Class	Class Limits	Frequency
1	1–10	0
2	11–20	0
3	21–30	3
4	31–40	4
5	41–50	5
6	51–60	18
7	61–70	20
8	71–80	15
9	81–90	9
10	91–100	2

7   A thumb tack can land in one of 2 ways, point up or point down

(a) Drop 50 tacks and record the number of times each position occurs.

(b) Based on your results, is a thumb tack more likely to land point up or point down?

(c) Based on your results, what is the probability of a thumb tack landing point up?

8   A histogram shows the frequency distribution of the normal pulse rates of students. If you select a student at random, what is the probability of each of the following pulse rates?

(a) less than 60   (b) more than 80

(c) between 60 and 80

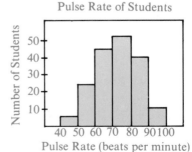

Pulse Rate of Students

Number of Students

Pulse Rate (beats per minute)

Applications: Predicting Wildlife Populations

Predictions are also used when samples are taken. Based on the sample, predictions are made about the population.

To determine how many fish might be in a lake, the following procedure is often used.

Step A: A sample of 136 fish is caught. These fish are tagged and released back into the lake.

Step B: Later a sample of fish is taken and the data are recorded.

number of fish caught, 396	number of tagged fish, 6

The data are used to predict the fish population. Use n to represent the number of fish in the lake.

$$\frac{\text{number of fish in lake}}{\text{number of original tagged fish}} = \frac{\text{number of fish in sample}}{\text{number of tagged fish in sample}}$$

$$\frac{n}{136} = \frac{396}{6}$$

$$n = \frac{136 \times 396}{6}$$

$$n = 8976$$

To the nearest 100, there are about 9000 fish in the lake.
Check your work with a calculator.

9 The Department of Fisheries released 1350 tagged pickerel fingerlings into Lake Trask. Of 8000 fish caught a week later, 270 were tagged. About how many fish would you expect to be in the lake?

10 Of a herd of deer, 86 were tagged. Some time later 7 out of 168 deer sighted were tagged. Estimate the deer population. What assumption did you make?

11 To estimate the polar bear population, 18 bears were tagged and released. Out of 128 polar bears sighted, 6 bears were tagged. Estimate the polar bear population.

12 The Department of Fisheries recorded 73 lake trout in Lake Nosbining out of a total catch of 750 fish. How many fish, out of a catch of 1200, would you expect to be lake trout?

13 The Georgian Bay Islands National Park has an area of 1424 ha. If 3 bears were spotted in a region of 24 ha, how many bears would you expect to be in the park?

13.11 Simulations

Real-life situations can be imitated in probability experiments. The experiments provide estimated probabilities. Such experiments are called **simulations**.

Example   What is the probability that, in a group of 5 people, at least 2 people were born in December?

Solution   Assume that the probability of being born in December is $\frac{1}{12}$ or $0.08\overline{3}$.

Method 1   Take 12 beans, paint a red dot on one of them and place all the beans in a bag. One trial consists of drawing a bean from the bag, replacing it and drawing again until 5 draws have been made. Use 20 trials. Record the results.

Trial	1	2	3	4	5	6	7	8	9	10	11	12	13	14	15	16	17	18	19	20
Number of times red dot	/		/		//			/		/	///		//	//	//		//		/	
bean is drawn	1	0	1	0	2	0	0	1	0	1	3	0	2	2	2	0	2	0	1	0

Estimate the probability of at least 2 people out of 5 being born in December.

$$P \doteq \frac{\text{number of times the red dot bean was drawn at least 2 out of 5 times}}{\text{number of trials}}$$

$$= \frac{6}{20}$$

$$= \frac{3}{10} \text{ or } 0.3$$

Method 2   Make a spinner with 12 equal sectors. Identify one sector as December. One trial consists of spinning the spinner 5 times. Use 20 trials. Record the results.

What is the degree measure of each sector?

Trial	1	2	3	4	5	6	7	8	9	10	11	12	13	14	15	16	17	18	19	20
Number of times		//	/		/	/	/	/	/				/		//				/	
spinner points to D	0	2	1	0	1	1	1	1	1	0	0	0	1	0	2	0	0	0	1	0

Estimate the probability of at least 2 people out of 5 being born in December.

$$P \doteq \frac{\text{number of times the spinner pointed to D at least 2 out of 5 times}}{\text{number of trials}}$$

$$= \frac{2}{20}$$

$$= \frac{1}{10} \text{ or } 0.1$$

Method 3   Use a table of random digits. (See page 489.) One trial consists
of selecting 15 (3 × 5) consecutive digits at random. Read
them as 3-digit numbers. Since the probability of being born in
December is 0.083, a 3-digit number less than or equal to 083
represents a December birth.

503 267 339 408 077 922 397 | 456 309 538 363 219 371 222 088
567 664 162 373 300 066 188 | 585 699 847 690 599 249 213 883
471 946 899 126 718 609 101↓208 604 067 056 378 | 576 968 645   067 < 083
745 125 508 483 546 078 998 022 103 730 287 923 410 168 418   056 < 083
591 504 309 563 533 573 862 948 933 626 641 878 595 382 790

Use 20 trials. Record the results.

Trial	1	2	3	4	5	6	7	8	9	10	11	12	13	14	15	16	17	18	19	20
Number of numbers less than 083	/		/		/	/	//		/	/	//		//		/		//	/	/	/
	1	0	1	0	1	1	2	0	1	1	2	0	2	0	1	0	2	1	1	1

Estimate the probability of at least 2 people out of 5 being born in December.

$$P \doteq \frac{\text{number of times at least 2 out of 5 numbers were less than or equal to 083}}{\text{number of trials}}$$

$$= \frac{4}{20}$$

$$= \frac{1}{5} \text{ or } 0.2$$

The accuracy of the probability is greater when more trials are used.
Consider all three experiments.

$$P \doteq \frac{\text{number of favourable outcomes}}{\text{number of possible outcomes}}$$

$$= \frac{6 + 2 + 4}{3 \times 20}$$

$$= \frac{12}{60}$$

$$= \frac{1}{5} \text{ or } 0.2$$ Thus the probability that, in a group of 5 people, at least
2 people were born in December is about 0.2.

13.11   Exercise

B 1   In a family of 3 children, you want to find the probability that exactly 2
of the children are boys.

(a) What assumption do you make about the probability of a child being a boy?

(b) Simulate the birth of 3 children by tossing 3 coins and letting a tail
represent a boy. Perform 30 trials. Record the results in a table.

(c) Estimate the probability. Divide the number of times that 2 out of 3
coins showed tails by 30.

2 Use your table from Question 1 to estimate each probability.

   (a) 3 girls   (b) first-born a boy   (c) at least 2 girls

3 A quiz consists of 8 true/false questions. You want to find the probability of obtaining a perfect score by guessing.

   (a) What assumption do you make about the probability of guessing the correct answer to a true/false question?

   (b) Simulate guessing the answers by rolling a die 8 times and letting the even numbers represent a correct guess. Perform 30 trials. Record the results in a table.

   (c) Estimate the probability of a perfect score on the quiz.

4 Use your table from Question 3 to estimate each probability.

   (a) passing the quiz (at least 4 correct guesses)

   (b) just passing (exactly 4 correct guesses)

5 An ice cream shop serves 5 flavours of milk shakes. You want to find how many people must be served a milk shake before one milk shake of each flavour is served.

   (a) What assumption do you make about the probability of a person ordering any given flavour of milk shake?

   (b) Simulate serving milk shakes by starting at any point in a table of random digits and counting the number of digits until you have 1 to 5 at least once. Ignore the other digits.

```
941| 803  385 926  480  667  090  042  646  721 540 313 826 200 106   8 digits
767| 700  872 736  123  213  840  516  795  588 615 285 952 978 427   before at
986 |2|78 |4|6|5| 689 |5|68 69|2| 65|3| |4|99 |1|04 882 503 277 364 189 704   least 1 of
996  071  799 476  805  321  695  739  031  609 100 017 494 079 630   each of
787  765  654 490  242  316  977  462  560  408 088 397 449 001 566   1 to 5 occurs
```

   Perform 20 trials. Record the results in a table.

   (c) Find the number of people by finding the average of the trials.

For Questions 6 to 11,

▶ Identify the assumptions you are making about the probability.

▶ Select a suitable simulation model.

▶ Perform an experiment and answer the question.

6 What is the probability that, in a group of 4 people, all of them were born between July 1 and December 31?

7 Each box of cereal has 1 of 10 model spaceships. How many boxes of cereal must be opened to obtain a complete set of the models?

8 Lila wears her blue angora sweater twice as often as she wears any of her other 4 sweaters. What is the probability that Lila will wear her blue angora sweater the next time she wears a sweater?

9 In a family of 5 children find the probability of each.
(a) 0 boys   (b) 3 boys   (c) at least 2 girls

10 A traffic light at an intersection is green for 30 s, red for 30 s and amber for 10 s. What is the probability that the next time you approach the intersection the light will be green?

PSP 11 The knight in chess makes a move by moving two squares in one direction and then one square in the perpendicular direction as shown by the diagrams.
Can the knight move to every square of the grid shown without landing in the same square twice?

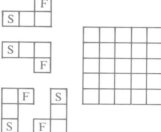

Computer Use

When a lot of data are involved, a program can assist you in doing tedious calculation.

► Examine the program at the right. What is the program designed to do?

► Use data from this section and try the program. Do you need to make any adjustments in the program for the data you choose?

```
10 DIM X(100)
15 INPUT N
20 LET S = 0
30 FOR I = 1 TO N
40 INPUT X(I)
50 LET S = S + X(I)
60 NEXT I
70 LET M = S/N
80 PRINT "THE MEAN IS", M
90 END
```

From Math History

Blaise Pascal, a mathematician, used what he knew to develop what he did not know. Historically, many people used this method not only in mathematics but also in medicine, science and astronomy. Pascal's study of the geometry of Euclid at the age of 12 gave him a thirst for mathematics. He prepared important material on the study of conics (circles, ellipses, parabolas, etc.). His interest in the roulette wheel provided him with the insight to discover the properties of the cycloid, a geometric curve. Correspondence between Pascal and another great mathematician, Fermat was the beginning of probability theory. To this day, there are parts of mathematics named after Pascal. Do you know what a Pascal triangle is?

13.12 PSP Problem Solving: Using Strategies

To solve the following problems, you need to devise a strategy. Refer to the list of strategies you have placed in your *Problem Solving Plan* PSP .

As in your earlier work, you need to know the answers to these important questions:

I What information am I asked to find?
II What information am I given?

13.12 Exercise

B 1 A name is spelled using the pattern at the right.
(a) How many different ways can you spell ELIZABETH?
(b) Make a similar diagram to show your name. How many different ways can you spell your name?

2 Sometimes numbers behave in unusual ways.

$$1 + 2 = 3 \qquad 1 + 2 + 3 = 6 \qquad 1 + 2 + 3 + 4 = 10$$
$$1^3 + 2^3 = 3^2 \quad 1^3 + 2^3 + 3^3 = 6^2 \quad 1^3 + 2^3 + 3^3 + 4^3 = 10^2$$

Explore whether the above pattern is true for all natural numbers.

3 What is the last digit of the value of 3^{3333}?

4 A two-digit number is equal to 8 times the sum of its digits. Find the number.

5 Find the next 3 letters for each pattern. Give reason(s) for your choices.
(a) A D G J M   (b) T T T F F S S

6 What is the least positive number that when divided by 4, 5 or 7 leaves a remainder of 3?

Math Tip

▶ It is important to clearly understand the vocabulary of mathematics in order to solve problems. Make a list of all the new words you have learned. Provide an example of your own for each word.

▶ Make a list of the strategies you have used in this chapter for problem solving. Place them in your *Problem Solving Plan* PSP .

Practice Test

1   List two advantages and two disadvantages for each data gathering method.
    (a) questionnaire   (b) telephone survey

2   Use an example to illustrate when a census would be preferable to a sample.

3   A sample was taken of the ages of people attending an art exhibition.
        26 39 24 14 49 15 8 23 17 41 7 28 13 25 35 46 61 18 13 35 26 58 12 21 16
        11 36 5 12 25 35 26 17 21 27 12 15 13 42 55 48 16 10 9 70 64 35 32 17 19
    (a) Construct a stem-and-leaf plot for the data.
    (b) In which age group do the most data occur?

4   A survey of 50 people provided data on their preferred type of television viewing
        Drama 12   Sport 15   Comedy 18   Other 5
    (a) What is the percent for each category?
    (b) Construct a circle graph to show the data.

5   The masses of 30 eggs were measured   49.8 62.3 47.3 55.9 61.3 52.8 50.7 65.5
    in grams and recorded.   52.4 50.8 63.4 49.9 53.6 57.4 51.2 41.6
    (a) Organize the data in a frequency table. 57.9 56.3 49.3 53.5 58.0 61.4 60.4 55.1
                                                 59.2 67.1 61.5 47.7 50.8 54.7
    (b) Display the data in a histogram.

6   The number of people visiting the zoo is given for a 1-week period.
    Mon. 475   Tue. 823   Wed. 765   Thu. 648   Fri. 1289   Sat. 1425   Sun. 1325
    Draw a suitable graph to display the data.

7   Calculate the mean, the median and the mode of 24, 18, 17, 16, 20, 30 and 16.

8   (a) Make a tree diagram to show the possible outcomes of rolling a die
        and tossing two coins.
    (b) Using the tree diagram, find the probability of each of the following.
        (i) an even number and two heads
        (ii) a prime number, one head and one tail

9   Identify a suitable simulation model for predicting some probability about
    each of the following. Explain your choice.
    (a) sex of a child
    (b) month of birth
    (c) six different snack foods

                                              P
                                            A   A
                                          T   T   T
                                        T   T   T   T
PSP 10 How many different ways can   E   E   E
         you spell PATTERN using   R   R
         the diagram at the right?   N

Cumulative Review (10–12)

1   Each relation rule occurs in the form $p \to \blacksquare p^2 + \square$. Find the relation
    rule in each of the following.

(a)
$p \to ?$	
1	3
3	35
4	63
2	15

(b)
$p \to ?$	
4	49
2	13
3	28
1	4

(c)
$p \to ?$	
2	18
4	78
1	3
3	43

2   For the line,
    (a) what is the x-intercept?
    (b) what is the y-intercept?
    (c) what is its slope?

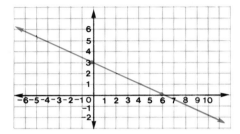

3   Draw the graphs of the pair of
    equations. Find their point of
    intersection.
    $y = 17 - 3x \qquad 2x + 3y = 16$

4   When the Barnes sold their house for \$140 000, they paid a 6% real estate
    commission. What was the commission in dollars?

5   To buy a car, the Zacharias borrowed \$10 000 at $9\frac{1}{2}\%$/a for two years
    compounded annually. Find the amount of the loan.

6   In a snack food the ratio of seeds to nuts to dried fruit is 3:4:5. How
    many grams of each would you expect to get in a 480-g package?

7   Theresa and Rod live in cities 405 km apart. Theresa left to meet Rod and
    half an hour later Rod left to meet Theresa. Two hours after Rod left
    they met. They both travelled at the same speed. What was it?

8   Simplify
    (a) $(y + 3)(y + 5)$ (b) $(y - 2)(y - 3)$ (c) $(x + 3)^2$
    (d) $(x + 4y)^2$ (e) $(x - 4)(x + 3)$ (f) $(x + 5)(x - 8)$
    (g) $(x + 2y)(x + 3y)$ (h) $(x - 3y)(x - 2y)$ (i) $(a - 6b)(3a - 2b)$
    (j) $(2x + 3y)^2$ (k) $(5 - m)(3 - m)$ (l) $(6 - 3m)(7 + 2m)$

9   Factor fully.
    (a) $p^2 - 6p + 9$ (b) $n^2 - 9n + 20$ (c) $3a^2 + 9ab + 6b^2$
    (d) $81m^2 - 4n^2$ (e) $2y^2 + 2y - 4$ (f) $25a^2 - 40ab + 16b^2$

14 Using Transformations: Concepts and Skills

Language of transformations, concept of transformations, translations and reflections, line and point symmetry, rotations and dilatations, using co-ordinates, tiling patterns, glide reflections, testing for transformations, distortions, half turns, applications, strategies for problem solving

Introduction

As you learn new concepts and skills in mathematics, you increase your store of strategies for problem solving. Throughout this text you have developed a framework for a *Problem Solving Plan* **PSP** . A plan will help you develop your ability to solve problems in any situation, whether in mathematics or another discipline. Throughout your study, you have continued to build your plan by placing skills and strategies in the appropriate part of the *Problem Solving Plan* **PSP** .

In this chapter, you will study the properties and applications of translations, reflections, rotations and dilatations which collectively are called *transformations*.

PSP | **Problem Solving Plan**

Step A: Understand the problem.
 • What are you asked to find?
 • What are you given?

Step B: Decide on a strategy.

Step C: Apply the strategy.
 Do the work.

Step D: Check your solution.

Step E: Write a final statement.

If the shape, size or position of a figure changes, then the figure is said to have undergone a transformation. You will use the skills and strategies in this chapter to learn about the properties of figures. As the chapter unfolds, place the skills and strategies in the appropriate part of your *Problem Solving Plan* **PSP** .

▶ In plane geometry, you study relations among figures and properties of figures.

▶ In co-ordinate geometry, you use co-ordinates to locate points and figures on the plane. You learn important strategies and skills for solving problems.

▶ In transformational geometry, you study the properties of a figure as its shape, size or position changes.

14.1 Working with Transformations

If you begin with a shape such as the one shown, you can transform it in a number of ways.

You can change its position

▶ by sliding it.   ▶ by flipping it.   ▶ by turning it.

                    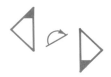

In each of the above, the shape has undergone a **transformation**. For each transformation, the mathematician asks two important questions.

▶ What has changed?   ▶ What has not changed? (What is invariant?)

Transformations are another part of your study of geometry. This section introduces you to the vocabulary of transformations. Place these words in your vocabulary list.

Translations

A **translation** maps rectangle ABCD onto rectangle A'B'C'D'. Rectangle A'B'C'D' is the **translation image**.

A ⟶ A'
B ⟶ B'   B' is read as B prime.
C ⟶ C'   B' is the image of B.
D ⟶ D'

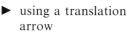

Translations can be described in different ways.

▶ using words   ▶ using a translation   ▶ using symbols
  right 3, down 2   arrow $[+3, -2]$

down 2 units

right 3 units

Reflections

A **reflection** about a line *l* maps △HJK onto △H'J'K'.

△H'J'K' is the **reflection image**.
The line *l* is the **line of reflection**.

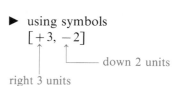

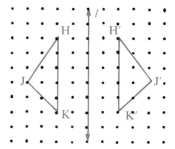

Rotations

A **rotation** about a point O maps △PQR
onto △P′Q′R′.

△P′Q′R′ is the **rotation image**.

O is the **centre of rotation**. The direction is
either clockwise (cw) ↻ or counter-clockwise
(ccw) ↺. The amount of rotation in the
diagram is 90° or $\frac{1}{4}$ turn clockwise.

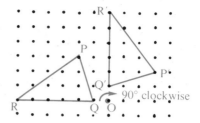

14.1 Exercise

A Review the types of transformations.

1. Transformations are applied to the figure
   shown. The images are shown below. Identify
   the type of transformation used for each.

(a)   (b)   (c)

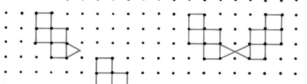
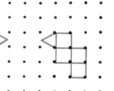

2. A transformation is used to create each logo. Identify the type of
   transformation used for each.

(a)   (b)   (c)   (d)

(e)   (f)   (g)   (h)

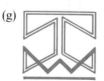

3. List examples from the world around you of each of the transformations
   discussed in this section.

B 4 Each figure has been translated. Describe the translation.

(a)

(b)

(c)

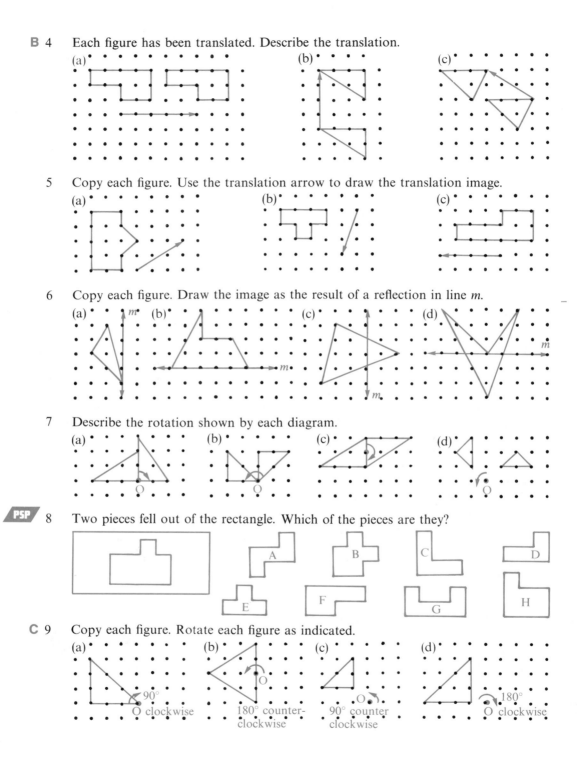

5 Copy each figure. Use the translation arrow to draw the translation image.

(a)

(b)

(c)

6 Copy each figure. Draw the image as the result of a reflection in line *m*.

(a) *m*   (b)   (c)   (d)   *m*

7 Describe the rotation shown by each diagram.

(a)   (b)   (c)   (d)

8 Two pieces fell out of the rectangle. Which of the pieces are they?

A   B   C   D

E   F   G   H

C 9 Copy each figure. Rotate each figure as indicated.

(a)   (b)   (c)   (d)

90°
O clockwise

180° counter-
clockwise

90° counter
clockwise

180°
O clockwise

14.2 Constructions: Translations and Reflections

In this section, you will construct translation images and reflection images.

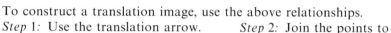

Translation

$\triangle A'B'C'$ is the translation image of $\triangle ABC$.
$\overrightarrow{PQ}$ is the translation arrow.

$$\overline{AA'} = \overline{BB'} = \overline{CC'} = \overline{PQ}$$
$$\overline{AA'} \parallel \overline{BB'} \parallel \overline{CC'} \parallel \overline{PQ}$$

To construct a translation image, use the above relationships.

Step 1: Use the translation arrow. Locate points S', T' and U'.   *Step 2:* Join the points to draw $\triangle S'T'U'$.

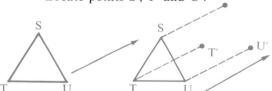
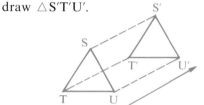

Reflection

$\triangle P'Q'R'$ is the reflection image of $\triangle PQR$.
$\overleftrightarrow{ST}$ is the reflection line.

$$\overline{PP'} \perp \overleftrightarrow{ST}, \overline{QQ'} \perp \overleftrightarrow{ST}, \overline{RR'} \perp \overleftrightarrow{ST}$$
$$\overline{PD} = \overline{P'D}, \overline{QE} = \overline{Q'E}, \overline{RF} = \overline{R'F}$$

To construct a reflection image, use the above relationships.

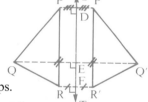

Step 1: Locate R', S' and T'.   *Step 2:* Join the points to draw $\triangle R'S'T'$.

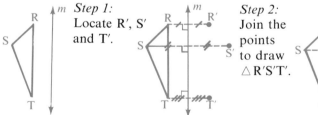

14.2 Exercise

A 1 $\triangle S'T'U'$ is the translation image of $\triangle STU$.

(a) Which line segments would have the same length as $\overline{AB}$?
(b) Which line segments are parallel to $\overline{AB}$?

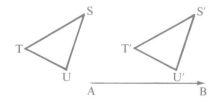

2   △P′Q′R′ is the reflection image of △PQR.

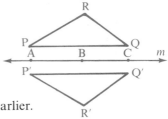

(a) Which pairs of line segments have the same length?

(b) Which line segments are perpendicular to line *m*?

B   To do constructions, use the skills you have learned earlier.

3   Draw any △DEF. Use the translation arrow shown.

(a) Construct the translation image of △DEF.

(b) List the relationships between the construction line segments and the translation arrow.

4   Draw any rectangle STUV. Use the translation arrow shown.

(a) Construct the translation image of rectangle STUV.

(b) List the relationships between the construction line segments and the translation arrow.

5   Copy the diagram.

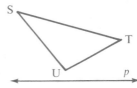

(a) Use the reflection line. Construct the reflection image of △STU.

(b) List the relationships between the construction line segments and the reflection line.

 6   Study the diagram. Which line segment, *c*, *d*, *e* or *f*, continues the line segment of which *a* and *b* are part? Do not use a ruler!

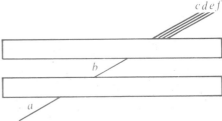

C 7   Copy each diagram. Construct the reflection image of each figure with respect to its reflection line.

(a)

(b)

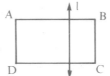

(c)

Math Tip

Make a list of new math words as you meet them in this chapter. Provide an example of your own to illustrate each word. Refer to the *Math Tip* at the end of Section 14.10.

14.3 Constructing Rotations

In this section you will construct rotation images.

△A′B′C′ is the rotation image of △ABC.
O is the centre of rotation.
90° clockwise is the angle of rotation.

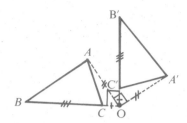

$$\angle AOA' = \angle BOB' = \angle COC' = 90°$$
$$\overline{OA} = \overline{OA'} \qquad \overline{OB} = \overline{OB'} \qquad \overline{OC} = \overline{OC'}$$

To construct a rotation image, use the above relationships. Rotate ∠PQR about O through an angle of 90° clockwise.

Step 1: Locate points P′, Q′ and R′.

 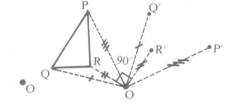

Step 2: Join the points to draw △P′Q′R′.

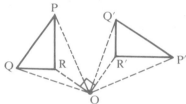

To indicate a 90° or 180° turn, the following vocabulary is often used.

▶ half turn $\left(\frac{1}{2}\text{ turn}\right)$ or 180° turn   ▶ quarter turn $\left(\frac{1}{4}\text{ turn}\right)$ or 90° turn

In the exercise, you will explore rotations with half and quarter turns.

14.3 Exercise

A 1 How many degrees are in each turn?
(a) half turn   (b) quarter turn

2 △S′T′U′ is the rotation image of △STU about the rotation centre O.

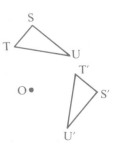

(a) Which pairs of line segments have the same length?
(b) What is the measure of the rotation angle?
(c) Which angles are equal to the rotation angle?

3 Square P′Q′R′S′ is the rotation image of square
PQRS about the rotation centre O.

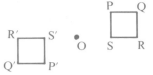

(a) Which pairs of line segments have the same length?

(b) What is the measure of the rotation angle?

(c) Which angles are equal to the rotation angle?

B To do constructions, use the skills you have learned earlier.

4 Make a copy of △DEF and the rotation
centre O. Construct the rotation image
about O for each of the following.

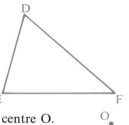

(a) 90° turn clockwise

(b) 180° turn counter-clockwise

5 Make a copy of △PQS and the rotation centre O.

(a) Construct the rotation image △P′Q′S′ about O.

(b) Which pairs of line segments are congruent?

(c) Which angles are equal to the rotation angle?

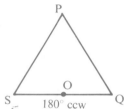

6 Make a copy of each diagram. Use the rotation centre O. For each
diagram construct the rotation image for a half turn.

(a) clockwise   (b) counter-clockwise

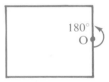

What do you notice about the position of the image and original figure
for (a) and (b)?

 7 To answer the question, you may need to interpret it from a different
point of view. The answer you provide must answer the question asked!
Describe a way to throw a rubber ball so that it will not bounce off a
surface but will return to you. You cannot attach anything to the ball to
make it return!

C 8 Make a copy of each diagram. Construct the rotation image for a quarter
turn clockwise. Use the rotation centre O.

(a)   (b)   (c)

Line and Point Symmetry

A figure has **line symmetry** or **reflectional symmetry** if a line can be drawn through it so that one half of the figure reflects onto the other half of the figure. The figure at the right has 2 lines of symmetry.

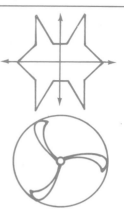

A figure has **point** or **rotational symmetry** if it can be rotated about a point onto itself. The figure at the right can be turned to match its original position. After three such turns it is in its original position. This figure is said to have **rotational symmetry of order 3**.

---

9 ► How many lines of symmetry does each figure have?
  ► What is the order of rotational symmetry for each figure?

(a)   (b)   (c)   (d)   (e)   (f)

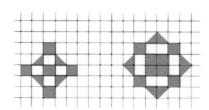

(g) square   (h) kite   (i) isosceles triangle
(j) rhombus   (k) equilateral triangle (l) parallelogram

10 (a) Figures with rotational symmetry of order 1 are not considered to have rotational symmetry. Why?
  (b) Does every figure with line symmetry have point symmetry? If your answer is no, give an example.
  (c) Does every figure with point symmetry have line symmetry? If your answer is no, give an example.

11 Squared paper is used to create designs that have symmetry. Create two designs that have
  (a) reflectional symmetry.
  (b) rotational symmetry.

14.4 Constructing Dilatations

If you change the size of a figure, either by making it larger or smaller, you are using a **size transformation** or a **dilatation**. Each diagram shows a dilatation with respect to a **dilatation centre** O.

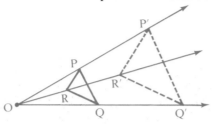 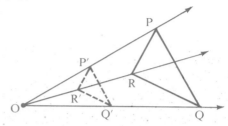

$\overline{P'Q'} = 2\overline{PQ}$

└─ 2 is called the **scale factor**.

$\overline{P'Q'} = \frac{1}{2}\overline{PQ}$

$\frac{1}{2}$ is called the **scale factor**.

The corresponding lengths, $\overline{OP}$ and $\overline{OP'}$, $\overline{OQ}$ and $\overline{OQ'}$, $\overline{OR}$ and $\overline{OR'}$, are related by a scale factor. This relationship is used to construct dilatation images.

14.4 Exercise

B 1 Make a copy of each figure and its dilatation centre, O. Construct the dilatation image.

(a) scale factor 3

(b) scale factor 2

2 Make another copy of each figure in Question 1. Then construct the dilatation image for each scale factor

(a) $\frac{1}{2}$

(b) $1\frac{1}{2}$

3 Draw each square and its dilatation centre, O, as shown.

▶ Construct the dilatation image for each figure for a scale factor of 3.

▶ Construct the dilatation image of each figure for a scale factor of $\frac{1}{2}$.

(a)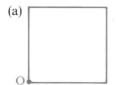
(b)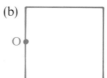
(c)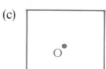
(d)

14.5 Translations and Co-ordinates

You have used symbols like [+4, +1] to show the translation which relates △ABC and △A′B′C′.

You can use your skills with co-ordinates to represent translations and to explore properties of translations.

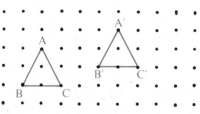

△XYZ and its translation image △X′Y′Z′ are shown. The co-ordinates of the corresponding vertices are related. The translation is given by [6, 0].

original points   image points

X(−4, 3)   ⟶   X′(2, 3)
Y(−5, −2)   ⟶   Y′(1, −2)
Z(−2, −2)   ⟶   Z′(4, −2)

Add 6 to the x co-ordinate.   The y co-ordinate remains the same.

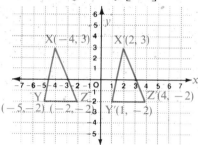

Mapping notation is used to show the translation as $(x, y) \longrightarrow (x + 6, y)$.

14.5 Exercise

A Use your skills with co-ordinates to explore the properties of translations.

1   A translation is applied to obtain the image of figure ABCDE.
   - (a) Write the co-ordinates of corresponding points.
   - (b) How are the x co-ordinates related?
   - (c) How are the y co-ordinates related?
   - (d) Complete the mapping for the translation $(x \ y) \longrightarrow (?, ?)$.

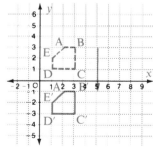

2   A translation is applied to obtain the image of figure PQRST. Repeat parts (a) to (d) in Question 1.

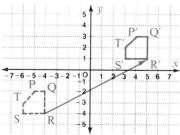

3 Find the co-ordinates of the image of each figure. Why do the mappings shown describe translations?

(a) $(x, y) \longrightarrow (x - 2, y)$

(b) $(x, y) \longrightarrow (x, y + 3)$

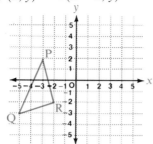

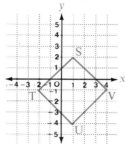

(a)   (b)

4 The mapping for a translation is given by

$$(x, y) \longrightarrow (x + 1, y - 2).$$

Find the co-ordinates of the image of each figure.

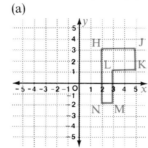

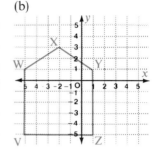

5 Copy and complete the chart for each translation.

	Original point	Image point	Mapping
(a)	(2, 3)	(4, ?)	$(x, y) \longrightarrow (x + ?, y - 3)$
(b)	(5, ?)	(?, 0)	$(x, y) \longrightarrow (x - 2, y + 1)$
(c)	(3, 4)	(−6, ?)	$(x, y) \longrightarrow (x - ?, y - 1)$
(d)	(−7, −8)	(?, −5)	$(x, y) \longrightarrow (x + 1, y + ?)$

B Questions 6 to 16 explore the properties of translation using co-ordinates and are based on these two triangles.

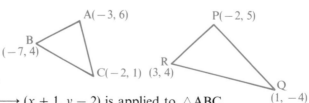

6 A translation given by $(x, y) \longrightarrow (x + 1, y - 2)$ is applied to $\triangle ABC$.
(a) Find the co-ordinates of A′, B′ and C′.
(b) Find the slopes of $\overline{AA'}$, $\overline{BB'}$ and $\overline{CC'}$. What do you notice?

7 A translation given by $(x, y) \longrightarrow (x - 2, y + 3)$ is applied to $\triangle PQR$.
(a) Find the co-ordinates of P′, Q′ and R′.
(b) Find the slopes of $\overline{PP'}$, $\overline{QQ'}$ and $\overline{RR'}$. What do you notice?

8 Use your results in Questions 6 and 7. Write a probable conclusion.

9 Calculate each of the following distances. What do you notice?
(a) $\overline{AA'}$, $\overline{BB'}$ and $\overline{CC'}$ (b) $\overline{PP'}$, $\overline{QQ'}$ and $\overline{RR'}$

10   Use your results in Question 9 to write a probable conclusion.

11   Find the slopes of each pair of sides.
      (a) $\overline{AC}$ and $\overline{A'C'}$, $\overline{AB}$ and $\overline{A'B'}$, $\overline{BC}$ and $\overline{B'C'}$ What do you notice?
      (b) $\overline{PQ}$ and $\overline{P'Q'}$, $\overline{PR}$ and $\overline{P'R'}$, $\overline{QR}$ and $\overline{Q'R'}$ What do you notice?

12   Use your results in Question 11. Write a probable conclusion about the
      slopes of corresponding sides of a figure and its image under a translation.

13   Calculate the lengths of each pair of sides.
      (a) $\overline{AC}$ and $\overline{A'C'}$, $\overline{AB}$ and $\overline{A'B'}$, $\overline{BC}$ and $\overline{B'C'}$ What do you notice?
      (b) $\overline{PQ}$ and $\overline{P'Q'}$, $\overline{PR}$ and $\overline{P'R'}$, $\overline{QR}$ and $\overline{Q'R'}$ What do you notice?

14   Use your results in Question 13. Write a probable conclusion about the lengths
      of corresponding sides of a figure and its image under a translation.

15   Compare the measures of each pair of angles.
      (a) $\angle BAC$ and $\angle B'A'C'$, $\angle ABC$ and $\angle A'B'C'$, $\angle BCA$ and $\angle B'C'A'$
          What do you notice?
      (b) $\angle PQR$ and $\angle P'Q'R'$, $\angle PRQ$ and $\angle P'R'Q'$, $\angle RPQ$ and $\angle R'P'Q'$
          What do you notice?

16   Use your results in Question 15. Write a probable conclusion about the
      corresponding angles of a figure and its image under a translation.

17   A translation given by $(x, y) \longrightarrow (x - 3, y + 4)$ is applied to the square
      with co-ordinates   A(5, −3),   B(9, −1),   C(7, 3)   and   D(3, 1).
      (a) Find the co-ordinates of A′, B′, C′ and D′.
      (b) Test the conclusions that you found in Questions 6 to 16 for this
          translation.

18   (a) Plot the points A(−3, 3), B(2, −2) and C(−6, −3). The **sense** of the
          points A, B, C written in order is **clockwise** (cw) and of A, C, B
          written in order is **counter-clockwise** (ccw).
      (b) Find the co-ordinates of A′, B′ and C′ for the translation
          $(x, y) \longrightarrow (x - 3, y + 2)$.
      (c) Are the points A′, B′ and C′ clockwise or counter-clockwise?
      (d) Choose a polygon of your own. Record the co-ordinates. Repeat
          steps (a) to (c).

19   Use your results in Question 18. Write a probable conclusion about the
      sense of vertices in a figure and its image under a translation.

20   Refer to your results in the previous questions. When a translation is applied to a figure,

▶ what changes?   ▶ what is invariant?

PSP 21   The sum, S, of the first n natural numbers $S = 1 + 2 + 3 + \cdots + n$ is given by $S = \dfrac{n(n + 1)}{2}$.

(a) Find the sum of the first 20 natural numbers.

(b) Use your answer in (a) to help you find the sum $21 + 22 + 23 + \cdots + 49 + 50$.

(c) What is the last digit of the value of $3^{50 + 51 + 52 + \cdots + 499 + 500}$?

C 22   The translation $(x, y) \longrightarrow (x + 2, y - 2)$ is applied to the polygon with co-ordinates A$(-4, 4)$, B$(-8, 4)$, C$(-8, 0)$, D$(-2, -5)$ and E$(2, -1)$.

(a) Find the slopes of $\overline{AE}$ and $\overline{CD}$. What do you notice?

(b) Find the slopes of $\overline{A'E'}$ and $\overline{C'D'}$. What do you notice?

(c) Classify $\triangle ABC$ and $\triangle A'B'C'$. What do you notice?

Calculator Use

Throughout this text, you have been encouraged to use a calculator to do mathematics.

▶ Review the use of each of these keys. Refer to your manual to provide further suggestions on the use of each key.

| $\sqrt{x}$ | $1/x$ | $+/-$ | $\%$ | x^2 | y^x | MS | MR | M+ | M− | π | C | AC | $\sqrt[x]{x}$ |

▶ For each of the above, select an example from the text to illustrate the use of the key. Use the examples to review the keys for future use in mathematics.

From Math History

Throughout the text, you have seen glimpses of the lives and contributions of various people of mathematics. As well you have learned various anecdotes about the mathematics used in history. From the list that follows, choose three people and investigate their lives and contributions. Only last names are provided and the names do not occur in any special order. Cramer, Sylvester, Lagrange, Napier, Ore, Gauss, Birkhoff, Cantor, Klein, Hilbert, Poincare, Noether, Jordan, Newton, Bernoilli, DeMoivre, Hardy, Euler, Hilbert, Shannon, Boole, Peano, Laplace, Möbius, Weyl, Hamilton, Artin, Bolzano, Venn, Fermat, Cauchy, Euclid, Kovalevsky, Pythagoras, Lipschitz, Zermelo, Thales, Archimedes, Dedekind, Leibnitz, Markov, Dantzig, Argand

14.6 Using Co-ordinates: Reflections

For a translation such as $(x, y) \rightarrow (x + 1, y - 2)$, you found that for the original figure and the image figure the following were **invariant** (did not change).

▶ the length of corresponding sides
▶ the slope of corresponding sides
▶ the measure of corresponding angles
▶ the sense of the vertices

In this section you will explore whether these properties are also invariant for reflections.

$\triangle ABC$ is reflected in the y-axis. $\triangle A'B'C'$ is the reflection image of $\triangle ABC$. The co-ordinates of the corresponding vertices are related.

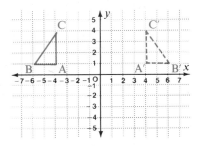

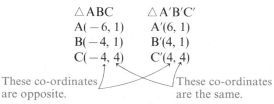

$\triangle ABC$	$\triangle A'B'C'$
$A(-6, 1)$	$A'(6, 1)$
$B(-4, 1)$	$B'(4, 1)$
$C(-4, 4)$	$C'(4, 4)$

These co-ordinates are opposite.   These co-ordinates are the same.

The previous reflection in the y-axis can be shown using mapping notation.

$$(x, y) \longrightarrow (-x, y)$$

PSP   Remember: Ask yourself,
▶ What has changed?
▶ What is invariant?

14.6 Exercise

A Use your skills with co-ordinates to explore the properties of reflections.

1 The line of reflection used is the x-axis.
   (a) Write the co-ordinates of corresponding points.
   (b) How are the x co-ordinates related?
   (c) How are the y co-ordinates related?
   (d) Complete the mapping $(x, y) \longrightarrow (?, ?)$.

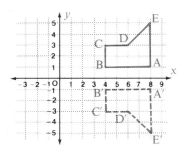

2 Copy and complete the chart for each reflection.

Co-ordinates of original	Co-ordinates of image	Line of reflection
$(4, ?)$	$(?, 5)$	x-axis
$(?, 5)$	$(3, ?)$	y-axis
$(-6, -3)$	$(-6, 3)$	?
$(7, 2)$	$(-7, 2)$	?

B Questions 3 to 15 use your skills with co-ordinate geometry to explore properties of reflections.

3 A triangle is reflected in the y-axis.

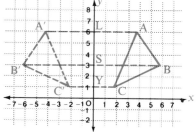

(a) Compare the lengths of $\overline{LA'}$ and $\overline{LA}$, $\overline{SB'}$ and $\overline{SB}$, $\overline{YC'}$ and $\overline{YC}$. What do you notice?

(b) Compare the measures of $\angle A'LS$ and $\angle ALS$, $\angle B'SY$ and $\angle BSY$, $\angle C'YL$ and $\angle CYL$. What do you notice?

4 A triangle is reflected in the x-axis.

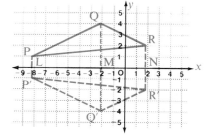

(a) Compare the lengths of $\overline{PL}$ and $\overline{P'L}$, $\overline{QM}$ and $\overline{Q'M}$, $\overline{RN}$ and $\overline{R'N}$. What do you notice?

(b) Find the measures of $\angle PLN$ and $\angle P'LN$, $\angle QMN$ and $\angle Q'MN$, $\angle RNM$ and $\angle R'NM$. What do you notice?

5 Based on the results of Questions 3 and 4, write a probable conclusion about the line of reflection and the line segment joining a point and its image.

6 $\triangle ABC$ has co-ordinates A(2, 7), B(3, 1) and C(−4, 4).

(a) Draw this triangle and reflect it in the y-axis.

(b) Compare the slopes of $\overline{AB}$ and $\overline{A'B'}$, $\overline{BC}$ and $\overline{B'C'}$, $\overline{CA}$ and $\overline{C'A'}$. What do you notice?

(c) Compare the lengths of $\overline{AB}$ and $\overline{A'B'}$, $\overline{BC}$ and $\overline{B'C'}$, $\overline{CA}$ and $\overline{C'A'}$. What do you notice?

(d) Compare the measures of $\angle A$ and $\angle A'$, $\angle B$ and $\angle B'$, $\angle C$ and $\angle C'$. What do you notice?

7 Repeat Question 6 for $\triangle ABC$ except reflect the triangle in the x-axis.

8 Based on your results in Questions 6 and 7, write a probable conclusion about each of the following.

(a) the slopes of corresponding sides of a figure and its image under a reflection in an axis

(b) the lengths of corresponding sides of a figure and its image under a reflection in an axis

(c) the measures of corresponding angles of a figure and its image under a reflection in an axis

9   Square ABCD has co-ordinates A(-4, 3), B(3, 3), C(3, -4) and D(-4, -4).

(a) Draw the image of square ABCD reflected in the x-axis.

(b) Compare the sense of the vertices of the original figure and the image. (Are they clockwise or counter-clockwise?)

(c) Which co-ordinates, x or y, would remain the same when a figure is reflected in the x-axis?

(d) Which co-ordinates, x or y, would remain the same when a figure is reflected in the y-axis?

(e) Which points of the square remain fixed when you reflect it in the x-axis?

(f) Which points of the square would remain fixed when you reflected it in the y-axis?

10 A quadrilateral PQRS has co-ordinates given by P(-6, 5), Q(-4, 8), R(-2, 2) and S(-7, -3).

(a) Draw the figure and reflect it in the y-axis.

(b) Compare the sense of the vertices of the original figure and the image. (Are they clockwise or counter-clockwise?)

(c) Which co-ordinates, x or y, remain the same when reflected in the y-axis?

(d) Which co-ordinates, x or y, would remain the same when reflected in the x-axis?

11 (a) Draw parallelogram ABCD with co-ordinates, A(-4, 2), B(4, 1), C(2, -4) and D(-6, -3). Which sides are parallel?

(b) Reflect parallelogram ABCD in the y-axis.

(c) Compare the slopes of $\overline{A'B'}$ and $\overline{D'C'}$, $\overline{A'D'}$ and $\overline{B'C'}$. What do you notice?

12 Repeat Question 11 except reflect the parallelogram in the x-axis.

13 (a) Refer to your results in the previous questions. When a reflection is applied to a figure,

▶ what changes?   ▶ what is invariant?

(b) Compare the reflection properties with those for translations. Which properties are alike? Which properties differ?

PSP 14 (a) Estimate which of the following pipe systems carries more water. Do not calculate!

System 1: 5 pipes each with a diameter of 10 cm
System 2: 10 pipes each with a diameter of 5 cm

(b) Calculate the answer in (a).

C 15 (a) Mark any parallelogram PQRS on the Cartesian plane.

(b) Reflect the parallelogram in the y-axis.

(c) Compare the slopes of $\overline{P'Q'}$ and $\overline{S'R'}$, $\overline{P'S'}$ and $\overline{Q'R'}$. What do you notice?

Applications: Reflections and Rebounds

You can use your skills with reflections to hit a ball, B, and place it in the hole, H. The edge of the table is used as the line of reflection. The ball, B, cannot go directly to H. You need to do a reflection or a rebound.

Step 1:
Use side $\overline{SY}$.

Step 2:
Find the image H′ by construction.

Step 3:
Shoot the ball at side $\overline{SY}$ to reflect at R.

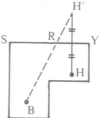

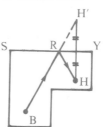

You may need to construct more than one image point to shoot the ball, B, into the hole, H. Locate H″ which is the image of H′. Shoot the ball at H″.

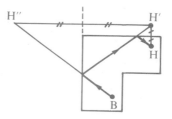

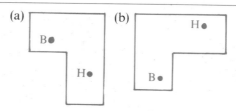

16   Make a copy of each diagram. Show the position of the hole, H, and the ball, B.

▶ Decide on the line of reflection.

▶ Do the needed construction to shoot the ball into the hole in one shot.

17   A grid is placed over each playing surface.

▶ Make a copy of each diagram.

▶ Find the co-ordinates of the points at which the ball must rebound to make a hole-in-one (you sink the ball in one shot).

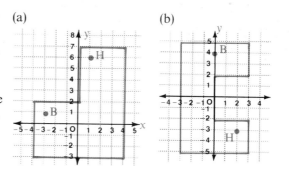

14.7 Rotations and Co-ordinates

In your previous work with rotations, you learned that for each rotation you need to indicate

▶ amount of rotation   ▶ direction of rotation   ▶ rotation centre.

You can use your skills with co-ordinate geometry to explore properties of rotations.

△ABC is rotated and the image triangle is △A'B'C'. Remember to indicate clearly the

▶ amount of rotation
        90°

▶ direction of rotation
        counter-clockwise

▶ rotation centre
        origin

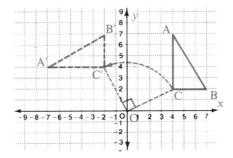

As you explore rotations again ask yourself,

▶ What has changed?   ▶ What is invariant? **PSP**

∠C'OC is referred to as the angle of rotation

14.7 Exercise

A Throughout this exercise, the centre of rotation is the origin.

1. The amount and direction of rotation can be expressed in three different forms. Complete the table.

	$\frac{1}{4}$ turn cw	$-90°$
90° cw (clockwise)		
90° ccw (counter-clockwise)		
180° cw		
180° ccw		

B Questions 2 to 17 explore the properties of rotations.

2. Copy each figure. Draw its image for the given rotation.

(a) $\frac{1}{2}$ turn cw

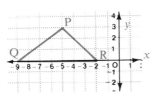

(b) $\frac{1}{2}$ turn ccw

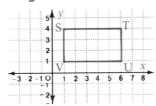

(c) $\frac{1}{4}$ turn ccw

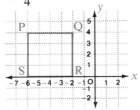

3   Copy each figure. Draw its image for the given rotation.

(a) $+90°$ (b) $-180°$ (c) $-90°$

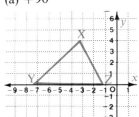   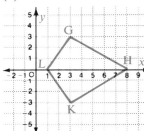   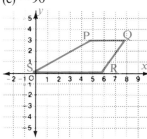

4   For each rotation in Questions 2 and 3 list the co-ordinates of the original figure and its image. Then write a mapping to show the rotation.

5   Use your results in Questions 2 to 4. If a figure is rotated about the origin for each angle of rotation, use a mapping to show the relation.

(a) 90° cw   (b) 90° ccw   (c) 180° cw   (d) 180° ccw

6   Predict the co-ordinates of the image figure for each figure. How can you check your predictions?

(a) 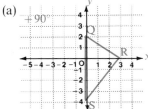   (b)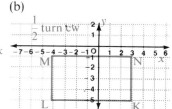

Questions 7 to 9 are based on the diagram at the right.

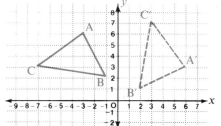

7   (a) Find the measures of $\angle AOA'$, $\angle BOB'$ and $\angle COC'$. What do you notice?

(b) How do the measures in (a) compare to the measure of the angle of rotation?

(c) Compare the lengths of $\overline{OA}$ and $\overline{OA'}$, $\overline{OB}$ and $\overline{OB'}$, $\overline{OC}$ and $\overline{OC'}$. What do you notice?

8   (a) Compare the measures of corresponding angles of the original figure and the image figure. What do you notice?

(b) Compare the measures of corresponding sides of the original figure and the image figure. What do you notice?

(c) Compare the slopes of the corresponding sides of the original figure and the image figure. What do you notice?

(d) Compare the sense of the vertices of the original figure and the image figure. (Are they clockwise or counter-clockwise?)

9   (a) Based on your results, when △ABC is rotated to △A′B′C′
        ▶ what changes?   ▶ what is invariant?
    (b) Test your answers in (a). Use other figures and rotate them.

10 △ABC has co-ordinates A(3, −2), B(7, −3) and C(4, −6). Find the
    co-ordinates of the image of △ABC for each of the following rotations.
    (a) 90° cw   (b) 90° ccw   (c) 180° cw   (d) 180° ccw
    What do you notice about your answers in (c) and (d)?

11 Square ABCD has co-ordinates A(3, 3), B(3, −3), C(−3, −3) and D(−3, 3).
    (a) Rotate the square 90° clockwise about the origin. Plot the image points.
        What do you notice?
    (b) Repeat (a) for each turn.
        ▶ 180° cw   ▶ 270° cw   ▶ 360° cw

12 (a) Repeat the steps of the previous question using rectangle PQRS with
        P(4, 6), Q(4, −6), R(−4, −6) and S(−4, 6).
    (b) How do your results above compare with your results for the square?
        (How are your results alike? How are they different?)

13 How are lines of symmetry related to your results
    (a) for the square in Question 11?   (b) for the rectangle in Question 12?

14 △ABC with vertices A(−4, 1), B(−9, 2) and C(−5, 6) is rotated 180°
    counter-clockwise about the origin.
    (a) Find the co-ordinates of A′, B′ and C′.
    (b) Compare the slopes of $\overline{AB}$ and $\overline{A′B′}$, $\overline{BC}$ and $\overline{B′C′}$, $\overline{AC}$ and $\overline{A′C′}$. What
        do you notice?

15 △DEF with vertices D(5, 1), E(8, −3) and F(3, −3) is rotated 90°
    clockwise about the origin.
    (a) Find the co-ordinates of D′, E′ and F′.
    (b) Compare the slopes of $\overline{DE}$ and $\overline{D′E′}$, $\overline{DF}$ and $\overline{D′F′}$, $\overline{EF}$ and $\overline{E′F′}$.
        What do you notice?
    (c) Repeat steps (a) and (b) except rotate △DEF in a counter-clockwise direction.

16 (a) Based on your results in Questions 14 and 15, write a probable conclusion.
    (b) How would you test your work in (a)?

17 Refer to your results in the previous questions. When a rotation is applied
    to a figure,
    ▶ what changes?   ▶ what is invariant?

Applications: Tiling Patterns

A design in which one or more polygons are used to cover a plane is called a **tiling pattern**.

In this design the basic shape is an isosceles triangle. Translation and reflection are used to create the tiling pattern.

In this design a rhombus and an equilateral triangle are the basic shapes. Reflections are used to create the tiling pattern.

You can apply your skills with transformations to create designs. Many people have used tiling patterns to create art. Maurits Cornelis Escher (1898–1972) used skills in geometry to create his world famous art.

To create a tiling pattern based on Escher's work, follow these steps.

▶ Start with a grid.　　▶ Use the grid and repeat a construction.　　▶ Add some design and detail.

 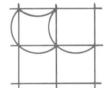 

18 Use two of these shapes. Create a tiling pattern. Repeat with two other shapes.

19 (a) How many different shapes can be made using 4 squares sharing at least 1 common side?

   (b) Which of the shapes in (a) can be used to tile a plane?

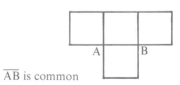

$\overline{AB}$ is common

20 Choose your own grid pattern. Create an "Escher" type tiling pattern.

14.8 Glide Reflections

So far in your study of transformations, you have explored the properties of translations, reflections and rotations when they have been applied to a figure.

What if you apply more than one transformation to a figure?

A **glide reflection** is an example of a transformation that is a combination of two transformations. In a glide reflection, a figure is translated and then the image is reflected in a reflection line parallel to the translation as shown by the following.

Step 1: A translation given by

$$(x, y) \rightarrow (x + 3, y)$$

is applied to $\triangle XYZ$.

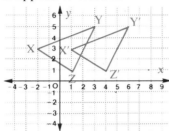

Step 2: The translation is followed by a reflection in the x-axis.

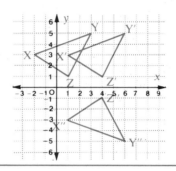

14.8 Exercise

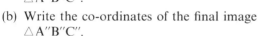

B Use your skills with co-ordinates to explore the properties of glide reflections.

1. (a) *Step 1:*
   Find the image $\triangle A'B'C'$ of $\triangle ABC$ if it is translated by the mapping $(x, y) \rightarrow (x, y - 3)$.

   Step 2:
   Then reflect the image in the y-axis to obtain $\triangle A''B''C''$.

   (b) Write the co-ordinates of the final image $\triangle A''B''C''$.

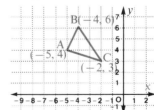

2. (a) Draw the final image of $\triangle PQR$ for the glide reflection given by the translation $(x, y) \rightarrow (x - 5, y)$ followed by a reflection in the x-axis.

   (b) Measure and compare $\angle P$ and $\angle P''$, $\angle Q$ and $\angle Q''$, $\angle R$ and $\angle R''$. What do you notice?

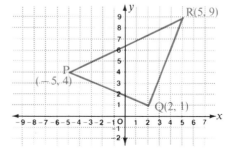

(c) Measure and compare the lengths of sides $\overline{PQ}$ and $\overline{P''Q''}$, $\overline{QR}$ and $\overline{Q''R''}$, $\overline{RP}$ and $\overline{R''P''}$. What do you notice?

(d) Calculate and compare the slopes of sides $\overline{PQ}$ and $\overline{P''Q''}$, $\overline{QR}$ and $\overline{Q''R''}$, $\overline{RP}$ and $\overline{R''P''}$. What do you notice?

(e) Compare the sense of the vertices of $\triangle PQR$ and $\triangle P''Q''R''$. (Are they clockwise or counter-clockwise?)

3   What if you reverse the steps in the previous questions? Try it. Repeat the steps except apply the reflection first followed by the translation. What do you notice?

4   A glide reflection is defined by the translation $(x, y) \rightarrow (x, y + 4)$ followed by a reflection in the y-axis.

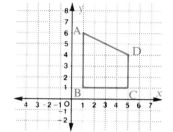

(a) Draw the final image of the quadrilateral ABCD.

(b) Find the lengths of corresponding sides of ABCD and its image. What do you notice?

(c) Find the measures of corresponding angles of the quadrilateral and its image. What do you notice?

(d) Find the slopes of corresponding sides of the quadrilateral and its image. What do you notice?

(e) Compare the sense of the vertices of the original figure and its image.

5   What if you reverse the steps in the previous question? Try it. Repeat the steps except apply the reflection first followed by the translation. What do you notice?

6   Refer to your results in the previous questions. When a glide reflection is applied to a figure,
   ► what changes?   ► what is invariant?

Computer Use

You have learned various strategies for problem solving. The computer is an invaluable aid for exploring some aspects of mathematics as well as for performing repeated tedious calculations.

► Make a list of the various ways in which computers have been used to help you explore problems as well as do calculations.

► Continue to find out more about computers and their applications, especially their use in mathematics.

14.9 Dilatations and Co-ordinates

When a polygon is translated, reflected or rotated, the resulting image polygon is congruent to the original polygon. For this reason, these transformations are often called **congruence transformations.**

In this section you will explore the properties of a **dilatation**.

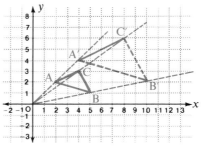

The diagram shows how $\triangle ABC$ is related to $\triangle A'B'C'$ by the mapping $(x, y) \rightarrow (2x, 2y)$.

The 2 in the mapping $(x, y) \rightarrow (2x, 2y)$ is the **scale factor** or **dilatation factor**.

The origin is the **dilatation centre**.

The size of the image has changed but the shape seems to be the same. The dilatation is *not* a congruence transformation.

Again as you explore dilatations ask yourself,

▶ What has changed?   ▶ What is invariant? **PSP**

14.9 Exercise

A Use your skills with co-ordinates to explore the properties of dilatations.

1   Each of the following are sets of points in the original figure and the image for a dilatation. Use the pattern. Find the missing co-ordinates.

(a) $(1, 3) \rightarrow (2, 6)$
$(-2, 5) \rightarrow (-4, 10)$
$(-2, 1) \rightarrow (?, 2)$
$(x, y) \rightarrow (?, ?)$

(b) $(-2, -4) \rightarrow (1, 2)$
$(6, -2) \rightarrow (-3, ?)$
$(?, -4) \rightarrow (1, ?)$
$(x, y) \rightarrow (?, ?)$

(c) $(3, 0) \rightarrow (1\frac{1}{2}, 0)$
$(2, -1) \rightarrow (?, -\frac{1}{2})$
$(5, 2) \rightarrow (?, ?)$
$(x, y) \rightarrow (?, ?)$

2   What is the dilatation factor for each of the dilatations in Question 1?

3   Copy each figure and draw its image for the given dilatation.

(a) $(x, y) \rightarrow \left(\frac{1}{2}x, \frac{1}{2}y\right)$

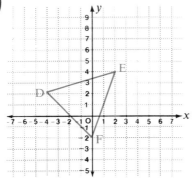

(b) $(x, y) \rightarrow (3x, 3y)$

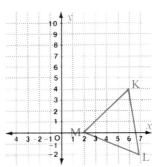

B Questions 4 to 9 are based on the diagram. A dilatation $(x, y) \rightarrow (2x, 2y)$ is applied to $\triangle ABC$ to obtain the image $\triangle A'B'C'$.

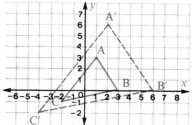

4 (a) Compare the lengths of $\overline{AC}$ and $\overline{A'C'}$, $\overline{BC}$ and $\overline{B'C'}$, $\overline{AB}$ and $\overline{A'B'}$. What do you notice?

   (b) Compare the ratios $\dfrac{A'B'}{AB}$, $\dfrac{A'C'}{AC}$, and $\dfrac{B'C'}{BC}$.

What do you notice?

5 (a) Compare the measures of corresponding angles. What do you notice?

   (b) Compare the areas of the triangles. What do you notice?

6 (a) Use your results in Questions 4 and 5. Why can you write $\triangle ABC \sim \triangle A'B'C'$ ($\triangle ABC$ is similar to $\triangle A'B'C'$)?

   (b) Write a probable conclusion about your results.

7 (a) Compare the lengths of $\overline{OA}$ and $\overline{OA'}$, $\overline{OB}$ and $\overline{OB'}$, $\overline{OC}$ and $\overline{OC'}$. What do you notice?

   (b) How is your answer in (a) related to your answer in Question 4?

   (c) Write a probable conclusion about your results.

8 (a) Compare the slopes of $\overline{AC}$ and $\overline{A'C'}$, $\overline{AB}$ and $\overline{A'B'}$, $\overline{BC}$ and $\overline{B'C'}$. What do you notice?

   (b) Write a probable conclusion about your results.

9 Compare the sense of the vertices of the original and image triangle. (Are they clockwise or counter-clockwise?)

10 $\triangle DEF$ has vertices D(2, 8), E(4, 4) and F(10, 2).

   (a) Find the co-ordinates of $\triangle D'E'F'$ if the dilatation is given by $(x, y) \rightarrow \left(\dfrac{1}{2}x, \dfrac{1}{2}y\right)$.

   (b) Compare the lengths of corresponding sides. What do you notice?

   (c) Compare the measures of corresponding angles. What do you notice?

   (d) Compare the slopes of corresponding sides. What do you notice?

   (e) What is the dilatation factor?

   (f) What other lengths in your diagram are reduced by the dilatation factor in (e)?

   (g) Compare the sense of the vertices for the original and image triangle.

   (h) Compare the areas of the original triangle and the image triangle.

11 Refer to your results in the previous questions. When a dilatation is applied to a figure,

   ▶ what changes?   ▶ what is invariant?

14.10 Testing for Transformations

The properties of transformations that you have found can be used to determine which transformation or transformations have been applied to a figure.

Example (a) What type of transformation maps $\triangle ABC$ onto $\triangle A'B'C'$? Be sure to give any information needed to identify the transformation.

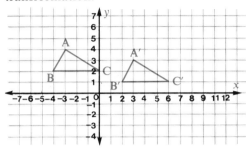

(b) What is the mapping for the transformation?

Solution (a) **PSP** Think: From the diagram, it appears that the transformation is a translation. Examine the properties of the image and original figure. Then you can determine the transformation.

▶ Since corresponding sides are equal in length, it is not a dilatation.

▶ Since the slopes of corresponding sides are equal, it is not a reflection, a glide reflection or a 90° rotation.

▶ Since the sense of the corresponding vertices is the same, it is not a reflection.

Thus the transformation is a translation.

(b) The transformation is the translation given by the mapping $(x, y) \rightarrow (x + 6, y - 1)$.

PSP Think: Is my answer reasonable?
Check: $A(-3, 4) \rightarrow A'(3, 3)$
$B(-4, 2) \rightarrow B'(2, 1)$
$C(0, 2) \rightarrow C'(6, 1)$ ✓

For translations, reflections and rotations, the lengths of corresponding sides are congruent. Any transformation that preserves length is an **isometry**.

Many words in mathematics derive their meaning from Greek. Isometry is from Greek, *isos* meaning same and *metria* meaning measure.

For an isometry, the original figure and the image are congruent. A dilatation is not an isometry since corresponding sides are not equal in length. The original figure and the image for a dilatation are similar in shape but not congruent.

14.10　Exercise

A　In Question 1 you are asked to summarize the properties of transformations. This is a useful skill for making comparisons to learn and remember properties.

1　Copy and complete the chart for translations, reflections, rotations, dilatations and glide reflections. Use true (T) or false (F).

		Translations	Reflections
(a)	Corresponding sides are congruent.		
(b)	Corresponding angles are congruent.		
(c)	Slopes of corresponding sides are equal.		
(d)	The sense of the vertices is preserved.		
(e)	The image figure is congruent to the original figure.		
(f)	The transformation is related to a line of symmetry.		
(g)	The transformation is related to a centre.		

B 2　For each diagram, the original and image figure are given. Identify and describe the transformation.

(a)

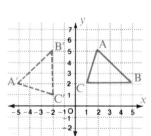

(b)

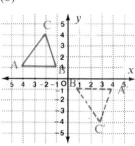

(c)

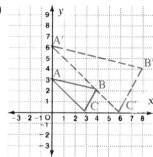

(d)

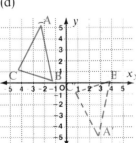

(e)

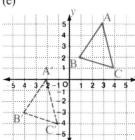

(f)

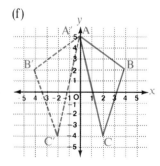

3　(a) For which transformations in Question 2 is the original triangle congruent to the image triangle?

　　(b) Which of the above transformations are isometries?

4 Apply the following transformation to △ABC to find the image △A′B′C′. Determine which type of transformation is represented.

(a) $(x, y) \rightarrow (x - 2, y + 2)$ (b) $(x, y) \rightarrow (x, -y)$

(c) $(x, y) \rightarrow \left(\dfrac{1}{2}x, \dfrac{1}{2}y\right)$ (d) $(x, y) \rightarrow (-y, x)$

(e) $(x, y) \rightarrow (x - 3, y)$ and then reflected in the x-axis

(f) reflected in the y-axis and then $(x, y) \rightarrow (x, y + 4)$

5 Refer to your results in the previous question.
   (a) For which transformations is △ABC congruent to its image triangle?
   (b) Which of the transformations are isometries?

6 Transformations have been applied to △ABC and to polygon PQRSTU.
   (a) Describe each transformation related to △ABC.
   (b) Describe each transformation related to polygon PQRSTU.

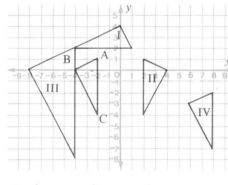

7 Which of the transformations in Question 6 are isometries?

8 Which does not belong? agemi gurefi xtreve strabuct ranantivi

Math Tip: The Next Step

▶ Many of the strategies and suggestions for solving problems can be used in your work later in mathematics. Summarize them in a list now. When you solve a problem, you must organize your planning and your thoughts.

Complete the various steps of your *Problem Solving Plan* **PSP** for use at a later time.

▶ Throughout this text, you were encouraged to record new math words and to illustrate them with an example. Keep all of these for your future study of mathematics. How complete is your list?

14.11 Distortions on a Grid

You can distort the shape of a figure in many ways if you use distorted grids as follows.

Start with a figure.

A

Use a larger grid B to magnify the figure.

B

You can use a smaller grid C to reduce the figure.

C

Use a grid D that has been stretched horizontally.

D

Use a grid E that has been stretched vertically.

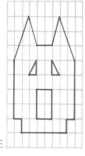

E

You can also use a mapping to describe a distortion.

Square ABCD has co-ordinates A(-2, 0), B(0, 2), C(2, 0) and D(0, -2).

Find the image figure for the transformation $(x, y) \rightarrow \left(2x, \dfrac{1}{2}y\right)$.

Plot the original figure.

Plot the image A'B'C'D'.

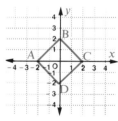

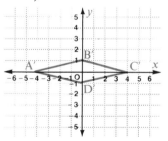

14.11 Exercise

B Use grids and co-ordinate axes to draw the following distortions.

1   Draw a distorted image of each figure.

(a) Use grid D.

(b) Use grid E.

(c) Use grid C.

(d) Use grid E.

2 Make a larger copy of the distorted grid. Use the grid to copy each figure.

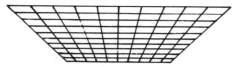

(a)

(b)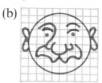

3 Make a larger copy of the distorted grid. Use the grid to copy each figure.

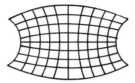

(a)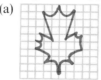

(b)

4 Make a larger copy of the distorted grid. Use the grid to copy each figure.

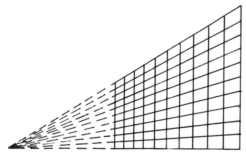

(a)

(b)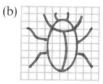

5 Figure ABCD is given with co-ordinates A(0, 4), B(6, 4), C(6, 0) and D(0, 0).
(a) Plot figure ABCD.
(b) Predict the effect on figure ABCD if you apply the mapping $(x, y) \rightarrow (\frac{1}{2}x, y)$.
(c) Apply the mapping to figure ABCD and plot figure A'B'C'D'. How close was your prediction?

6 Figure PQRS is given by the co-ordinates P(−6, 1), Q(1, 8), R(5, 4) and S(−2, −3).
(a) Predict the effect on the figure if you apply the mapping $(x, y) \rightarrow (x, \frac{3}{2}y)$.
(b) Find the co-ordinates of P', Q', R' and S'. Draw the image. How close was your prediction?

7 Figure ABCD is given by the co-ordinates A(−2, 0), B(3, 6), C(11, 6) and D(6, 0)
(a) Predict the effect on figure ABCD if you apply the mapping $(x, y) \rightarrow (\frac{1}{2}x, 2y)$.
(b) Draw the image A'B'C'D'. How close was your prediction?

14.12 The Half Turn

You can use your skills with co-ordinates to explore
properties of special relations. A half turn (180°) can be
clockwise or counter-clockwise. When you apply a half
turn about the point O to △PQR, you obtain the image
△P′Q′R′. To explore properties ask yourself,

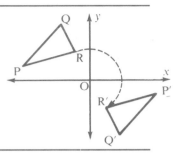

▶ What has changed?　　▶ What is invariant?

The exercise explores the properties of a half turn.

14.12 Exercise

B 1 $\overline{AB}$ is given by the co-ordinates A(4, 6) and B(−2, 1). A half turn about the
origin is applied to $\overline{AB}$. Find the slope of $\overline{AB}$ and $\overline{A'B'}$. What do you notice?

2 (a) Find the image of $\overline{CD}$ and of $\overline{EF}$ when a half turn is applied about the origin.
　　$\overline{CD}$　C(3, −5) D(−2, 1)　　　$\overline{EF}$　E(−3, −4) F(5, 2)
(b) Find the slopes of each line segment and its image. What do you notice?

3 △STU is given by the co-ordinates S(2, −1), T(6, −2) and U(1, −3). A
half turn clockwise about the origin is applied to △STU. Find the slopes
of $\overline{ST}$ and $\overline{S'T'}$, $\overline{TU}$ and $\overline{T'U'}$, $\overline{SU}$ and $\overline{S'U'}$. What do you notice?

4 Based on your results, write a probable conclusion about the slope of a
line segment and its image after a half turn about the origin.

5 Figure PQRS has co-ordinates P(−1, 0), Q(−2, −3), R(−5, −4) and
S(−4, −1). A half turn about the origin is applied to the figure.
(a) What has not been affected by the rotation?　　(b) What has changed?

6 $\overline{RS}$ is given by the co-ordinates R(0, 6) and S(−6, −1). A half turn about
the origin is applied to $\overline{RS}$. Compare the measures of $\overline{OR}$ and $\overline{OR'}$, $\overline{OS}$
and $\overline{OS'}$. What do you notice?

7 (a) Figure STRV, with co-ordinates S(5, 3), T(8, 0), R(5, −3) and V(2, 0) is
　　rotated 180° clockwise about the origin.　　Find the image.
(b) M(4, 2) is on the original figure. What are the co-ordinates of M′?
(c) Find the length of $\overline{OM}$ and $\overline{OM'}$. What do you notice?
(d) Choose any point, P, on the figure. Calculate the lengths $\overline{OP}$ and $\overline{OP'}$.
　　What do you notice?

8 Based on your results in the previous questions, list the properties of a
half turn applied to a figure about a point.

Year-End Review

1. Simplify each of the following.
   (a) $[4(-8)] \div [4(-4)]$
   (b) $-3(-8 \div 2) - 9$
   (c) $\dfrac{-9(6) \div (-3)}{(-3)(3)}$
   (d) $\dfrac{(12-4)(-12)(-4)}{[(-2)(-2)]^2}$
   (e) $4^2 - 3^2 - 2^2 \div (4-3-2)^2$
   (f) $-160 \div (4) + 2[-3(8-4)]$

2. Calculate.
   (a) 3^0
   (b) 2^{-3}
   (c) $(2^3)^0$
   (d) 3^{-1}
   (e) $\dfrac{1}{3^{-2}}$
   (f) $\left(\dfrac{1}{2}\right)^{-2}$
   (g) $\dfrac{1}{(-2)^{-3}}$
   (h) $\dfrac{1}{3^{-3}}$
   (i) $2^{-3} \times 2^2$
   (j) -2^4
   (k) $3^{-1} + 3^{-2}$
   (l) $2^{-2} + 2^{-3} - 2^2$

3. (a) Calculate a decimal for $\dfrac{18}{999}$ and for $\dfrac{120}{999}$. What do you notice about your answers?

   (b) Use the pattern in your answers in (a) to predict a decimal for $\dfrac{456}{999}$.

   (c) Check your prediction in (b) by calculating the decimal for $\dfrac{456}{999}$.

4. Find the length of the path XY if $a = 3$ and $b = -1$.

5. Find the solution set for each of the following.
   (a) $\dfrac{x}{15} - \dfrac{x}{10} = x + \dfrac{31}{15}$
   (b) $89 + (x + 5)^2 = (x - 5)(x - 6)$

6. (a) A rectangle is four times as long as it is wide. The perimeter is 120 m. Find the dimensions of the rectangle.
   (b) Find the length of the diagonal.

7. You wish to paint all the surfaces of each shape. Which shape would require the most paint?

   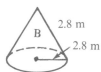

   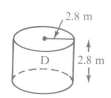

8   A rough sketch of a figure is shown. Construct the figure accurately using a straight-edge and compasses.

9   Simplify each of the following.
(a) $y(y - 3) + 5(y + 5)$ (b) $2y(2y - 1) + 3(y - 6)$
(c) $-3x(2x - 1) + 5(3x - 6)$ (d) $-4x(2x - 3) - 5(x - 7)$
(e) $2(x - 4)(x + 5) - 3(x + 5)(x - 2)$ (f) $x^2 + 2(x - 1)(x + 2) - 3(x^2 - 1)$

10   (a) Construct $\triangle ABC$ so that $\angle ABC = 45°$, $\angle ACB = 60°$ and $\overline{BC} = 6$ cm.
     (b) Measure the remaining sides.   (c) Construct the median from A to $\overline{BC}$.

11   Show that A$(-2, 5)$, B$(0, 2)$ and C$(4, -4)$ are collinear.

12   At a sale John paid $54.70 including 5% sales tax for a record player.
     (a) Find the sale price of the record player.
     (b) If the discount given at the sale was 25%, find the original selling price of the record player.

13   Harry and Bill live 190 km apart and start toward each other on mini-bikes. After 5 h they meet. If Bill travels 2 km/h faster than Harry, how fast do they drive their mini-bikes?

14   (a) Find an expression for the perimeter of the rectangle.
     (b) If the perimeter of the rectangle is less than 42 units, what are the possible dimensions of the rectangle $r \in W$?

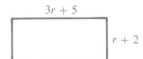

15   The area of a square is $25x^2y^2$. Find an expression for the sides.

16   The area of a rectangle is $4x^2 - 8x$. If the length is $4x$, find an expression for the width.

17   Decide on the most effective way of showing the following information using a graph. Give reasons for your choice. The average price of a share on a stock market each month is shown.

January	$23.50	May	$20.50	September	$20.50
February	$21.00	June	$20.75	October	$21.50
March	$21.50	July	$20.00	November	$22.00
April	$21.50	August	$19.50	December	$22.75

18   A mapping for a translation is given by $(x, y) \rightarrow (x + 1, y + 2)$. Find the co-ordinates of the image of a square ABCD with vertices A$(5, 2)$, B$(-1, 2)$, C$(-1, -4)$ and D$(5, -4)$.

Table of Square Roots: 1 to 100

n	$\sqrt{n}$	n	$\sqrt{n}$	n	$\sqrt{n}$	n	$\sqrt{n}$	n	$\sqrt{n}$
1	1.000	21	4.583	41	6.403	61	7.810	81	9.000
2	1.414	22	4.690	42	6.481	62	7.874	82	9.055
3	1.732	23	4.796	43	6.557	63	7.937	83	9.110
4	2.000	24	4.899	44	6.633	64	8.000	84	9.165
5	2.236	25	5.000	45	6.708	65	8.062	85	9.220
6	2.449	26	5.099	46	6.782	66	8.124	86	9.274
7	2.646	27	5.196	47	6.856	67	8.185	87	9.327
8	2.828	28	5.292	48	6.928	68	8.246	88	9.381
9	3.000	29	5.385	49	7.000	69	8.307	89	9.434
10	3.162	30	5.477	50	7.071	70	8.367	90	9.487
11	3.317	31	5.568	51	7.141	71	8.426	91	9.539
12	3.464	32	5.657	52	7.211	72	8.485	92	9.592
13	3.606	33	5.745	53	7.280	73	8.544	93	9.644
14	3.742	34	5.831	54	7.348	74	8.602	94	9.695
15	3.873	35	5.916	55	7.416	75	8.660	95	9.747
16	4.000	36	6.000	56	7.483	76	8.718	96	9.798
17	4.123	37	6.083	57	7.550	77	8.775	97	9.849
18	4.243	38	6.164	58	7.616	78	8.832	98	9.899
19	4.359	39	6.245	59	7.681	79	8.888	99	9.950
20	4.472	40	6.325	60	7.746	80	8.944	100	10.000

Table of Random Digits: 000 to 999

```
302 068 416 505 346 808 242 349 956 892 265 546 092 488 336 201 057 728 343 640 895 202 076 619 431
809 229 534 531 633 874 682 353 794 607 039 713 764 623 563 527 794 604 069 799 480 655 454 224 163
186 408 090 103 644 774 892 279 486 409 124 305 294 429 903 019 884 456 332 049 041 294 453 190 852
806 288 827 206 422 754 358 536 443 239 557 307 438 468 847 699 863 930 558 362 302 114 600 193 879
561 451 088 502 255 677 218 380 672 059 585 703 955 914 203 172 855 871 751 277 363 227 400 302 089
296 316 999 001 673 088 446 143 823 127 813 138 477 779 987 249 241 394 580 874 690 595 366 060 061
221 135 036 015 710 844 616 339 385 911 155 745 130 754 364 167 217 550 050 439 443 283 754 354 725
430 842 575 965 692 648 655 436 558 359 446 124 353 779 993 137 282 748 196 546 096 829 270 129 882
503 267 339 408 077 922 397 456 309 538 363 219 371 222 088 567 664 162 373 300 066 188 585 699 847
690 599 249 213 883 471 946 899 126 718 609 101 208 604 067 056 378 576 968 645 745 125 508 483 546
078 998 022 103 730 287 923 410 168 418 591 504 309 563 533 573 862 948 933 626 641 878 595 382 790
711 796 541 265 500 140 801 419 617 350 978 444 204 287 951 998 038 981 383 818 013 289 767 711 802
411 225 172 869 786 814 095 987 251 378 566 619 428 951 992 157 907 064 933 622 526 816 046 626 637
999 007 478 742 047 998 025 258 954 941 793 637 992 160 607 025 588 592 470 924 432 766 677 204 298
149 041 487 362 290 698 826 199 210 812 144 745 128 920 333 065 536 458 418 560 413 323 549 014 078
941 803 385 926 480 667 090 042 646 721 540 313 826 200 106 767 700 872 736 123 213 840 516 795 588
615 285 952 978 427 986 278 465 689 568 692 653 499 104 882 503 277 364 189 704 996 071 799 476 805
321 695 739 031 609 100 017 494 079 630 787 765 654 490 242 316 977 462 560 408 088 397 449 001 566
632 824 147 265 515 749 243 219 357 583 790 693 680 304 186 414 392 711 800 450 046 541 252 511 600
200 126 688 537 408 095 966 671 046 805 328 287 934 643 824 144 697 781 919 316 984 306 322 609 097
646 731 247 079 565 585 704 983 331 089 341 511 595 362 281 674 118 584 737 092 281 670 003 723 473
954 929 546 095 971 570 767 720 560 424 884 676 176 634 903 025 314 868 829 268 269 193 821 078 936
691 612 211 948 938 737 091 201 067 018 430 848 725 407 033 263 665 129 825 160 592 464 676 193 894
229 532 601 165 011 926 466 746 161 487 368 029 354 723 485 471 969 612 194 779 977 450 051 700 872
718 606 002 809 224 094 775 906 046 650 615 288 889 348 919 321 687 505 369 072 601 167 295 407 033
```

Glossary

This glossary is a quick reference for the meanings of certain selected words and phrases that you need to know while doing mathematics. For some words and phrases, a diagram or example is provided.

► The use of this glossary should be combined with references to the *index* at the back of this text.

► Throughout this text, *Math Tips* suggest that you compile your own vocabulary list. Your vocabulary list, together with this glossary, will provide you with a useful dictionary to help you now, as well as in your advanced mathematics studies. *You cannot do or speak mathematics if you do not know the meanings of words.* Learn the vocabulary well.

abscissa: the horizontal or *x* co-ordinate of an ordered pair on the Cartesian Plane.

acute angle: an angle with measure between $0°$ and $90°$.

acute triangle: a triangle in which each angle measures less than $90°$.

additive inverse: the additive inverse of a number n is the number $-n$ so that $n + (-n) = 0$.

adjacent angles: a pair of angles sharing a common vertex and ray with no intersection of interior points.

alternate angles: $\angle 4$, $\angle 6$ and $\angle 3$, $\angle 5$ are pairs of alternate angles.

altitude of a triangle: the perpendicular distance from a base to the opposite vertex.

angle: a figure formed by two rays with a common end point.

approximate number: a number obtained by rounding a decimal number.

arc: a part of a curve; for a circle, a part of its circumference.

area: the number of square units needed to cover a surface.

average: the average of n numbers is the sum of the numbers divided by n; also called the arithmetic mean or mean.

axes (singular **axis**): the intersecting number lines or scales of a graph.

axis of symmetry: see *line of symmetry*.

bar graph: a diagram that uses bars to display data or information.

base (of a polygon): any side may be referred to as a base; in a triangle the base is usually the side to which an altitude is drawn.

base (of a power): the number that is the repeated factor in a power.

binomial: an algebraic expression with two terms.

bisector (of an angle): a ray or line that bisects an angle into two congruent angles.

bisector of line segment: a line that divides a line segment into two congruent parts.

broken-line graph: a graph that displays data by joining points representing data with line segments.

capacity: the amount of substance a container can hold (the amount of space enclosed).

central angle: the angle formed by any two radii.

centre (of a circle): the point that is the same distance from any point on the circle.

chord (of a circle): a line segment joining any two points on the circle.

circle: a closed figure such that all of its points are the same distance from a fixed point, the centre.

circle graph: a diagram that uses a circle to display data or information.

circumference: the distance around a circle.

coefficient: the numerical coefficient is the numerical part of a term; e.g. 5 in $5xy$; the literal coefficient is the letter part of a term; e.g. xy in $5xy$.

common factor: a number or variable that divides evenly into two or more terms.

complementary angles: a pair of angles for which the sum of their measures is $90°$.

composite number: a number with three or more factors.

concurrent: having a point in common; a point at which three or more lines intersect.

congruence transformation: a transformation for which the original and image figures are congruent.

congruent figures: figures that have the same shape and size.

corresponding angles: pairs of corresponding angles are given by $\angle 2$, $\angle 6$; $\angle 4$, $\angle 8$; $\angle 7$, $\angle 3$; and so on.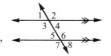

cube root: a cube root of a number is a number which, when cubed, produces the given number.

data: facts or pieces of information.

deduction: a conclusion based on data obtained by a process of reasoning.

degree (Celsius): a unit for measuring temperature; 45°C means forty-five degrees Celsius.

degree (measure of an angle): a unit for measuring an angle. 1° is 1/360 of a complete turn.

degree of a monomial: the sum of the exponents of the literal factors making up the term; e.g. the degree of $2a^3bc$ is 5.

degree of a polynomial: the greatest degree of the degrees of its terms; e.g. the degree of $3x^4 + 2x^2 - 8x$ is 4.

diagonal: in a polygon, a line segment that joins two vertices that are not adjacent.

diameter: a line segment containing the centre of the circle with endpoints on the circle.

dilatation: a transformation for which the original and image figures are similar.

distributive property: for all real numbers, a, b, c
$a(b + c) = ab + ac \quad (b + c)a = ba + ca$.

equation: a statement showing equality.

equiangular triangle: a triangle in which all angles have equal measures.

equilateral triangle: a triangle in which all sides have equal measures; a triangle with three lines of symmetry.

equivalent decimals: decimal numbers that represent the same number.

equivalent equations: equations that have the same solution set.

equivalent expressions: expressions that represent the same number for the same value of the variable(s); e.g. $5x$ and $3x + 2x$ are equivalent expressions for all values of x.

equivalent fractions: fractions that name the same number.

equivalent ratios: ratios that name the same simplest-form ratio.

exponent: a number that shows the number of times equal factors are multiplied; e.g. 2^3 means to multiply 3 equal factors of 2

face: a flat or plane surface of a polyhedron.

factor: any number or variable that evenly divides a term is a factor of the term; the factors of $2xy$ are 2, x and y.

factored form: an expression in which the terms are written as a product of factors; e.g. $2(a + 3b)$ is the factored form of $2a + 6b$.

formula: a concise statement or equation written in mathematical symbols used to express a relationship existing among quantities.

frequency: for a set of data, the number of items in a specified category.

frequency table: a diagram used to record the frequency for a set of data.

graph: a display of information or data using a pictorial method; see *bar graph*, *broken-line graph*, *circle graph*.

greatest common factor: the greatest number or variable that divides evenly into two or more terms.

hypotenuse: the side opposite the right angle in a right triangle.

identity: an equation which is true for every value of the variable; e.g. $2(x + 3) = 4x - 2x + 6$ is an identity.

identity (operation): for addition, 0 is the identity since for any number k, $0 + k = k$; for multiplication, 1 is the identity since for any number k, $1 \times k = k$.

image: the figure produced by a transformation.

improper fraction: a fraction in which the numerator is greater than the denominator.

inequality: a statement that one quantity or expression is not equal to another quantity or expression.

inequation: a statement showing inequality.

integer: one of the numbers of the set $\{\ldots, -3, -2, -1, 0, +1, +2, +3, \ldots\}$.

integral factor: a factor that is an integer.

interest: money earned or paid for investing or borrowing money.

intersecting lines: lines with a point in common.

inverse operations: addition and subtraction are inverse operations; multiplication and division are also inverse operations.

irrational number: a number that is not rational; a number when expressed as a decimal does not terminate or repeat; see *rational number*.

isosceles triangle: a triangle with 2 sides of equal measure; a triangle with one line of symmetry.

kite: a quadrilateral with two pairs of equal adjacent sides.

like terms: terms that have the same literal coefficient.

line of reflection: a line that is used to obtain the reflection image.

line of symmetry: a line that divides a figure into two congruent parts; also referred to as axis of symmetry or mirror line; a figure with a line of symmetry is said to have reflectional symmetry.

lowest terms: a fraction or rational is in lowest terms if the numerator and denominator have only the number 1 as a common factor.

mean: see *average*.

measure of central tendency: a measure that shows how data are clustered to show trends; see *mean, median, mode*.

median: the middle value of a set of data; the line segment joining a vertex of a triangle to the midpoint of the opposite side.

mirror line: see *line of symmetry*.

mode: the member of a set of data that occurs most frequently.

monomial: an algebraic expression with one term.

multiplicative inverse: the multiplicative inverse of a non-zero number k is the number $\frac{1}{k}$ for which $k \times \frac{1}{k} = 1$; also called reciprocal.

negative of a number: for any number a, $-a$ is the negative of the number.

obtuse angle: an angle with measure between $90°$ and $180°$.

obtuse triangle: a triangle with an obtuse angle.

ordinate: the vertical or y-co-ordinate of an ordered pair on the Cartesian Plane.

origin: the point at which the horizontal or x-axis and the vertical or y-axis intersect.

outcome: a result obtained in an experiment, etc.

parallel lines: two lines in the same plane that do not have any points in common.

parallelogram: a quadrilateral with opposite sides parallel.

perimeter: the distance around a closed figure; for a circle, its circumference.

perpendicular bisector: a line that bisects a line segment and meets it at a right angle.

perpendicular lines: two or more lines that meet at right angles.

polygon: a simple closed figure made of line segments; special names are used for polygons: pentagon (5 sides); hexagon (6 sides); septagon (7 sides); octagon (8 sides).

polynomial: an algebraic expression.

pre-image point: a point to which a transformation is applied.

prime factors: factors of a number that are prime; see *prime number, factor*.

prime number: a number evenly divisible only by 1 and itself.

principal square root: the positive square root of a number.

probability: the numerical measure of the likelihood that an event will happen; the number of favourable outcomes divided by the number of possible outcomes.

proportion: an equation that shows the equality of two ratios.

Pythagorean theorem: in any right triangle, the square of the measure of the hypotenuse is equal to the sum of the squares of the measures of the other two sides.

quadrant: one of four regions formed by two intersecting perpendicular lines.

quadrilateral: a polygon of four sides.

radical: the indicated root of a quantity; $\sqrt{2}$ is a radical; radical sign $\sqrt{}$.

radius: the distance from the centre to any point on the circle; half the diameter.

range: the difference between the greatest and least values of a set of data.

range of a variable: the set of all possible values of a variable.

rate: a comparison of unlike quantities with different units of measure.

ratio: a comparison of like quantities with the same units of measure.

rational number: a number that can be expressed as the quotient of two integers (provided the divisor is not zero).

ray: a part of a line with one end point.

real number: a number that is either rational or irrational; see *rational number, irrational number*.

rectangle: a quadrilateral with opposite sides equal and angles that measure 90°.

reflection: a congruence transformation that maps a figure onto its image by a reflection in a line.

reflectional symmetry: see *line of symmetry*.

reflex angle: an angle with measure between 180° and 360°.

regular polygon: a polygon with all sides and all angles equal in measure.

rhombus: a quadrilateral with all sides equal in measure.

right angle: an angle with measure 90°.

root of an equation: the value of the variable that makes the left side equal to the right side.

rotation: a congruence transformation that maps a figure onto its image by turning about a point; rotation angle is the amount and direction of the rotation; rotation centre is the point about which the rotation takes place.

rotational symmetry: a figure that fits onto itself more than once during a complete rotation about a point has rotational symmetry.

sample: a part of a group or population that is studied in order to predict information about the entire group or population.

scale: the ratio of distance on the scale diagram to the actual distance.

scalene triangle: a triangle with all sides of unequal length.

scientific notation: a method of writing large and small numbers using powers of ten.

similar figures: figures that are the same shape, but not always the same size; corresponding sides of similar figures are in the same proportion.

similarity transformation: a transformation for which the original and image figures are similar.

slope of a line: the ratio of the rise to the run.

square: a quadrilateral with equal sides and all right angles.

square number: a number that can be expressed as a power with the exponent 2; e.g. $36 = 6^2$.

square root: the square root of a number is the number which, when multiplied by itself, produces the number.

straight angle: an angle with measure 180°.

supplementary angles: a pair of angles with a sum of their measures equal to 180°.

surface area: the total area of all the faces or surfaces of a solid.

symbols: $<$ is less than; $>$ is greater than; $\leq$ is less than or equal to; $\geq$ is greater than or equal to; $\doteq$ is approximately equal to; $\cong$ is congruent to; $\parallel$ is parallel to; $\perp$ is perpendicular to; ... and so on; $\in$ is a member of; $\sim$ is similar to; $\sqrt{}$ radical.

transformation: a mapping of a figure that changes the figure's position, size or shape; see *translation, reflection, rotation, dilatation*.

translation: a congruence transformation that maps a figure onto its image so that each point on its image is the same distance from each corresponding point on the figure.

transversal: a line that intersects two or more lines.

trapezoid: a quadrilateral with one pair of parallel sides.

triangle: a polygon with three sides.

trinomial: an algebraic expression with 3 terms.

variable: a symbol used to represent any number or members of a set of numbers.

variable expression: an algebraic expression with variables.

vertex (plural vertices): the common point of two rays of an angle; the point where two sides of a polygon meet; the point where three or more faces of polyhedron meet.

vertically opposite angles: angles opposite to each other formed by two intersecting straight lines.

volume: the amount of space, measured in cubic units, occupied by a solid.

Answers

CHAPTER 1

1.1 Exercise, page 10
Inventory 1: 1.a)54 **b)**72 **c)**63 **d)**153 **e)**100 **f)**251 **g)**5255 **h)**4912
2.a)36 **b)**36 **c)**34 **d)**345 **e)**848 **f)**569 **g)**523 **h)**609 **i)**277 **3.a)**315
b)108 **c)**152 **d)**4698 **e)**1472 **f)**2380 **g)**18 441 **h)**47 124 **i)**49 980
4.a)86 **b)**38 **c)**84 R3 **d)**39 R2 **e)**68 **Inventory 2: 1.a)**2.97 **b)**1.99
c)7.95 **d)**39.3 **e)**2.53 **f)**1.572 **g)**11.34 **h)**0.0632 **2.a)**4.2 **b)**5.41
c)0.311 **d)**4.6 **e)**6.78 **f)**11.431 **g)**20.69 **h)**2.15 **3.a)**1.5 **b)**2.8
c)0.12 **d)**9.12 **e)**0.135 **f)**73.5 **g)**148.35 **h)**1.795 **4.a)**1.3 **b)**3.4 **c)**6.8
d)3.08 **e)**5.6 **f)**0.043 84 **g)**43 **h)**43 **Inventory 3: 1.a)**$\frac{1}{3}$ **b)**$\frac{1}{6}$ **c)**$\frac{5}{8}$

d)$\frac{4}{5}$ **e)**$\frac{2}{3}$ **2.a)**$1\frac{3}{5}$ **b)**$3\frac{1}{4}$ **c)**$2\frac{5}{7}$ **d)**$3\frac{1}{3}$ **e)**$2\frac{5}{8}$ **3.a)**$\frac{7}{4}$ **b)**$\frac{7}{3}$ **c)**$\frac{37}{7}$ **d)**$\frac{19}{4}$ **e)**$\frac{17}{5}$

4.a)$\frac{4}{5}$ **b)**$\frac{5}{8}$ **c)**$\frac{3}{8}$ **d)**$\frac{7}{8}$ **e)**$\frac{7}{9}$ **5.a)**$\frac{1}{5}$ **b)**$\frac{5}{8}$ **c)**$3\frac{7}{9}$ **d)**$3\frac{1}{5}$ **e)**$4\frac{2}{9}$ **6.a)**$\frac{1}{12}$ **c)**$\frac{1}{24}$

d)$\frac{1}{2}$ **e)**$\frac{1}{2}$ **7.a)**$\frac{1}{10}$ **b)**$\frac{3}{8}$ **c)**$2\frac{2}{5}$ **d)**$2\frac{2}{3}$ **e)**12 **8.a)**$\frac{2}{3}$ **b)**$1\frac{1}{2}$ **c)**$\frac{1}{4}$ **d)**3 **e)**$1\frac{13}{20}$

Inventory 4: 1.a)19 360 **b)**19 400 **c)**19 000 **2.a)**0.8 **b)**0.78
c)2.50 **d)**9.416 **3.a)**33.617 **b)**7.6 **c)**14.19 **d)**2.16 **4.a)**869.3 **b)**6.62
c)14 705 **d)**3515 **e)**78.02 **f)**1.479 **g)**546 **h)**506 **5.a)**7 cans
@ 63¢ **b)**8 singles **c)**2 slacks **6.a)**$8.05 **b)**$7.55 **c)**$50.75

1.2 Exercise, page 14
3.a) + **b)** > **c)** × **d)** = **e)** ÷ **f)** + **g)** < **h)** − **4.a)**36 + 25 > 50

b)36 − 12 < 6 × 5 **c)**12 + 30 > 30 − 12 **d)**$\frac{36+48}{2} = 7 \times 6$

e)$8^2 < 7^2 + 6^2$ **5.a)**9 **b)**29 **c)**20 **d)**4 **e)**5 **f)**6 **g)**7 **h)**25 **i)**55 **6.a)**6
b)3 **c)**10 **d)**1 **e)**10 **f)**6 **7.a)**B **b)**A:2, B:6 **8.a)**1 **b)**70 **c)**420; (c)
9.a)9 **b)**2 **c)**23 **d)**252 **10.a)**180 **b)**7 **c)**10 **d)**18 **e)**36 **f)**2 **g)**2 **h)**2
i)12 **j)**8 **11.a)** < **b)** > **c)** < **d)** > **e)** = **f)** < **g)** = **h)** =
12.a)30, 33, 36, . . . **b)**6, 9, 12, 15, 18, 21 **c)**6, 9, 12
d)24, 27, 30, 33 **13.a)**28, 32 **b)**27, 30, 33 **c)**{ } or ϕ
14.a)18, 20, 22, . . . **b)**1, 3, 5, 7, 9, 11 **c)**13, 15, 17, 19 **d)**105
e)10, 11, 12, . . . **f)**54, 72, 90 **g)**38 **h)**18, 36, 54, 72, 90
15. Answers will vary. **a)**12 + 36 = 48 ÷ 1 **b)**5 ÷ 2 < 28 ÷ 2
c)2 + 3 × 4 = 14 **d)**15 < (27 + 13) ÷ 2 **e)**8 < (4 + 2) × 3
f)6 + 2 > 8 − 3 **g)**1 × 2 + 8 ÷ 4 < 5³
h)2 > (4 × 5 + 1) ÷ 3 − 6

1.3 Exercise, page 18
1.a)11 **b)**42 **c)**11 **d)**5 **2.a)**1674 **b)**28.5 **c)**51 211 **d)**8071 **3.a)**32
b)243 **c)**64 **d)**216 **4.a)**18 747 **b)**3801.6 **c)**23.6 **5.** A: 56, B: 205,
C: 21 672, D: 37, E: 19; 21 989 **6.a)**168.3 **b)**200.8 **c)**73.35
d)6.98 **e)**29 958 **f)**4563.6 **8.a)**$10.50 **b)**$6.75 **c)**$13.00
9.a)$2.63 **b)**$3.17 **c)**$3.42 **10.** $3.23 **11.a)**8 **b)**16 **c)**32

1.4 Exercise, page 21
1.a)2, 3 **b)**3, 2 **c)**2, 4 **d)**3, 4 **e)**4, 3 **f)**4, 2 **g)**5, 2 **h)**2, 5
2. 8, 9, 16, 81, 64, 16, 25, 32 **3.a)**3^5 **b)**2^4 **c)**5^3 **d)**4^6
4.a)2 × 2 × 3 **b)**2 × 2 × 2 × 2 **c)**4 **5.a)**2 **b)**8 **c)**5 **d)**9 **e)**9 **f)**16
g)9 **h)**15 **i)**10 **j)**8 **6.a)**5 **b)**6 **c)**24 **d)**4 **7.a)**12 **b)**30 **c)**50 **d)**72
e)24 **f)**48 **8.a)**72 **b)**36 **c)**72 **d)**36 **e)**144 **f)**144 **9.a)**25: {1, 5, 25};
16: {1, 2, 4, 8, 16}; 36: {1, 2, 3, 4, 6, 9, 12, 18, 36};
27: {1, 3, 9, 27}; 48: {1, 2, 3, 4, 6, 8, 12, 16, 24, 48};

49: {1, 7, 49}; 72: {1, 2, 3, 4, 6, 8, 9, 12, 18, 24, 36, 72};
99: {1, 3, 9, 11, 33, 99} **b)**4, 9, 25, 49 **10.a)**2, 3, 5, 7, 11, 13,
17, 19 **b)**23, 29, 31, 37 **c)**41, 43, 47, 53, 59 **d)**61, 67, 71, 73, 79
11.b)127, 131, 137, 139 **12.** 48 **13.a)(i)**8 **(ii)**16 **(iii)**128 **(iv)**128
b)same **14.b)**2^5, 2^6, 3^7, 3^6, 10^8 **15.a)(i)**100 000 **(ii)** 100
(iii)1000 **(iv)**1000 **b)**same **16.b)**8^4, 5^4, 2^4, 8^3

1.5 Exercise, page 24
1.a)11 **b)**29 **c)**15 **2.a)**{8, 14, 20} **b)**{18, 24, 30} **3.a)**{4, 12, 20}
b){7, 15, 23} **4.a)**2, 5, 8, 11, 14 **b)**26, 37, 50, 65, 82 **c)**170,
209, 252, 299, 350 **5.a)**10 **b)**18 **c)**1 **d)**2 **6.a)**{8, 12, 16, 20}
b){3, 7, 12} **c)**{21, 96, 225} **d)**{0, 3, 9} **e)**{2, 3, 4}
f){15, 35, 63, 99, 143} **7.a)**13 **b)**23 **c)**2 **d)**60 **e)**10 **f)**41 **g)**120
h)41 **i)**9 **j)**55 **k)**2 **l)**9 **m)**0 **n)**200 **o)**240 **p)**3600 **q)**81 **r)**81 **s)**8
t)0 **8.a)(i)**576 **(ii)**576 **9.a)**1600, 1600 **10.a)(i)**16 **(ii)**16
11.a)(i)16 **(ii)**16

1.6 Exercise, page 26
1.a)5 **b)**2 **c)**10 **d)**3 **e)**11 **f)**1 **2.a)**{0, 1, 2, 3} **b)**{0, 1, 2, 3}
c){0, 1, 2, 3} **3.a)**{2} **b)**{4} **c)**∅ **d)**{3} **4.a)**{0, 1, 2, . . . , 12}
b){6, 7, 8, . . .} **c)**{0, 1, . . . , 6} **d)**{8, 9, 10, . . .} **e)**{4, 5, 6, . . .}
f){0, 1, 2, 3, 4, 5} **g)**{9} **h)**{4} **i)**{4, 5, 6, . . .} **j)**{4} **k)**{1}
l){4} **m)**{2} **n)**{4} **5.a)**4 **b)**12 **c)**0 **d)**5 **e)**10 **f)**3 **6.a)**0, 1, 2
b)16, 17, 18, . . . **c)**36 **d)**6, 7, 8, . . . **e)**0, 1, 2 **f)**17
g)4, 5, 6, . . . **h)**10, 11, 12, . . . **i)**3 **7.a)**{2, 3, 4, . . .} **b)**{1}
c){4, 5, 6, . . .} **d)**{3, 6, 9, 12} **e)**{0, 1, 2, 3} **f)**{0, 1, 2, 3}

1.8 Exercise, page 31
1. 19 planes **2.** 160 g **3.** 16 cm × 22 cm **4.** A $230, B $310,
C $460 **5.** 8100 **6.** 73 days **7.** 846 553 km **8.** 1318 stations
9. 255 600 boxes **10.** 4990 points **11.a)** no distance given
b) Nile **c)**65 d 3 h 20 min

1.9 Exercise, page 33
1. 27 **2.** 55 **3.** 12 **4.a)**6 **b)**12 **c)**1 **d)**8 **e)**0 **5.** 1, 3, 5, 7, 9
6.a)neither **b)**they are not **7.** vife

8.

3	2	1
7	9	4
5	8	6

9.a)207 **b)**32 **c)**Quebec **10.a)**50 **b)**49
11.b)83, 61, 50, 49, 16 **c)**Boston and
Quebec **13.a)**Boston and Quebec; Montreal
and Buffalo; Buffalo and Hartford
b)Quebec, Montreal, Hartford

Practice and Problems, page 36
1.a)1221 **b)**2.51 **c)**16.74 **d)**$\frac{11}{15}$ **e)**$11\frac{1}{4}$ **2.a)**130 **b)**2.855 **c)**5.53

d)$\frac{3}{8}$ **e)**$1\frac{9}{10}$ **3.a)**756 **b)**0.85 **c)**0.0036 **d)**$\frac{3}{14}$ **e)**28 **4.a)**52 **b)**1.3

c)0.16 **d)**$1\frac{3}{32}$ **e)**$2\frac{26}{45}$ **5.a)**9.2 **b)**152.9 **c)**6.6 **6.a)**17 **b)**3 **c)**84

7.a)283.2 **b)**17.86 **c)**1.5 **8.a)**10 × 10; 10^2
b)2 × 2 × 2 × 2 × 2 × 2; 2^6 **c)**10 × 10 × 10 × 10; 10^4
d)2 × 2 × 2; 2^3 **e)**5 × 5 × 5; 5^3 **9.a)**4 **b)**6 **c)**18 **10.a)**18
b)36 **c)**80 **11.a)**10 **b)**5 **12.a)**{4} **b)**{3} **c)**{0, 1, 2, . . . , 9}
d){3, 4, 5, . . .} **e)**{0, 1, 2, 3} **13.** 10.0 cm × 6.5 cm

1.a)40.70 **b)**5.818 **c)**87.849 **2.a)**$1\frac{13}{20}$ **b)**$\frac{9}{16}$ **c)**$\frac{1}{2}$ **d)**$1\frac{1}{12}$ **3.a)**24.22
b)7.191 **c)**3.06 **4.a)**17 **b)**144 **c)**18 **5.a)**2, 5, 32 **b)**5^2, 25
c)3^4, 4 **6.a)**100 000 000 **b)**1 000 000 **c)**1000 **d)**1000 **e)**100
f)1000 **7.a)**2 **b)**48 **8.a)**7 **b)**9 **c)**72 **d)**6 **9.a)**{4} **b)**{3, 4, 5, ...}
c){0, 1, 2, 3, 4, 5} **d)**{2} **10.** \$4.50 **11.** 4

CHAPTER 2

2.1 Exercise, page 40
1.a)-6 **b)**$+\$12$ **c)**$+14$ **d)**$+8$ **e)**-8 **f)**-6 **2.a)**2 **b)**-1 **c)**3
d)-18 **e)**36 **f)**48 **3.a)**3 m left **b)**4 m right **c)**12 m left
d)15 m right **e)**36 m left **f)**no movement **4.a)**$+8840$
b)-1130 **c)**$+5630$ **d)**$+41$ **5.a)**5 **b)**1 **c)**8 **d)**-3 **e)**5 **f)**2 **6.a)**$<$
b)$>$ **c)**$>$ **d)**$<$ **e)**$<$ **f)**$>$ **g)**$<$ **h)**$<$ **7.a)**-13, -9, 0, 2, 6
b)-103, -99, -87, 100, 101 **c)**-21, -18, -15, -12, -5
d)-29, -17, -13, 24, 36 **8.a)**45, 27, -8, -19, -23
b)15, 13, -14, -16, -17 **c)**5, 1, -1, -3, -8 **d)**109, 95,
-96, -101, -108 **9.a)**12 km

2.2 Exercise, page 43
1.a)$-3 < -2 < 5$ **b)**$-3 < 3 < 4$ **c)**$-12 < 4 < 12$
d)$-8 < -3 < 1$ **e)**$-5 \leqq -1 \leqq 12$ **f)**$-7 \leqq 2 \leqq 7$
2.a){4, 5, 6, ...} **b)**{..., 3, 4, 5} **c)**{..., -5, -4}
d){-3, -2, -1, ...} **e)**{5, 6, 7} **f)**{0} **3.a)**greater than 0 *or*
greater than or equal to 1 **b)**less than -3, *or*, less than
or equal to -4 **c)**less than 3 *or* less than or equal to
2 **d)**greater than -9 and less than -4, *or*, greater than
-9 and less than or equal to -5, *or*, greater than or
equal to -8 and less than -4, *or*, greater than or equal to
-8 and less than or equal to -5 **4.a)**{-4, -3, -2, ...}
b){-3, -2, -1, ...} **5.a)**{0, 1} **b)**{..., -1, 0, 1}
6. (a), (iv); (b), (i); (c), (ii); (d), (iii) **7.a)**{3, 4, 5, ...}
b){0, 1, 2, 3} **c)**{-1, 0, 1, ...} **d)**{..., -4, -3, -2} **e)**{0, 1}
f){-11, -10, -9, ...} **8.a)**{4} **b)**{-2} **c)**{-2, 0, 2, 4, ...}
d){10, 12, 14, ...} **9.a)**A: {-1, 0, 1, 2} B: {-2, -1, 0, 1, 2}
C: {-1, 0, 1, 2, 3} D: {-2, -1, 0, 1, 2, 3} **10.a)**{4, 5}
b){-2, -1, 0, 1, 2} **c)**{-3, -2, -1} **d)**{-8, -7, -6, -5,
-4, -3} **e)**{-16, -15, -14, -13, -12} **f)**{-1, 0}
11. Answers may vary. **a)**$x > 0$ **b)**$x < -1$ **c)**$-3 \leqq x < 0$
d)$x > 1$ **e)**$x < -3$ **f)**$x > 15$ **g)**$x < -28$ **h)**$-30 < x < -25$
12. Answers may vary. **a)**$x \geqq 1$ **b)**$x \leqq -2$ **c)**$-3 \leqq x \leqq -1$
d)$x \geqq 2$ **e)**$x \leqq -4$ **f)**$x \geqq 16$ **g)**$x \leqq -29$ **h)**$-29 \leqq x \leqq -26$

2.3 Exercise, page 46
2.a)$+3$ **b)**-3 **c)**$+4$ **d)**-3 **3.a)**$+7$ **b)**-7 **c)**$+3$ **d)**-3
4.a)$+8$ **b)**$+2$ **c)**-8 **d)**-8 **5.a)**$+5$ **b)**-5 **c)**$+1$ **d)**-1
6.a)$+1$ **b)**$+2$ **c)**-5 **d)**$+1$ **e)**-1 **f)**-9 **g)**0 **h)**0 **i)**-6 **7.a)**-3
b)-8 **c)**3 **d)**-2 **e)**-2 **f)**-9 **g)**6 **h)**0 **i)**-1 **j)**-12 **k)**-8 **l)**1
8.a)-4 **b)**-10 **c)**-3 **d)**5 **9.a)**2 **b)**4 **c)**4 **d)**-1 **e)**7 **f)**0 **g)**-3
h)0 **i)**-7 **j)**1 **k)**-12 **l)**-6 **m)**9 **n)**-11 **o)**0 **11.** 5°C,
-2°C, -6°C, 1°C, -4°C, -6°C, -10°C, -11°C, -6°C,
0°C, 9°C, -4°C, 0°C, 8°C, -3°C, 0°C

2.4 Exercise, page 49
1.a)$+7$ **b)**-5 **c)**$+2$ **d)**-2 **2.a)**-1 **b)**$+3$ **c)**-2 **d)**$+1$ **e)**-1

---

f)$+15$ **g)**-15 **h)**$+15$ **i)**$+3$ **3.a)**$+6$, $+5$ **b)**-1, -2 **4.a)**$+7$,
$+8$, $+9$, $+10$ **b)**$+7$, $+8$, $+9$, $+10$ **5.a)**$+8$ **b)**$+19$ **c)**$+3$
d)-6 **e)**-1 **f)**-5 **g)**$+6$ **h)**$+4$ **i)**-9 **6.b)**(i)$+17$ (ii)-3
(iii)$+2$ (iv)-18 **7.a)**2 **b)**-3 **c)**-25 **d)**17 **e)**-8 **f)**54 **g)**62
h)-6 **8.a)**-1 **b)**1 **c)**-7 **d)**-8 **e)**-4 **f)**-6 **9.a)**-1 **b)**7 **c)**1
d)-2 **e)**2 **f)**6 **10.a)**-1 **b)**-5 **c)**11 **d)**-14 **e)**2 **f)**0 **g)**8 **h)**-3
11.a)-4 **b)**-1 **c)**16 **d)**-23 **e)**28 **f)**-9 **12.a)**$>$ **b)**$>$ **c)**$<$
d)$<$ **13.** 72

2.5 Exercise, page 51
1.a)$+2$°C **b)**$+18$°C **c)**-11°C **2.a)**-47°C **b)**20°C **c)**-5°C
d)-7°C **3.** -5°C **4.** -9°C **5.a)**-29°C **b)**$+29$°C **6.** -24°C
7. -88°C **8.a)**-3°C **b)**-4°C **c)**-8°C **d)**-15°C
9. (d) **10.a)**St. John's **b)**Frobisher Bay **11.a)**Whitehorse
b)Vancouver **13.a)**Regina **b)**Regina **14.a)**-2 **b)**$+25$ **c)**-18
d)-12 **e)**$+38$ **15.a)**$+2$ **b)**-4 **c)**$+2$ **d)**-1 **e)**-2; Joelle
16.a)-1 **b)**$+1$ **c)**-2 **d)**0; Barb

2.6 Exercise, page 55
1.a)$+4$, 0, -4, -8, -12 **b)**-16, -20 **2.a)**$+4$, 0, $+4$, -8
b)$+1$, 0, -1, $+4$ **3.** -12, -12 **4.a)**-3, 0, $+3$, $+6$ **b)**$+9$,
$+12$ **5.a)**-18, -12, $+1$, 0, -6; $(-2)(-6) = +12$,
$(-3)(-6) = +18$, $(-4)(-6) = +24$ **b)**-14, -7, 0, -7,
$+14$; $(-3)(-7) = +21$, $(-4)(-7) = +28$,
$(-5)(-7) = +35$ **6.a)**-15 **b)**-12 **c)**$+15$ **d)**-20
7.a)negative **b)**positive **c)**positive **d)**negative **e)**negative
f)positive **8.a)**WAR **b)**BALE or BEAL or ELBA

2.7 Exercise, page 57
1.a)-1 **b)**-12 **c)**$+4$ **d)**$+28$ **e)**-12 **f)**$+72$ **g)**-24 **h)**0
i)$+42$ **j)**-60 **k)**$+60$ **l)**-7 **2.a)**-4 **b)**-15 **c)**12 **d)**12 **e)**-12
f)6 **g)**-24 **h)**-18 **i)**-72 **j)**72 **3.a)**-6 **b)**-6 **c)**$+12$ **d)**$+24$
e)-32 **f)**-54 **4.a)**-12 **b)**$+30$, **c)**-6; (b) **5.** -6, -15, 0,
20, 0, -12, -40 **6.** 9, 10, 0, 2, 12, 0, -12 **7.a)**15 **b)**84 **c)**18
d)120 **e)**-240 **f)**15 **g)**144 **h)**0 **i)**108 **8.a)**4 **b)**9 **c)**16 **d)**16 **e)**4
f)25 **g)**-8 **h)**-1 **i)**-27 **j)**-18 **k)**24 **l)**64 **9.a)**-8 **b)**-8
c)-16 **d)**16 **e)**36 **f)**-1 **g)**-36 **h)**-25 **i)**25 **j)**-125
10.b)(i)-32 (ii)-35 (iii)54 (iv)-65 **11.a)**-10 **b)**3 **c)**4 **d)**-2
e)6 **f)**-8 **g)**12 **h)**-16 **12.a)**-9, -6, -3, 0, 3, 6 **b)**-15,
-10, -5, 0, 5 **c)**12, 6, 0, -6, -12 **d)**-20, -12, -4, 12, 20
13.a)$+$, $-$ **b)**(i)-1 (ii)-1 (iii)1 **14.** Answers may vary.
a)$(-2) + (-3) = -5$, **b)**$(-2) - (+1) = -3$
c)$(+5) + (-3) = +2$ **d)**$(-4)(+2) = -8$

2.8 Exercise, page 59
1.a)$+4$ **b)**-4 **c)**$+4$ **d)**-4 **2.a)**-4 **b)**-8 **c)**$+4$ **d)**$+8$
3.a)$+5$ **b)**-5 **c)**-5 **d)**$+5$ **e)**-6 **f)**-6 **g)**$+6$ **h)**$+6$ **i)**-6
j)-6 **4.a)**like signs **b)**unlike signs **c)**(i)$+5$ (ii)-5 (iii)-5
(iv)$+5$ **5.a)**positive **b)**negative **c)**positive **d)**negative
e)negative **f)**positive **6.a)**-4 **b)**-6 **c)**$+7$ **d)**-10 **e)**$+6$
f)$+7$ **g)**-5 **h)**$+6$ **i)**-5 **j)**$+1$ **k)**$+4$ **l)**-4 **m)**-2 **n)**$+2$
o)-25 **p)**$+45$ **7.a)**$+3$ **b)**-5 **c)**0 **d)**-2 **e)**-1 **f)**-8 **g)**$+11$
h)-5 **i)**$+10$ **8.** -23, -16, 13, -12, -13, -35, 13 **9.a)**-4
b)-3 **c)**$+7$ **d)**$+15$ **10.a)**63 **b)**-3 **c)**-54 **d)**-8 **e)**39 **f)**7
g)-88 **h)**-108 **i)**27 **j)**0 **k)**0 **l)**0 **11.a)**6 **b)**25 **c)**48 **d)**-3
e)-6 **f)**48 **g)**6 **h)**-3 **i)**-3 **j)**12 **k)**-5 **l)**49 **12.a)**4 **b)**-28

c)-11 **d)**52 **e)**-18 **f)**-36 **g)**-2 **h)**13 **13.a)**-3 **b)**24 **c)**18
d)-85 **e)**-13 **14.a)**5 **b)**8 **15.a)**-10 **b)**-4 **c)**-18 **d)**8 **e)**-2
f)4 **g)**-6 **h)**-15 **i)**-8 **j)**22 **k)**-12; FLOEBERG BAY

2.9 Exercise, page 62

1.a)-15 **b)**10 **c)**-5 **d)**1 **e)**5 **f)**20 **2.a)**-9 **b)**-4 **c)**76 **d)**-180
e)-12 **f)**-4 **4.a)**-5 **b)**37 **c)**20 **d)**-43 **e)**-24 **f)**-1
5.a)-18 **b)**25 **c)**55 **d)**4 **e)**13 **f)**6 **6.a)**3 **b)**1 **c)**-2 **d)**1 **7.a)**0
b)22 **c)**-4 **8.** A: -6, B: 21; B **9.a)**-3 **b)**-40 **c)**-16 **d)**8
10.a)15 **b)**6 **c)**-12 **d)**33 **e)**8 **f)**45 **g)**-27 **h)**-18
11. 320 saves **12.a)**-6 **b)**-1 **c)**-60 **d)**-8 **e)**-7; (e)
13.a)-9 **b)**$+7$ **c)**0 **d)**0 **e)**0 **f)**0 **g)**1 **h)**-1 **i)**-5 **14.a)**zero
b)the integer **c)**zero **15.a)**-15, -15 **b)**-66, -66 **c)**52, 52
d)-6, -6 **e)**-21, -21 **f)**$+9$, $+9$ **g)**-4, 4 **h)**18, -18
i)11, -11 **j)**1, -1 **16.** (a), (c) **17.a)**36 **b)**-48 **c)**-30 **d)**26 **e)**36
f)22 **g)**4 **h)**26 **i)**-48; (a), (e); (b), (i); (d), (h) **18.a)**6 **b)**-66 **c)**20

2.10 Exercise, page 65

1.a)4 **b)**-11 **c)**8 **d)**950 **2.a)**20 **b)**8 **c)**48 **d)**134 **3.** $-2°C$
4. $-22°C$ **5.** -7, -1, -12 **6.b)**$-4°C$ **7.** -38 m **8.** -7780 m
9.a)-16 **b)**-2 **c)**negative **10.** Jennifer and Joseph, Samuel
and Samantha, Christina and James **11.a)**-68 g **b)**-8.5 g
12. $-6°C$ **13.** $6°C$ **14.a)**$-32°C$ **b)**24 km/h **c)**$-40°C$ **d)**$-42°C$
15.a)$-28°C$ **b)**$-24°C$ **16.** $-35°C$ **17.** $-40°C$ **18.** 24 km/h

2.11 Exercise, page 69

1.a)2 **b)**3 **c)**5 **d)**10 **e)**8 **2.a)**-1 **b)**3 **c)**5 **d)**15 **e)**0 **f)**5 **g)**5 **h)**5
3.a)$>$ **b)**$<$ **c)**$>$ **d)**$<$ **4.a)**9 **b)**5 **c)**9 **d)**10 **5.a)**$>$ **b)**$<$ **c)**$=$
d)$<$ **6.a)**-6 **b)**-12 **c)**9 **d)**11 **e)**0 **f)**-7 **g)**18 **h)**3 **i)**4 **j)**1
k)-1 **l)**24 **7.** -4 **8.a)**-2 **b)**4 **c)**4 **d)**2 **e)**0 **f)**6 **g)**11 **h)**7
i)-4 **j)**-4 **k)**4 **l)**-3 **9.a)**(i)0, 0 (ii)12, 12 (iii)12, 12
10.a)(i)0, 0 (ii)16, 16 (iii)16, 16

2.12 Exercise, page 73

1.a)2, 6, 24 **b)**120 **c)**3 628 800 **2.a)**2 **b)**6 **c)**12 **3.** 362 880
4.a)6 **b)**1 **5.** 41 **6.a)**3 **b)**10 **7.** 44 **8.** 107 **9.** 22 **10.** 6 days.

Practice and Problems, page 74

1.a)$+6$ **b)**-5 **c)**$+4$ **2.a)**-13, -4, -1, 8, 9
b)-19, -15, -13, 12, 18 **3.a)**$\{\ldots, -5, -4, -3\}$
b)$\{-1, 0, 1, \ldots\}$ **c)**$\{-1, 0, 1, 2, 3\}$
d)$\{-4, -3\}$ **4.a)**7 **b)**-7 **c)**3 **d)**-3 **e)**-4 **f)**0 **g)**-4 **h)**1
5.a)-6 **b)**8 **c)**9 **d)**-9 **e)**-12 **f)**-7 **g)**2 **h)**13 **6.a)**8 **b)**-8
c)-8 **d)**8 **e)**-54 **f)**9 **g)**36 **h)**-55 **7.a)**5 **b)**-5 **c)**-5 **d)**4
e)-1 **f)**-11 **8.a)**-4 **b)**2 **c)**31 **9.a)**5 **b)**-8 **c)**17 **d)**-3
10. $92°C$ **11.a)**-2 **b)**10 **c)**9 **d)**-9

Practice Test, page 75

1.a)101, 97, -95, -99, -102 **b)**333, 33, 3, -3, -33
2.a)$\{\ldots, -5, -4, -3\}$ **b)**$\{-5, -4, -3, -2\}$
c)$\{-3, -2, -1, 0, 1, 2\}$ **3.a)**1 **b)**1 **c)**0 **d)**-1 **e)**-6 **f)**-7
g)1 **h)**3 **i)**3 **j)**-9 **4.a)**5 **b)**-7 **5.a)**-8 **b)**-3 **c)**-4 **d)**-8 **e)**12
f)2 **g)**16 **h)**-12 **6.a)**18 **b)**-9 **c)**-9 **d)**2 **e)**-2 **f)**-4 **g)**-12
h)-4 **i)**63 **7.a)**1 **b)**18 **c)**-20 **d)**10 **8.a)**1 **b)**66 **9.** $75°C$ colder
10.a)$-3°C$ **b)**$+6°C$ **11.a)**-28 **b)**5 **c)**1 **d)**35

CHAPTER 3

3.1 Exercise, page 79

1.a)$\dfrac{-3}{2}$ **b)**$\dfrac{-10}{-3}$ **c)**$\dfrac{-2}{5}$ **2.a)**$-\dfrac{1}{2}$, $\dfrac{2}{-4}$, $\dfrac{1}{-2}$ **b)**$\dfrac{4}{5}$, $\dfrac{-4}{-5}$; $\dfrac{-4}{5}$, $\dfrac{4}{-5}$

c)$\dfrac{7}{8}$, $\dfrac{-7}{-8}$; $\dfrac{-7}{8}$, $\dfrac{7}{-8}$, $-\dfrac{7}{8}$ **3.a)**$\dfrac{1}{-4}$, $\dfrac{-1}{4}$ **b)**$\dfrac{-2}{3}$ **c)**$\dfrac{5}{3}$

5.a)-2 **b)**2 **c)**2 **d)**4 **e)**-4 **f)**5 **6.a)**$<$ **b)**$<$ **c)**$>$ **d)**$<$

7. Answers may vary. **a)**$-\dfrac{4}{5}$, $\dfrac{-4}{5}$ **b)**$-\dfrac{2}{3}$, $\dfrac{-4}{6}$ **c)**$-\dfrac{1}{2}$, $\dfrac{-1}{2}$

d)$-\dfrac{3}{5}$, $\dfrac{-6}{10}$ **e)**$\dfrac{3}{9}$, $\dfrac{9}{27}$ **f)**$-\dfrac{3}{4}$, $\dfrac{-3}{4}$ **9.a)**$-\dfrac{2}{5}$ **b)**$-\dfrac{1}{5}$ **c)**$-\dfrac{2}{3}$

d)$\dfrac{3}{10}$ **e)**$-\dfrac{1}{2}$ **f)**$\dfrac{6}{5}$ **g)**5 **h)**$-\dfrac{3}{4}$ **i)**$-\dfrac{4}{5}$ **j)**$\dfrac{3}{2}$ **10.a)**1 **b)**-1 **c)**$-\dfrac{1}{3}$

d)-1 **11.a)**16 **b)**15 **c)**18 **d)**-6 **e)**-15 **f)**-5 **12.a)**$>$ **b)**$<$

c)$<$ **d)**$<$ **13.a)**$-\dfrac{4}{3}$, $\dfrac{-3}{5}$, $\dfrac{1}{-3}$ **b)**$\dfrac{-3}{2}$, $\dfrac{-2}{5}$, $\dfrac{1}{3}$ **c)**$\dfrac{-1}{2}$, $-\dfrac{2}{5}$, $\dfrac{3}{10}$

14.a)$-2\dfrac{3}{4}$ **b)**$-3\dfrac{1}{3}$ **c)**$-2\dfrac{2}{5}$ **d)**$3\dfrac{3}{4}$ **e)**$-2\dfrac{6}{7}$ **15.a)**$-\dfrac{7}{2}$ **b)**$-\dfrac{21}{4}$

c)$\dfrac{8}{3}$ **d)**$-\dfrac{17}{10}$ **e)**$\dfrac{6}{1}$ **16.a)**$<$ **b)**$>$ **c)**$<$ **d)**$=$ **e)**$=$ **f)**$>$

3.2 Exercise, page 81

1.a)$\dfrac{-2}{4}$, $\dfrac{1}{4}$ **b)**$\dfrac{6}{8}$, $\dfrac{-5}{8}$ **c)**$\dfrac{-8}{12}$, $\dfrac{-9}{12}$ **d)**$\dfrac{-5}{15}$, $\dfrac{-6}{15}$ **e)**$\dfrac{-5}{10}$, $\dfrac{-3}{10}$

2.a)-9 **b)**3 **c)**-5 **d)**-11 **e)**18 **3.a)**$-\dfrac{1}{2}$ **b)**$-\dfrac{1}{2}$ **c)**$-1\dfrac{9}{20}$ **d)**$\dfrac{1}{10}$

e)$-\dfrac{7}{10}$ **f)**$\dfrac{11}{15}$ **g)**$-\dfrac{1}{6}$ **h)**$-1\dfrac{7}{20}$ **4.a)**$\dfrac{1}{2}$ **b)**$-\dfrac{1}{3}$ **c)**$-\dfrac{1}{5}$ **d)**$1\dfrac{1}{8}$

e)$-\dfrac{1}{12}$ **f)**$\dfrac{11}{24}$ **g)**$1\dfrac{11}{20}$ **h)**$-\dfrac{7}{12}$ **5.a)**1 **b)**$-\dfrac{9}{10}$ **c)**$\dfrac{7}{10}$ **d)**$-\dfrac{7}{8}$

e)$-\dfrac{7}{12}$ **f)**$-1\dfrac{5}{12}$ **g)**$-\dfrac{1}{2}$ **h)**$-1\dfrac{1}{6}$ **i)**$-1\dfrac{1}{20}$ **j)**$1\dfrac{4}{15}$ **k)**$\dfrac{5}{8}$

l)$-1\dfrac{3}{10}$ **6.a)**0 **b)**$\dfrac{1}{3}$ **c)**$\dfrac{2}{3}$ **d)**$2\dfrac{1}{4}$ **e)**$-\dfrac{1}{6}$ **f)**$\dfrac{1}{4}$ **7.a)**$\dfrac{1}{12}$ **b)**$1\dfrac{1}{4}$ **c)**$-1\dfrac{5}{12}$

d)$\dfrac{7}{12}$ **e)**$\dfrac{11}{12}$ **f)**$1\dfrac{11}{12}$ **8.a)**$1\dfrac{1}{6}$ **b)**$-1\dfrac{1}{4}$ **c)**$\dfrac{1}{2}$ **d)**1 **9.** $1\dfrac{7}{24}$ **10.a)**$\dfrac{1}{6}$ **b)**$1\dfrac{7}{8}$

c)$-\dfrac{5}{8}$ **d)**$-2\dfrac{3}{10}$ **e)**$\dfrac{3}{4}$ **f)**$-\dfrac{2}{3}$ **g)**$-3\dfrac{3}{10}$ **h)**$3\dfrac{1}{4}$ **i)**$1\dfrac{1}{12}$ **j)**$-\dfrac{11}{24}$ **k)**$\dfrac{5}{6}$

l)$-1\dfrac{3}{4}$ **m)**$-\dfrac{7}{8}$ **n)**$5\dfrac{4}{5}$ **o)**$-1\dfrac{5}{6}$ **11.a)**$>$ **b)**$<$ **13.a)**$-2\dfrac{3}{10}$ **b)**$-2\dfrac{3}{4}$

c)1 **d)**$3\dfrac{2}{3}$

3.3 Exercise, page 86

1.a)$-\dfrac{1}{10}$ **b)**$\dfrac{2}{15}$ **c)**$-\dfrac{1}{5}$ **d)**$-\dfrac{1}{4}$ **e)**$\dfrac{3}{10}$ **f)**1 **2.a)**$-\dfrac{8}{9}$ **b)**$-1\dfrac{7}{8}$ **c)**0

d)$1\dfrac{7}{15}$ **e)**$-2\dfrac{1}{6}$ **f)**0 **3.a)**3 **b)**$-\dfrac{3}{2}$ **c)**$\dfrac{1}{3}$ **d)**-3 **e)**$\dfrac{2}{5}$ **f)**$-\dfrac{2}{9}$ **4.a)**$\dfrac{3}{2}$

b)2 **c)**$-\dfrac{8}{3}$ **d)**$\dfrac{9}{2}$ **5.a)**$-\dfrac{16}{25}$ **b)**$4\dfrac{1}{4}$ **c)**$-7\dfrac{1}{2}$ **d)**0 **e)**14 **f)**$4\dfrac{3}{4}$

g)$\dfrac{-3}{14}$ **h)**$-4\dfrac{31}{50}$ **6.a)**$\dfrac{1}{15}$ **b)**$-\dfrac{1}{20}$ **c)**$\dfrac{3}{16}$ **d)**0 **e)**$1\dfrac{37}{128}$ **f)**$16\dfrac{1}{2}$ **7.a)**$\dfrac{4}{9}$

b)$\frac{1}{9}$ c)$\frac{9}{4}$ d)$\frac{4}{25}$ e)$-\frac{3}{4}$ f)$-\frac{1}{6}$ g)$-\frac{1}{18}$ 8.a)$\frac{3}{8}$ b)3 c)$\frac{3}{4}$ d)-2 e)$-\frac{7}{15}$
f)$\frac{1}{4}$ 9.a)$-1\frac{1}{3}$ b)$2\frac{1}{4}$ c)$\frac{8}{15}$ d)$\frac{2}{3}$ e)$\frac{2}{3}$ 10.a)$\frac{3}{8}$ b)-1 c)$\frac{1}{3}$ d)$\frac{1}{3}$ e)$\frac{3}{4}$
11. 17 **12.** \$227 500.00 **13.** \$223 560.00 **14.** \$2 070 000.00
15.a)\$37 614.25 **b)**\$36 739.50 **c)**\$874.75 **16.a)**\$4500.00
b)\$109 520.00 **17.** (a) **18.** 2240 shares

3.4 Exercise, page 89

1.a)$1\frac{5}{8}$, $1\frac{5}{8}$ **2.a)**$\frac{1}{24}$, $\frac{-5}{24}$ **3.a)**$-1\frac{3}{10}$, $-1\frac{19}{30}$ **4.a)**$-\frac{4}{5}$, $-1\frac{9}{16}$
5.a)$-\frac{3}{8}$, $-\frac{3}{8}$ **6.c)**$-\frac{3}{5}$ **d)**$-\frac{1}{15}$ **7.a)**$\frac{1}{2}$ **b)**$\frac{7}{12}$ **c)**$\frac{1}{8}$ **d)**$-2\frac{1}{4}$
e) 2 **f)**$-\frac{5}{9}$ **8.a)**$\frac{1}{2}$ **b)**$\frac{1}{5}$ **c)**$-\frac{1}{5}$ **d)**$\frac{4}{5}$ **e)**$\frac{1}{4}$ **f)**-4 **9.a)**$\frac{4}{5}$ **b)**$1\frac{1}{20}$
c)$-29\frac{1}{2}$; (b) **10.a)**$-\frac{2}{5}$ **b)**$1\frac{5}{27}$ **c)**$-1\frac{1}{9}$; (c) **11.b)**$7\frac{1}{5}$ **12.a)**-12
b)$-\frac{1}{8}$ **c)**$\frac{1}{18}$ **d)**$-\frac{217}{240}$ **13.a)**$\frac{1}{6}$ **b)**$\frac{43}{48}$ **14.a)**$\frac{5}{12}$ **b)**1 **c)**$-\frac{9}{16}$ **d)**$-2\frac{5}{6}$
e)$\frac{25}{36}$ **f)**$-\frac{11}{16}$ **g)**$-\frac{4}{3}$ **h)**$-\frac{5}{18}$ **16.** $\frac{-557}{1840}$ **15.b)**

Vehicle	Combination of each type of vehicle																							
wagon	1	1	1	1	1	2	2	2	2	2	3	3	3	3	4	4	4	5	5	5	6	6	7	8
bicycle	3	6	9	12	15	1	4	7	10	13	2	5	8	11	3	6	9	1	4	7	2	5	3	1
tricycle	10	8	6	4	2	10	8	6	4	2	8	6	4	2	6	4	2	6	4	2	4	2	2	2

3.5 Exercise, page 93

1. 4 h **2.** $2\frac{11}{12}$ h **3.** Twice **4.** Garry $1\frac{1}{4}$ min, Brad $1\frac{2}{3}$ min
5. $9\frac{1}{3}$ cans **6.** $3\frac{3}{11}$ min **7.** $\frac{11}{40}$ **8.** $23\frac{1}{4}$ points **9.** $8\frac{3}{4}$ trips **10.** $2\frac{1}{2}$ cups
11. 10 flats **12.** $79\frac{5}{8}$ bags **13.** $+6$ points **14.a)**$\frac{21}{40}$ **b)**$\frac{3}{20}$ **c)**$\frac{3}{5}$
d)carrot-nut **15.a)**10, 11, 12 **b)**13, 14 **16.a)**$\frac{1}{10}$ **b)**$\frac{3}{10}$ **c)**$\frac{9}{20}$

3.6 Exercise, page 95

1.a)$3.\overline{23}$ **b)**$3.\dot{7}$ **c)**$2.3\overline{5}$ **d)**$0.01\overline{23}$ **2.a)**0.25 **b)**$0.\dot{6}$ **c)**0.75 **d)**0.125
e)$0.\overline{18}$ **f)**$-0.\dot{1}$ **3.** Terminating: (a), (d), (f); Periodic: (b), (c), (e) **4.a)**35, 2 **b)**18, 2 **c)**6, 1 **d)**36, 2 **e)**259, 3 **f)**6, 1 **g)**63, 2
h)074, 3 **i)**6, 1 **j)**2, 1 **k)**407, 3 **l)**428 571, 6 **5.a)**$\frac{12}{23}$ **b)**$-\frac{3}{17}$
c)$\frac{2}{17}$ **d)**$-\frac{3}{20}$ **e)**$\frac{7}{30}$ **f)**$\frac{5}{29}$ **g)**$-\frac{4}{25}$ **h)**$\frac{26}{27}$ **i)**$\frac{21}{22}$ **j)**$-\frac{11}{27}$ **6.a)**0.571
b)0.531 **c)**0.559 **d)** 0.517 **e)**0.485; Johnson, Harris
7.a)0.423 **b)**0.403 **c)**0.365 **d)**0.345 **e)**0.335 **8.** 36 years
9.a)$0.\overline{09}$, $0.\overline{18}$, $0.\overline{27}$ **c)**$0.\overline{36}$ **10.a)**0.5, 0.05 **c)**0.005 **11.a)**0.234, 0.255, 0.276 **c)**0.298 **12.a)**$0.\overline{142\ 857}$, $0.\overline{285\ 714}$, $0.\overline{428\ 571}$
b)$0.\overline{571\ 428}$, $0.\overline{714\ 285}$ **c)**$\frac{6}{7}$

3.7 Exercise, page 98

1.a)1 **b)**1 **c)**2 **d)**0 **2.a)**$\frac{1}{5}$ **b)**$-\frac{1}{4}$ **c)**$\frac{31}{50}$ **d)**$-1\frac{3}{4}$ **e)**$\frac{3}{10}$ **f)**$-\frac{9}{25}$ **g)**$\frac{3}{20}$
h)$\frac{8}{25}$ **i)**$\frac{1}{8}$ **j)**$-\frac{1}{20}$ **3.a)**10 **b)**100 **c)**both **d)**100 **4.a)**$1\frac{1}{3}$ **b)**$-1\frac{23}{99}$
c)$\frac{4}{9}$ **d)**$3\frac{4}{33}$ **e)**$-2\frac{5}{11}$ **5.a)**$\frac{5}{9}$ **b)**$\frac{1}{3}$ **c)**$\frac{8}{9}$ **d)**$1\frac{4}{9}$ **e)**$3\frac{2}{3}$ **f)**$\frac{5}{33}$
g)$2\frac{7}{11}$ **h)**$\frac{82}{99}$ **i)**$1\frac{4}{11}$ **j)**$\frac{35}{111}$ **k)**$1\frac{19}{333}$ **l)**$2\frac{275}{333}$ **6.a)**$\frac{16}{45}$ **b)**$\frac{1}{2}$
c)$\frac{31}{45}$ **d)**$\frac{3}{5}$ **e)**$\frac{52}{165}$ **f)**$3\frac{5}{33}$ **g)**$\frac{23}{495}$ **h)**$2\frac{1}{3}$ **i)**$\frac{409}{990}$ **j)**$4\frac{41}{90}$ **k)**$\frac{97}{300}$
l)$\frac{16}{495}$ **7.a)**$\frac{1}{2}$, $\frac{1}{2}$ **b)**same **8.a)**$\frac{3}{5}$, $\frac{3}{5}$ **b)**same **c)**$\frac{3}{10}$ **9.a)**$\frac{4}{9}$ **b)**$\frac{2}{9}$
c)$\frac{3}{9}$, $\frac{5}{9}$, $\frac{8}{9}$ **10.a)**$\frac{2}{45}$ **b)**$\frac{1}{18}$, $\frac{4}{45}$, $\frac{89}{90}$ **c)**$\frac{1}{225}$, $\frac{1}{100}$ **11.b)**5040 ways

3.8 Exercise, page 101

1.a)3.2 **b)**4.2 **c)**5.8 **d)**3.5 **e)**7.1 **2.a)**6.32 **b)**8.66 **c)**9.43 **d)**4.58
e)7.42 **3.a)**2.45 **b)**4.90 **c)**7.62 **d)**8.72 **e)**7.00 **f)**9.70 **g)**8.06
h)3.61; (e) **4.a)**83 **b)**82.9921 **5.a)**5 **b)**-3 **c)**8 **d)**10 **e)**-15
f)16 **g)**0.6 **h)**0.9 **i)**1.5 **j)**2.5 **6.a)**15.0 mm **b)**18.7 mm **c)**20.9 mm
7.a)9.8 m **b)**25.9 m **c)**42.6 m **8.a)**17.32 **b)**14.42 **c)**28.28
d)18.71 **e)**15.49 **f)**26.46 **g)**13.23 **h)**36.06 **9.** 22.4 m × 22.4 m
10.a)19.49 m × 19.49 m **b)**78.0 m **c)**\$315.80 **11.** 1881
12. 22.4 cm **13.a)**24.0 km **b)**33.9 km **c)**39.1 km **d)**50.5 km
e)75.8 km **f)**112.0 km **14.** 34.3 km **15.** 31.7 km **16.** 50.5 km
17. 65.4 km **18.a)**107.2 km **b)**16.5 km

3.9 Exercise, page 104

1.a)9.22 **b)**5.48 **c)**3.32 **d)**4.80 **e)**10.49 **f)**12.37 **g)**2.41 **h)**3.63
i)1.45 **j)**4.20

3.10 Exercise, page 106

1.a)11.7 **b)**25.0 **c)**11.3 **d)**15.0 **e)**25.0 **f)**27.3 **2.a)**13 **b)**9.8
c)6.7 **d)**13.4 **e)**16 **f)**23.7 **g)**18.4 **h)**19.8 **i)**13.7 **3.a)**19.2 **b)**11.4
c)8.9 **d)**12 **4.a)**8.2 m **b)**4.9 m **c)**16.5 m **5.a)**106.1 m **b)**244.9 m
c)282.9 m **6.a)**2.7 m **b)**233.9 cm **c)**10.3 m **7.** 5.0 m **8.** 6.7 m
9. 80.0 m **10.a)**85, 58; 76, 67 **b)**75, 57; 93, 39; 48, 84; 66, 66

3.11 Exercise, page 109

1. Rational: (a), (b), (c), (d), (e), (g), (h), (j), (k), (l), (n)
Irrational: (f), (i), (m) **3.a)**2 decimal places **b)**6 decimal places
c)$\frac{355}{113}$ **5.a)**Subtraction is not closed for natural numbers.
b)Multiplication is associative for the integers. **c)**There is
a multiplicative identity for fractions. **d)**Division is not
commutative for rational numbers. **e)**Division is distributive
over addition for whole numbers. **f)**Irrationals are not
closed under addition.

3.13 Exercise, page 112

1.a)R **b)**I **3.a)**Domain R **b)**-1 is not included in Set A.

c)$2\frac{1}{2}$ is not an integer. **5.a)**$\{x\,|\,x > -1, x \in R\}$

b)$\{x\,|\,x < -1, x \in R\}$ **c)**$\{x\,|\,x \geqq 2, x \in R\}$ **d)**$\{x\,|\,x < 4, x \in I\}$
e)$\{x\,|\,x > 2, x \in R\}$ **f)**$\{x\,|\,x \geqq -6, x \in I\}$ **g)**$\{x\,|\,x < -4, x \in R\}$
h)$\{x\,|\,x \geqq 6, x \in R\}$ **i)**$\{x\,|\,x > 6, x \in I\}$ **j)**$\{x\,|\,x \leqq 0, x \in R\}$
7.a)$\{x\,|\,{-2} \leqq x < 1, x \in R\}$ **b)**$\{x\,|\,7 < x \leqq 11, x \in R\}$
c)$\{x\,|\,0 \leqq x \leqq 3, x \in I\}$ **d)**$\{x\,|\,{-6} \leqq x < -3, x \in R\}$
e)$\{x\,|\,5 < x \leqq 8, x \in R\}$ **f)**$\{x\,|\,{-3} \leqq x \leqq 1, x \in I\}$
g)$\{x\,|\,0 < x < 3, x \in R\}$ **h)**$\{x\,|\,{-4} \leqq x \leqq -2, x \in I\}$
9.a)is not greater than **b)**is not less than **c)**is not greater than or equal to **d)**is not less than or equal to **10.a)**84 years

3.14 Exercise, page 115
1.c)4 **2.c)**4 **3.a)**18.5 cm **4.** white square **5.** 30 **6.** 6
7. 37 sharks, 63 whales

3.15 Exercise, page 117
1.a)462 canes **b)**\$115.50 **2.** From the top clockwise: 10, 15, 14, 13, 12, 7, 8, 9 Centre: 11 **3.** 21

Practice and Problems, page 118
1.a)$\frac{1}{5}$ **b)**$-\frac{2}{3}$ **c)**$1\frac{1}{3}$ **d)**-8 **e)**$\frac{4}{21}$ **2.a)**$-\frac{2}{5}$ **b)**$\frac{1}{6}$ **c)**$-\frac{7}{10}$ **d)**$\frac{2}{3}$ **3.a)**$\frac{1}{6}$
b)$-1\frac{1}{2}$ **c)**$1\frac{1}{2}$ **d)**$\frac{4}{9}$ **4.a)**$\frac{4}{15}$ **b)**-3 **c)**$-\frac{1}{2}$ **5.a)**$\frac{7}{8}$ **b)**$-2\frac{1}{4}$ **c)**$\frac{1}{4}$
6.a)73, 2 **b)**72, 2 **c)**481, 3 **d)**714 285, 6 **7.a)**$\frac{3}{4}$ **b)**$\frac{9}{20}$ **c)**$\frac{37}{99}$
d)$1\frac{3}{10}$ **8.** 21.3 cm **9.a)**8.4 **b)**11.6, 4.4 **10.** 3.8 m

Practice Test, page 119
1.a)$<$ **b)**$>$ **c)**$>$ **d)**$<$ **2.a)**$-\frac{1}{3}$ **b)**$\frac{8}{9}$ **c)**$-1\frac{1}{2}$ **d)**$\frac{2}{7}$ **e)**$1\frac{5}{6}$ **f)**$-2\frac{5}{6}$
g)$-8\frac{1}{6}$ **h)**$4\frac{7}{8}$ **i)**$-1\frac{1}{2}$ **j)**$-1\frac{1}{3}$ **k)**$-1\frac{1}{3}$ **3.a)**0.7 **b)**-0.375 **c)**$1.\overline{7}$
d)$-0.8\overline{3}$ **4.a)**$\frac{2}{25}$ **b)**$\frac{4}{9}$ **c)**$1\frac{23}{33}$ **d)**$-\frac{5}{12}$ **5.** $12\frac{3}{4}$ **6.** $4\frac{2}{3}$ **7.** 66.0 m
8. 8.0 m **9.** 29.7 cm

CHAPTER 4

4.1 Exercise, page 122
1.a)16 **b)**18 **c)**6 **2.a)**15 **b)**12 **c)**60 **3.a)**1 **b)**-8 **c)**-3 **d)**-18
e)-6 **f)**-12 **g)**-3 **h)**3 **i)**15 **j)**0 **k)**-24 **l)**76 **m)**-5 **n)**-6 **o)**10
p)8 **q)**64 **r)**-8 **4.a)**-24 **b)**6 **c)**-3 **d)**3 **e)**13 **f)**24 **g)**-4 **h)**-9
5.a)-3 **b)**3 **6.a)**13 **b)**-1 **c)**-2 **d)**-1 **7.a)**-9 **b)**4 **c)**20 **d)**0

4.2 Exercise, page 124
1.a)$2x + 3y$ **b)**$4a$ **c)**$3b$ **d)**$2x + 2y$ **e)**$a + 3b$ **f)**$4m + 3n$
2.a)(b), (c) **b)**(a), (d), (e), (f) **3.a)**a, $3a$, $-a$; $2b$, $4b - 6b$
b)$2x$, $-4x$; $-3y$, $-2y$, $-5y$ **c)**$2x^2$, $-2x^2$, $-3x^2$, $-x^2$
d)a^2, $4a^2$; $2a$, $-3a$, $-5a$ **e)**x^2, $-x^2$; y^2, $-y^2$; $2xy$, $-3xy$
f)$6y$, $-3y$, $-2y$; 8, 6 **4.a)**A: 10, B: 10 **5.a)**A: $x^2 + x$, B: $x^2 + x$
6.a)$4a + 4b$ **b)**$3a + 3b$ **c)**$3a + 3b + 2c$ **d)**$4m + 3n$ **e)**$6m$

f)$3x + 3y + 2z$ **g)**$3a + 4b$ **h)**$5x + 3y$ **i)**$3a + 4b + 3c$
j)$6a + 7b$; monomials: (e); binomials: (a), (b), (d), (g), (h),
(j); trinomials: (c), (f), (i) **7.a)**$5x - 5y$ **b)**$5x$ **c)**$-3y$ **d)**$7a$
e)0 **f)**$3x$ **g)**$5y$ **h)**$-2y$ **i)**$5y + 4$ **8.a)**$3a - b$ **b)**$9x - 8$ **c)**$x + y$
d)$3x$ **e)**$2a - b$ **f)**$2a - b$ **g)**$3x$ **h)**$x + y$ **i)**$3x$ **j)**$x + y$
k)$4y - 5x$ **l)**$10k - 8m$; equivalent: (c), (h), (j); (d) (g), (i);
(e), (f) **9.a)**-36 **b)**-5 **c)**-1 **d)**-12 **e)**-8 **f)**-33 **10.** A: 7,
B: -13, C: -1; B **11.a)**30.7 **b)**-25.5 **c)**-44.5 **12.a)**5 **b)**no
13.a)2, 3 **b)**-7, 4 **14.** 30 km **15.a)**$9x$ **b)**$21x + 2$ **c)**$16x + 4$
d)$14x + 2$ **16.a)**54 units, 128 units, 100 units, 86 units
b)90 units, 212 units, 164 units, 142 units **17.a)**$4x$ units
b)$3y$ units **18.a)**$8x$ units **b)**96 units $\times$ 48 units

4.3 Exercise, page 128
1. (a), D; (b), F; (c), E; (d), A; (e), B; (f), C **2.a)**(i)-5 (ii)5
(iii)13 (iv)-13 **b)**(i) and (ii), (iii) and (iv) **3.a)**8, -8 **b)**-7, 7
c)-10, 10 **d)**-7, 7 **4.a)**$-3x$ **b)**$2x$ **c)**$4x^2$ **d)**$-2xy$ **e)**$4x^2y$
f)$g - h$ **g)**$a + b$ **h)**$-e + f$ **i)**$-x^2 - 2x + 5$ **j)**$k^2 + 3k - 6$
k)$-3x + 2y$ **l)**$-y^2 + 2y + 5$ **5.a)**3 **b)**4 **c)**3 **d)**1 **e)**5 **f)**2
6.a)$m + 3$ **b)**$x + y$ **c)**$m + n$ **d)**$x - 6y$ **e)**$4a + 2b$ **f)**2
g)$14m - n$ **7.a)**2 **b)**5 **c)**-7 **8.a)**$-x - y$ **b)**$7a - b$ **c)**$-2m$
d)$4y^2 - 3x^2$ **e)**$3y^2 + xy$ **f)**$x^2 - 3x + 11$ **g)**$-4m^2 - 3m - 3$
9.a)$4x^2 - 6$ **b)**$8ab + 2b$ **c)**$7g^2 - 3g$ **d)**$m^2 - 4m + 1$
e)$3p^2 + p + 8$ **f)**$-x^2y - 2xy + 5$ **10.** 204 km^2 **11.** A: 2,
B: -19, C:-25 **13.** A by 4 units **14.** A: $-m + 4n$,
B: $-6m + 4n$ **15.a)**$4x + 14$ **b)**$\overline{LN} = 46$ units,
$\overline{LM} = 22$ units, $\overline{NM} = 26$ units **c)**94 units **16.a)**(i) 72 units
(ii) 127 units (iii) 226 units **b)**$x = 20$ **17.a)**$5x + 5y$ **b)**$x + 7y$
c)$18x + 22y$

4.4 Exercise, page 131
1.a)$5(y + 23)$ **b)**$\frac{1}{2}n - \frac{1}{3}n$ **2.a)**$10n$ **b)**$5(n - 1)$ **c)**$50n$ **3.a)**$n - 15$
b)$\frac{2}{3}n$ **c)**$2n$ **d)**$n - \frac{1}{2}n$ **4.a)**$k + 3$ **b)**$2k$ **c)**$\frac{1}{2}(k - 3)$ **d)**$\frac{2}{3}(k + 1)$
5.a)$l - 8$, l **b)**$2w$, w **c)**l, $\frac{1}{2}l - 3$ **d)**w, $2w + 3$ **e)**l, $\frac{1}{2}l + 2$
6.a)$35n + 25$ **b)**$15n - 20$ **c)**$6n + 10$ **d)**$105n + 25$ **e)**$21n + 2$
f)$16n + 20$ **g)**$36n + 54$ **h)**$93n - 48$ **7.** 27 cats, 62 birds
8. horizontal symmetry, BED, BID, HEX, BOX, HIDE,
DECK, ECHO, KICKED **9.a)**twice a number increased
by 5 **b)**a number decreased by 8 **c)**six times a number
d)three times a number decreased by 1 **e)**five times a number
decreased by that number **f)**seven more than half the number
g)fifteen decreased by twice a number **h)**two-thirds the sum
of a number and 1 **i)**half of a number which has been
decreased by 1 **j)**half of the sum of a number and twice
the number **10.** $5x - 6y$ **11.** $-x - 2y$ **12.** $7x - 4y$
13. $-5a - 6b$ **14.** $3a + 5b$ **15.** $-10a + 6b$ **16.** $-4x + 3y$
17. $11a + 2b$ **18.** $a - 4b$ **19.** $-2x^2 - 11xy$ **20.** $8m$ **21.** $-ab - b$
22. $2m^2 + 9n^3$ **23.** $5v + 10vw + 5w$

4.5 Exercise, page 134
1.a)\$3.25 **b)**\$4.25 **c)**\$5.25 **d)**\$21.25 **2.a)**\$9.88 **b)**\$5.20 **c)**\$23.90
3.a)2293 m **b)**108 m **4.a)**\$247.02 **b)**\$317.50 **c)**\$292.88
5.a)12 adults **6.a)**210 **b)**2520 **c)**168 **7.** \$467.80

4.6 Exercise, page 137
1.a)$6x$ **b)**$-6y$ **c)**$-10k$ **d)**$-3y$ **e)**$6y$ **f)**$3x$ **g)**$20x^2$ **h)**$-6xy$
i)$-18ab^2$ **j)**$-6y^2$ **2.a)**$3x + 18$ **b)**$2y + 8$ **c)**$48 + 8y$ **d)**$6x + 8$
e)$-16y - 4$ **f)**$-6y + 3$ **g)**$-6x + 12y$ **h)**$-56 + 24y$
i)$3x - 18y$ **j)**$-2m + 6n$ **k)**$15m + 35n$ **l)**$-12m + 4n$
3.a)$3x - 6$ **b)**$-y - 3$ **c)**$-4y + 10$ **d)**$-2y + 4$ **e)**$-6x + 4y$
f)$-6a - 15b$ **g)**$12a - 8b$ **h)**$-30y + 15x$ **i)**$-15x + 6y$
4.a)$5x + 6$ **b)**$x + 10$ **c)**$-2y - 12$ **d)**$-3a + 24$ **e)**$-8a + 5$
f)$-8m$ **g)**15 **h)**$-4a + 28$ **i)**$-17x - 4$ **j)**$-3x + 8$ **k)**$23m + 12$
l)$-9x - 20$ **5.a)**$x - 6$ **b)**$5m - 15$ **c)**$-7m + 23$ **d)**$-3m - 14$
e)$7y - 63$ **f)**$7y - 81$ **g)**$6x$ **h)**$m + 14$ **6.a)**7 **b)**7 **c)**(b)
7.a)$-14, -17, -18$ **b)**$-5, -2, -1$ **c)**$40, -8, -24$
8.a)25¢ **b)**$13.75 **c)**$6.25 **9.a)**$5k + 3$ **b)**$5.7p - 13.2$
c)$-2.7w + 10.8$ **d)**$1.4m + 0.5$ **e)**$-0.9q - 1.8$ **f)**$0.5b - 36.82$
10.a)0.2 **b)**-20.5 **c)**-28 **d)**-25 **11.a)**$15x - 5$ **b)**$7x - 17$
12.a)$18x$ **b)**90 units, 180 units **13.** 105 line segments

4.8 Exercise, page 141
1.c)K **2.b)**M **3.a)**X **b)**Q **c)**J **d)**N **4.a)**N **b)**S **c)**S **d)**S **5.a)**T **b)**K
6.a)68 **b)**70 **7.** $92 + 7954 = 8046$ **9.** 4

Practice and Problems, page 143
1.a)2 **b)**-2 **c)**-2 **d)**-2 **2.a)**$7a + 9$ **b)**$5c - 8$ **c)**$-2m^2 - 3mn$
d)$3x^2 + 2x + 6$ **3.a)**34 **b)**0 **c)**21 **d)**-18 **4.** $8x + 28$ **5.a)**$k + 3$
b)$c - 2$ **c)**$w + 3$ **d)**$5k$ **e)**$10m + 10$ **6.a)**$27.50 **b)**$42.50
c)$50.00 **d)**$110.00 **7.a)**$3a + b$ **b)**$-a - b$ **c)**$3a$ **8.a)**-8
b)5 **c)**-36 **d)**18 **e)**8 **f)**-13 **9.** 21 **10.** 1

Practice Test, page 144
1.a)$2d + 2$ **b)**$3w^2 - w$ **c)**$-2q$ **d)**$4y - x$ **2.a)**92.3 **b)**17.4 **c)**-0.8
3. 2 units **4.a)**$x + 5$ **b)**$p - 5q$ **c)**$3k + 18$ **d)**$-3y^2 - 9y + 7$
e)$6x - 5y$ **f)**$-4ab + 3b^2$ **5.a)**$\frac{1}{2}n$ **b)**$9n$ **c)**$4(n - 3)$ **d)**$n + \frac{2}{3}n$
6.a)$-u - c$ **b)**$2d + 5h$ **7.a)**$3.00 **b)**$10.50 **c)**$12.75 **d)**$22.50
8.a)$5p - 35q$ **b)**$-2y - 10$ **c)**$x + 8$ **d)**$k + 14$ **e)**$-4w^2 + w$
f)$5p^2 - 46$ **g)**$m - 4.5$ **h)**$2.55y - 5.1z$ **9.** 12 096

Cumulative Review, page 145
1.a)99.1 **b)**154.8 **c)**3.9 **d)**3960.0 **e)**8.5 **f)**54.0 **g)**34.6 **h)**20.7
i)836.5 **j)**903.2 **k)**207.4 **l)**4.3 **m)**50.7 **n)**4.8 **o)**2.1 **2.a)**$10 \times 10 \times 10$; 10^3 **b)**$2 \times 2 \times 2 \times 2 \times 2$; 2^5 **c)**$3 \times 3 \times 3$; 3^3 **d)**$5 \times 5 \times 5$;
5^3 **e)**$10 \times 10 \times 10 \times 10 \times 10$; 10^5 **3.a)**32 **b)**17 **c)**18 **d)**72 **e)**2
f)2 **g)**20 **h)**133 **i)**27 **4.a)**-21 **b)**6 **c)**-17 **5.a)**9 **b)**6 **c)**-18 **d)**1
e)-1 **f)**-8 **g)**0 **h)**36 **i)**64 **j)**0 **k)**0 **l)**4 **6.a)**$-1.\dot{3}$ **b)**4.6 less
7.a)$-\frac{1}{2}$ **b)**$\frac{15}{32}$ **c)**$-\frac{9}{64}$ **d)**$\frac{9}{256}$ **e)**$-\frac{3}{16}$ **8.** 3.0 m

CHAPTER 5

5.1 Exercise, page 149
2.a)5 **b)**-2 **c)**5 **d)**6 **3.b)**7 **4.a)**5 **b)**6 **c)**-4 **d)**-3 **e)**$-\frac{1}{2}$ **f)**-11
5.a){2} **b)**{0} **c)**{3} **d)**{3} **e)**{10} **f)**{6} **6.a)**4 **b)**5 **c)**6 **d)**8 **e)**6
f)2 **7.a)**2 **b)**4 **c)**-3 **d)**4 **e)**-3 **f)**-3 **g)**2 **h)**4 **i)**-3 **j)**4 **k)**-3 **l)**2
8. (a), (c), (e), (g) **9.** (a), (c), (d), (e) **10.** 4 pennies, 6 nickels,
12 dimes, 8 quarters **11.** 1029 m

5.2 Exercise, page 152
1.a)subtract 8 **b)**multiply by 4 **c)**divide by 6 **d)**add 6
e)subtract -3 **f)**multiply by -2 **2.a)**4 **b)**10 **c)**-9 **d)**9 **e)**12
f)-8 **3.a)**3 **b)**12 **c)**$\frac{1}{6}$ **d)**24 **e)**2 **f)**24 **g)**-6 **h)**-15 **4.a)**23 **b)**17
c)-56 **d)**-9 **e)**18 **f)**-26 **g)**-8 **h)**12 **5.a)**12 **b)**5 **c)**-52 **d)**20
e)2.4 **f)**9 **g)**2 **h)**-5 **6.a)**{3.3} **b)**{7.7} **c)**{3.25} **d)**{-3.4}
e){-10.8} **f)**{5.9} **g)**{3.3} **h)**{-12.4} **i)**{-11.1} **7.** 4

5.3 Exercise, page 153
1.a)6 **b)**-11 **c)**-5 **d)**2 **e)**9 **f)**l **g)**10 **h)**15 **i)**9 **j)**-8 **k)**-2 **l)**-3
m)-42 **n)**-72 **o)**-6 **p)**3 **4.a)**5 **b)**2 **c)**16 **d)**-2 **e)**l **f)**6 **5.a)**6
b)2 **c)**28 **d)**4 **e)**5 **f)**2 **6.a)**5 **b)**1 **c)**2 **d)**5 **e)**4 **f)**2 **7.a)**{-5} **b)**{8}
c){9} **d)**{10} **e)**{-2} **f)**{10} **8.a)**5.2 **b)**1.9 **c)**1.8 **d)**3.3 **e)**2.1
f)4.2 **9.** 50 people **10.** $(4 \times 8 + 4 \div 2 - 8 - 3) \times (3 - 3) = 0$

5.4 Exercise, page 156
1.a)$2y - 6$ **b)**$18 - 3y$ **c)**$-2x + 12$ **d)**$-8y + 24$ **e)**$9 - 6y$
f)$-6y + 12$ **g)**$2x + 8$ **h)**$10 - 3x$ **i)**$x + 8$ **j)**$10x$ **k)**$3x - 12$
l)$-3x - 20$ **2.a)**$\frac{1}{6}x$ **b)**$\frac{7y}{12}$ **c)**$\frac{2y}{15}$ **3.b)**$\frac{1}{2}$ **4.a)**14 **b)**6 **c)**3 **d)**8
e)5 **f)**4 **g)**$-2\frac{1}{2}$ **h)**$-\frac{1}{2}$ **5.a)**15 **b)**0 **c)**{5} **6.a)**{6} **b)**{4} **c)**$\left\{2\frac{1}{2}\right\}$
d){11} **e)**{6} **f)**{15} **g)**$\left\{\frac{1}{2}\right\}$ **h)**{2} **7.a)**3 **b)**0.4 **c)**-2 **d)**1.5 **e)**4
f)14 **g)**40 **8.a)**$\frac{1}{12}$ **b)**10 **c)**30 **d)**2 **e)**20 **f)**-12 **g)**15 **h)**-75 **i)**33

9. -60 **10.a)**2 **b)**3 **c)**10 **d)**2 **e)**-6 **f)**-5 **11.a)**4 **b)**$2\frac{2}{3}$ **c)**3 **d)**5

e)$-8\frac{1}{2}$ **f)**22 **12.** 24 **13.** $3^3 + 3$ **14.** 5 zones **15.** 15 brothers

16. $33\frac{2}{7}$ h **17.** Twice **18.** 6 zones **19.** 28 years **20.** 5 events

5.5 Exercise, page 159
1. $6x + 4 = 40$ **2.** $4x + 4 = 160$ **3.** $20y = 400$ **4.** $6x - 2 = 154$
5. $\overline{AB} = 10$ m, $\overline{AC} = 11$ m, $\overline{BC} = 16$ m **6.a)**(i) 222 m
(ii)178 m (iii)135 m **7.a)**$\overline{EF} = 4$ m, $\overline{FG} = 9$ m, $\overline{HG} = 12$ m,
$\overline{EH} = 9$ m **b)**$\overline{AB} = \overline{BC} = \overline{ED} = \overline{EF} = 3.5$ m, $\overline{CD} = 7$ m
$\overline{HG} = 14$ m, $\overline{AH} = \overline{FG} = 10.5$ m **8.** 32 subscriptions
9. 32 cattle **10.** A and D **11.a)**$12h + 3$ **b)**wrist 8, palm 5,
fingers 14 **12.a)**$k - 0.4$ **b)**5.4 m **13.a)**$16t + 6.8$
b)snapping 26.3 kg, alligator 98.3 kg **14.a)**$11k - 5$
b)nitrogen 6 kg, phosphorus 20 kg, potash 24 kg **15.a)**$20a$
b)49 cm³ oxygen, 191 cm³ nitrogen **16.a)**$12a + 6$ **b)**24 g

5.6 Exercise, page 163
1.a)$2j - 2 = 20$ **b)**$2j + 5 = 30$ **c)**$j = 8$ **2.a)**$4w + 4 = 30$
b)$2w^2 - w = 40$ **3.a)**$2s - 200 = 750$ **b)**$2s + 150 = 890$
c)$s = 330$ **4.a)**20, 28 **b)**48 **c)**15 **5.a)**24, 25, 26 **b)**$-48, -49,$
-50 **6.a)**12 m × 36 m **b)**12 cm × 20 cm **7.** Peach 92 m,
Fenwick 91 m, Lombard 124 m **8.** Andrea $750, Julie
$1000, Laura $500 **9.** Scott $9, Max $7, Sam $14 **10.**
Abigail $500, Klaus $1500, Jerome $750 **11.** Bridget $321,
Kelsey $642, Wayne $963 **12.** Sam 395, Bruce 195, Les 545
14. 6 **15.** 5 km

5.7 Exercise, page 165

1.a)$3x + 1 = 13$ **b)**$8n = 24$ **c)**$n - 5 = 19$ **d)**$2n - 6 = 8$
2.a)twice a number **b)**a number increased by 5
c)five less than a number **d)**one more than twice a number
e)three reduced by twice a number **f)**two-thirds of a number
g)a number increased by twice the number **h)**three more than
half a number **i)**ten reduced by half a number **j)**five less
than one-third of a number **3.** 45, 46 **4.** 25, 26 **5.a)**180 **b)**216
6. 42 eyes **7.a)**58, 17 **b)**5 **8.** 61 girls, 73 boys **9.** 15, 45 **11.** 192

5.8 Exercise, page 167

1. Virja \$600, Yannak \$500 **2.** 27, 28, 29 **3.** Tanya \$25,
Janet \$16, Fraser \$48 **4.** 7, 23 **5.** diskette \$4.25, cassette \$2.50
6. 16 **7.** large 83¢, small 68¢ **8.a)**122 **b)**134th and
135th digits

5.9 Exercise, page 169

1.a)$5n$ **b)**$50n$ **c)**$25d + 150$ **d)**$30n - 10$ **e)**$5q - 20$ **2.a)**$k + 5$,
$k - 6$ **b)**$k + 7$, $k - 4$ **c)**$m + 2$, $m - 9$ **d)**$2p + 5$, $2p - 6$
e)$30 - p$, $19 - p$ **3.** 4 years **4.** 3 nickels, 6 dimes, 12 quarters
5. marsupial 57 years, orangutan 19 years **6.** me 37 years,
son 11 years **7.** me 31 years, daughter 5 years **8.** 11 nickels,
32 dimes **9.** Jerry 6 years, Elaine 18 years **10.** 7 dimes,
23 quarters **12.** me 15 years, father 45 years
13. me 42 years, daughter 12 years

5.10 Exercise, page 172

1.a)$16x$ **b)**$8x + 2$ **c)**$12x - 2$ **2.a)**$6w - 4$ **b)**$10w + 8$ **c)**$8w$
d)$6w + 12$ **3.** 14 cm × 20 cm **4.** 5 m × 12 m **5.a)**16 m × 22 m
b)352 m² **6.a)**8 m **b)**624 m² **7.** Rose 5 years, Shirley
22 years **8.a)**64 m × 125 m **b)**8000 m² **c)**flag by 2600 m²
9. 9 m × 27 m **10.a)**28 m × 56 m **b)**168 m **11.** 4.0 m **12.** 1 cut

5.11 Exercise, page 174

1.a)\$7.50 **b)**\$15.00 **c)**\$8.13 **d)**\$15.63 **2.a)**\$0.08x **b)**\$0.12y
c)\$0.065m **d)**\$(0.09m + 45) **3.a)**\$46.00 **b)**\$66.50
c)\$(100 - 0.02m) **d)**\$(45 + 0.02n) **4.a)**multiplied by 100 **b)**50
5.a)50 **b)**100 **6.** \$4000 @ 8%, \$2000 @ 12% **7.** \$2400 **8.** \$600
9. \$250 @ 8%, \$500 @ 11% **10.** \$4800 @ 9%, \$3600 @ 12%
11. 85% **12.b)**lost \$8.33 **13.** 9 **14.** 40 **15.** 250 programs
16. 20 fish **17.** 2 h **18.** 60 **19.** 45 non-sporting, 30 sporting

5.12 Exercise, page 179

1.a)50 **b)**142.5 **c)**840 **d)**32 **2.a)**$\dfrac{A}{w}$ **b)**$\dfrac{V}{S}$ **3.a)**$\dfrac{V - k}{2}$ **b)**$\dfrac{V - \mu}{a}$
4.a)$\dfrac{t}{3} - s$ **b)**$\dfrac{P}{2} - l$ **5.a)**$x = 6 - y$ **b)**$x = 3 - 2y$ **c)**$x = \dfrac{y + 4}{2}$
d)$x = \dfrac{y + 8}{2}$ **e)**$x = \dfrac{6 - 3y}{2}$ **f)**$x = 3y - 4$ **6.a)**$P = \dfrac{I}{rt}$ **b)**$r = \dfrac{I}{Pt}$
c)$t = \dfrac{I}{Pr}$ **7.a)**$P = \dfrac{A}{1 + rt}$ **b)**$r = \dfrac{A - P}{Pt}$ **c)**$t = \dfrac{A - P}{Pr}$ **8.a)**$l = \dfrac{A}{w}$,
116 **b)**$b = \dfrac{2A}{h}$, 24 **c)**$h = \dfrac{2A}{a + b}$, 16 **d)**$l = \dfrac{P}{2} - w$, 32
e)$s = \sqrt{A}$, 43 **f)**$h = \dfrac{A}{b}$, 89 **9.a)**650 **b)**18 **c)**6 **d)**1.6 **e)**48 **f)**38

g)661.25 **h)**45 **10.a)**$x = \dfrac{y - b}{2}$ **b)**$x = \dfrac{y - b}{m}$ **c)**$m = 3 - \dfrac{v}{k}$
d)$b = \dfrac{2A}{h}$ **11.a)**$h = \dfrac{2A}{b}$ **b)**8, 9, 4.5, 2.5 **12.** 31 wins

13.a)5 fouls **b)**1 foul **c)**8 fouls **14.** 34 m **15.a)**$V = \dfrac{d}{t} + s$
b)8, 26, 9.6 **16.b)**1.0, 1.3, 1.6, 2.0, 2.4 **17.b)**4, 1.5 **18.** 77.4 m²

5.13 Exercise, page 183

1.a)$m > 3$ **b)**$p > 5$ **c)**$x \le 6$ **d)**$x \ge 2$ **e)**$p < -2$ **f)**$t \ge 2$
g)$t \ge -2$ **h)**$r < 8$ **i)**$t < 7$ **2.a)**$\{x \mid x > 1, x \in I\}$
3.a)$\{y \mid y \ge 3, y \in I\}$ **5.a)**$y < 8$ **b)**$x \ge 9$ **c)**$y \le 22$ **d)**$x < 6$
e)$m > 6$ **f)**$k \ge -1$ **6.a)**$x \ge 3\dfrac{1}{2}$ **b)**$y > 6$ **c)**$y \le -6$ **d)**$m < 2$
e)$p \ge -4$ **f)**$x < 3$ **g)**$p \ge 4$ **h)**$k \le -1\dfrac{1}{2}$ **i)**$y > \dfrac{1}{3}$ **7.a)**$x > -9$,
$x \in R$ **8.a)**$y < 11$ **b)**$x > 6$ **c)**$m \le -7$ **d)**$y \le -1$ **9.** $y \ge 14$,
$y \in I$ **10.** $n > 5$ **11.** $n > -16$, $n \in R$ **12.** $n < 24$, $n \in I$
13. 12 cola, 9 orange, 24 ginger **14.** 12 quarters, 3 dimes,
6 nickels; 10 quarters, 2 dimes, 5 nickels; 8 quarters,
1 dime, 4 nickels; 6 quarters, 0 dimes, 3 nickels

5.14 Exercise, page 185

1.a)$25x + 10x + 50 = 155$ **b)**$2n + 7 = 3n - 5$
c)$b - 1 + b - 3 = 22$ **d)**$2f + \dfrac{2}{3}f = 200$
e)$n + 1 + n + 2 - (n + 3) = n$ **2.** 16 girls **3.** Cliff 48 km,
Craig 96 km **4.** 9, 27 **5.a)**147 students, 62 adults **b)**\$1.75
6.a)300 m **b)**21.4 m × 21.4 **7.** Two boys 32 h each, two boys
64 h each **8.** 40 pages, 260 pages **9.** Mary Rose \$4, John \$8,
Melanie \$16 **10.** Me 36 years, daughter 14 years **11.** Won 34,
lost 17, tied 27 **12.** Johann 110, Swelm 22, Hann 12 **13.** \$800
14. 16 m × 19 m **15.** won 16, tied 14, lost 48 **16.** 11 years
17. \$2.00 **18.** Brian 66, Nora 82, Alan 50 **19.** lost \$224

5.15 Exercise, page 188

4. 125 **5.** Shirley and Alex, Frank and Rose Mary,
Margie and John

Practice and Problems, page 189

1.a)4 **b)**-5 **c)**3 **d)**2 **2.a)**1 **b)**11 **c)**-18 **d)**-42 **e)**15 **f)**3
g)$n \le 9$ **h)**-3 **i)**$y > 15$ **j)**3 **k)**$x \ge 10$ **l)**-19 **m)**$-\dfrac{1}{2}$
3. Yesterday 29, Today 65 **4.a)**5, 8 **b)**28, 29, 30 **5.** 8 horses
6. Andrea $k + 3$, Pamela $2k$, $2k + 3$ **7.** Andrea 7,
Pamela 14 **8.** 15 m × 42 m **9.** \$3 000

Practice Test, page 190

1.a)2 **b)**20 **c)**$y \ge 4$ **d)**1.4 **e)**-2 **f)**8 **g)**2.5 **h)**$y \ge -1.5$ **i)**11 **j)**4
k)$x < 6$ **l)**9 **m)**4 **n)**3 **2.a)**7 **b)**9 **c)**6.4 **3.** 13 goals
4. 16, 23 **5.** 11 dimes, 9 quarters **6.** \$2575 @ 12%,
\$1925 @ 8% **7.** 10 nickels, 7 dimes, 9 quarters
8. Rejean 15 years, Gilbert 14 years **9.** 11 cm × 27 cm,
8 cm × 30 cm **10.** \$2000 @ $6\dfrac{1}{2}$%, \$3000 @ 8% **11.** \$2.50

6.1 Exercise, page 193
1.a)62.4 cm **b)**96.1 km **c)**464.4 m **2.a)**80.0 cm, 251.2 cm
b)330.0 cm, 1036.2 cm **c)**4.3 m, 27.0 m **d)**9.1 km, 57.1 km
3. A: 89.5 m, B: 90.5 m, C: 88.8 m, greatest perimeter B
4.a)13.7 m, 10.0 m, 143.8 m **b)**4.5 cm, 105.8 cm **c)**6.2 km,
74.0 km **5.a)**48.5 m **b)**43.5 cm **c)**28.8 m **6.** 105 m **7.** 50.4 m
8.a)$335.58 **b)**$177.69 **c)**$209.69 **9.a)**218.2 cm, 458 turns
b)10.2 m, 98 turns **c)**13.6 m, 73 turns **10.** 12 flares
11. 41 639.5 km **12.a)**92.0 m **b)**36.2 m **c)**3.6 m **13.a)**10.0 cm
14.a)239.6 m **b)**1 m/s or 3.6 km/h **15.** 26

6.2 Exercise, page 196
1.a)33.9 m² **b)**8.4cm² **c)**70.4 cm² **d)**80.5 m² **e)**1.3 m²
f)642.1 cm² **g)**118.6 m² **h)**44.2 m² **i)**11.7 cm² **j)**120.7 m²
k)75.4 cm² **2.a)**4.6 cm **b)**6.5 cm **c)**6.4 m **d)**9.3 m **3.** 28.2 cm
4. 161.7 cm² **5.** 171.9 cm² **6.** 6.2 m **7.** 46.8 cm² **8.** 725.5 km²
9. 8.6 m **10.a)**366.2 cm² **b)**5.9 m² **11.a)**98.5 m² **12.b)**increases
by $(2r + 1)\pi$ square units **13.** 394 strips **14.** 3.8 m **15.a)**6
b)6 **16.a)**$\pi R^2 - \pi r^2$ **b)**$4r^2 - \pi r^2$ **c)**$4r^2 - \pi r^2$ **17.a)**154.8 m²
b)99.2 m² **18.a)**48.9 m² **b)**180.0 cm² **c)**43.2 m² **d)**6.0 m²
e)34.7 m² **f)**8.3 m²

6.3 Exercise, page 199
1.a)semi-circle: 36.2 m², triangle: 55.2 m² **b)**91.4 m²
2.a)70.6 cm² **b)**11.0 m² **c)**103.4 cm² **d)**8.6 m² **e)**13.0 cm²
f)11.9 m² **3.a)**1109.3 m² **b)**$484.86 **4.a)**6 **b)**6.0 cm **c)**4.0 cm
d)12.0 cm² **e)**72.0 cm² **f)**3*bh* **5.** $A = \dfrac{nbh}{2}$ **6.a)**181.4 cm²
b)734.4 cm² **c)**1002.2 cm² **d)**864.9 m²

6.4 Exercise, page 203
1.a)6 **b)**square **c)**400.0 cm² **d)**2400.0 cm² **2.c)**6.56 m², 3.68 m²,
9.43 m² **d)**39.3 m² **3.c)**1.2 cm², 1.6 cm², 1.5 cm², 1.5 cm²,
2.0 cm² **d)**7.8 cm² **4.b)**3.24 cm² **c)**2.16 cm² **d)** 11.9 cm² **5.b)**4
c)30.66 cm² **d)**122.6 cm² **6.a)**36.2 m² **b)**96.6 m² **c)**24.6 m²
7.a)1004.8 cm² **b)**50.2 cm × 12.0 cm **8.a)**11.3 m²
9.a)241.3 cm² **b)**60.0 cm² **10.a)**12.6 cm **b)**2.3 cm **11.a)**C:
103.7 cm², B: 180.6 cm², E: 201.2 cm², A: 254.3 cm²,
D: 486.0 cm² **12.** 530.7 cm² **13.b)**Cube sides 9.13 cm,
Cylinder with *r* = 8.45, *h* = 1 or *r* = 8.0 cm, *h* = 2.0 cm, or
r = 7.5 cm, *h* = 3.1 cm, etc. **14.** 4950 L **15.a)**100%
b)Area increases $3\pi r^2 + \pi rs$ **c)**Area of curved surface doubles.
Area of the base quadruples.

6.5 Exercise, page 205
1.a)11.6 m³ **b)**14.5 m³ **c)**9.8 m³ **d)**7.7 m³ **2.a)**trapezium
b)8.3 m² **c)**29.9 m³ **3.a)**semi-cylinder **b)**13.0m³ **4.a)**63.7 cm³
b)2.3 m **c)**4.8 cm **5.a)**151.8 m³ **6.a)**80.4 m³ **7.a)**9.7 m³
b)49 470 kg **8.** 27.4 m³ **9.a)**11.8 L **b)**9.2 L **10.a)**1526.9 m³
b)65 trips **11.a)**213.8 L **b)**235.2 L **12.**4.5 m³ **14.** halved
15.a)$V = \pi h(R^2 - r^2)$ **b)**3.5 m³ **16.a)**4673.3 cm³ **b)**3.2 m
17.a)1.5 m³ **b)**7854 kg

6.6 Exercise, page 208
1.a)A: 64.0 cm³, B: 25.5 cm³, C: 23.4 cm³, D: 21.3 cm³ **b)**D

c)$V = \dfrac{1}{3}s^3 h$ **3.a)**A: 201.0 cm³, B: 80.1 cm³, C: 73.4 cm³,
D: 69.5 cm³ **b)**D **c)**$V = \dfrac{1}{3}\pi r^2 h$

6.7 Exercise, page 211
1.a)60.5 m³ **b)**48.4 m³ **c)**1296.3 cm³ **d)**215.0 m³ **e)**721.2 cm³
f)330.6 cm³ **g)**44.6 m³ **2.a)**10.8 cm³ **b)**29.1 m³ **c)**75.4 m³
d)192.1 cm³ **3.a)**229.7 m³ **b)**229 730.8 L **4.a)**B: 15.0 m³,
A: 22.5 m³, D: 40.3 m³, C: 60.5 m³, E: 332.9 m³ **5.a)**8.6 cm³
b)6.3 m **c)**4.3 cm **6.** 4397.0 m³ **7.a)**34.7 cm³ **b)**6.9 cm
8. 5.5 cm³ **9.** cone: 34.3 m², hemisphere 68.6 m³ **11.a)**6 h
b)student's own name **12.a)**151.5 g **b)**160.9 cm³
c)tennis by 14.1 cm² **13.a)**117.8 cm³ **b)**36.7% **14.** halved

6.8 Exercise, page 213
1.a)B: 1722.2 cm³, C: 991.4 cm³ **b)**2713.6 cm³ **2.a)**250.0 m³
b)68 881.9 m³ **c)**412.6 m³ **d)**37.4 m³ **e)**208.6 m³ **f)**2829.8 cm³

6.9 Exercise, page 214
1. maximum 65.2 m³ **2.** B.C. is not possible on a dated coin
since the birth of Christ was not known. **3.** IX + II = XI
4. 533 packages **5.** 114 games **6.** 13

Practice and Problems, page 215
1.a)6.5 cm **b)**3.8 m **c)**5.4 cm **2.** $518.96 **3.a)**14.3 cm² **b)**58.3 m²
c)33.8 cm² **4.** 141.5 m² **5.** 4069.4 cm² **6.a)**27.0 m
7.a)X: 609.3 cm³, Y: 643.1 cm³, Z: 607.9 cm³; Y **b)**X

Practice Test, page 216
1. $1426.35 **2.** 468 **3.a)**50.8 m² **b)**18.7 cm² **4.a)**C: 55.4 m²,
A: 69.9 m², B: 74.2 m² **b)**C: 38.8 m³, B: 43.0 m³, A: 44.3 m³
5. 13.0 cm **6.** 1417.5 cm³ **7.** 3.1 m³ **8.** 108.9 m³ **9.a)**14.13 m³
b)86.8 m²

7.1 Exercise, page 219
2.a)32 **b)**243 **c)**15 625 **d)**a^5 **e)**b^5 **3.a)**8 **b)**27 **c)**5 **d)**a^4 **e)**b^3
4.a)16 **b)**729 **c)**81 **d)**a^6 **e)**b^9 **5.a)**m^2n^2 **b)**p^3q^3 **c)**s^5t^5 **d)**$8x^3$
e)$9a^2$ **6.a)**$\dfrac{a^2}{b^2}$ **b)**$\dfrac{c^3}{d^3}$ **c)**$\dfrac{a^4}{c^4}$ **d)**$\dfrac{m^3}{8}$ **e)**$\dfrac{y^2}{9}$ **7.a)**4 **b)**m^7 **c)**x^2y^2 **d)**m^6
e)$\dfrac{m^3}{n^3}$ **f)**a^2 **g)**x^9 **h)**$\dfrac{a^5}{b^5}$ **i)**a^5b^5 **j)**x^{15} **8.a)**x^5 **b)**a^6 **c)**a^6 **d)**t^6 **e)**m^{10}
f)b^6 **g)**a^3b^2 **h)**a^3b^3 **9.a)**x^6 **b)**a^6 **c)**m^{15} **d)**y^{10} **e)**y^{10} **f)**64 **g)**36
h)64 **i)**a^2b^4 **j)**a^3b^6 **k)**x^6y^4 **l)**$x^{15}y^9$ **m)**x^4y^{12} **n)**$y^{18}z^{12}$ **o)**$y^{10}z^6$
10.a)$\dfrac{x^3}{y^3}$ **b)**$\dfrac{a^4}{b^4}$ **c)**$\dfrac{x^3y^3}{k^3}$ **d)**$\dfrac{x^6}{y^3}$ **e)**$\dfrac{x^8}{y^6}$ **f)**$\dfrac{x^2y^2}{p^2}$ **g)**$\dfrac{m^{10}n^5}{k^{10}}$ **h)**$\dfrac{x^6y^3}{m^3n^6}$
i)$\dfrac{-a^3b^3}{c^3}$ **j)**$\dfrac{a^4b^2}{c^2}$ **11.a)**x^3 **b)**x **c)**x^4 **d)**4 **e)**1000 **f)**9 **g)**x^2y
h)$3y^3$ **i)** $-2x^3y$ **j)**x^4 **12.** 25, 39 **13.a)** -8 **b)**1 **c)**4 **d)**4 **e)** -2

7.2 Exercise, page 221
2.a)1 **b)**1 **c)**$\dfrac{1}{100}$ **d)**$\dfrac{1}{25}$ **e)**$\dfrac{1}{8}$ **3.a)**$\dfrac{1}{3}$ **b)**$\dfrac{1}{4}$ **c)**$\dfrac{1}{2^3}$ **d)**2 **e)**3^2 **4.a)**9 **b)**$\dfrac{1}{9}$

c)$-\dfrac{1}{9}$ d)-8 e)-9 5.a)1 b)2 c)1 d)4 e)1 6.a)$2x^{-1}$ b)$3x^{-1}$

c)$8x^{-2}$ d)mn^{-3} e)$2tx^{-2}$ f)abn^{-1} 7.a)$\dfrac{1}{x^2}$ b)$\dfrac{3}{x}$ c)$\dfrac{a}{x^3}$ d)$\dfrac{-2p}{n}$

e)$\dfrac{1}{4n^2}$ 8.a)1 b)32 c)1 d)10 e)$\dfrac{1}{2}$ f)64 g)$\dfrac{1}{25}$ h)16 i)4 j)1 k)1

l)256 m)27 n)2 o)$-\dfrac{1}{8}$ p)$\dfrac{1}{16}$ q)$\dfrac{3}{2}$ r)9 9.a)$x^{-1}y$ b)a^3

c)$4^{-1}xy^{-2}$ d)$y^{-3}z^5$ e)xy^{-2} f)a^3b g)a^4b^{-2} h)$a^{-2}b$ 10.a)11 b)11 11.a)x^{3m+n} b)x^{2m+n} c)x^{2m+2} d)x^{4a}

7.3 Exercise, page 224

1.a)1 b)$\dfrac{1}{9}$ c)4 d)10 e)$\dfrac{3}{2}$ 2.a)$-\dfrac{1}{8}$ b)$-\dfrac{1}{8}$ c)-8 3.a)-2 b)-4 c)16

d)1 e)$-\dfrac{1}{8}$ f)$\dfrac{1}{4}$ 4.a)2 b)$\dfrac{5}{6}$ c)$3\dfrac{1}{2}$ d)$1\dfrac{1}{3}$ e)$\dfrac{1}{9}$ f)3 g)1 h)$\dfrac{4}{9}$ i)$-\dfrac{3}{4}$ j)-8

5.a)$\dfrac{1}{2}$ b)$-\dfrac{1}{64}$ c)$-\dfrac{1}{27}$ d)$2\dfrac{1}{2}$ e)5 f)$\dfrac{11}{18}$ g)$\dfrac{9}{16}$ h)$\dfrac{27}{8}$ 6.a)$\dfrac{1}{18}$ b)$4\dfrac{4}{5}$

c)$28\dfrac{1}{2}$ d)$\dfrac{1}{81}$ e)$\dfrac{1}{4}$ f)$\dfrac{6}{5}$ g)$\dfrac{9}{17}$ h)$\dfrac{9}{8}$ 7.a)1 b)$16\dfrac{1}{8}$ c)$2\dfrac{4}{13}$ d)$3\dfrac{1}{2}$; 1,

$2\dfrac{4}{13}$, $3\dfrac{1}{2}$, $16\dfrac{1}{8}$ 8.a)4 b)$\dfrac{1}{4}$ c)1 d)4 e)$\dfrac{1}{4}$ f)$-\dfrac{1}{4}$ g)$\dfrac{2}{3}$ h)$3\dfrac{2}{3}$ i)$\dfrac{1}{4}$ j)3

k)6 l)$-\dfrac{5}{6}$ 9. T

7.4 Exercise, page 226

1.a)3 b)2 c)-3 2.a)4.69 b)3.89 c)8.96 3.a) 640 b)3060 c)0.0637 d)0.0093 4.a)4.86×10^5 b)9.32×10^6 c)4.53×10^{-4} d)1.35×10^{-3} 5.a)6360 b)0.000 321 c)421 000 d)0.000 000 040 8 6.a)3860 b)0.009 32 c)0.0404 d)5 980 000 7.a)9.866 05 b)4.93 -04 c)1.2 -07 d)3.9 06 8.a)683 b)0.009 25 c)0.000 020 2 d)4 510 000 9.a)2.86 + E04 b)3.21 − E04 c)3.45 − E03 d)6.96 + E07

7.5 Exercise, page 227

1.a)2.30×10^3 b)2.300×10^3 c)1.5×10^4 d)8.5×10^{-1} e)8.5×10^{-3} f)1.203×10^4 g)4.80×10^4 h)9.60×10^{-5} 2.a)4.1×10^8 b)1.4×10^2 c)2.1×10^{-1} 3.a)5.53×10^6 b)2×10^5 4. 1.3×10^7 cells 5. 2.5×10^{-18} g 6. 3.6×10^9 microseconds, 3.2×10^{13} microseconds 7. 9.5×10^{20} protons 8.a) chord, altitude, cube, prime, data 9.a)15 137 280 L b)15 936.5 m

7.6 Exercise, page 229

1.a)10^7 b)7 2.b)A: 3; B: 6 3.b)3 4.a)6 b)6 c)4 d)5 5.a)2 b)3 c)1 d)1 e)4 f)2 g)-3 h)2 i)9 j)3 k)2 l)-4

7.7 Exercise, page 231

1.a)m^8 b)x^7 c)p^6 d)y^9 2.a)$-6m$ b)$-15b$ c)$6k$ d)$9n$ e)$10r$ 3.a)$-6xy$ b)$-9y^2$ c)$12mn$ d)$-6a^2b$ e)$6x^4$ f)$-8y^5$ g)$8m^6$ h)$-6a^4$ i)$-6x^4y^2$ j)$-18a^5b^2$ k)$-6a^2b^3$ l)$18a^5$ 4.a)$-28a^2$ b)$12my$ c)$6x^3y$ d)$-6a^3$ e)$-6x^6y$ f)$12x^4$ g)0 h)$-3x^3y^9$ 5.a)$9y^2$ b)$4m^4$ c)$9a^2b^2$ d)$16x^4y^2$ e)$9x^4y^6$ 6.a)-36 b)36 c)-72 d)-216 e)-432 7.a)$-30abc$ b)$5mnp$ c)$-3stv$ d)$-6x^3y^3$ e)$10a^7b^2$ f)$12s^5t^5$ 8.a)$4.8x^5$ b)$-3.33a^3b^2$ c)$-1.4m^2n$ d)$-1.23p^3q^3$ e)$-2.42x^3y^4$ f)$1.44x^4$ 9.a)41.0

b)246.2 c)46.8 d)73.9 e)-362.0 f)9.4 10.a)$-3.36abc$ b)$-0.825mnp$ c)$-7.735stv$ d)$-9.50x^2y^2$ e)-16.908 $75a^2b^2$ f)26.316 $62s^2t^2$ 11.a)black △ b)red ○ 12.a)A: $36x^2y^2$, B: $2x^3y^2$, C: $6x^3y$ b)A: $24xy$, B: $4xy + 2x^2y$, C: $4x^2 + 6xy$ 13.a)A: 9216 square units, 384 units, B: 4096 square units, 320 units, C: 6144 square units, 352 units b)A c)A 14.a)$30x^2$ b)$12x^2$ c)$18x^2$ d)72, 1800

7.8 Exercise, page 234

1.a)$6xy$ b)$-6xy$ c)$6x^2$ d)$-6x^2$ e)$3x^3$ f)$6xy$ g)$48a^3$ h)$-x^3y^4$ 2.a)$-3x^2 + 3x - 3y$ b)$-2xy - 2z$ c)$-9a + 18b - 9c$ d)$8p - 12q$ e)$5m - 15n$ f)$-2x^2 - 2xy + 2y^2$ g)$-20a + 12a^2$ h)$3p - 15q + 3q^2$ i)$-4x^2 + 4xy + 4y^3$ 3.a)$-3x^2 + 3xy$ b)$-2m^2 - 2mn$ c)$4x^3 - 4x^3y$ d)$18a^2 - 12ab$ e)$3m^3n + 2m^2n^2$ f)$18x^2y - 12y^3$ 4.a)$5x^2y + 5x^2y^2 - 5xy^2$ b)$-2p^3 + 2p^2 - 2pq$ c)$2x^3 - 6x^2 - 2x$ d)$-3a^3 + 6a^2 + 3a$ e)$-2m^3 + 6m^2n - 2mn^2$ f)$-2a^3 + 3a^2b - a^2c$ 5.a)20 b)8 c)-12 d)7 e)-14 f)-4 6.a)$5x^2 + 6$ b)$p + 10$ c)$24 - 3a$ d)$-17x^2 - 4x$ e)$23mn + 12m$ f)$-6y + 3y^2$ 7.a)-8 b)-10 c)84 d)-36 e)-16 f)-22 8.a)$0.5x^2 - 0.5xy$ b)$1.5a - 3.6b$ c)$0.9p^4 - 0.99p^3$ d)$3.2m^3 - 5.12m^2$ e)$1.4x^3 - 0.7x^2 + 3.08x$ f)$-0.6k^3 + 1.26k^2 - 1.92k$ 9.a)2.025 b)-1.62 c)5.13 d)1.98 e)1.08 f)-2.43 10. D

7.9 Exercise, page 236

1.a)m b)x c)y d)1 2.a)$3y$ b)$-3x$ c)$-3a^3$ d)$-3m$ 3.a)$3y$ b)$3y$ c)4 d)m^3 e)-1 f)x^2 g)$5xy$ h)$-m^3$ 4.a)$3m$ b)$-2b$ c)$2a$ d)$-6n$ e)$-8c$ f)8 g)$-10mn$ h)$3x^2y$ i)$-4b$ j)-3 k)$3m$ l)$-2m$ 5.a)$2p$ b)$-4s^2$ c)$-6m$ d)$6p^2$ e)$-2n^2$ f)$-4a$ 6.a)-6 b)-16 c)144 d)-6 7. 75 8. 6 tens, 4 fives, 2 twos, 1 one 9.a)$6xy$ b)$4ab$ c)$4xy^2$ 10.a)$-x^2$ b)$\dfrac{x}{y}$ c)$\dfrac{-3}{2b^2}$ d)$6y$ e)$\dfrac{8k}{25}$ f)$\dfrac{5x}{12a}$ 11.a)$\dfrac{4}{x}$ b)$\dfrac{-1}{5y}$ c)$\dfrac{18x}{49}$ d)$\dfrac{8}{-xy}$ e)$\dfrac{-3a}{2}$ f)$\dfrac{-1}{4ax}$ 12.a)x^2 b)$\dfrac{b^2}{2a}$ c)$4a^2$ d)$\dfrac{5}{x}$ e)$\dfrac{16m^2}{-n^3}$ f)$\dfrac{1}{t}$ 13.a)$\dfrac{5a^2}{6b^2}$ b)$\dfrac{25a^2}{16b^2}$ c)$\dfrac{4a^2}{9b^2}$ d)$1\dfrac{7}{8}$

7.10 Exercise, pages 239

1.a)$2y + 6$ b)$4m + 8$ c)$2b - 3$ d)$5y + 4$ e)$-4m - 3$ f)$6y^2 + 4y$ 2.a)$y + 6$ b)$2y - 8$ c)$4y + 1$ d)$2y - 1$ e)$6 - y$ f)$6b - 12c$ g)$8y - 4$ h)$-5n + 2$ 3.a)$3a + 4$ b)$5m - 2x$ c)$-2x + 3x^2$ d)$3y + 4$ e)$4x^2 - 2y^2$ f)$3n + 2m$ 4.a)-9 b)-1 c)-13 5.a)$3 + x - 4x^2$ b)$2 - k + 8k^2$ c)$3x^2 + 2x - 5$ d)$2y - 1 + x$ e)$y - xy - x$ f)$-a^2 + 2a + b$ g)$-3x + 2y - 5xy$ h)$-3am + 2m + 6a$ 6.a)$4x^2y + x$ b)82 units 7.a)$4x^2y - 3xy$ b)30 units, 120 units d)900 square units 8.a)$1 = 3^{3-3}$, $2 = (3 + 3) \div 3$, $3 = 3 \times 3 \div 3$, $4 = 3 \div 3 + 3$ b)$6 = 3 \times 3 - 3$, $9 = 3 + 3 + 3$

7.11 Exercise, page 241

1.a)$5t$ b)y c)$\dfrac{13p}{4}$ d)$-\dfrac{2s}{3}$ e)$5k$ 2.a)$\dfrac{7y + 24}{12}$ b)$\dfrac{3p + 5}{9}$ c)$\dfrac{3x - 19}{6}$ 3.b)$\dfrac{7x - 5}{10}$ 4.b)$\dfrac{-y - 21}{6}$ 5.a)$\dfrac{7y}{4}$ b)$\dfrac{11a}{3}$ c)$\dfrac{13p}{20}$ 6.a)$\dfrac{7}{2a}$ b)$\dfrac{1}{x^2}$ c)$\dfrac{4x}{a}$ d)$\dfrac{2}{3x}$ e)$\dfrac{3 - 2y}{2y^2}$ f)$\dfrac{2}{m}$ 7.a)$\dfrac{7x - 8}{4}$

b) $\dfrac{y-14}{6}$ **c)** $\dfrac{10x-9}{8}$ **d)** $\dfrac{-41m-96}{6}$ **e)** $\dfrac{x+7}{12}$ **f)** $\dfrac{56k-63}{10}$

8.a) $\dfrac{37}{20}$ **b)** -1 **c)** -3 **9.a)** 3 **b)** $-4\dfrac{1}{6}$; (a)

7.12 Exercise, page 244

1.a) 3 **b)** 8 **c)** -4 **d)** $6a$ **e)** $4ab$ **f)** $3x^2$ **g)** $4a$ **h)** $5ab$ **i)** x^2 **j)** x **k)** ab
l) $2xy$ **2.a)** 2 **b)** 2π **c)** $1-2y$ **d)** $y-2$ **e)** $-3x+2y-5xy$
f) $-3am+2m+6a$ **3.a)** $6(1-2x)$ **b)** $x(5x-3)$ **c)** $3(3y-4x)$
d) $xy(5-3y)$ **e)** $2x(x-3)$ **f)** $a(a-2)$ **g)** $b(4a-b)$ **h)** $4(y^2-4)$
i) $14a(2a-b)$ **j)** $mn(36-25mn)$ **k)** $3(2x^2-4x+5)$
l) $5(m^3-5m^2+3)$ **m)** $25(2a^2+3ab+b^2)$
n) $10xy(x^2y^2+2xy-1)$ **4.a)** 15 **b)** 36 **c)** -90 **d)** -12 **e)** 30
f) 126 **g)** -63 **h)** 84 **i)** -198 **5.a)** $3a(7-4a)$ **b)** $a(b^2+14)$
c) $k^2(2-3k+8k^2)$ **d)** $xy(x^2-2xy-y^2)$ **e)** $5b(4-5b)$
f) $20a^2b^2$ **g)** $-2y(2y-1+x)$ **h)** $xy(x-xy-y)$
i) $3(3x^2-4xy-2y^2)$ **6.a)** $2x+3y$ **b)** $x-6y$ **c)** $1+2y$
d) x^3-7y^2 **e)** $-2x-3y$ **f)** x^2+2x+3

7.13 Exercise, page 245

1. 28 **2.** $VI + IV = X$ **3.** 50

Practice and Problems, page 246

1.a) 3^6 **b)** x^5 **c)** a^6 **d)** 3^4 **e)** m^4 **f)** c^2 **g)** 2^6 **h)** x^6 **i)** a^{15} **2.a)** $4x^3$
b) $\dfrac{-4c^2}{x^3}$ **c)** $\dfrac{4}{b^6}$ **d)** $\dfrac{-5}{b^2}$ **3.a)** 5 **b)** $\dfrac{1}{9}$ **c)** 1 **d)** $-\dfrac{5}{6}$ **4.a)** 8.5×10^5
b) 3.45×10^6 **c)** 1.25×10^{-4} **d)** 3.904×10^{-3} **5.a)** 3.0×10^5
b) 3.6×10^3 **c)** 1.08×10^9 km **6.a)** 5 **b)** 2 **c)** 3 **7.a)** $8a^2$ **b)** $-12a^2c$
c) d^3 **d)** $-2k^7$ **e)** $3n^3$ **f)** $2y^5$ **g)** $2p^3q$ **h)** x^4y **8.a)** $-6d^2$ **b)** $6k^4$
c) $-8r+12$ **d)** $6f^2-15fw$ **9.a)** $5x$ **b)** $15y$ **c)** $4x$ **d)** $-4x$ **e)** $2hk$
f) $-3y$ **10.a)** $n+3$ **b)** $-2k+6$ **c)** $-4b+8c$ **d)** $n-2$
11.a) $3(3-4y)$ **b)** $b(5a-3b)$ **c)** $y(5x^2-x+y)$
d) $2q(p^2-2p+4q)$ **e)** $3k(k-3+4k^3)$ **f)** $3m^2n^2(1-3mn)$

Practice Test, page 247

1.a) 2^5 **b)** n^5 **c)** 3^4 **d)** q^5 **e)** 3^6 **f)** m^{12} **g)** $8t^3$ **h)** a^2c^2 **i)** $8k^{12}$ **j)** $27x^6$
2.a) 1 **b)** $\dfrac{1}{16}$ **c)** 9 **d)** $-\dfrac{2}{9}$ **e)** $\dfrac{3}{4}$ **3.a)** $-1\dfrac{5}{9}$ **b)** 4 **c)** -3 **d)** -3
4.a) 4.5×10^6 **b)** 2.9×10^{-5} **c)** 3.92×10^{-7} **5.a)** $52\,000\,000$
b) $0.001\,95$ **c)** $0.000\,000\,28$ **6.** 24.0 g **7.a)** 3 **b)** 1 **c)** -1
8.a) $-12x^2y$ **b)** $-21g^2k$ **c)** $36d-8d^2$ **d)** $-14p^3+2p^2$
9.a) -8 **b)** -153 **10.a)** $-8h$ **b)** $-9x^2$ **c)** $3-2k$ **d)** $5q-3p$
11. $6xy-3y$, 60 square units **12.a)** $5x(x-3)$ **b)** $3b(3a^2-4)$
c) $2x^2(x^3-2x-4)$

Cumulative Review, page 248

1.a) $3a-2b$ **b)** $-2x+2y$ **c)** $5y-6$ **d)** $32-4y$ **e)** $4y-18$
f) $-2y-1$ **g)** $-m-1$ **h)** $2p-12q$ **i)** $4x-14$ **j)** $-5a+b$
2.a) $10x-6y$ **b)** $4x+6y$ **c)** $4x-4y$ **d)** $10x-6y$; (a) and (d)
3.a) 4 **b)** -67 **4.a)** 2 **b)** $-2\dfrac{1}{2}$ **c)** -4 **d)** $y\geq7$ **e)** 24 **f)** 28 **g)** 11
h) $m>8$ **i)** 4 **5.a)** $u=\dfrac{2d-tv}{t}$ **b)** $x=\dfrac{y-a+mb}{m}$ **6.** 24
7. Bill 14 years, John 26 years **8.** 4 cm $\times18$ cm
9. $200 at 6%, $1200 at 9% **10.a)** 94.5 cm

CHAPTER 8

8.1 Exercise, page 251

2. Answers may vary. **a)** $\overrightarrow{BD}$, $\overrightarrow{AC}$ **b)** $\overrightarrow{ED}$, $\overrightarrow{EC}$, $\overrightarrow{EB}$, $\overrightarrow{EA}$
c) $\overrightarrow{CD}$, $\overrightarrow{ED}$, $\overrightarrow{EC}$ **d)** $\angle AEB$, $\angle BEC$, $\angle CED$ **4.a)** $\overrightarrow{PQ}$, $\overrightarrow{PR}$, $\overrightarrow{PS}$,
$\overrightarrow{QR}$, $\overrightarrow{QS}$, $\overrightarrow{RS}$ **b)** $\angle AOB$, $\angle AOC$, $\angle AOD$, $\angle BOC$, $\angle BOD$,
$\angle COD$ **5.a)** $28°$ **b)** $90°$ **c)** $130°$ **7.a)** $\angle CFD$, $\angle DFE$, $\angle AFB$,
b) $\angle EFC$, $\angle EFA$ **c)** $\angle AFC$, $\angle BFD$ **d)** $\angle BFC$, $\angle AFD$,
$\angle EFB$ **e)** $\overrightarrow{AC}$, $\overrightarrow{BD}$ **f)** $\overrightarrow{AF}\perp\overrightarrow{EF}$, $\overrightarrow{FC}\perp\overrightarrow{EF}$ **9.** Answers may
vary. **a)** $\overrightarrow{AD}$, $\overrightarrow{CF}$; $\overrightarrow{HE}$, $\overrightarrow{CF}$ **b)** $\overrightarrow{AD}$, $\overrightarrow{HE}$ **c)** A, Q, D; H, S, R
d) $\overrightarrow{HE}\perp\overrightarrow{BG}$ **10.** Answers may vary. **a)** $\angle PQC$, $\angle CQD$;
$\angle SRC$, $\angle CRE$ **b)** $\angle PSH$, $\angle PSR$; $\angle PSH$, $\angle HSG$
c) $\angle CQD$, $\angle DQF$; $\angle CRE$, $\angle ERF$ **d)** $\angle CQD$, $\angle AQF$;
$\angle CRE$, $\angle HRF$ **11.** S **12.a)** $30°$ **b)** $90°$ **c)** $50°$ **d)** $180°$ **e)** $70°$
f) $140°$ **13.a)** obtuse **b)** acute **c)** reflex **d)** right

8.2 Exercise, page 254

2.a) equilateral **b)** isosceles **c)** scalene **3.a)** acute **b)** right **c)** obtuse
d) equiangular **4.a)** square **b)** rectangle **c)** parallelogram
d) rhombus **e)** trapezoid **f)** kite **5.** Answers may vary.
a) $\angle EAD$, $\angle ADE$
b) $\angle ADC$, $\angle CBA$
c) $\angle DEA$, $\angle DEC$
7.a) angle **b)** rhombus
c) square **d)** subtract
e) multiply **f)** percent
8.a) true **b)** true **c)** false
d) false **e)** true **f)** true

11.a)

Name	V	F	E
tetrahedron	4	4	6
hexagon	8	6	12
octagon	6	8	12
dodecahedron	20	12	30
icosahedron	12	20	30

11.c) (iv)

8.3 Exercise, page 257

7.a) $\overrightarrow{AC}=\overrightarrow{BD}$ **9.** 48 **10.a)** false **b)** true **c)** false **d)** true **e)** true

8.4 Exercise, page 261

1.e) inductive **2.e)** inductive **3.e)** inductive **4.a)** All equal $60°$.
d) inductive **5.a)** $\angle LMN\cong\angle PMO$, $\angle LMP\cong\angle NMO$
b) $\angle DEF\cong\angle DFE$ **c)** $\angle TUV\cong\angle TVU$, $\angle TVU\cong\angle WVX$,
$\angle TVW\cong\angle UVX$ **9.d)** deductive **10.d)** deductive **11.**

Coin	\multicolumn{14}{c}{Combination of coins which total \$1.}													
dime	0	0	0	0	1	1	1	1	2	2	2	2	3
quarter	0	1	2	3	4	0	1	2	3	0	1	2	3	0
nickel	20	15	10	5	0	18	13	8	3	16	11	6	1	14

dime	3	3	4	4	4	5	5	5	6	6	7	7	8	9	10
quarter	1	2	0	1	2	0	1	2	0	1	0	1	0	0	0
nickel	9	4	12	7	2	10	5	0	8	3	6	1	4	2	0

8.5 Exercise, page 265

1.a) $40°$ **b)** $30°$ **c)** $k°=x°=120°$, $y°=60°$ **d)** $90°$ **2.a)** $121°$
b) $x°=y°=55°$ **c)** $k°=m°=y°=60°$ **d)** $50°$
3.a) $\angle A=\angle C=45°$, $\angle B=90°$ **b)** $\angle E=80°$,
$\angle D=\angle F=50°$ **4.a)** $x°=45°$, $y°=90°$ **b)** $x°=50°$,
$y°=130°$ **c)** $50°$ **d)** $y°=k°=80°$, $m°=n°=100°$
e) $k°=90°$, $m°=70°$, $y°=160°$ **f)** $x°=y°=45°$,
$m°=135°$, $k°=p°=22.5°$ **g)** $p°=70°$, $x°=y°=80°$
h) $k°=30°$, $m°=90°$, $x°=y°=u°=60°$ **5.** $82.5°$, $97.5°$
6.a) $60°$, $120°$, **b)** $29°$, $61°$ **7.a)** $71°$, $109°$ **b)** $67°$ **c)** $58°$, $122°$

8.a)78° **b)**acute **9.** $\angle A = 22.5°$, $\angle B = 67.5°$, $\angle C = 90°$
10. $\angle A = 65°$, $\angle B = 25°$, $\angle C = 90°$ **12.a)**60° **b)**$2x° = 60°$,
$3x° = 90°$, $m° = y° = 45°$ **c)**$x° = 80°$, $y° = 30°$

8.6 Exercise, page 267

1.a)corresponding **b)**alternate **c)**interior angles on the same side of the transversal **d)**corresponding **e)**corresponding **f)**corresponding **g)**interior angles on the same side of the transversal **h)**alternate **2.** Answers will vary.
a)$\angle$ AOR, $\angle$ ORQ **b)**$\angle$ EOP, $\angle$ ORQ **c)**$\angle$ POR, $\angle$ QRO **d)**$\angle$ GPO, $\angle$ QPB **6.** Page 89 **7.** Answers may vary.
a)alternate: $\angle$ AFH, $\angle$ FGD; $\angle$ BFG, $\angle$ FGC; corresponding: $\angle$ AFE, $\angle$ CGE **b)**All alternate and corresponding angles are equal. **c)**$\angle$ AFG, $\angle$ CGF **d)**All interior angles on the same side of the transversal have a sum of 180°.
8.a) Alternate angles are equal. **b)**Interior angles on the same size of the transveral are supplementary. **c)**Corresponding angles are equal. **9.** Not Meet: (b), (c); meet: (a), (d), (e)
10. (a), (c), (g), (i)

8.7 Exercise, page 271

1.a)69° **b)**123° **c)**95° **d)**69° **2.a)**$\overrightarrow{AB}\|\overrightarrow{EF}$ **b)**$\overrightarrow{PQ}\|\overrightarrow{RS}$ **c)**$\overrightarrow{AB}\|\overrightarrow{CD}$, $\overrightarrow{AC}\|\overrightarrow{BD}$ **3.a)**$\overrightarrow{BE}\|\overrightarrow{CD}$ **b)**$\overrightarrow{DE}\|\overrightarrow{GF}$ **c)**$\overrightarrow{RW}\|\overrightarrow{SU}$ **4.a)**$k° = x° = y° = 100°$ **b)**$k° = x° = y° = 60°$ **c)**$x° = 150°$, $y° = 70°$, $z° = 30°$ **d)**$x° = 30°$ **e)**$x° = 150°$, $y° = 75°$ **f)**$x° = 120°$, $y° = 60°$ **5.** 45°, 135° **6.** 25°, 60°, 95° **8.** 84 **9.a)**$x° = 65°$, $y° = 75°$, $k° = 40°$ **b)**$x° = 40°$, $y° = 30°$, $k° = 110°$ **c)**100°

8.9 Exercise, page 278

6. 90 **7.** 12, 14 or -12, -14

8.11 Exercise, page 285

1.a)$x° + y° = 180°$ **b)**$x° = 2y°$ **c)**$\overrightarrow{OQ} \perp \overrightarrow{PR}$ **d)**$k = p$
2.a)$x° = 90°$, $y° = 30°$ **b)**40° **c)**$x° = 30°$, $y° = 60°$
d)$x° = 50°$, $y° = 40°$, $m° = 90°$ **3.a)**5 **b)**$x = 4$, $y = 6$ **c)**10
d)$x° = 60°$, $y° = 120°$ **4.a)**$x° = 100°$, $y° = 90°$ **b)**120°
c)$x° = 25°$, $y° = 83°$ **d)**$m° = 90°$, $y° = 45°$, $k° = 40°$
5.a)10 cm **b)**$k° = 90°$, $y° = 40°$ **c)**$x° = y° = k° = 45°$
6. C, D, K, O, X **7.** 90° **8.a)**60° **b)**60° **c)**60° **d)**8 cm **e)**8 cm

8.13 Exercise, page 288

1. 28 **2.** 1 h 5 min 36.6 s **3.** 178 132.3 km **4.** I, O, V, W, X
5. 10, 11, 12, or -12, -11, -10 **6.** 35 **7.** 12, 24, 36, 48

Practice and Problems, page 289

1. 15°, 105° **3.a)**$\angle$ PQR $= \angle$ TQS, $\angle$ PQT $= \angle$ RQS **b)**$\angle$ B $= \angle$ C **c)**$\angle$ W $= \angle$ Y, $\angle$ X $= \angle$ Z **4.a)**$a° = 59°$, $b° = 121°$ **b)**$m° = 40°$, $n° = p° = 70°$ **c)**$a° = 80°$, $b° = 60°$, $c° = 120°$ **d)**$m° = n° = p° = 65°$, $q° = 50°$ **8.a)**$y° = 25°$, $x° = 50°$ **b)**$x° = y° = z° = 39°$ **c)**$x° = 65°$, $y° = 130°$ **d)**$x° = y° = 65°$, $z° = 130°$

Practice Test, page 290

1. Answers may vary. **a)**$\overrightarrow{FH}$ **b)**$\overrightarrow{AB}$ **c)**$\overrightarrow{CD}$ **d)**$\overrightarrow{AB}\|\overrightarrow{CD}$
e)$\angle$ BFE **f)**$\angle$ AFE **g)**$\angle$ CGH, $\angle$ HGD **h)**$\angle$ EFB, $\angle$ AFG
2.a)$\angle A = \angle B$, $\angle$ ACD $= \angle$ BCE, $\angle$ ACB $= \angle$ DCE
b)$\angle F = \angle H$, $\angle K = \angle G$ **c)**$\angle$ JKN $= \angle$ KNP,

$\angle$ JKP $= \angle$ KPQ, $\angle$ LKP $= \angle$ KPN, $\angle$ LKN $= \angle$ KNM, $\angle$ KNP $= \angle$ KPN, $\angle$ KNM $= \angle$ KPQ, $\angle$ JKP $= \angle$ LKN
6.a)$a° = 42°$, $b° = 65°$ **b)**$\angle$ P $= 31°$, $\angle$ Q $= 93°$, $\angle$ R $= 56°$
c)$a° = 18°$, $b° = 135°$, $d° = e° = 45°$ **d)**$x° = 70°$, $y° = 90°$,
$z° = 20°$ **e)**$x° = 104°$, $y° = 32°$, $z° = 72°$ **f)**$x° = 45°$
g)$y = 3$ cm **h)**$x° = 220°$, $y° = 110°$

CHAPTER 9

9.2 Exercise, page 295 **6.b)**2.0 cm **7.a)**3.1 cm **b)**4.0 cm
8. the circumcentre **10.** circumcentre

9.3 Exercise, page 297

2.b)right isosceles **d)**45°, 45° **3.c)**60°, 60° **4.a)**$\angle$ C $= 49°$,
$\angle$ F $= 71°$, $\overline{CF} = 4.6$ cm **b)**$\angle$ P $= 60°$, $\overline{PS} = 4.9$ cm, $\overline{PT} = 6.8$ cm
c)$\angle$ H $= 48°$, $\angle$ G $= \angle$ J $= 66°$

9.4 Exercise, page 299

1.b) Each equal to 7.1 cm. **2.b)**Each equal to 7.2 cm.
3.b)rhombus **c)**$\angle$ A $= \angle$ C $= 120°$ **d)**$\angle$ B $= \angle$ D $= 60°$
4.b)equal **5.b)**equal **7.b)**33.9 cm² **8.** 12

9.5 Exercise, page 301

1.b)$\overline{AB} = 6$ cm or $\angle$ C $= 37°$ **4.c)**no **5.b)**yes **c)**no
d)$\overline{AB}$, $\overline{CD}$, $\overline{GH}$ **7.** (c), (d), (e), (g), (h) **8.** 1 triangle: (a), (d), (e), (g), (i), (k), (l); 2 triangles: (b), (h), (m); 0 triangles: (c), (f), (j)
11. unique: (a), (b), (c), (d); more: (e), (f)

9.6 Exercise, page 305

1.a)$\angle$ D $\cong \angle$ M, $\angle$ E $\cong \angle$ N, $\angle$ F $\cong \angle$ P, $\overline{DE} \cong \overline{MN}$, $\overline{EF} \cong \overline{NP}$, $\overline{DF} \cong \overline{MP}$ **b)**$\angle$ S $\cong \angle$ U, $\angle$ T $\cong \angle$ V, $\angle$ P $\cong \angle$ M, $\overline{ST} \cong \overline{UV}$, $\overline{TP} \cong \overline{VM}$, $\overline{SP} \cong \overline{UM}$ **c)**$\angle$ P $\cong \angle$ S, $\angle$ Q $\cong \angle$ T, $\angle$ R $\cong \angle$ V, $\overline{PQ} \cong \overline{ST}$, $\overline{QR} \cong \overline{TV}$, $\overline{PR} \cong \overline{SV}$
2.a)$\triangle$ ABC $\cong \triangle$ DEF (SSS) **b)**$\angle$ A $\cong \angle$ D, $\angle$ B $\cong \angle$ E, $\angle$ C $\cong \angle$ F **3.a)**$\triangle$ HJG $\cong \triangle$ KLM (SAS) **b)**$\angle$ H $\cong \angle$ K, $\angle$ G $\cong \angle$ M, $\overline{HG} \cong \overline{KM}$ **4.a)**$\triangle$ DEF $\cong \triangle$ TSR (ASA)
b)$\angle$ F $\cong \angle$ R, $\overline{DF} \cong \overline{TR}$, $\overline{EF} \cong \overline{SR}$ **6.a)**$\overline{BD} = \overline{CD}$, $\angle$ ADB $= \angle$ ADC **b)**SAS **c)**$\overline{AB} = \overline{AC}$, $\angle$ B $= \angle$ C, $\angle$ BAD $= \angle$ CAD **7.a)**3.6 cm **b)**$x° = 50°$, $y° = 40°$, $e = 5.6$ cm, $p = 8.7$ cm **9.** $h = 3.2$ cm, $j = 4.6$ cm, $x° = y° = 45°$

9.7 Exercise, page 308

4.a)$\angle$ A $\cong \angle$ F, $\angle$ B $\cong \angle$ D, $\angle$ C $\cong \angle$ E (SAS) **b)**$\angle$ T $\cong \angle$ B $\cong \angle$ U $\cong \angle$ F, $\angle$ A $\cong \angle$ D (SSS) **c)**Alternate angles: $\angle$ HML $\cong \angle$ INK, $\angle$ GML $\cong \angle$ JNK; corresponding angles: $\angle$ KMH $\cong \angle$ KNJ, $\angle$ HML $\cong$ JNL, $\angle$ KMG $\cong \angle$ KNI, $\angle$ GML $\cong \angle$ INL; vertically opposite angles: $\angle$ GMK $\cong \angle$ HML, $\angle$ KMH $\cong \angle$ GML, $\angle$ INK $\cong \angle$ JNL, $\angle$ INL $\cong \angle$ KNJ
d)$\angle$ DCO $\cong \angle$ BAO, $\angle$ CDO $\cong \angle$ ABO (SAS), $\angle$ OCD $\cong \angle$ ODC $\cong \angle$ OAB $\cong \angle$ OBA (base angles of isosceles triangle) **e)**$\angle$ PTQ $\cong \angle$ STR (vertically opposite angles,) $\angle$ Q $\cong \angle$ R, $\angle$ P $\cong \angle$ S (alternate angles) **5.a)**$\overline{AC} \cong \overline{DF}$, $\overline{BC} \cong \overline{EF}$ (ASA) **b)**$\overline{GJ} \cong \overline{GH}$, $\overline{JK} \cong \overline{HK}$ (ASA) **c)**$\overline{KM} \cong \overline{NM}$, $\overline{LM} \cong \overline{OM}$ (AAS) **d)**$\overline{QR} \cong \overline{TU}$, $\overline{PR} \cong \overline{SU}$ (AAS) **6.a)**radii of circle **b)**base angles of isosceles triangle **c)**ASA **d)**corresponding sides of congruent triangles; 90° **8.a)**SAS **b)**SAS **9.a)**90°

2.a)24 **b)**15 **3.a)**$x = 14$, $y = 10$ **b)**$y° = m° = 65°$, $x° = 40°$, $p° = 75°$ **c)**$a° = 44°$, $b° = c° = k° = m° = 68°$, $x = 4$
4.a)$\angle RUV \cong \angle STV$, $\angle VRU \cong \angle VST$ **b)**8 **c)**8 m **5.a)**10 **b)**7 **c)**5.3 **d)**10 **e)**6.8 **6.a)**$\triangle ABC \sim \triangle DEF$, $y = 22.5$, $k = 27.0$
6.a)$\triangle ABC \sim \triangle DEF$, $y = 22.5$, $k = 27.0$
b)$\triangle GHI \sim \triangle KJL$, $x = 12$, $y = 16$ **c)**$\triangle SVW \sim \triangle UTW$, $x = 3.1$, $y = 3.8$ **7.a)**36 **b)**$\dfrac{AC}{45} = \dfrac{48}{36}$ **c)**60 **8.b)**9.9 m **9.** 13.8 m
10.a)30.6 m **b)**11.9 m **11.a)**166.7 m **12.** 1.1 m **13.a)**17 **b)**71

1.a)$\triangle ACE \sim \triangle BCD$ (AAA) **b)**$\dfrac{\overline{AE}}{\overline{BD}}$ **c)**31.9 **d)**31.9 m
2. 12.0 m **3.** 21.7 m **4.** 7.8 m **5.** 6.3 m **6.** 7.3 m **7.** 34.9 m
8. 6.0 km

1.a)120.0 km **b)**97.5 km **c)**273.0 km **2.a)**1.5 cm **b)**5 cm **c)**15 cm **3.a)**225.0 cm **b)**0.4 cm **4.a)**360 cm **b)**405 cm **c)**990 cm **5.a)**1:267 **b)**11.2 cm **c)**6.2 cm **7.a)**3081.8 km **b)**76.3 cm **c)**938.7 km **d)**62.5 cm **10.** Answers may vary. 1:20
11. Answers may vary. 1:12

2. 3, 5; 5, 7; 11, 13; 17, 19; 29, 31; 41, 43; 59, 61; 71, 73;
3. 2520 **4.** centre: 13, from top clockwise: 9, 10, 11, 12, 17, 16, 15, 14 **5.** 12

Practice and Problems, page 323
1. (a)–(iii), (b)–(iv), (c)–(i), (d)–(ii) **3.a)**(a), (c) **4.** $\angle W = 84°$, $\angle G = 51°$, $\overline{GW} = 3.6$ cm **7.a)**$\dfrac{\overline{AB}}{\overline{DE}} = \dfrac{\overline{BC}}{\overline{EF}} = \dfrac{\overline{AC}}{\overline{DF}} = 2$
b)2 **c)**congruent **8.** 4.2 m **9.a)**130 km **b)**6.3 cm

Practice Test, page 324
3.a)true **b)**false **c)**true **d)**true **e)**false **4.c)**$\angle YZX = 87°$, $\angle ZXY = 48°$, $\overline{XZ} = 5.7$ cm **5.c)**135°, 45°, 135° **6.a)**ASA **b)**ASA **c)**AAS **7.** 25.0 m **8.** Answers may vary. 1:400

CHAPTER 10

1.a)(2, 2) **b)**(−5, 2) **c)**(2, −3) **d)**(−2, −2) **e)**(5, −7) **f)**(−7, 2) **g)**(−5, 5) **h)**(0. −6) **2.a)**A **b)**S **c)**J **d)**I **e)**Q **f)**L **3.a)**(−6, 0), (2, 0) **b)**On x-axis **4.a)**(0, 6), (0, 2)(0, −6) **b)**On y-axis **5.b)**D, F, J, V **6.** (0, 0) **7.b)**U, H, V, J, D **8.a)**I **b)**E **9.a)**I **b)**II **c)**IV **d)**II **e)**III **10.a)**L(0, 2), W(0, 6) **b)**N(0, −6) **c)**Q(2, 0), M(5, 0) **d)**P(−6, 0) **11.b)**straight line **12.b)**straight line **13.b)**parallelogram **14.b)**square **15.** D(−6, −4) **16.** D(0, 4) **17.b)**$1 = 4 \times 4 \div 4 \div 4$, $2 = 4 \div 4 + 4 \div 4$, $3 = (4 + 4 + 4) \div 4$, $4 = 4 + (4 − 4) \times 4$, $5 = (4 \times 4 + 4) \div 4$, $6 = (4 + 4) \div 4 + 4$, $7 = 4 + 4 − 4 \div 4$, $8 = (4 + 4) \times 4 \div 4$, $9 = 4 + 4 + 4 \div 4$, $10 = 4 + 4 + 4 − \sqrt{4}$
18. READ PAGE 114 **19.** BAD **20.** SET **21.** REDIVIDER

1.a)9, 12, 15, 18, 21, 24, 27, 30 **2.d)**20 km, 44 km, 64 km **e)**1.5 h, 4.5 h, 6 h **3.c)**2.4 cm, 8.0 cm, 9.0 cm **d)**17.5 g, 27.5 g,

35.0 g **5.a)**4.9 **b)**4.899 **c)**(b) **d)**(b) **6.a)**3.2 **b)**3.162 **c)**greater than **7.a)**3.7 **b)**5.7 **c)**4.4 **d)**5.3 **e)**2.6 **f)**5.1 **8.a)**22.9 m **b)**71.6 m **c)**42.5 m **9.** Answers are approximate. **a)**25 km/h **b)**53 km/h **c)**82 km/h **10.a)**6.9 m **b)**15.0 m **c)**24.6 m **11.a)**term, power, base, ratio, rate, graph **12.c)**6.25 s

1.a)1 **b)**−1 **c)**3 **d)**−3 **e)**5 **2.a)**4 **b)**44 **c)**19 **d)**4 **e)**44 **4.a)**$y = x$ **b)**$y = −x + 2$ **c)**$y = x + 4$ **5.a)**(−3, 6), (−2, 1), (−1, −2), (0, −3), (1, −2), (2, 1), (3, 6) **6.a)**$x \to x + 1$ **b)**$x \to x^2$ **c)**$x \to 2$

1. (a), (c), (d), (e) **2.a)**B **b)**C, L **c)**E **d)**I, N **8.a)**$0 \to 0$, $1 \to 4.5$, $2 \to 9.0$, $3 \to 13.5$, $4 \to 18.0$ **c)**$11.25 **d)**3.5 h

1.a)4, 2 **b)**−3, −6 **c)**5, −1 **d)**6, 3 **e)**−1, 1 **f)**−5, 6
2.a)(−4, 0), (0, 3) **b)**(5, 0), (0, −3) **c)**(−5, 0), (0, 1) **3.b)**3 **c)**(3, 0) **4.b)**8 **c)**(0, 8) **5.b)**x-intercept 3, y-intercept −12 **c)**(3, 0), (0, −12) **6.a)**3, −9 **b)**7, 7 **c)**2, −6 **d)**3, 2 **e)**3, −4 **f)**−6, 3 **8.c)**$y = −\dfrac{1}{2}x + 2$, $y = −3x + 2$ **9.c)**$y = x − 3$
10. (0, −2) **12.b)**A and D, B and E, C and F

1.a)4, 6, $\dfrac{2}{3}$ **b)**6, −4, −$1\dfrac{1}{2}$ **c)**4, 2, 2 **4.a)**$\dfrac{1}{2}$ **b)**$\dfrac{1}{2}$ **c)**$\dfrac{1}{2}$; the same
6. (a), (c), (d) **8.a)**Roll the egg down a very gentle slope. **b)**Riding (horse shoes) **c)**He was at the North Pole.
9.a)2 **b)**2 **c)**−3 **d)**3 **e)**$\dfrac{1}{2}$ **f)**−$\dfrac{2}{3}$ **10.a)**(i)2 (ii)−1 (iii)−$\dfrac{3}{2}$

1. $\overline{AB} = 4$, $\overline{CD} = 6$, $\overline{EF} = 2$, $\overline{GH} = 9$, $\overline{IJ} = 10$, $\overline{KL} = 8$, $\overline{MN} = 4$, $\overline{PQ} = 3$, $\overline{RS} = 7$, $\overline{TU} = 6$ **2.a)**9.2 **b)**9.4 **c)**7.8 **3.** 6.7 **4.a)**9 **b)**3 **c)**10.4 **d)**2.2 **5.** $\overline{AB} = 9.9$, $\overline{CD} = 8.5$, $\overline{AB}$ **6.b)**$\overline{PQ} = \overline{PR} = 6.3$, $\overline{QR} = 5.7$ **c)**isosceles **7.b)**E(−2, 1), F(4, 0) **c)**$\overline{EF} = 6.1$, $\overline{AC} = 12.2$; $\overline{AC} = 2\overline{EF}$ **8.b)**$\overline{DH} = \overline{HF} = 5.4$, $\overline{GH} = \overline{HE} = 5.4$ **9.**136 squares **10.b)**$\overline{AB} = \overline{BC} = \overline{CD} = CA = 6.4$ **c)**square

1.a)(−4, −2) **b)**(6, 5) **c)**(5, −4) **2.c)**(2, 3) **3.a)**(1, 1) **b)**(0, 2) **c)**(1, −1) **d)**(6, 4) **e)**(−3, 4) **f)**(2, 6) **4.** (−1, 2) **5.** (9, 2) **6.** (2, 6) **8.b)**2 h, 8 km

1. pareg **2.** Erik 1, Axel 26, Fred 35 **3.** X − V − I = IV **4.** $98 + 7 − 6 + 5 − 4 + 3 − 2 − 1 + 0 = 100$ **5.** 6 $20's, 3 $5's, 8 $1's, 2 $50's

Practice and Problems, page 348
1. V **2.b)**15 g **c)**6.5 cm **3.a)**(−2, 1), (−1, 2), (0, 3), (1, 4) (2, 5) **5.a)**6, 6 **b)**4, −10 **c)**4, 8 **8.a)**90° **b)**$\overline{AB} = \overline{AC} = 4.5$, $\overline{BC} = 6.3$ **c)**10 square units **9.** (2, 5) **10.** (−2, 4)

1.b)M **2.b)**2.6 s **c)**45 m **3.a)**$(-3, 8)$, $(-2, 3)$, $(-1, 0)$, $(0, -1)$, $(1, 0)$, $(2, 3)$, $(3, 8)$ **5.** ℓ: 1, -2, $-\frac{1}{2}$; m: 1, 2, $\frac{1}{2}$; n: 3, 2, $\frac{3}{2}$

8.b)$\overline{AC} = \overline{BD} = 7.6$ **9.** $(1, 3)$ **10.** 4

Cumulative Review, page 350

1.a)$12x^4y$ **b)** $-6x^2y^2$ **c)**$3xy + 3xy^2 - 3y^2$ **d)** $-4x^3 + 28x$
e)$\frac{-8x^2}{y}$ **f)**$\frac{9}{x}$ **g)** $-x + 2$ **h)** $-y + 3$ **2.a)** -6 **b)**$\frac{-3}{2}$ **c)**3 **d)**12

3.a)19 **b)** -2 **c)**$\frac{1}{2}$ **4.a)**$3(4 - k)$ **b)**$5x(3x - 1)$ **c)**$4ab(a - 2 + 4b)$

5.a)72°, 18° **b)**30°, 150°, **c)**40°, 140° **d)**40°, 80° **7.a)**$x° = 40°$, $y° = 80°$, $z° = 60°$ **b)**60° **c)**$x° = 35°$, $y° = 110°$ **8.** 6.0 m

---

CHAPTER 11

11.1 Exercise, page 353

1.a)0.36 **b)**0.04 **c)**1.25 **d)**0.005 **e)**0.095 **f)**0.1175 **g)**2.65 **2.a)**36%
b)6% **c)**146% **d)**$\frac{1}{2}$% **e)**37.5% **f)**250% **g)**$\frac{1}{100}$% **3.a)**30% **b)**80%

c)150% **d)**0.5% **e)**175% **f)**87.5% **g)**187.5% **4.a)**20% **b)**$33\frac{1}{3}$%

c)400% **d)**17.8% **5.a)**60 **b)**2.232 **c)**450 **d)**18.75 **6.a)**5250
b)96 000 **c)**450 **d)**360 **7.a)**72 **b)**200 **c)**5% **d)**20% **e)**320 **f)**6
8. 65 **9.** 50.8% **10.** \$24.50 **11.** 180 **12.** 120 **13.** 72% **14.a)**62 kg
b)18.9 kg **15.a)**2040 people **b)**38.8% **c)**18.7% **16.** Yes.
3 quarters, 1 dime, 2 nickels, 1 cent. **17.a)**\$260 **b)**\$3510
18.a)106% **b)**\$45 050

11.2 Exercise, page 356

1.a)5% **b)**\$150 000 **c)**\$625 **2.a)**26.7%, \$190 **b)**\$35.25, \$270.25
c)\$75.00, \$91.50 **3.a)**\$258.75, \$172.50 **b)**15.90, \$63.60
c)15%, \$67.99 **4.a)**\$5.60, \$75.55 **b)**\$124, \$130.20
c)12%, \$349.44 **5.** \$186 **6.** 31.6% **7.**\$434 to \$949 **8.** \$5715

9.

	Nfld.	P.E.I	N.B., Que., N.S.	Ont., Sask.	B.C.	Man.	Alt.
a)	\$40.88	\$39.79	\$39.42	\$39.06	\$38.69	\$38.33	\$36.50
b)	\$156.74	\$152.55	\$151.15	\$149.75	\$148.35	\$146.95	\$139.95
c)	\$10.63	\$10.34	\$10.25	\$10.15	\$10.06	\$9.96	\$9.49
d)	\$62.70	\$61.02	\$60.46	\$59.90	\$59.34	\$58.78	\$55.98

12.a)N.B., Que., N.S. **b)**Man. **c)**P.E.I. **d)**Ont., Sask.
13. \$68.85 **14.** \$5202

11.3 Exercise, page 360

1.a)0.09 **b)**0.0775 **c)**0.125 **d)**0.0825 **e)**0.1175 **2.a)**$\frac{1}{2}$ **b)**$\frac{1}{3}$ **c)**$4\frac{1}{2}$

3.a)\$67.50 **b)**\$11.25 **c)**\$29.69 **4.a)**\$840.00 **b)**\$463.50 **c)**\$1309.38
d)\$1023.00 **5.** John **6.** \$900.21 **7.** Mara in Canada, Nina in

Germany, Serena in France **8.a)**1 year **b)**$8\frac{1}{2}$% **c)**\$2000

d)\$32.50 **e)**61d **f)**14%

11.4 Exercise, page 362

1.a)1.367 631 **b)**1.573 519 4 **c)**1.1881 **d)**1.302 260 1
e)1.171 659 4 **f)**277 289 1 **g)**1.452 400 5 **h)**1.378 842 8

2.a)\$3419.08 **b)**1038.57 **c)**\$1632.28 **3.a)**\$5832.00 **b)**\$2800.86
c)\$1461.54 **4.a)**\$20 073.38 **b)**\$23 613.58 **c)**\$26 141.40
d)\$30 499.72 **5.a)**\$2494.94 **b)**\$2257.50 **c)**\$237.44 **6.** \$2000;
\$783.63 **9.a)**\$2306.26 **b)**\$1087.08 **c)**\$2986.09

11.5 Exercise, page 365

1.a)1:2 **b)**4:1 **c)**2:4:1 **d)**3:5 **e)**1:2:4 **f)**2:5 **g)**1:2:1 **h)**1:3:2
i)10:1 **j)**1:10 **k)**5:3:2 **l)**1:2:4 **2.a)**1:4 **b)**2:1 **c)**25:9 **d)**1:8
e)6:1 **f)**9:200 **g)**8:1 **h)**9:50 **3.** Answers will vary. **a)** 6:8 **b)**6:16
c)10:18 **d)**4:6 **e)**4:6:8 **f)**2:4:2 **g)**8:14 **h)**10:6 **i)**6:20 **j)**2:6:12
4.a)61¢/L **b)**\$9.33/m **c)**\$1.78/L **5.a)**2 goals for 5 shots
b)1.4¢/g **c)**3.75 pages per minute **d)**\$3.95/h **6.a)**5 m/s
b)22 km/h **c)**15 100 km/h **d)**8 m/min **7.a)**9 **b)**10 **c)**26 **d)**50
e)5 **f)**15 **g)**4 **h)**30 **8.a)**20 **b)**5 **c)**27 **d)**4.5 **e)**13.5 **f)**12 **g)**9 **h)**5
9.a)2, 6 **b)**12, 20 **c)**20, 5 **d)**4, 10 **e)**3, 3, **f)**18, 9 **g)**6, 15 **h)**10, 5
10.a)720 **b)**1296 **11.a)**288 **b)**\$1170 **12.a)**56 L **b)**12 L **c)**6 L
d)40 L **14.a)**12.81 m **15.a)**344

11.6 Exercise, page 369

1.a)$7y$ **b)**$10y = 50$ **c)**15 g of M, 35 g of N **2.a)**$12x$ **b)**$19x = 114$
c)Robin 72 h, Dom 42 h **3.a)**5:3 **b)**225 g **4.a)**$4y$, $6y$ **b)**4 L
5.a)900 **b)**\$3150 **6.a)**72, 90 **b)**935, 1105 **c)**864, 540 **7.** Brad \$279,
Kelly \$232.50 **8.a)**5:2 **b)**520 kg **9.** 60 kg nitrogen, 15 kg
phosphorus, 15 kg potash **10.** 12 kg nitrogen, 40 kg
phosphorus, 48 kg potash **11.** George \$120, Susan \$90,
Bruce \$150 **12.** 108, 180, 216 **13.** 116, 290, 638 **14.** 112 dimes
16.a) Danny \$744.03, Michael \$425.16 **b)**36.4% **17.a)**91 g
b)39.3% **18.a)**350 kg **b)**364 kg **19.a)**60% **b)**480 g
20. 280 kg **21.a)**36 kg **b)**40%, 48% **22.** 500 kg

11.7 Exercise, page 373

1. 60 km/h **2.** 15 km/h **3.** 2 h **4.** 3 h **5.** 33 m **6.** 44.8 m **7.a)**6 h
b)35 km/h **c)**560 km **d)**30 s **e)**120 m/min **f)**8.5 h **8.a)**4.1 km/h
b)1.2 m/s **9.** 14 m/s **10.** 19.8 km/h **11.** dog **12.** 90 kg **13.** 12 d
14. 37 km/h **15.** 45.62 km/h **16.** 0.07 km/h faster

11.8 Exercise, page 376

2. $60x + 10$ **3.** $60x + 10 = 70$ **4.** $x = 1$ **5.** 50 km **7.** $\frac{25x}{2}$ **8.** $\frac{25x}{2} =$

2500 **9.** $x = 200$ **10.** 5 h **11.b)**$80x + 100x = 450$ **c)**$x = 2.5$
d)2.5 h **12.b)**$6x + 450 = 1650$ **c)**$x = 200$ **d)**200 km/h, 350 km/h

11.9 Exercise, page 379

1.a)$x + 2$ **c)**$3x + 3(x + 2) = 54$ **d)**$x = 8$ **f)**Jennifer 8 km/h,
Adrianna 10 km/h **2.a)**$3x$ **c)**$15x + 240x = 255$ **d)**$x = 1$
f)He travelled 3 h by car. **3.** 250 km **4.** 45 km **5.** 300 km/h,
450 km/h **6.** 44 km/h, 56 km/h **7.a)**50 km/h **8.** 40 km/h
9.a)6 km/h **10.** 1.5 h **11.** 52 **12.** 2.4 km

11.10 Exercise, page 382

1.d)2.5 h **2.d)**10 min **3.c)**4 h **4.b)**17 km/h **5.** 9 h **6.** 77

11.11 Exercise, page 384

1.c)faster 690 km, slower 630 km **2.c)**walking 13 km/h,
cycling 39 km/h **3.** 45 km/h, 90 km/h **4.** 8 km/h, 22 km/h
5.a)24 min **b)**8.8 km **6.a)**7 h **b)**700 km **7.a)**4 km/h **b)**2 km

8. 9 h **9.** 7 km/h **10.** 18 km **11.** 26 children **12.** 2 h
13.a)3630 km **b)**90 km **14.** 650 km/h **15.** 60 km/h **16.** 4.5 h
17.a)510 km/h **b)**$V + 40$ **c)**L1011: $d = 1020$, $v = 510$;
DC9: $d = 2(V + 40)$, $v = V + 40$ **d)**$2(V + 40) + 1020 = 2000$
e)450 km/h

11.12 Exercise, page 388
1.a)140 g **b)**original: 140; New: $(400 + x)$, $(140 + x)$
c)$0.48(400 + x) = 140 + x$ **d)**100 g **2.a)**81 g **b)**5%: 81;
10%: $(1620 + n)$, $(81 + n)$ **c)** $0.1(1620 + n) = 81 + n$ **d)**90 g
3.a)1200 kg **b)**original: 1200; new: $(3000 + y)$, $(1200 + y)$
c)$0.55(3000 + y) = 1200 + y$ **d)**1000 kg **4.** 400 g
5. 1000 non-fiction **6.** 10.4 kg **7.b)**30 kg **8.** 500 g **9.** 210 g
10. 7 kg **11.** 18 kg **12.a)**450 kg **b)**60 kg **c)**22.5 kg

11.13 Exercise, page 390
1. 8 **2.a)**120 **b)**1 **3.a)**1.26 m^3 **b)**72 tiles **4.** 14, 16, and -16, -14
5. Page 200 **6.** 63

Practice and Problems, page 391
1.a)97.5 **b)**70 **c)**20 **d)**75 **e)**80 **f)**600 **2.** \$162.62 **3.** \$1700
4. \$6564.66 **5.a)**1:3 **b)**4:3 **c)**3:1:2 **d)**3:7 **6.a)**21 **b)**8, 5 **c)**2, 21
7.a)60, 72 **b)**80°, 80°, 20° **8.a)**82 km/h **b)**$\dfrac{500}{y}$ km/h **9.** 7 h
10. 3 h **11.** 0.27 kg **12.** -131

Practice Test, page 392
1. 417% **2.** \$12 050 **3.** \$110.33 **4.a)**\$3446.71 **b)**\$3150.00
c)\$296.71 **5.a)**16 **b)**4 **c)**12, 20 **d)**6, 6 **e)**12, 6 **f)**20, 5 **6.** 30, 18
7. 1.2 kg **8.** 15 kg **9.a)**$6k^2$ km **b)**$5d$ hours **10.** Diane 15 km/h,
Jack 10 km/h **11.** 1.4 kg

CHAPTER 12

12.1 Exercise, page 394
1.a)$x^2 + 9x + 20$ **b)**$x^2 + 9x + 20$ **c)**same **2.a)**$x^2 + 13x + 42$
b)$2x^2 + 7x + 3$ **3.a)**$x^2 + 9x + 18$ **b)**$y^2 + 12y + 35$
c)$a^2 + 8a + 16$ **d)**$k^2 + 14k + 48$ **e)**$m^2 + 11m + 30$
f)$n^2 + 10n + 25$ **4.a)**$x^2 + 6x + 5$ **b)**$a^2 - a - 12$
c)$m^2 - 3m - 40$ **d)**$x^2 - 5xy + 6y^2$ **e)**$k^2 + 4k - 5$
f)$48 + 14x + x^2$ **5.a)**$a^2 - 9$ **b)**$x^2 - 25$ **c)**$4y^2 - 9$
d)$9m^2 - 36$ **e)**$36 - 4m^2$ **f)**$64 - 9x^2$ **6.a)**$x^2 + 9x + 18$
b)$y^2 - 2xy - 63x^2$ **c)**$4t^2 - 12t + 9$ **d)**$k^2 - 36$ **e)**$y^4 - 36$
f)$30 + x - x^2$ **7.a)**$3x^2 + 7xy + 2y^2$ **b)**$6c^2 + 16cd - 6d^2$
c)$3a^2 + 7ab + 2b^2$ **d)**$6y^2 - 13xy + 6x^2$ **e)**$6y^2 - 5xy + x^2$
f)$18k^2 - 9ks - 2s^2$ **8.a)**$2x^2 - 5x - 3$ **b)**$3x^2 - 16x + 5$
c)$16x^2 - 8x + 1$ **9.a)**$(2x + 1)(x - 3)$ **b)**$3x^2 - 5x - 3$
10.a)$(2y - 3)(y + 3)$ **b)**$2y^2 + 3y - 9$ **11.a)**625 **b)**1225 **c)**2025
d)3025 **12.a)**A: $x^2 + 2x + 1$, B: $x^3 + 3x^2 + 3x + 1$, C: $x^4 +$
$4x^3 + 6x^2 + 4x + 1$, D: $x^5 + 5x^4 + 10x^3 + 10x^2 + 5x + 1$
b)$x^6 + 6x^5 + 15x^4 + 20x^3 + 15x^2 + 6x + 1$

12.2 Exercise, page 396
2.a)$x^2 + 2xy + y^2$ **b)**$m^2 - 6m + 9$ **c)**$4y^2 + 24y + 36$
d)$9 + 6m + m^2$ **e)**$9y^2 - 6y + 1$ **f)**$9x^2 - 6xy + y^2$
g)$9 + 12b + 4b^2$ **h)**$9x^2 + 12xy + 4y^2$ **3.a)**$x^2 + 10x + 25$
b)$y^2 - 12y + 36$ **c)**$9 - 6y + y^2$ **d)**$25 + 10b + b^2$
e)$m^2 - 6mn + 9n^2$ **f)**$4m^2 + 24mn + 36n^2$

g)$4m^2 - 12mn + 9n^2$ **h)**$25x^2 - 20xy + 4y^2$ **4.a)**$x^2 + 6x + 9$
b)$y^2 - 8y + 16$ **c)**$4y^2 + 4y + 1$ **d)**$36 + 36y + 9y^2$
e)$64 - 32x + 4x^2$ **5.** (a), (b), (d)

12.3 Exercise, page 397
1.a)x^2 **b)** $+ 5y$ **c)** $- 15$ **d)**m^2 **e)** $- 5x$ **f)** $+ y^2$ **2.a)**$y^2 - 10y + 9$
b)$2x^2 + 16x + 32$ **c)**$3y^2 + 4y - 15$ **d)**$m^2 + 9m + 14$ **e)**$6a^2 -$
$2a - 28$ **f)**$2y^2 - 18$ **g)**$x^2 - 8x + 12$ **h)**$4x^2 + 26x - 14$
i)$m^4 - 11m^2 + 30$ **3.a)**$t^2 + 10t + 24$ **b)**$m^2 - 5m + 6$
c)$2x^2 - 17x - 9$ **d)**$3t^2 - 6t - 9$ **e)**$x^4 + 5x^2 - 24$ **f)**$8 + 10a + 2a^2$
4.a)$x^2 - 4y^2$ **b)**$9m^2 - 4y^2$ **c)**$25a^2 - 4b^2$ **5.a)**$k^2 - k - 12$
b)$2x^2 + 5x + 2$ **c)**$y^2 - 16$ **d)**$4y^2 + 12y + 9$ **e)**$30 + y - y^2$
f)$x^2 - 9$ **g)**$y^2 + 8y + 16$ **h)**$30s^2 + 33s + 9$ **i)**$4x^2 - 1$
j)$2y^2 + 8y - 64$ **k)**$30y^2 + 2y - 4$ **l)**$9 - 4a^2$ Binomials: (c),
(f), (i), (l) Trinomials: (a), (b), (d), (e), (g), (h), (j), (k)

6.a)$x^2 - \dfrac{1}{4}$ **b)**$x^2 - x + \dfrac{1}{4}$ **c)**$4x^2 + 6x + \dfrac{9}{4}$ **d)**$16x^2 - 4x + \dfrac{1}{4}$

e)$a^2 - 4b^2c^2$ **f)**$x^2y^2 - 6xy + 9$ **g)**$a^2b^2 - 9$ **h)**$9x^2 - 4x + \dfrac{4}{9}$

i)$4y^2 - 10y + \dfrac{25}{4}$ **j)**$x^2y^2 - 6xy + 9$ **k)**$x^4 + 2x^2 + 1$

l)$\dfrac{1}{4} - p + p^2$ **7.a)**$12x^2 - 23x + 10$ **b)**$14x - 14$

c)Multiplication **d)**Addition **8.a)**$3w - 31$
b)$3w^2 - 67w + 372$ **c)**$8w - 86$ **9.** 29.1%

12.4 Exercise, page 399
1.a)$y^2 + 5xy - 24x^2$ **b)**$18y^2 - 36y + 18$ **c)**$15k^2 + 60k + 45$
d)$36y^2 - 24y + 4$ **e)**$8c^2 + 16c - 24$ **f)**$12x^4 - 7x^2 - 49$
2.a)$4x^2 - 22x + 24$ **b)** $- 18x^2 + 3xy + 3y^2$ **3.a)**$2x^2 - 8x + 6$
b)$3y^2 + 12y - 36$ **c)** $- 6a^2 + 14a + 40$ **d)** $- 3m^2 + 24m - 45$
e) $- 16x^2 - 84x + 72$ **f)**$100 - 45y + 5y^2$ **4.a)**$3x^2 - 6x + 3$
b) $- 8x^2 + 24xy - 18y^2$ **5.a)**$2x^2 - 4x + 2$ **b)**$3y^2 + 12y + 12$
c) $- 128 + 32a - 2a^2$ **d)** $- 3m^2 - 36m - 108$
e)$75 - 60x + 12x^2$ **f)** $- 9y^3 + 12y^2 - 4y$ **6.a)**$2a^2 + 8$
b)$3a^2 + 2a + 3$ **c)**$4x$ **d)**$a^2 + 2a + 1$ **7.a)** $- x^2 + 20x - 63$
b)(i) $- y^2 + 10y - 23$ (ii)$5x^2 - 2x + 5$ **8.a)**0 **b)**0 **9.a)**$4a^2 - 4$
b) $- a^2 + 12a - 35$ **c)** $- y^2 - 6y - 48$ **d)**$4x^2 - 20x + 28$
e)$3a^2 - 11a + 12$ **f)** $- y^2 - 42y - 57$ **10.a)** $- 48$ **b)**4 **c)**250 **d)**17
11.a)A: $2x - 3$ B: $2x - 5$, C: $2x - 7$, D: $2x - 9$ **b)**E: $2x - 11$,
F: $2x - 13$ **c)**$2x - 51$ **12.a)**A: $- 27$, B: $- 52$, C: $- 272$, A

12.5 Exercise, page 402
1.b)5 **2.a)**$\{ - 2\}$ **3.a)**1 **b)**2 **c)**2 **d)**3 **e)**40 **4.** A: 3 units × 3 units,
B: 7 units × 7 units **5.** 8 m × 8 m **6.** 10 m × 18 m,
14 m × 7 m **7.** 12, 13 **8.a)**Lesley 08:41, Michael 08:28
b)13 min **9.** 31 m × 34 m

12.6 Exercise, page 404
1. (b), (c), (d), (g), (i), (l) **2.a)**4 **b)**y^2 **c)**$4a$ **d)**25 **e)**$9y^2$
f)$12ab$ **3.a)**$(y + 2)^2$ **b)**$(x - 3)^2$ **c)**$(a + 6)^2$ **d)**$(m - 5)^2$
e)cannot be factored **f)**$(1 + 2x)^2$ **g)**$(x - 3y)^2$ **h)**$(2x + y)^2$
i)$(3a - 2b)^2$ **j)**$(3 - 4y)^2$ **k)**$(2a + 3b)^2$ **l)**$(3m - 5n)^2$ **m)**$(x - 6y)^2$
n)$(9 - 2y)^2$ **o)**$\left(a + \dfrac{1}{2}\right)^2$ **p)**$(a^2 - 1)^2$ **q)**$(1 - 2y^2)^2$ **r)**$\left(y - \dfrac{3}{2}\right)^2$

4.a)$2(a + 3)^2$ **b)**$3(y − 3)^2$ **c)**$a(3x + 2)^2$ **d)**$b(y − 2x)^2$
e)$x(2x + 1)^2$ **f)**$y(y − 3)^2$ **g)**$a(2a − b)^2$ **h)**$n(3m − 2n)^2$
i)$2a(3a − 4b)^2$ **5.a)**49 **b)**49 **6.** 5

12.7 Exercise, page 406
1.a)6, 3 **b)**−2, −6 **c)**6, 1 **d)**−10, −3 **e)**9, 2 **f)**−2, −7
2.a)$m + 3$ **b)**$n − 2$ **c)**$c + 6$ **d)**$a + 9$ **e)**$d − 3$ **f)**$y − 7$ **3.a)**$m − 8$
b)$t − 1$ **c)**$p + 7$ **d)**$k − 3$ **e)**$w + 8$ **f)**$z − 1$ **4.a)**$(x − 9)(x − 2)$
b)$(y + 4)(y + 2)$ **c)**$(m + 3)(m + 9)$ **d)**$(n − 6)(n − 5)$ **e)**$(5 − a)^2$
f)$(h + 6)(h + 2)$ **g)**$(t + 5)(t + 1)$ **h)**$(6 − m)(3 − m)$ **i)**$(m + 7)$
$(m + 2)$ **j)**$(t − 12)(t − 8)$ **k)**$(y − 9)(y − 1)$ **l)**$(d + 4)(d + 9)$
m)$(x − 5)(x + 2)$ **n)**$(y + 3)(y − 2)$ **o)**$(m − 2)(m + 1)$ **p)**$(t − 10)$
$(t + 3)$ **q)**$(x + 14)(x − 1)$ **r)**$(m + 9)(m − 2)$ **s)**$(t − 6)(t + 4)$ **t)**$(y$
$− 6)(y + 5)$ **u)**$(x + 4)(x − 1)$ **5.a)**$(k + 5)(k − 1)$ **b)**$(x + 7)(x + 5)$
c)$(m + 11)(m − 1)$ **d)**$(x − 3)(x + 4)$ **e)**$(y + 9)(y + 1)$ **f)**$(t − 6)$
$(t + 8)$ **g)**$(m + 6)(m − 7)$ **h)**$(s + 5)(s − 10)$ **i)**$(t − 4)(t − 5)$
j)$(7 − x)(8 − x)$ **k)**$(x − 17)(x + 5)$ **l)**$(y + 3)(y + 5)$ **6.a)**$(m + 4n)$
$(m + 2n)$ **b)**$(a − 2b)(a + b)$ **c)**$(t + 8n)(t + n)$ **d)**$(x − 6y)(x − 2y)$
e)$(p + 4q)(p − 5q)$ **f)**$(b − 4c)(b + 5c)$ **7.a)**$2(x − 4)(x − 2)$
b)$y(y + 12)(y + 2)$ **c)**$2(x + 9)(x + 2)$ **d)**$4(m + 13)(m − 2)$
e)$x(x + 12)(x − 4)$ **f)**$a(a − 3)(a − 9)$ **g)**$3(y − 6)^2$ **h)**$2(x − 6)$
$(x + 7)$ **i)**$b(b + 27)(b − 3)$ **j)**$3(m + 26)(m − 2)$ **k)**$2(x − 4)(x − 14)$
l)$x(x + 6)(x − 8)$ **8.** $(x − 2)$ m **9.** $(x + 10)$ km/h **10.a)**$x + 10$
b)$y + 27$ **c)**$s + 8$ **d)**$a − 4$ **e)**$y + 9$ **f)**$y + 6$ **g)**$k + 11$ **h)**$y − 4$
11. Canada 23, U.S.A. 11 **12.a)**26, −26 **b)**+2, −2, +5, −5,
+10, −10, +23, −23 **c)**+1, −1, +8, −8, +19, −19

12.8 Exercise, page 408
1.a)6 **b)**x **c)**1 **d)**$3a$ **e)**$3a$ **f)**5 **2.a)**$(a − b)(a + b)$ **b)**$(y − x)(y + x)$
c)$(a − 2b)(a + 2b)$ **d)**$(x − 1)(x + 1)$ **e)**$(2m − 3n)(2m + 3n)$
f)$(3k − 4m)(3k + 4m)$ **g)**$(1 − 5y)(1 + 5y)$ **h)**$(4y − 5x)(4y + 5x)$
i)$2(m − 6)(m + 6)$ **j)**$(2t − 5s)(2t + 5s)$ **k)**$2(7 − 3m)(7 + 3m)$
l)$(6 − x)(6 + x)$ **3.a)**$3(m − 4)(m + 4)$ **b)**$2(x − 8)(x + 8)$ **c)**$2(7 − y)$
$(7 + y)$ **d)**$3(5x − 1)(5x + 1)$ **e)**$2(3m − 2)(3m + 2)$ **f)**$2(5 − 4m)$
$(5 + 4m)$ **g)**$2(5y − 1)(5y + 1)$ **h)**$3(6 − m)(6 + m)$ **i)**$2(6 − 7y)$
$(6 + 7y)$ **j)**$a(x − 10)(x + 10)$ **k)**$m(m − 6)(m + 6)$ **l)**$x(x − 4)(x + 4)$
4.a)$(mn − 5)(mn + 5)$ **b)**$(xy − 2)(xy + 2)$ **c)**$(10 − ab)(10 + ab)$
d)$(8 − mn)(8 + mn)$ **e)**$(xy − 3)(xy + 3)$ **f)**$(ab − k)(ab + k)$
g)cannot be factored **h)**$(1 − 5ab)(1 + 5ab)$ **i)**$m^2(n^2 − 6)$
j)$16p^2(q − 1)(q + 1)$ **k)**$4(5m − 4n)(5m + 4n)$
l)$(5xy − 1)(5xy + 1)$ **m)**$\left(\frac{x}{3} − 5\right)\left(\frac{x}{3} + 5\right)$ **n)**$\left(x − \frac{1}{2}\right)\left(x + \frac{1}{2}\right)$
o)$x^2y^2(xy − 1)(xy + 1)$ **p)**$4\left(\frac{x}{5} − 4\right)\left(\frac{x}{5} + 4\right)$ **5.** 24, 54, 84
6.a)$(a^2 + 1)(a + 1)(a − 1)$ **b)**$(4m^2 + n^2)(2m + n)(2m − n)$
c)$4(2y^2 + 5x^2)(2y^2 − 5x^2)$ **d)**$(1 + 4b^2)(1 + 2b)(1 − 2b)$
7.a)$(x − 2)(x + 2)(x − 1)(x + 1)$ **b)**$(x^2 − 2)(x − 3)(x + 3)$

12.9 Exercise, page 410
1.a)2; 396 **b)**4, 30; 884 **c)**2, 30; 896 **d)**50; 2496
2.a)$(60 − 3)(60 + 3)$; 3591 **b)**$(30 − 3)(30 + 3)$; 891
c)$(20 + 4)(20 − 4)$; 384 **d)**$(70 − 2)(70 + 2)$; 4896 **3.a)**2; 484
b)30; 1024 **c)**3; 1849 **d)**70; 4624 **e)**3; 5329 **f)**60; 3844
4.a)391 **b)**1584 **c)**3575 **d)**1596 **5.a)**140 **b)**279 **c)**9200 **d)**5000
6.a)3969 **b)**361 **c)**841 **d)**9409 **e)**4624 **f)**8281 **7.a)**8096 **b)**183

c)2304 **d)**9999 **e)**4884 **f)**1444 **g)**6000 **h)**2401 **i)**10 201
8.a)188.4 m² **b)**577.8 cm² **9.a)**369.0 m² **b)**2080.0 m²
c)6400.0 m² **10.** 352.0 m² **11.** 78.5 m² **12.** Answers will vary.
13.b)A

12.10 Exercise, page 413
1. $x(x + 4)$ **2.** $3a(1 + 2b)$ **3.** $(x − 4)(x − 7)$ **4.** $(x − 6)(x + 4)$
5. $ab(c + d)$ **6.** $9x^2(4x − 1)$ **7.** $(y + 7)(y − 2)$ **8.** $2(a − 1)(a + 1)$
9. $(5x^2 − 4y^2)(5x^2 + 4y^2)$ **10.** $(y − 7)(y − 9)$ **11.** $(x − 20)(x − 4)$
12. $2(x^2 + 2)$ **13.** $3(a − b)(a + b)$ **14.** $(x + 3)(x + 4)$ **15.** $(m − 10)$
$(m + 1)$ **16.** $(x − 2)(x + 2)(x − 3)(x + 3)$ **17.** $(a + 8)(a + 1)$
18. $(4x − 1)^2$ **19.** Cannot be factored. **20.** $(m + 4)(m − 2)$
21. $a(1 − 4a)$ **22.** $2(n − 5)(n + 5)$ **23.** $(y − 3)(y + 1)$ **24.** $−6x^2$
25. $−(x + y)^2$ **26.** $8(y − 2)(y + 2)$ **27.** $10(x − y)(x + y)$
28. $−(a + b)^2$ **29.** $b(a − b)(a + b)$ **30.** $10(3x − 10)(3x + 10)$
31. $3(y^2 − 12y + 12)$ **32.** $(x − 12)(x + 12)$ **33.** $(a − 8)(a + 8)$
34. $(m^2 + 9)(m − 2)(m + 2)$ **35.** $(12 − y)(12 + y)$ **36.** $3(x − 4)$
$(x + 4)$ **37.** $(9x^2 + 1)(3x + 1)(3x − 1)$ **38.** $(−6 + y)(4 + y)$
39. $3(a − 3b)(a + 3b)$ **40.** $(5m − 4n)(5m + 4n)$ **41.** $2(n + 5)(n − 2)$
42. $2(x + 3)(x − 4)$ **43.** $4(n + 4)(n − 5)$ **44.** $(m^2 + 1)(m − 2)(m + 2)$
45. $2a(a^2 − 2)$ **46.** $8(x^2 − 3y^2)$ **47.** $(a + 7b)(a − 8b)$ **48.** $(b − 7)$
$(b − 8)$ **49.** $x(x − y)(x + y)$ **50.** $5m(1 − 5m)$ **51.** $(m^2 + 4)(m + 1)$
$(m − 1)$ **52.** $(y − 2)^2(y + 2)^2$ **53.** $10(x − 2)(x − 1)$ **54.** $9(2x^2 + 1)$
55. $(x^2 + y^2)(x + y)(x − y)$ **56.** $\left(\frac{1}{2}x − 1\right)^2$ **57.** $(x + 6)(x − 3)$
58. $x(1 − y)(1 + y)$ **59.** $2(x − 2)(x + 2)$ **60.** $(5 − n)(5 + n)$
61. $(y − 12)(y + 2)$ **62.** $(m + 8)(m − 2)$ **63.** $(x + 16)(x + 2)$
64. $4(3x − y)(3x + y)$ **65.** $a(a + 5)(a − 2)$ **66.** $(x − 9)(x − 12)$
67. $2a(x − 2b)(x + 2b)$ **68.** $(6x − 5y)(6x + 5y)$ **69.** $2y^2(y + 4)$
70. $3(a + 1)^2$ **71.** $(x − 2y)(x + 2y)$ **72.** $(m^2 + 4)(m + 3)(m − 3)$
73. $(1 + 2x)(1 + 36x)$ **74.** $(x^2 + 1)(x + 1)(x − 1)$
75. $(y − 4)(y + 4)(y − 1)(y + 1)$

12.11 Exercise, page 414
1.a)$−2, −5$ **b)**$3, −2$ **c)**$5, 3$ **d)**$0, −4$ **2.a)**$−3, −2$ **b)**$−3, 4$
c)$4, −4$ **d)**$5, −1$ **3.a)**$−3$ **b)**$−2$ **c)**3 **d)**2 **4.a)**$−4, −5$ **b)**$3, −10$
c)$0, −6$ **d)**$6, −6$ **e)**$3, 4$ **f)**$\frac{3}{2}, −\frac{3}{2}$ **5.a)**$−5, −6$ **b)**$7, −5$ **c)**$6, 7$
d)$3, −7$ **6.b)**$−3, 5$ **7.a)**$3, −2$ **b)**$−3, 5$ **c)**$6, 7$ **d)**$4, −2$ **e)**$−3, −5$
f)$7, −3$ **8.a)**$0, 2.1$ **b)**$0, −3.6$ **c)**$0, −2.2$ **d)**$0, 6.2$ **e)**$0, 3.6$ **f)**$−1, 1.6$
9.a)$2.1, 3$ **b)**$−4, −3.2$ **c)**$−2, 4.5$ **d)**$5, −2.2$ **10.a)**$−2, 1.4$ **b)**$1, 3.2$
c)$3, −1.8$ **d)**$4.1, 2$ **11.** 11, 88, 101, 111, 181, 609, 619, 808,
818, 888, 906, 916, 1001, 1111, 1691, 1881, 1961

12.12 Exercise, page 416   **2.a)**95 **b)**98 **4.** 24 fish

Practice and Problems, page 417
1.a)$a^2 + 5a + 6$ **b)**$a^2 + a − 6$ **c)**$2a^2 − 8a + 6$ **d)**$2c^2 + 7c + 3$
e)$2x^2 + x − 21$ **f)**$9k^2 − 16$ **2.a)**$(x − 3)(x + 5)$ **b)**$x^2 + 2x − 15$
3.a)$(2a + 3)^2$ **b)**$4a^2 + 12a + 9$ **4.a)**$2m^2 − 5m − 3$ **b)**$2h^2 + 7h + 6$
c)$4m^2 − 1$ **d)**$9r^2 + 6r + 1$ **e)**$28 + 3y − y^2$ **f)**$10x^2 + x − 3$
5.a)$4a^2 − 6$ **b)**$6x^2 − 3x + 37$ **6.a)**2 **b)**$−3, −5$ **7.a)**4 **b)**4 **c)**4 **d)**1 **e)**12
f)16 **8.a)**$(x + 3)(x + 2)$ **b)**$(y + 3)(y − 9)$ **c)**$(x − 6)^2$ **d)**$(y − 6)(y − 5)$
e)$(a + 3b)^2$ **f)**$2(5p + q)^2$ **9.a)**$(x − 9)(x + 9)$ **b)**$(2y − 5)(2y + 5)$
c)$(3a − 4b)(3a + 4b)$ **d)**$(x − 11)(x + 11)$ **e)**$\left(p − \frac{1}{2}\right)\left(p + \frac{1}{2}\right)$

f)$(8 - m)(8 + m)$ **g)**$9\left(k - \dfrac{1}{9}\right)\left(k + \dfrac{1}{9}\right)$ **h)**$(4x^2 - 3y^2)(4x^2 + 3y^2)$

Practice Test, page 418
1.a)$p^2 - 3p - 10$ **b)**$w^2 + 7w + 12$ **c)**$k^2 - 16k + 63$
d)$x^2 - 2xy - 3y^2$ **e)**$4a^2 - 12a + 9$ **f)**$25q^2 - 1$
g)$35 + 2b - b^2$ **h)**$9x^2 - 24xy + 16y^2$ **i)**$27k^2 + 15k - 2$
j)$15p^2 - 17pq - 4q^2$ **k)**$16x^2 - 81$ **l)**$-63 - 16x - x^2$
2.a)$x^2 - 2x$ **b)**$y^2 - 2y - 26$ **c)**$2y^2 - 10y + 9$ **d)**$11x^2 - 31x +$
13 **e)**$3n^2 + 17n + 25$ **f)**$-2x^2 - 20x + 52$ **g)**$2k^2 + 5k - 54$
h)$8n - 34$ **3.a)**-13 **b)**24 **c)**-6 **d)**$\dfrac{3}{2}$, 5 **e)**7, -3 **f)**4, 5 **4.** 11, 14

5.a)$(x + 3)(x + 5)$ **b)**$(w - 6)(w + 5)$ **c)**$2(p + 2)(p - 1)$ **d)**$(x -$
$2y)(x + 2y)$ **e)**$(m^2 + 4)(m + 3)(m - 3)$ **f)**$(5x^2 + y^2)(5x^2 - y^2)$
g)$4(y - 3)(y + 5)$ **h)**$(a - 6)^2$ **i)**$(x + 5)(x - 1)$
j)$5(x - 2y)(x + 2y)$ **k)**$2(y + 3)(y - 7)$ **l)**$(1 + 2y)(1 + 36y)$
6.a)$(x - 4)$ m **b)**$(x + 2)$ cm **7.a)**2496 **b)**9000 **c)**961 **d)**891
e)300 **f)**2401 **8.a)**576.0 m² **b)**1004.8 cm²

CHAPTER 13

13.1 Exercise, page 420
10. Peter cycles, Steven swims, Pitman lifts weights.
11.a)clustered **b)**stratified **c)**census **d)**random **12.** Nfld.
240, Ont. 3600, N.S. 360, Man. 430, N.B. 300, Sask. 410, P.E.L
50, Alta. 860, Que. 2650, B.C. 1020 **13.a)**39 **b)**30 **c)**6 **14.** (b)

13.2 Exercise, page 424
1.b)50 **c)**4, 5, 3, 7, **2.c)**6 **3.a)**Total number of fish. **b)**11.1%
4.b)have a mass of 2.0 kg or more **5.d)**73.3%
6.b)$3:30 - 3:59$ **c)**57.8% **8.b)**57.1% **c)**42.9% **9.** 4 **10.a)**14
b)77.5% **11.b)**24 **c)**52 and 66 **d)**12%

13.3 Exercise, page 428
1.b) Rena 12, Helen 16, Jeremy 6, Greg 10 **2.b)**10 **c)**971
4.c)22.7% **d)**7.6% **5.b)**14.1% **8.** 1

13.4 Exercise, page 430
1.a)24.4% **b)**23.6% **c)**8.3% **d)**79.2% **3.b)**227.0 g **4.b)**100°
c)27.8% **d)**(i)$34 766.68 (ii)$20 885.02 **6.b)**511.4 **8.a)**T, F, S
b)M, N, T

13.6 Exercise, page 434   **2.b)**4 **c)**2 **5.** 27

13.7 Exercise, page 437
1.a)none **b)**increase **c)**decrease **2.** mode **3.a)**mean **b)**mode
4.a)169, 169, 160 **b)**mode **5.a)**158, 178, 73 **b)**median
6.a)$40-50$ **b)**$90-100$ **7.a)**$60-70$ **b)**$20-30$, $60-70$, $70-80$
9.c)28% **d)**24% **f)**48% **10.b)**10 **11.** 23 **12.** 22.4 **13.** 55.9
14.a)34.8 **15.b)**26 **c)**25.2

13.8 Exercise, page 441
2.a)$\dfrac{1}{6}$ **b)**$\dfrac{1}{6}$ **c)**$\dfrac{1}{2}$ **d)**0 **3.a)**$\dfrac{1}{3}$ **b)**$\dfrac{4}{9}$ **c)**$\dfrac{2}{9}$ **d)**0 **4.a)**$\dfrac{2}{5}$ **b)**$\dfrac{3}{10}$ **5.** $\dfrac{17}{25}$ **6.a)**$\dfrac{1}{2}$, $\dfrac{1}{2}$
7.a)$\dfrac{1}{4}$ **b)**$\dfrac{1}{4}$ **c)**$\dfrac{1}{2}$ **9.a)**$\dfrac{1}{8}$ **b)**$\dfrac{3}{8}$ **c)**$\dfrac{3}{8}$ **d)**$\dfrac{3}{8}$ **11.a)**$\dfrac{1}{2}$ **b)**$\dfrac{3}{10}$ **c)**$\dfrac{1}{5}$ **12.a)**10
b)100 **13.b)**$\dfrac{1}{36}$, $\dfrac{1}{6}$ **c)**7 **14.a)**mean **b)**mode **c)**statistics
d)average **e)**sample

13.9 Exercise, page 443
1.a)$\dfrac{7}{250}$ **b)**$\dfrac{243}{250}$; 1 **2.a)**$\dfrac{1}{9}$ **b)**$\dfrac{8}{9}$; 1 **3.a)**$\dfrac{5}{18}$ **b)**$\dfrac{5}{6}$ **c)**$\dfrac{5}{18}$ **4.a)**$\dfrac{1}{2}$ **b)**$\dfrac{1}{13}$
c)$\dfrac{3}{4}$ **d)**$\dfrac{10}{13}$ **e)**$\dfrac{1}{2}$ **5.a)**$\dfrac{1}{9}$ **b)**$\dfrac{8}{9}$ **c)**$\dfrac{7}{9}$ **6.** 58% **7.a)**$\dfrac{1}{6}$ **b)**$\dfrac{1}{2}$ **c)**$\dfrac{7}{12}$ **d)**$\dfrac{29}{36}$ **e)**$\dfrac{2}{3}$
f)$\dfrac{5}{6}$ **8.a)**$\dfrac{3}{8}$ **b)**$\dfrac{7}{8}$ **9.a)**$\dfrac{1}{5}$ **b)**$\dfrac{4}{5}$ **c)**$\dfrac{7}{75}$ **d)**$\dfrac{68}{75}$

13.10 Exercise, page 445
1.a)4 **2.a)**166 **b)**156 **c)**192 **3.a)**478 **b)**522 **4.a)**24 **b)**66 **6.a)**$\dfrac{16}{19}$ **b)**$\dfrac{11}{76}$
c)$\dfrac{14}{19}$ **8.a)**$\dfrac{6}{35}$ **b)**$\dfrac{2}{7}$ **c)**$\dfrac{19}{35}$ **9.** 40 000 **10.** 2064 **11.** 384 **12.** 117 **13.** 178

13.12 Exercise, page 452   **3.** 3 **4.** 72 **5.a)**P, S, V **b)**E, N, O **6.** 143

Practice Test, page 453
3.b)$10-19$ years **4.a)**Drama 24%, Sport 30%, Comedy 36%,
Other 10% **7.** 20, 18, 16 **8.b)**(i)$\dfrac{1}{8}$ (ii)$\dfrac{1}{4}$

Cumulative Review, page 454
1.a)$p \to 4p^2 - 1$ **b)**$p \to 3p^2 + 1$ **c)**$p \to 5p^2 - 2$ **2.a)**(6, 0)
b)(0, 3) **c)**$-\dfrac{1}{2}$ **3.** (5, 2) **4.** $8400 **5.** $11 990.25 **6.** seeds 120 g,
nuts 160 g, fruit 200 g **7.** 90 km/h **8.a)**$y^2 + 8y + 15$
b)$y^2 - 5y + 6$ **c)**$x^2 + 6x + 9$ **d)**$x^2 + 8xy + 16y^2$
e)$x^2 - x - 12$ **f)**$x^2 - 3x - 40$ **g)**$x^2 + 5xy + 6y^2$
h)$x^2 - 5xy + 6y^2$ **i)**$3a^2 - 20ab + 12b^2$ **j)**$4x^2 + 12xy + 9y^2$
k)$15 - 8m + m^2$ **l)**$42 - 9m - 6m^2$ **9.a)**$(p - 3)^2$
b)$(n - 4)(n - 5)$ **c)**$3(a + 2b)(a + b)$ **d)**$(9m + 2n)(9m - 2n)$
e)$2(y + 2)(y - 1)$ **f)**$(5a - 4b)^2$

CHAPTER 14

14.1 Exercise, page 457
1.a)translation **b)**reflection **c)**rotation **2.a)**rotation
b)translation **c)**rotation **d)**reflection **e)**rotation **f)**reflection
g)reflection **h)**translation **4.a)**$(x, y) \to (x + 5, y)$
b)$(x, y) \to (x, y + 4)$ **c)**$(x, y) \to (x - 3, y + 2)$ **7.a)**$-90°$
b)90° **c)**$-180°$ **d)**90° **8.** A, D

14.2 Exercise, page 459
1.a)$\overline{SS'}$, $\overline{TT'}$, $\overline{UU'}$ **b)**$\overline{SS'}$, $\overline{TT'}$, $\overline{UU'}$ **2.a)**$\overline{PR}$, $\overline{P'R'}$; $\overline{RB}$, $\overline{R'B}$;
$\overline{QC}$, $\overline{Q'C}$ **b)**$\overline{PP'}$, $\overline{QQ'}$, $\overline{RR'}$ **3.b)**$\overline{DD'} \cong \overline{EE'} \cong \overline{FF'}$,
$\overline{DD'} \parallel \overline{EE'} \parallel \overline{FF'}$ **4.b)**$\overline{SS'} \cong \overline{TT'} \cong \overline{UU'} \cong \overline{VV'}$;
$\overline{SS'} \parallel \overline{TT'} \parallel \overline{UU'} \parallel \overline{VV'}$ **5.b)**$\overline{SS'}$, $\overline{TT'}$, $\overline{UU'} \perp p$, $\overline{SS'} \parallel \overline{TT'} \parallel \overline{UU'}$
6. e

14.3 Exercise, page 461
1.a)180° **b)**90° **2.a)**$\overline{OS} \cong \overline{OS'}$, $\overline{TU} \cong \overline{T'U'}$, $\overline{OU} \cong \overline{OU'}$ **b)**90°
c)$\angle TOT' \cong \angle SOS' \cong \angle UOU'$ **3.a)**$\overline{OP} \cong \overline{OP'}$,
$\overline{OQ} \cong \overline{OQ'}$, $\overline{OR} \cong \overline{OR'}$, $\overline{OS} \cong \overline{OS'}$ **b)**180°
c)$\angle POP' \cong \angle QOQ' \cong ROR' \cong \angle SOS'$ **5.b)**$\overline{OP} \cong \overline{OP'}$,
$\overline{OQ} \cong \overline{OQ'}$, $\overline{OS} \cong \overline{OS'}$ **c)**$\angle POP' \cong \angle QOQ' \cong \angle SOS'$
7. Throw the ball straight up into the air. **9.a)**4, 8 **b)**6, 6
c)4, 4 **d)**3, 3 **e)**0, 6 **f)**4, 4 **g)**4, 4 **h)**1, 2 **i)**1, 1 **j)**2, 2 **k)**3, 3 **l)**0, 2

14.5 Exercise, page 465
1.a)A′(2, -1), B′(3, -1), C′(3, -3), D′(1, -3), E′(1, -2)

d)$(x, y) \rightarrow (x, y - 4)$ **2.a)**$P'(4, 3)$, $Q'(5, 3)$, $R'(5, 1)$, $S'(3, 1)$, $T'(3, 2)$ **d)**$(x, y) \rightarrow (x + 9, y + 5)$ **3.a)**$P'(-5, 2)$, $Q'(-7, -3)$, $R'(-4, -2)$ **b)**$S'(1, 5)$, $T'(-2, 2)$, $U'(1, -1)$, $V'(4, 2)$

4.a)$H'(3, 1)$, $J'(6, 1)$, $K'(6, -1)$, $L'(4, -1)$, $M'(4, -4)$, $N'(3, -4)$ **b)**$V'(-4, -7)$, $W'(-4, -1)$, $X'(-1, 1)$, $Y'(2, -1)$, $Z'(2, -7)$ **5.a)**0, 2 **b)**−1, 3 **c)**3, 9 **d)**−6, 3 **6.a)**$A'(-2, 4)$, $B'(-6, 2)$, $C'(-1, -1)$ **b)**All −2 **7.a)**$P'(-4, 8)$, $Q'(-1, -1)$, $R'(1, 7)$ **b)**All $-\frac{3}{2}$ **9.a)**$\overline{AA'} \cong \overline{BB'} \cong \overline{CC'} = \sqrt{5}$ **b)**$\overline{PP'} \cong \overline{QQ'} \cong \overline{RR'} = \sqrt{13}$ **11.a)**$m_{\overline{AC}} = m_{\overline{A'C'}} = -5$, $m_{\overline{BC}} = m_{\overline{B'C'}} = -\frac{3}{5}$, $m_{\overline{AB}} = m_{\overline{A'B'}} = \frac{1}{2}$ **b)**$m_{\overline{PQ}} = m_{\overline{P'Q'}} = -3$, $m_{\overline{PR}} = m_{\overline{P'R'}} = -\frac{1}{5}$, $m_{\overline{QR}} = m_{\overline{Q'R'}} = 4$ **13.a)**$\overline{AC} \cong \overline{A'C'} = \sqrt{26}$, $\overline{AB} \cong \overline{A'B'} = 2\sqrt{5}$, $\overline{BC} \cong \overline{B'C'} = \sqrt{34}$ **b)**$\overline{PQ} \cong \overline{P'Q'} = 3\sqrt{10}$, $\overline{PR} \cong \overline{P'R'} = \sqrt{26}$, $\overline{QR} \cong \overline{Q'R'} = 2\sqrt{17}$ **15.a)**$\angle BAC \cong \angle B'A'C'$, $\angle ABC \cong \angle A'B'C'$, $\angle BCA \cong \angle B'C'A'$ **b)**$\angle PQR \cong \angle P'Q'R'$, $\angle PRQ \cong \angle P'R'Q'$, $\angle RPQ \cong \angle R'P'Q'$ **17.a)**$A'(2, 1)$, $B'(6, 3)$, $C'(4, 7)$, $D'(0, 5)$ **18.b)**$A'(-6, 5)$, $B'(-1, 0)$, $C'(-9, -1)$ **c)**clockwise **21.a)**210 **b)**1065 **c)**3 **22.a)**Both $-\frac{5}{6}$ **b)**Both $-\frac{5}{6}$

14.6 Exercise, page 469
1.a)$A(8, 1) \rightarrow A'(8, -1)$, $B(4, 1) \rightarrow B'(4, -1)$, $C(4, 3) \rightarrow C'(4, -3)$, $D(6, 3) \rightarrow D'(6, -3)$, $E(8, 5) \rightarrow E'(8, -5)$
b)unchanged **c)**opposites **d)**$(x, y) \rightarrow (x, -y)$ **2.a)**−5, 4 **b)**−3, 5 **c)**x-axis **d)**y-axis **3.a)**$\overline{L'A'} \cong \overline{LA}$, $\overline{SB'} \cong \overline{SB}$, $\overline{YC'} \cong \overline{YC}$ **b)**$\angle A'LS \cong \angle ALS$, $\angle B'SY \cong \angle BSY$, $\angle C'YL \cong \angle CYL$ **4.a)**$\overline{PL'} \cong \overline{P'L}$, $\overline{QM'} \cong \overline{Q'M}$, $\overline{RN'} \cong \overline{R'N}$ **b)**$\angle PLN \cong \angle P'LN$, $\angle QMN \cong \angle Q'MN$, $\angle RNM \cong \angle R'NM$ **6.b)**$m_{\overline{AB}} = -6$, $m_{\overline{A'B'}} = 6$, $m_{\overline{BC}} = -\frac{3}{7}$, $m_{\overline{B'C'}} = \frac{3}{7}$, $m_{\overline{CA}} = \frac{1}{2}$, $m_{\overline{C'A'}} = -\frac{1}{2}$
c)$\overline{AB} \cong \overline{A'B'} = \sqrt{37}$, $\overline{BC} = \overline{B'C'} = \sqrt{58}$, $\overline{CA} = \overline{C'A'} = 3\sqrt{5}$
d)$\angle A \cong \angle A'$, $\angle B \cong \angle B'$, $\angle C \cong \angle C'$
9.b)original: clockwise, image: counterclockwise **c)**x **d)**y
e)x co-ordinates **f)**y co-ordinates **10.b)**original: clockwise, image: counterclockwise **c)**y **d)**x **11.a)**$\overline{AB} \parallel \overline{CD}$, $\overline{AD} \parallel \overline{BC}$
c)$m_{\overline{A'D'}} = m_{\overline{D'C'}} = \frac{1}{8}$, $m_{\overline{A'D'}} = m_{\overline{B'C'}} = -\frac{5}{2}$ **14.b)**System I.

14.7 Exercise, page 473
1.a)$\frac{1}{4}$ turn, $+90°$ **b)**$\frac{1}{2}$ turn, $-180°$ **c)**$\frac{1}{2}$ turn, $+180°$

2.a)$P(-5, 3) \rightarrow P'(5, -3)$, $Q(-9, 0) \rightarrow Q'(9, 0)$, $R(-2, 0) \rightarrow R'(2, 0)$; $(x, y) \rightarrow (-x, -y)$ **b)**$S(1, 4) \rightarrow S'(-1, -4)$, $T'(6, 4) \rightarrow T'(-6, -4)$, $U(6, 1) \rightarrow U'(-6, -1)$, $V(1, 1) \rightarrow V'(-1, -1)$; $(x, y) \rightarrow (-x, -y)$ **c)**$P(-6, 4) \rightarrow P'(-4, -6)$, $Q(-2, 4) \rightarrow Q'(-4, -2)$, $R(-2, 0) \rightarrow R'(0, -2)$, $S(-6, 0) \rightarrow S'(0, -6)$; $(x, y) \rightarrow (-y, x)$ **3.a)**$X(-3, 4) \rightarrow X'(-4, -3)$, $Y(-7, 0) \rightarrow Y'(0, -7)$, $Z(-1, 0) \rightarrow Z'(0, -1)$; $(x, y) \rightarrow (-y, x)$ **b)**$G(3, 3) \rightarrow G'(-3, -3)$, $H(8, 0) \rightarrow H'(-8, 0)$, $K(3, -3) \rightarrow K'(-3, 3)$, $L(1, 0) \rightarrow L'(-1, 0)$; $(x, y) \rightarrow (-x, -y)$ **c)**$P(5, 3) \rightarrow P'(3, -5)$, $Q(8, 3) \rightarrow Q'(3, -8)$, $R(6, 0) \rightarrow R'(0, -6)$, $S(0, 0) \rightarrow S'(0, 0)$; $(x, y) \rightarrow (y, -x)$ **5.a)**$(x, y) \rightarrow (y, -x)$ **b)**$(x, y) \rightarrow (-y, x)$ **c)**$(x, y) \rightarrow (-x, -y)$ **d)**$(x, y) \rightarrow (-x, -y)$ **6.a)**$Q'(-2, 0)$, $R'(0, 3)$, $S'(4, 0)$ **b)**$K'(-3, 5)$, $L'(4, 5)$, $M'(4, 1)$, $N'(-3, 1)$

7.a)equal **b)**equal to the angle of rotation **c)**$\overline{OA} \cong \overline{OA'}$, $\overline{OB} \cong \overline{OB'}$, $\overline{OC} \cong \overline{OC'}$ **10.a)**$A'(-2, -3)$, $B'(-3, -7)$, $C'(-6, -4)$ **b)**$A'(2, 3)$, $B'(3, 7)$, $C'(6, 4)$ **c)**$A'(-3, 2)$, $B'(-7, 3)$ $C'(-4, 6)$ **d)**$A'(-3, 2)$, $B'(-7, 3)$, $C'(-4, 6)$ **14.a)**$A'(4, -1)$, $B'(9, -2)$, $C'(5, -6)$ **b)**$m_{\overline{AB}} = m_{\overline{A'B'}} = -\frac{1}{5}$, $m_{\overline{BC}} = m_{\overline{B'C'}} = 1$, $m_{\overline{AC}} = m_{\overline{A'C'}} = -5$ **15.a)**$D'(1, -5)$, $E'(-3, -8)$, $F'(-3, -3)$ **b)**$m_{\overline{DE}} = -\frac{4}{3}$, $m_{\overline{D'E'}} = \frac{3}{4}$, $m_{\overline{DF}} = 2$, $m_{\overline{D'F'}} = -\frac{1}{2}$, $m_{\overline{EF}} = 0$, $m_{\overline{E'F'}} = \infty$ **c)**$D'(-1, 5)$, $E'(3, 8)$, $F'(3, 3)$; $m_{\overline{DE}} = -\frac{4}{3}$, $m_{\overline{D'E'}} = \frac{3}{4}$, $m_{\overline{DF}} = 2$, $m_{\overline{D'F'}} = -\frac{1}{2}$, $m_{\overline{EF}} = 0$, $m_{\overline{E'F'}} = \infty$

14.8 Exercise, page 477
1.a)$A'(-5, 1)$, $B'(-4, 3)$, $C'(-2, 0)$ **b)**$A''(5, 1)$, $B''(4, 3)$, $C''(2, 0)$ **2.a)**$P''(-10, -4)$, $Q''(-3, -1)$, $R''(0, -9)$ **b)**$\angle P \cong \angle P''$, $\angle Q \cong \angle Q''$, $\angle R \cong \angle R''$ **c)**$\overline{PQ} \cong \overline{P''Q''}$, $\overline{QR} = \overline{Q''R''}$, $\overline{RP} = \overline{R''P''}$ **d)**$m_{\overline{PQ}} = -m_{\overline{P''Q''}}$, $m_{\overline{QR}} = -m_{\overline{Q''R''}}$, $m_{\overline{RP}} = m_{\overline{R''P''}}$ **e)**$\angle PRQ$ counterclockwise, $\angle P''Q''R''$ clockwise **3.** Same results **4.a)**$A''(-1, 10)$, $B''(-1, 5)$, $C''(-5, 5)$, $D''(-5, 9)$

14.9 Exercise, page 479
1.a)-4, $(2x, 2y)$ **b)**$1, -2, 2, \left(-\frac{x}{2}, -\frac{y}{2}\right)$ **c)**$1, \left(\frac{5}{2}, 1\right), \left(\frac{x}{2}, \frac{y}{2}\right)$

2.a)2 **b)**$-\frac{1}{2}$ **c)**$\frac{1}{2}$ **4.a)**$\overline{AC} = 2\overline{A'C'}$, $\overline{BC} = 2\overline{B'C'}$, $\overline{AB} = 2\overline{A'B'}$ **b)**All equal to 2 **5.a)**equal **b)**$\triangle ABC = 2\triangle A'B'C'$ **7.a)**$\overline{OA} = 2\overline{OA'}$, $\overline{OB} = 2\overline{OB'}$, $\overline{OC} = 2\overline{OC'}$ **8.a)**$m_{\overline{AC}} = m_{\overline{A'C'}}$, $m_{\overline{AB}} = m_{\overline{A'B'}}$, $m_{\overline{BC}} = m_{\overline{B'C'}}$ **10.a)**$D'(1, 4)$, $E'(2, 2)$, $F'(5, 1)$ **b)**$\overline{D'E'} = \frac{1}{2}\overline{DE}$, $\overline{E'F'} = \frac{1}{2}\overline{EF}$, $\overline{F'D'} = \frac{1}{2}\overline{FD}$ **c)**equal corresponding angles **d)**corresponding slopes are equal **e)**$\frac{1}{2}$ **f)**$\overline{OD'}$, $\overline{OE'}$, $\overline{OF'}$ **g)**original ccw, image ccw **h)**$\triangle DEF = \frac{1}{2}\triangle D'E'F'$

14.12 Exercise, page 486
2.a)$C'(-3, 5)$, $D'(2, -1)$, $E'(3, 4)$, $F'(-5, -2)$ **6.** $\overline{OR} = \overline{OR'}$, $\overline{OS} = \overline{OS'}$ **7.a)**$S'(-5, -3)$, $T'(-8, 0)$, $R'(-5, 3)$, $V'(-2, 0)$ **b)**$M'(-4, -2)$ **c)**$\overline{OM} = \overline{OM'}$ **d)**$\overline{OP} = \overline{OP'}$

Year End Review, page 487
1.a)2 **b)**3 **c)**−2 **d)**24 **e)**3 **f)**−64 **2.a)**1 **b)**$\frac{1}{8}$ **c)**1 **d)**$\frac{1}{3}$ **e)**9 **f)**4
g)−8 **h)**27 **i)**$\frac{1}{2}$ **j)**16 **k)**$\frac{4}{9}$ **l)**$-\frac{29}{8}$ **3.a)**$0.0\overline{18}$, $0.\overline{120}$ **c)**$0.\overline{456}$ **4.** 24
5.a)$\{-2\}$ **b)**$\{-4\}$ **6.a)**12 m × 48 m **b)**49.5 m **7.** A 23.5 m², B 49.2 m², C 98.5 m², D 98.5 m²; C and D **9.a)**$y^2 + 2y + 25$
b)$4y^2 + y - 18$ **c)**$-6(x^2 - 3x + 5)$ **d)**$-8x^2 + 7x + 35$
e)$-x^2 - 7x - 10$ **f)**$2x - 1$ **12.a)**$52.10 **b)**$69.47
13. Harry 18 km/h, Bill 20 km/h **14.a)**$8r + 14$
b)8 units × 3 units, 11 units × 4 units, 5 units × 2 units
15. $5xy$ **16.** $x - 2$ **18.** $A'(6, 4)$, $B'(0, 4)$, $C'(0, -2)$, $D'(6, -2)$

Index